HYDROLOGY
AND
WATER QUANTITY
CONTROL

HYDROLOGY AND WATER QUANTITY CONTROL

Martin P. Wanielista
University of Central Florida

WILEY

John Wiley & Sons

New York • Chichester • Brisbane • Toronto • Singapore

Library of Congress Cataloging-in-Publication Data

Wanielista, Martin P.
    Hydrology and water quantity control/Martin P. Wanielista.
        p.   cm.
    Includes bibliographical references.

    1. Water-supply—Management.   2. Hydrology.   3. Runoff.
I. Title.   II. Title: Hydrology and water quantity control.

TD353.W337   1990
551.48—dc20   89-38369

Printed in the United States of America

10 9 8 7 6 5 4 3 2 1

ABOUT THE AUTHOR

Marty Wanielista is Professor of Engineering at the University of Central Florida in Orlando. He is a graduate of the University of Detroit, Manhattan College, and Cornell University. At the University of Central Florida, Dr. Wanielista teaches environmental and civil engineering courses, and this text has been used in one of his hydrology courses. Dr. Wanielista's course development integrates the basic scientific, engineering, and planning disciplines, introducing students to today's problems that can be solved by using hydrologic principles, ideas, and concepts. Dr. Wanielista began research in this area in 1968 and has several years' consulting experience, which is reflected in the practical example problems. He is a registered Professional Engineer in the State of Florida. He is the author of more than 130 articles and technical reports and has edited 8 books. For continuing service in education, research, and community leadership, he has received 18 awards and is an active member of 8 professional and technical organizations.

To Betty, Marlo, and Vicki

"What we leave for future generations is found in our children and writings. To have both is but a small sacrifice of time for the value derived."

PREFACE

Hydrology is the major discipline used to understand and design water management systems that are directly and indirectly related to the occurrence of water on, above, and below the earth's surface. Principles and concepts related to basic hydrologic processes and their use in analysis and design form a major part of this book. The hydrologic systems that one seeks to identify lend themselves to a variety of mathematical methods, both deterministic and probabilistic in nature. The presentations in this book bring together theoretical understanding with practical solution methods.

This textbook was developed in response to the educational needs of scientists, engineers, planners, and environmentalists to incorporate hydrologic concepts, ideas, and models into comprehensive water quantity studies. Comprehensive studies are necessary when water supplies are developed or land use changes are contemplated. The major emphasis is placed on (1) measurement and interpretation of hydrologic data, and (2) measurement and management of water volume and peak flows.

Organization

This text includes both basic hydrology, emphasizing an understanding of concepts, principles, and ideas of hydrologic processes, and applications of these methods. A process is one that is variable in time. This variability must be understood to adequately measure and use hydrologic data. Practical applications of hydrology concepts and principles are presented for water quantity considerations in the management of runoff volume and rate.

The book has been used primarily by third- and fourth-year undergraduate science and engineering students. However, graduate students have used the text. It is used in a course with three contact hours per week in a standard 16-week semester. Professionals working in hydrology and stormwater management may also use the book.

Chapter 1 and the first two sections of Chapter 2 are introductory lectures and, thus, proportionally less time is spent on them. Generally, equal time is spent on the remaining materials. Parts of Chapters 6 and 9 may be omitted by some teachers and used in a more advanced course. The problems at the end of each chapter have been solved and a solution manual is available for professors adopting the text. Also, professionals working with stormwater management system designs and analysis will find the end-of-chapter problems and text examples useful. In fact, many of the problems (example and end-of-chapter) use realistic data from research projects or consultations.

Computer programs on a diskette are included with this book. Not only will the computer programs aid in an understanding of basic hydrologic phenomena but they will also be useful in reducing the time it takes to solve a problem that has a large number of repetitive calculations. However, the text can be used without the computer programs. For the professional doing larger problems, the computer programs are also useful.

The text material is unique in (1) the presentation of basic hydrology concepts, (2) the integration of hydrologic, hydraulic, and quantity control, (3) the realistic problems, and (4) the coverage of topics, such as synthetic hydrographs, volume and peak discharge management, convolution, empirical frequency distributions, and related design criteria. Hydraulic principles are introduced and used where appropriate. Practicing engineers, hydrologists, and planners will find the material useful in completing comprehensive water quantity plans that are required by state and federal regulatory agencies.

Martin P. Wanielista

ACKNOWLEDGMENTS

I thank the scientists and engineers who provided written materials in the form of consulting reports, example tutorial problems, and reviews. Without their input, the practical application of the theory would not have been possible. Bernard L. Golding provided the initial encouragement for the book's development. Dr. J. P. Hartman provided an in-depth review of Chapter 10, and Dr. Y. A. Yousef reviewed Chapter 11. I am appreciative of the reviews of the manuscript in the different phases of completion that were provided by the publisher.

A special thanks go to George Cooper, who helped develop the computer programs. His attention to programming details made the programs very beneficial for both educational and practical use.

The text materials were reviewed by students in a hydrology course and a water resource course at the University of Central Florida. Special recognition is extended to Sara Mayo, Betty Wanielista, Cheryl Brooks, Jackie Goigel, Dawn Fetter, Bryon Russell, John Florio and Denver Stutler for their assistance in compiling, editing, typing, and proofreading.

M. P. W.

CONTENTS

5 Streamflow Measurements 121

6 Hydrographs 155

8 Flow Routing

9 Probability and Statistics for Hydrologic Descriptors

10 Groundwater Hydrology   345

11 Volume and Peak Discharge Management _____ **375**

············
············
············

1

INTRODUCTION

The study and practice of hydrology aids in explaining and quantifying the occurrence of water on, under, and over the earth's surface. Hydrology is both a scientific and engineering field of study. The subject area is derived from many basic sciences such as mathematics, physics, meteorology, and geology. In this text, methods for measurement and methodologies for the description and prediction of hydrologic processes are presented. Hydrologic processes are ones that vary with time and also change with geographic location. The quantities (volume and rate) of each process resulting from modifications to other hydrologic processes and land use conditions are the fundamental considerations in this text. Both theoretical and experimental descriptions are presented.

1.1

ORGANIZATION AND CONTENT OF THE TEXT

This chapter presents information concerning the content and organization of the text. Next, the social importance of hydrology, the value of accounting for the location of water (water budget), units of measurement, and computation aids are briefly introduced. To enforce the concepts and ideas of each chapter, some example problems are solved and then additional problems are found at the end of each chapter. The end-of-chapter problems recognize the complexity of hydrologic systems and provide repetition to learn problem-solving procedures. The computer programs on a diskette included with this book serve as teaching aids in addition to being computation aids. One computer diskette is provided.

Summary statements are also used to reinforce the material of each chapter. The summaries are listed before the problem sections of each chapter to highlight important ideas, issues, and concepts.

The text material is primarily used for the study of water quantity using basic hydrologic processes: precipitation, streamflow, runoff, evaporation, transpiration, infiltration, and storage. Both volumes and rates of flow are included for water quantity studies. Measurement techniques for each process are developed. Information to relate one process to other common processes of the hydrologic cycle are presented. Watershed and meteorological factors that affect these processes are developed. Quantification of the hydrologic processes is done by relating each process to easily available watershed and meteorological data. Concepts of probability and statistics are introduced as they relate to hydrology and water quantity management. The example problems and end-of-chapter problems are developed to aid in understanding hydrologic processes and the relationships among watershed, meteorological, and hydrologic processes.

Water quality is another consideration for the management of surface and ground waters. Water quality issues build on the basic concepts of this text. Hydrologic processes and measures can be applied to stormwater management for quality control. However, this text does not directly address the water quality issues. Other texts are available (Novotny and Chesters, 1981; Wanielista, 1983).

1.2

SOCIAL IMPORTANCE AND ENGINEERING RELEVANCE

Many aspects of social life are dependent on the economic availability and acceptable quality of water. The availability of water determines the basic existence of a society. Without sufficient water, there would be no life as it is known today. Thus, people educated and trained in a variety of water-related jobs are necessary. Modern society appears to be very dependent on water projects. Early societies used the water experts to help plan, design and build canals for transportation. Modern society has shifted the primary use of canals from transporting people and goods to irrigation, drainage, and potable water supply. With this shift comes greater interest in water quantity management. For example, along our highways there exists the need to manage waters to prevent flooding of adjacent lands. Also, as populations increase, the required volume of potable water increases. Thus, emphasis is on the volume of water and the rate of flow.

Planning is an important part of any society. Furthermore, this planning must conform to reasonable economic forecasts. Rate of flow and volume projections and protections must be planned. One can plan for future water requirements, but the plans must conform to some economic model requiring different levels of benefits to be estimated. These benefits usually can be expressed in both quantitative and qualitative ways. To warrant investment, costs are generally required to be less than the benefits expected. As a simple example, peak streamflow varies from year to year. Is it reasonable to provide protection against the very rare streamflow? The cost of this protection may be much greater than the losses from a flood. Thus, individuals in the planning area must be aware of the chance events associated with probable outcomes and incorporate economic considerations into the analysis.

The use of the concepts, ideas, and methods of hydrology are found in both the public sector of governments and the private sector of an economy. Individuals with hydrologic backgrounds can perform design calculations, collect hydrologic data, inspect construction, and conduct operations and maintenance activities. There are many types of hydrologic-related work including flood mitigation, roadway drainage, irrigation systems, navigation, water supply, pollution control, hydropower development, and ecological protection. Certainly, there is a tendency towards specialization, because details in design and operation are necessary. But also, there are needs for the individual with general knowledge about the many interactions of water projects. The material in this text introduces broad concepts, interactions, and design specifics related to the quantity of water.

1.3

WATER BUDGET OR MASS BALANCE

A water budget is an accounting of the volume or flow rate of water in all possible locations. Thus, it is a mass balance. One has to focus interest on a region and determine how the quantity of water in the region can be changed. The regional boundaries have to be determined across which water may move or be confined. Also, a time period must be specified.

A simple example of a budget is water from a parking lot. First, one must determine the surface boundaries of the parking lot that can contribute water to a collection point. The boundary may be defined on the surface as an

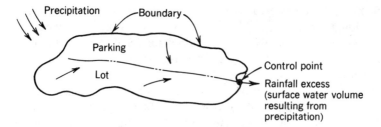

FIGURE 1.1   Parking lot water budget.

imaginary line bordering the surface area from which precipitation can be accumulated and routed to some control point. At the control point, a decision may be made on the volume and rate of discharge. The control point can be an inlet grate at the lowest elevation of the parking lot. If the parking lot is constructed with curbes to contain the water on site, the boundary is easily determined. A parking lot is shown schematically in Figure 1.1. A water budget for the parking lot depicted in Figure 1.1 is helpful to present the concepts of a mass balance. Assume that all precipitation remains on the surface of the parking lot and is routed to a control point. This water volume is given the term rainfall excess. The rate at which rainfall excess appears over time at a discharge (control) point is called runoff. A water budget can be written in volume terms (mass balance):

$$\text{Inputs} - \text{outputs} \pm \text{accumulation} = 0$$

If water is not stored on the parking surface, the accumulation term is zero with input equal to precipitation and output equal to rainfall excess, or:

$$\text{Rainfall excess} = \text{volume of precipitation} \tag{1.1}$$

If precipitation is abstracted by depression storage in the parking lot, then the water budget is altered as shown in Equation 1.2.

$$\text{Rainfall excess} = \text{precipitation} - \text{depression storage} \tag{1.2}$$

The complexity of a budget depends on the physical system and the ultimate use of the budget. Water budgets for large areas are complex with many parameters.

1.3.1 Global Water Budget

Available freshwater on earth comprises only about 3% of the total supply (Miller, 1986). More than 97% of the water on earth contains dissolved solids, which result in a salty taste. Direct human use and most industrial uses of salt water are possible only after some or most of the solids are removed. Other waters become unfit for municipal and industrial use when unwanted chemicals or rubbish are disposed of in them. Also biological changes can take place within the water resulting in a need for treatment before use.

Much of the freshwater is not readily available for use due to its remote locations. A majority of the freshwater (90%) is found in glaciers and polar ice caps. The small fraction of the total supply available for human consumption is estimated at about 4 billion billion liters. This is 400 million liters per person at a population of 10 billion people. It would appear then that water supply would not be a problem if remote sources could be made economically available and pollution could be minimized. Making water economically available is the major task.

On a global scale, the quantity of water is finite and its usable fraction can be altered (Wanielista et al., 1984). With a global water budget, one can establish water quality and quantity levels. Thus, the availability of water can be a matter of record, which provides responsible people with the database for decision making. This decision making can affect both water and land uses in a large region or a small council district. Useful storage must be monitored to ensure that there are no significant losses over time. When one of the inputs or outputs to the usable storage is significantly altered, changes will take place. These changes may be costly and life-styles may have to be altered. Life-style changes are already evident in places where usable water is in short supply. People must limit their consumption, which changes life-style.

1.3.2 Geographic Area Water Budgets

On a smaller scale, examples exist that indicate the value of a water budget. One such example is Amboseli National Park in southern Kenya. The park is located just north of Mount Kilimanjaro. Highly saline groundwater percolates from Kilimanjaro to Amboseli. The climate is arid, with on the average only 400 mm (16 in.) of rain per year.

After the early 1960s, the vegetation in the park changed along with the animal life that fed on the vegetation. What caused the changes? After an examination of a water budget for the area, it was found that precipitation on Kilimanjaro had increased dramatically. This caused groundwater levels to increase, which raised the groundwater levels beneath the lake beds in the National Park and caused a shift in the surface vegetation.

There are also examples of precipitation greatly exceeding watershed storage. In many cases, floods and subsequent damages can be reduced simply by storing water for release during dry periods. These examples show that simple water budgets are valuable and can provide operating guidelines for reservoir sizing.

Excessive precipitation is not the only problem. There are examples of too little precipitation causing drought conditions and rapid depletion of groundwater. This in turn causes an increased cost of water treatment. Subsidence, or sinkhole activity, has also been related to groundwater withdrawal. Possibly one of the most famous subsidence studies was conducted near Venice (Gambolati et al., 1974). Again, a water budget was used. The budget indicated a reduction in subsurface water occurred from pumping activities and could have caused the subsidence. Sinkhole activity in Florida and Texas has been related to groundwater withdrawal. A relatively complete history of sinkhole activities and related groundwater levels have been reported for the central Florida area. In the Houston–Galveston area, up to 3 m (9.8 ft) of subsidence has been noted and related to groundwater withdrawals. As pumps in wells remove great quantities of water from one of the United States most plentiful aquifers, about 1700 mi^2 of land has subsided. To prevent this subsidence, the source of water supply is being changed from groundwater to surface water and to practice more conservative use of water (*U.S. Water News*, 1985).

In Pennsylvania and other areas, increases in stormwater discharges to groundwaters were related to sinkhole activity. Possibly the increased volume and flow rates of stormwater being discharged to the aquifer caused dissolving of the limestone rock structure. Again, a water budget was used to estimate groundwater volume increases.

1.4

UNITS OF MEASUREMENT

Consistency among individuals in the reporting of data would increase the rate of knowledge transfer. The transfer of data is enhanced by modern definitions of primary and secondary units of measurement. The primary quantities are defined as mass, length, time, and temperature. A secondary quantity is one defined in terms of primary quantities. Examples of secondary quantities are volume in cubic meters (m^3), density in kilograms per cubic meter (kg/m^3), and rainfall intensity (mm/s). The U.S., or English customary System, and the International System of Units (SI) are both used in this text. It is important for hydrologists, planners, and engineers to understand and calculate with a knowledge of both systems of units. Thus, a mixture of SI and customary units is found in the text with conversion factors included. Some of the more common notation and dimensions for basic units of hydrology are shown in Table 1.1. A more complete notation list is shown in Appendix A.

TABLE 1.1   Some Common Hydrologic Symbols and Dimensions

PROPERTY	SYMBOL	CUSTOMARY	SI UNITS
Length	т	ft	m
Mass	Primary	lb	kg
Time	dimensions	s	s
Temperature	⊥	°F or °R	°C or K
Precipitation volume	P	in.	mm
Precipitation rate	i	in./hr	mm/hr
Rainfall excess	R	in.(ft^3)^a	mm(m^3)^a
Infiltration rate	f	in./hr	cm/hr
Velocity	v	ft/s	m/s
Area	A	ft^2	m^2
Volume	V	ft^3	m^3
Flow rate	Q	ft^3/s (CFS)	m^3/s
Concentration	C	lb/gal	mg/L

^{a} Volume (depth over an area).

□   **EXAMPLE PROBLEM 1.1**

From basic units, develop conversion factors for volumetric flow rate and area loadings.

Solution

For flow rate:

$$Q = \text{flow rate} = L^3/t \quad (\text{from cubic feet/second to meters}^3/\text{second})$$

$$= 1 \text{ ft}^3/\text{s} \times (0.3049 \text{ m/ft})^3 = 0.0283 \text{ m}^3/\text{s}$$

and area loadings:

$$\text{loadings} = M/L^2 \quad (\text{from lb/ac to kg/ha})$$

$$1 \text{ lb/ac} \times 0.454 \text{ kg/lb} \times 2.471 \text{ ac/ha} = 1.121 \text{ kg/ha}$$

A listing of conversion factors is presented in Appendix B and an abbreviated list is found within the front and back cover.   □

□   **EXAMPLE PROBLEM 1.2**

Using the conversion factors of Appendix B, convert 1 in. of rainfall over a 1 mi watershed to rainfall excess expressed as acre-feet, cubic feet, gallons, and cubic meters. Assume that all the rainfall is available as rainfall excess.

Solution

From a mass balance, rainfall excess is equal to rainfall, thus using the conversion tables of Appendix B:

a.   Conversion to acre-feet:

$$1 \text{ in.-mi}^2 \times 1 \text{ ft}/12 \text{ in.} \times 640 \text{ acres}/\text{mi}^2$$

$$= 53.33 \text{ acre-feet}/\text{in.-mi}^2$$

which agrees with the conversion factor under Miscellaneous in Appendix B.

b.   Conversion to cubic feet:
There are 43,560 ft^2/acre, thus $(53.33 \times 43,560)$ 1 in.-mi$^2 = 2.323$ $(10^6) \text{ ft}^3$

c.   Conversion to gallons:
There are 7.48 gal/ft^3, thus $(7.48 \times 2.323 \ (10^6))$ 1 in.-m$^2 = 17.38$ $(10^6) \text{ gal}$

d.   Conversion to cubic meters:
There are 35.314 ft^3/m^3, thus $(2.323 \ (10^6)/35.314)$ 1 in.-m$^2 = 65,781$ m^3, which agrees with the conversion factor under Miscellaneous in Appendix B.   □

1.5

COMPUTATION AIDS

Problems in hydrology frequently require repetitive and precise calculations. Some are solved by trial-and-error methods. Others require repeating the basic solution algorithm many times. Many aids for solving these problems have been developed over the years. Nomographs and coaxial graphs were popular about 25 years ago (1950–1965) and are still used today. These graphs make the computation procedure less complex and save time. Proper interpretation of the graphs is necessary and can be learned by those educated and trained in the subject matter. Starting in the 1960s, calculators of various types further streamlined the repetitive and routine calculations. Also, around the same time, computers were gaining popularity. In the early 1980s, the personal computer (PC) gained greater recognition as an aid to solving complex repetitive problems in hydrology. As more software developed, the availability of PCs increased and cost decreased. In the late 1980s, many researchers, planners, engineers, and hydrologists increased their dependency on computers.

1.6
COMPUTER PROGRAMS

To understand some of the complex problems for which hydrology can aid in solving, it is frequently necessary to use computer programs. There are many computer programs available to aid in solving these hydrologic processes. Computer programs are available with this book and can be used for educational or professional experience. The programs are resident on a computer diskette of standard $5\frac{1}{4}$in. size. These programs should be initialized on your computer and the menus reviewed. These programs are similar to those programs used by professionals (additional details in Appendix I). Similarity is found with input data and computation procedures. As with any computation aid, all programs are specific to certain types of problems and input data identification is very important.

1.7
SUMMARY

Brief summary statements to highlight important concepts, ideas, problems, and formulas are provided at the end of each chapter to reinforce material. Details related to the material must be obtained by reading the complete text and solving both the example problems in the chapter and problems at the end of the text. The depth of understanding can be increased by reading some of the references at the end of each chapter.

- Hydrology is the study of waters on, under, and over the earth's surface.
- Water quantity control can be understood knowing hydrologic principles. Both peak rates and volume control are studied in this text.
- The basic concept of a water budget is necessary to understand and interpret hydrologic data. A volume mass balance of rainfall and rainfall excess for a parking lot helps to illustrate the concept.
- Rainfall excess is the volume of water from rainfall that remains on the surface and is available for runoff, while runoff is the rate at which water is discharged from a watershed.
- A notation list is found in Appendix A.

- Conversion tables are found in Appendix B and on the inside of the front and back cover of the book.
- To expand an understanding of hydrologic processes, computer programs would be helpful.

1.8

PROBLEMS

1. List at least five hydrologic processes.
2. Explain in your own words and by means of an example how you can use hydrology and economics to aid in solving a problem related to a hydrologic process.
3. Convert and show all basic units for:
   a. Pounds/acre-day to kilograms/hectare-year
   b. Acre-feet to million gallons
   c. Cubic feet/second to cubic meters/second
   d. Inches/hour to millimeters/hour
   e. Liters/second to gallons/minute
4. What is a water budget? Explain at least three applications of a water budget to hydrologic systems.
5. Write an equation of a water budget for a parking lot that has on-site storage. Using common notation for precipitation volume, rainfall excess, and storage volume, show an equation to solve for rainfall excess. Using both the SI and U.S. customary set of units for the variables of your equation, define at least four consistent sets of units.

1.9

COMPUTER-ASSISTED PROBLEMS

1. Initiate the computer program diskette provided with this book. Obtain the menus of programs and locate at least one chapter of this book where the programs can be used. This exercise will start to familiarize you with the computer programs and the subject material.
2. Using your own disk, develop a computer program to convert any inputed data from pounds/acre-day to kilograms/hectare-year, from acre-feet to million gallons, from cubic feet/second to cubic meters/second, from inches/hour to millimeters/hour, and from liter/second to gallons/minute. Be sure to document the program well and make it user friendly. Print out the inputed data as well as the converted data along with the appropriate units.

1.10

REFERENCES

Gambolati, G., Gatto, P., and Freeze, R.A. 1974. "Predictive Simulation of the Subsidence of Venice," *Science* **183**, pp. 849–851.

Miller, G.T., Jr. 1986. *Living in the Environment—Concepts, Problems and Alternatives*. Wadsworth Publishing Co., Inc., Belmont, CA.

Novotny, V. and Chesters, G. 1981. *Handbook of Nonpoint Pollution: Sources and Management*. Van Nostrand-Reinhold, New York.

U.S. Water News, May 1985, "Houston's Subsidence Problem," **1** (11), pp. 1 and 17.

Wanielista, M.P., Yousef, Y.A., Taylor J.S., and Cooper C.D. 1984. *Engineering and The Environment*. Brooks/Cole Engineering Division, Wadsworth, Belmont, CA.

Wanielista, M.P. 1983. *Stormwater Management: Quality and Quantity Control*. Ann Arbor Science Publishers, Ann Arbor, MI.

....
....
....

2

METEOROLOGY AND THE HYDROLOGIC CYCLE

This chapter introduces some scientific explanations believed to be responsible for the occurrence and distribution of waters on the earth. The hydrologic cycle is a description of waters on, above, and below the earth's surface. To identify and quantify the distribution of waters, a mass balance of the hydrologic cycle is introduced. From the hydrologic cycle and the mass balance, the concepts and formulas related to the estimation of waters remaining on the ground after a precipitation event are introduced. Terms such as rainfall excess, runoff, and runoff coefficient are identified. Rainfall excess is the volume of rainfall that is available for intentional on-site surface storage or if not stored, it becomes runoff from the site. Runoff is the rate of flow at which rainfall excess is discharged from an area. The runoff coefficient relates both the runoff rate to precipitation rate and rainfall excess to precipitation volume. These are important terms used for hydrologic studies. Two additional terms of the hydrologic cycle to be defined are infiltration and evapotranspiration. Infiltration is the movement of water from the ground surface into the soil while evapotranspiration is the conversion of liquid water to water vapor from water surfaces, soils, and vegetation.

Meteorology also helps explain other hydrologic measures. Some measures with reference to the chapters which describe them are:

1. Volume, intensity, type and area distribution of precipitation in Chapter 3.
2. Infiltration and evapotranspiration in Chapter 4.
3. Flow rates and volumes of water transport in Chapters 5 and 8.
4. Flow rate and volume changes with time in Chapters 6 and 7.
5. Changes in groundwater flow rates and volumes in Chapter 10.

2.1

METEOROLOGY

Meteorology is the study of the atmosphere with special interest in weather and climate conditions. Weather conditions are those existing in a watershed or area at a specific time. Climate is the average of prevailing conditions over a period of years and is defined by measures of central tendency (average, median, etc.) or variability (standard deviation, range, etc.).

Weather conditions with ground cover, topography, and geology of an area determine surface water storage volumes and flow rates to a great extent. Description or prediction of storage and flow rates must begin with, or at least be related to, meteorological and geological conditions.

2.1.1   The Atmosphere

The atmosphere is the gaseous envelope surrounding the earth. It sustains life by cycling chemicals and water. For the study of hydrology, the complex atmosphere can be divided into three parts: dry air, water vapor, and impurities related to the hydrologic cycling of water.

The dry portion of air is a mixture of gases. If the gases were separated and brought to the same temperature and pressure, the relative volumes that the four principal gases would occupy are shown in Table 2.1. These four gases make up all but 0.003% of the atmosphere 15 miles (25 km) above the earth. Some of the other trace gases are helium, ozone, hydrogen, radon, neon, and krypton. Ozone is an important trace gas because it prevents ultraviolet radiation from reaching the earth's surface. The carbon dioxide and water vapor in the air cause radiation from the earth to be absorbed. This absorption causes temperature increases. The quantity of carbon dioxide is changing because of its consumption by vegetation, absorption by oceans, and production by animals, volcanoes, and the burning of fossil fuels. Changes in atmospheric gases, especially ozone and carbon dioxide will continue to be

TABLE 2.1 Volume of Four Gases
in the Atmosphere

GAS	PERCENTAGE
Nitrogen (N_2)	78.09
Oxygen (O_2)	20.95
Argon (Ar)	0.93
Carbon dioxide (CO_2)	0.03

examined to determine effects on the amount and distribution of water on the earth. Some investigators (Hansen, et al., 1981) predict dramatic effects on the earth's climate and weather which could change precipitation and evaporation rates.

2.1.2 Water Vapor

In the atmosphere of the earth, water vapor by weight is about 1.5×10^{13} metric tons. The atmosphere weight is 5.6×10^{15} metric tons. Water vapor must be present with temperature differences and other impurities for clouds and precipitation to form. Generally, water vapor occurs in the atmosphere about 18,000 ft above the earth (Petterssen, 1964). Within the earth's atmosphere, as distance from the earth increases, temperature in general will decrease. As temperature decreases, water vapor content will decrease. The amount of water vapor can be expressed as the pressure that vapor would exert in the absence of other gases, and is known as vapor pressure. The vapor pressure of water vapor saturating the air at 86°F (30°C) is about 1.18 in. of mercury (40 millibars [mbar]) while at 32°F (0°C), the vapor pressure is about 0.20 in. of mercury (7 mbar).

The atmosphere is infrequently saturated. The degree of saturation is expressed as the ratio of actual vapor pressure to that at saturation for a given temperature. This ratio is expressed as a percentage and is called relative humidity, or:

$$f = 100 \frac{e}{E} \qquad (2.1)$$

where
  f = relative humidity (%)
  e = actual vapor pressure (mbar)
  E = saturated vapor pressure (mbar)

As the relative humidity increases and approaches 100%, the chances for precipitation increases.

2.1.3 Solar Energy

Solar energy initiates the hydrologic cycle and influences climate. On the average, solar energy reaching the earth is approximately 0.5 Ly/min with the planet absorbing about 0.22 Ly/min. There are wide geographic differences in the net rate at which solar energy is received at the earth's surface. Snow, for example, can reflect about 80% while dark soil can absorb about 90% (Wanielista et al., 1984). These differences aid in air movements and serve to redistribute energy. The energy produces mass movements in the atmosphere and oceans and is the energy source for evaporation and transpiration. Evaporation occurs from water surfaces while transpiration is the loss of water from plant life. Of special interest for the understanding of the hydrologic cycle are the fundamental processes of conduction, convection, and radiation. Solar energy enters the hydrologic cycle by the radiation process. The redistribution of energy is done by conduction from the land and convection in the water bodies and atmosphere.

Conduction is the transport of air between adjacent layers if the layers are at different temperatures. A net transport of heat will result. Also, the amount of heat transfer is dependent on velocity and concentration. The degree of proportionality can be determined by laboratory measures and is expressed by the following.

For thermal conductivity:

$$q_x = K_T\left[(\Delta T)/x\right] \tag{2.2}$$

where

q_x = rate of transport of heat per unit area in the x direction (cal/cm^2-sec)
K_T = thermal conductivity constant at steady state (cal/deg-cm-sec)
ΔT = temperature differential (degrees centigrade)
x = distance (cm)

For concentration, Fick's law of diffusion can be used, and for velocity, Newton's law of viscosity can be used.

Convection is the movement of heat by the mass movement of air or water. It is one of the results of instability of the air or water masses, frequently caused by the potential energy in latent heat being converted into air currents. The rate at which the energy is released determines the meteorological conditions of rainfall and wind. Usually, stronger updrafts of air produce shorter rainfall durations. Another convective process—advection—is the transfer of heat by horizontal movement. The large-scale advective circulations of the atmosphere and the oceans are under the control of solar activity and the rotation of the earth.

2.1.4 Wind

Wind is the movement of air. The measures of wind are speed and direction. Wind speed is important because it can be related to water losses and precipitation events. In order for precipitation to occur, a sustained inflow of moist air is required. Winds provide the forces to sustain the moist air flow. Instruments for measuring wind speed are called anemometers. Common measures are kilometers per hour, miles per hour, meters per second, or knots.

If the world did not rotate, wind patterns would be established solely by thermal circulation. Winds would move towards the equator as warmer and lighter air would rise and be replaced by cooler dense air. Because of the earth's rotation, air mass (frontal) movements are from west to east. Solar energy and the earth's rotation are superimposed on thermal circulation. When air masses with different temperatures meet, precipitation can occur at the boundary (front).

During a day, wind speed and direction may change. These are called diurnal changes and are significant only near the ground. Examples are changes that result from temperature contrasts between land and water. Winds tend to blow from cooler bodies toward warmer ones. In the summer afternoons, winds tend to blow toward the warmer land from the cooler water bodies. Mountains also influence wind currents because of diurnal heating of the sides of mountains, which can cause unequal heating of air masses, causing wind currents. Heating loss from other heat sources (sand, pavement, buildings) also can set up wind movement.

Over any one of the major continents, there will exist prevailing winds, either called trade or westerly winds. Between the trade and westerlies are calm or lightly variable winds. Nevertheless, pressure systems make the direction and speed of winds generally variable with time. In the northern hemisphere, these pressure systems move across a continent spinning counterclockwise if a low pressure system and clockwise if a high pressure system.

2.1.5 Temperature

Temperature influences the form of precipitation and the rates of evaporation, transpiration, and snowmelt. It is one measure that has been related to the prediction and explanation of the occurrence and distribution of waters on the earth. The measurement of temperature and factors influencing the measurement will be discussed first.

The measurement of temperature requires consideration of air circulation and surfaces in the immediate vicinity of the measuring device. There are over 8500 stations in the United States for which records are compiled by a government agency. The recording stations are constructed of louvered, wooden shelters positioned about 1.5 m (4–5 ft) above the ground. The shelters are protected from direct sunlight, wind, and precipitation. The recording station will list daily maximum and minimum temperature values. Temperatures are expressed using the Celsius (°C), Fahrenheit (°F), or absolute scales. Mean daily temperatures are expressed in terms of the interval of data collection. There are a few hundred hourly recording stations in the United States. For hourly temperature data:

$$T_{avg} = \sum_{i=1}^{24} T_i/24 \qquad (2.3)$$

where

T_{avg} = average daily temperature, °F or °C
T_i = hourly temperature, °F or °C

If maximum and minimum data are collected, then the average temperature is defined as

$$T_{avg} = (T_{max} + T_{min})/2 \qquad (2.4)$$

where

T_{max} = maximum daily temperature, °C
T_{min} = minimum daily temperature, °C

The person using temperature data should know how averages were calculated because the average will vary with the method used.

Temperatures exhibit diurnal, seasonal, geographical, and elevation variations. Consequently, average conditions must be defined by time and location. An example of monthly variability with yearly averages is shown in Table 2.2 for a semitropical area in the northern hemisphere.

Under normal atmospheric conditions, temperatures will decrease with elevation. The mean decrease with increasing elevation is 0.7°C/100 m (3.8°F/1,000 ft). Thus, applying temperature data from one location (elevation) to a second location (elevation) may not be accurate. Tests of comparability would be advisable to establish deviations and levels of acceptable accuracy.

The temperature associated with saturated air is referred to as dewpoint temperature (T_D). Dewpoint temperature is easily obtained in the field or available from Weather Bureau records. Knowing the air and dewpoint temperature, an estimate of relative humidity can be obtained using

$$f = (112 - 0.1T + T_D)/(112 + 0.9T) \qquad (2.5)$$

where

f = relative humidity,
T = temperature, °C
T_D = dewpoint temperature, °C

The diurnal variation of atmospheric moisture is normally small with relative humidity being a maximum early in the morning.

2.1.6 The Variability of Data

Meteorological data change frequently, certainly daily and seasonally, but sometimes instaneously. As an example of change, consider the local climatological data in Table 2.3. Note the statistical data such as averages and departures from normal, which indicate variability in the data. For some studies, site-specific meteorological data are not available. Thus, data from the Weather Bureau or similar organizations located some distance from the study must be used and significant errors may be introduced. Equations used for description or prediction of hydrologic events could be tested for sensitivity of meteorological inputs. If necessary, field meteorologic data collected at a study site may be used, or at least statistically compared to longer records at permanent sites.

2.2

WEATHER SYSTEMS

The state of the atmosphere as measured by its temperature, water vapor, wind, and pressure determine the weather of a region. An understanding of the weather in a region will help explain some of the reasons for the existence of the hydrologic cycle and the measurement of the parameters of the cycle. The weather systems are related to types of precipitation events and air masses.

An air mass is a large air body whose physical properties (temperature, vapor, wind, pressure) are approximately constant in a horizontal plane. But violent changes occur on the border of the mass. These air masses can be found in the Arctic and Antarctic regions, subtropical ocean areas, and arid subtropical lands. The air masses will move from these regions. If the air mass is colder than the surface while in motion, precipitation will usually occur.

The border between air masses is called a front. Fronts are classified by the displacement of air. If cold air replaces warm air, a cold front results. A warm front results when warner air moves into an area. When warm air masses rise, cooling takes place and precipitation can result. Storm systems can be classified by the factors responsible for the lifting of air masses (wind or solar heating). There are four major types of storms:

1. Convective storms
2. Orographic storms
3. Cyclonic storms
4. Tropical cyclones

TABLE 2.2 Yearly and Monthly Temperature Averages

YEAR	JAN	FEB	MAR	APR	MAY	JUNE	JULY	AUG	SEPT	OCT	NOV	DEC	ANNUAL
						AVERAGE TEMPERATURE °F							
1934	62.2	59.8	65.4	70.8	76.4	60.0	81.8	82.0	79.6	75.0	67.2	60.4	71.7
1935	61.2	60.0	70.7	72.7	78.0	81.2	80.6	82.3	78.6	73.8	64.8	51.8	71.3
1936	58.6	56.9	63.9	69.8	74.5	77.8	81.6	81.0	79.4	76.8	64.4	62.8	70.6
1937	69.4	62.2	64.6	69.7	75.6	80.5	81.2	81.4	78.8	72.0	63.8	58.4	71.5
1938	59.3	65.2	70.2	70.4	77.0	77.8	79.6	81.2	78.3	70.2	66.6	57.8	71.1
1939	60.3	67.0	69.0	72.2	76.2	81.0	82.0	80.4	81.2	75.4	63.6	59.0	72.3
1940	50.4	57.5	64.8	68.4	73.8	80.0	80.6	82.3	78.2	70.9	64.6	63.8	69.8
1941	57.0	55.8	60.2	70.0	72.9	81.4	80.6	82.8	79.2	76.2	65.4	62.3	70.3
1942	56.6	57.0	65.1	70.0	76.6	80.8	84.5	82.4	81.3	74.1	68.2	63.2	71.7
1943	62.8	59.4	66.4	70.6	78.2	82.8	82.8	88.0	80.4	70.6	65.2	62.0	71.9
1944	58.8	68.2	69.6	72.9	75.2	82.8	82.1	83.0	82.5	72.6	65.4	58.3	72.6
1945	59.8	66.2	72.8	75.7	76.8	82.0	81.8	82.1	81.0	75.0	65.4	59.4	73.2
1946	62.3	63.3	68.8	72.5	78.4	79.8	82.6	82.8	80.9	76.0	73.9	66.8	74.0
1947	69.0	54.2	62.2	76.4	77.8	80.4	80.0	82.0	80.2	76.0	68.8	64.0	72.6
1948	58.0	66.0	71.5	74.1	79.0	82.6	82.0	82.0	80.6	73.2	73.7	67.4	74.2
1949	64.4	69.6	67.4	72.5	77.8	80.6	82.6	81.8	81.1	77.8	62.7	65.2	73.8
1950	68.2	65.1	66.5	67.1	78.0	83.0	81.5	82.3	80.2	77.0	63.5	57.7	72.5
1951	60.0	59.8	66.1	68.5	75.7	80.5	81.8	83.8	81.4	76.1	63.7	65.1	71.9
1952	62.5	61.1	67.3	67.8	77.4	83.0	82.5	82.5	80.5	73.3	65.6	58.0	71.8
1953	60.2	63.5	70.0	71.0	79.7	81.1	82.8	81.5	80.0	71.7	66.1	52.7	72.5
1954	61.9	62.2	64.1	74.1	75.3	81.1	81.4	83.5	80.9	72.1	63.2	57.3	71.4
1955	58.4	62.2	67.4	72.3	77.8	79.3	81.2	82.1	81.4	72.4	65.6	60.8	71.7

Year													
1956	53.1	65.5	65.7	70.2	77.8	79.9	82.1	82.5	78.3	73.4	63.8	64.5	71.6
1957	64.7	67.5	65.8	72.3	76.9	80.7	82.6	81.3	81.0	72.1	69.4	59.1	72.8
1958	52.9	52.4	63.7	71.4	75.6	82.0	82.6	82.7	81.9	72.7	71.3	60.6	70.8
1959	58.3	67.6	63.7	70.9	78.0	81.0	81.3	81.7	79.7	78.5	66.9	60.7	72.3
1960	60.5	59.7	60.9	72.0	76.0	79.5	83.1	83.3	80.3	77.2	69.9	57.6	71.1
1961	56.9	64.7	70.6	69.4	77.0	80.6	83.3	82.9	81.1	73.6	69.4	63.9	72.8
1962	60.9	68.4	63.7	70.3	79.8	81.6	83.9	82.8	80.6	75.0	63.0	57.7	72.3
1963	59.5	57.2	69.5	73.6	77.9	82.4	82.9	83.9	80.5	73.8	65.4	56.5	71.9
1964	58.5	58.3	68.1	74.1	77.1	82.4	81.6	82.8	79.8	72.5	70.5	64.4	72.5
1965	60.0	64.1	67.0	74.8	77.1	79.0	80.5	82.2	80.8	74.2	69.5	62.6	72.7
1966	58.7	62.3	64.4	70.5	77.4	78.0	82.3	82.3	80.1	75.8	65.8	60.1	71.5
1967	63.2	60.0	68.3	74.3	78.3	80.2	82.4	82.0	79.7	74.0	67.5	65.9	73.0
1968	59.6	54.8	61.4	73.5	76.7	78.8	81.3	82.3	80.3	74.3	63.4	58.7	70.4
1969	59.8	57.8	60.4	72.5	76.9	82.9	84.4	82.2	81.2	77.9	64.0	58.7	71.6
1970	55.1	58.7	67.0	75.8	77.7	81.8	83.8	82.3	83.6	77.0	63.4	64.6	72.6
1971	62.0	64.1	64.8	72.1	78.2	81.7	83.1	83.3	81.8	79.0	69.5	71.4	74.2
1972	68.9	62.0	68.7	72.7	77.4	82.2	83.2	82.8	81.8	76.8	68.9	66.1	74.3
1973	62.4	59.7	71.1	71.1	78.3	83.1	84.2	81.8	81.4	75.6	70.9	60.4	73.3
RECORD													
Mean	60.8	62.1	66.6	72.1	77.5	81.2	82.4	82.5	80.8	74.8	66.9	61.9	72.5
Max	71.7	73.3	77.8	83.3	88.4	91.0	91.8	91.6	89.3	83.7	77.3	72.7	82.7
Min	49.9	50.9	55.4	60.9	66.5	71.3	72.9	73.4	72.2	65.8	56.5	51.0	62.2

Latitude: 29 degrees 26 minutes north.
Longitude: 81 degrees 19 minutes west.
Source: National Oceanic and Atmospheric Administration. 1975. Annual Report, National Climatic Center, Acheville, NC.

TABLE 2.3 Example Climatological Data

LOCAL CLIMATOLOGICAL DATA

LATITUDE 28 DEGREES 26 MINUTES NORTH   LONGITUDE 81 DEGREES 19 MINUTES WEST

STATION: MCO
MONTH: MAR
YEAR: 1986

ELEVATION 96 FEET   TIME ZONE: EASTERN

DAY	TEMPERATURE DEGREES F				DEGREE DAYS (BASE 65)		PRECIPITATION			WIND			SUNSHINE				PEAK WIND
	MAXI-MUM	MINI-MUM	AVER-AGE	DEPARTURE FROM NORMAL	HEATING	COOLING	TOTAL WATER EQUIV	SNOW-FALL, ICE PELLETS	SNOW, ICE PELLETS OR ICE ON GROUND AT	AVG SPEED (MPH)	FASTEST MILE SPEED (MPH)	FASTEST MILE DIREC-TION	TOTAL (MIN)	% POS-SIBLE	SKY COVER SUNRISE-SUNSET	WEATHER OCCUR-RENCES	
1	53	42	48	−16	17	0	0.03	0.0	0	11.2	18	26	0	0	5	18	W 21
2	60	35	49	−16	17	0	0.00	0.0	0	9.1	14	29	0	0	0		NW 13
3	72	38	55	−9	10	0	0.00	0.0	0	8.5	14	25	0	0	5		W 22
4	73	52	63	−1	2	0	0.12	0.0	0	10.1	20	24	0	0	9		SW 25
5	66	48	57	−8	8	0	0.00	0.0	0	6.3	13	28	0	0	1	1	W 17
6	71	40	56	−9	9	0	0.00	0.0	0	9.9	18	28	0	0	5		SW 25
7	72	50	61	−4	4	0	0.00	0.0	0	7.6	10	29	0	0	0		NW 20
8	76	48	62	−3	3	0	0.00	0.0	0	7.6	14	08	0	0	9	18	E 13
9	79	59	69	3	0	4	0.00	0.0	0	10.1	15	12	0	0	10	1	SE 17
10	77	64	71	5	0	6	0.00	0.0	0	9.9	15	12	0	0	9		E 19
11	85	64	75	9	0	10	0.00	0.0	0	7.2	12	24	0	0	7	8	W 14
12	88	64	76	10	0	11	0.00	0.0	0	8.7	14	11	0	0	4	18	S 14
13	88	69	79	13	0	14	T	0.0	0	13.3	21	18	0	0	6		S 19
14	79	60	70	3	0	5	0.37	0.0	0	11.6	17	21	0	0	8	13	NW 24
15	77	61	69	2	0	4	0.90	0.0	0	8.2	20	31	0	0	10	13	NW 24
16	82	62	72	5	0	7	0.66	0.0	0	8.1	14	18	0	0	7	3	SW 16
17	82	63	73	6	0	8	0.00	0.0	0	5.9	12	07	0	0	5	1	NE 11
18	82	61	72	5	0	7	0.00	0.0	0	9.4	15	13	0	0	5	1	SE 15
19	87	68	78	11	0	13	0.15	0.0	0	10.9	18	18	0	0	8	1	S 18
20	88	60	74	6	0	9	0.00	0.0	0	11.9	17	20	0	0	7	1	SW 21
21	66	49	58	−10	7	0	0.15	0.0	0	9.6	14	33	0	0	7		N 16
22	59	44	52	−16	13	0	0.01	0.0	0	12.1	16	36	0	0	1		N 20
23	67	42	55	−13	10	0	0.00	0.0	0	9.5	13	02	0	0	0		N 15

Day	Max	Min	Avg	Dep	HDD	CDD	Precip	Snow	Wind				Sky	Wx	Dir
24	73	47	60	-8	5	0	0.00	0.0	8.2	14	06	0	0		E 13
25	77	54	66	-3	0	1	0.00	0.0	9.1	16	06	0	6		NE 20
26	79	61	70	1	0	5	T	0.0	8.5	14	07	0	7		E 14
27	78	60	69	0	0	4	0.02	0.0	7.1	12	06	0	9		NE 12
28	81	57	69	0	0	4	0.00	0.0	7.7	13	06	0	3	1	NE 15
29	79	59	69	0	0	4	0.14	0.0	7.8	13	07	0	6	18	NE 13
30	78	59	69	0	0	4	0.00	0.0	7.8	13	05	0	4	138	NE 14
31	79	59	69	0	0	4	0.00	0.0	7.2	13	07	0	4	1	NE 12
Sum	2353	1699			124	105	2.63	0.0	280.1		18	31		167	
Avg	75.9	54.8							9.0					5.4	
Misc.										21	18	31	0		

TEMPERATURE DATA

Average monthly	65.4
Departure from normal	-1.4
Highest 88 on 12, 13, 20	
Lowest 35 on 2	
Number of days with	
Max 32 or below	0
Max 90 or above	0
Min 32 or below	0
Min 0 or below	0
Heating degree days (base 65)	
Total this month	105
Departure from normal	37
Seasonal total	609
Departure from normal	-47
Cooling degree days (base 65)	
Total this month	124
Departure from normal	0
Seasonal total	218
Departure from normal	-53

PRECIPITATION DATA (INCHES)

Total for the month	2.63
Departure from normal	-0.57
Snowfall, ice pellets	none
Total for the month	0.0 in.
T-Trace	< 0.01 in.

WEATHER

Number of days-	
Clear (scale 0–3)	7
Partly cloudy (scale 4–7)	16
Cloudy (scale 8–10)	8
With 0.01 inch or more precip	10
With 0.10 inch or more precip	7
With 0.50 inch or more precip	2
With 1.00 inch or more precip	0

WEATHER SYMBOLS

1 = Fog
2 = fog w/visibility 1/4 mile or less
3 = Thunder
4 = Ice pellets
5 = Hail
6 = Glaze or rime
7 = Duststorm or sandstorm
8 = Smoke or haze
9 = Blowing snow
X = Tornado

Source: National Oceanic and Atmospheric Administration. 1986. Local Climatic and Data, March, National Climatic Center, Acheville, NC.

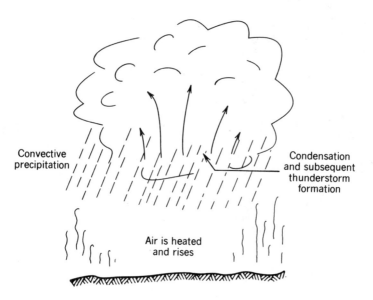

FIGURE 2.1   Convective storm.

2.2.1   Convective Storms

In the atmosphere, convection enables winds to be maintained by an upward and downward transfer of air masses of different temperatures. Convective storms result as warm, humid air rises into cooler overlying air (Figure 2.1). A common form of convective precipitation is the summer thunderstorm. The earth's surface is warmed by mid to late afternoon on a hot summer day. The surface imparts heat to the air mass directly above. The warmed air rises through the overlying air, and if the air mass has a moisture content equal to the condensation level, moisture will be condensed from the rising, rapidly cooling air. This may often result in a large volume of rain from a single thunderstorm.

Unequal cooling of air masses associated with large water bodies or "heat-islands" around metropolitan areas also can cause warm air to rise. Typically, these storms are very intense, are of short duration, and have wide area distribution.

2.2.2   Orographic Storms

Orography is the study of elevation relief between highlands (mountains) to other land and water features. Orographic precipitation results as warmer air rises over a high geographic feature such as a range of mountains and meets

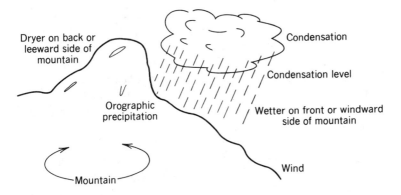

FIGURE 2.2 Orographic storm.

cooler air, as shown in Figure 2.2. Precipitation results if the rising air mass has a condensation level of moisture. Consequently, mountain slopes facing prevailing winds get more precipitation than the back, or leeward, slopes. The precipitation patterns of the Pacific coastal areas of North America are the result of significant orographic influences.

2.2.3 Cyclonic Storms

Cyclonic storms are caused by the rising or lifting of air as it converges on an area of low pressure. The movement of air is from high to low pressure areas

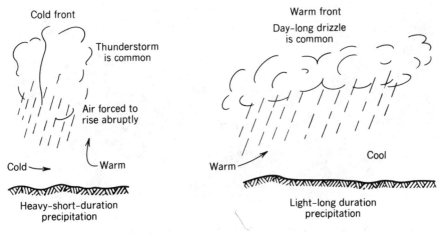

FIGURE 2.3 Cyclonic storms in mid-latitude.

and the boundary between air masses of different pressure is called a front. Frontal precipitation is formed from the lifting of warm air over cold air. Cold fronts are formed by cold air advancing under warmer air; a warm front is formed by warm air advancing over colder air (Figure 2.3). The intensity of precipitation associated with a cold front is usually heavy and covers a relatively small area, whereas less intense precipitation is associated with a warm front, but it covers a much larger area. Tornadoes and other violent weather phenomena are associated with cold fronts.

Cold fronts move faster than warm fronts, and, thus, warm air is lifted at a faster rate causing a higher intensity of precipitation. Cyclonic precipitation can also be associated with low pressure areas in the absence of frontal movements.

FIGURE 2.4 Tropical cyclone in North America, commonly called a hurricane (from U.S. National Environmental Satellite Service, NOAA).

2.2.4 Tropical Cyclones

A tropical cyclone is an intense cyclone with its source in the tropic regions where the surface water temperature is generally greater than 85°F (29°C). The wind speed is 75 mph and above. An example of a tropical cyclone in North America is shown in Figure 2.4. Note the center, or eye, and the counterclockwise wind movement. It is called a hurricane, but in the Far East it is termed a typhoon, and in the Indian Ocean it is called a cyclone. The waters must remain warm to sustain the winds and rain. A tropical cyclone must remain in warm waters to sustain the high winds and rain. Tropical cyclones have been known to cause more than 25 cm (10 in.) of rain on an area in a relatively short time period (12–24 hr). In most regions, tropical cyclones cause the greatest volume of rainfall per storm event.

2.3

HYDROLOGIC CYCLE

The hydrologic cycle is a simplified accounting of the complex interactions of meteorological, biological, chemical, and geological phenomena. It is the movement of water from surface water, groundwater, and vegetation to the atmosphere and back to the earth in the form of precipitation. The transfer of water from plant tissues to the atmosphere is called transpiration. Plants absorb water from the soil through the root system. Rainfall can be abstracted onto vegetation, intentionally stored in ponds, be abstracted by depression storage (unintentional small volumes), infiltrated into the soil, or be available for discharge (rainfall excess). Rainfall that infiltrates into the soil, moves or percolates to the water table. Some of this groundwater may help recharge the aquifers. Some infiltrated waters may evaporate or flow in the direction of surface waters. This is a simplified accounting of a very dynamic process, shown in Figure 2.5.

Some surface water will remain after infiltration, abstraction by vegetation, and depression storage has been filled. An example of depression storage is a hole in pavement that stores water. This depression storage is different from the intentional design of surface storage ponds to reduce rainfall excess and runoff.

2.3.1 The Hydrologic Cycle as a Mass Balance

Using a water budget to represent the hydrologic cycle, an equation to estimate surface water volumes can be developed. This equation is elementary but useful for surface water accounting where inputs and outputs vary with

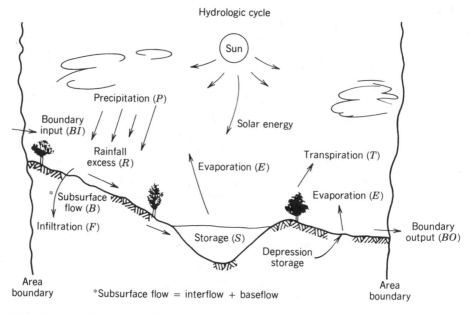

FIGURE 2.5   Hydrologic cycle.

time. Volume units are used and time is fixed for most elementary applications of the water budget. All elements of the hydrologic cycle are dependent in some way on each other. A schematic representation of a pond is helpful to develop a mass balance equation, shown in Figure 2.6. All variables that cross the boundary must be accounted for in equation form. Rainfall excess is usually separated from surface storage to denote its significance in stormwater management studies. An equation for the mass balance of Figure 2.6 is

$$\text{Inputs} - \text{outputs} = \text{change in storage}$$

$$P + R + B - F - E - T = \Delta S \tag{2.6}$$

where ΔS = change in storage volume. A boundary transfer can be net human consumptive uses from surface volumes and/or groundwater volumes. In the water budget, volumes are measured in units of cubic meters, liters, acre-feet, cubic feet, gallons, or inches and centimeters over the watershed area. Also, a common way to express quantities of surface waters is in discharge units (volume per unit time). In the United States, data on discharge are available from the U.S. Geological Survey (USGS, all years) and other state and federal environmental departments. Other countries publish similar data.

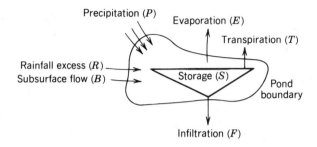

FIGURE 2.6 Schematic of hydrologic cycle.

It is often desired to perform a water budget for a specific time and on a specific watershed. The watershed of concern must be delineated to determine significant inputs over the time period. The time periods for analysis are chosen to be consistent with desired accuracy or storm event. Surface storage will change with time and is dependent on meteorological, geological, topographical, and human consumption factors.

2.3.2 Surface Water Supplies

One of the uses of the hydrologic cycle and a mass balance equation is in the estimation of surface storage. As an example, an area has an insufficient supply of water. Net input boundary exchanges may be increased by constructing reservoirs (water impoundments), restricting consumptive uses and importing water. Weather modifications are possible (however, not extensively used) for either increasing or decreasing precipitation. Geological surveys may indicate ways of directing subsurface runoff so that groundwater supplies are supplemented or transferred to surface waters. Thus, surface water inventories can be affected by various engineering projects. In addition to volume or inventory analysis of the hydrologic cycle, flow rates are important for establishing transport systems and quality degradation.

Storing and transferring a sufficient quantity of water from one location to another has been one of the major problems of society. Some questions related to surface storage and the hydrologic cycle are: What volume of water is stored in a surface reservoir and how does the volume change over time? What causes the water supply to be depleted or increased? How are the storage and releases managed?

Surface flows into a reservoir are necessary to maintain the beneficial uses of the reservoir. Adequate descriptions of these flow rates would be helpful to define flood levels, wildlife management, irrigation volumes, water-based recreation, and other social needs. Water quantity would be less of a problem if the source of usable, unpolluted water were located close to the users. Water is not always economically available at a particular location because rainfall quantities vary from one area to another. In addition, for one specific area, the stochastic (time-varying) aspects of rainfall must be considered for more reliable predictions of storage levels. Precipitation, evaporation, infiltration, and streamflows will be the material for latter chapters. The details for measurement and interpretation are necessary to use the basic mass balance of the hydrologic cycle as developed within this chapter.

2.3.3   Rainfall Excess

During a precipitation event, a mass balance of the total volume of rainfall onto and flow from an area is helpful to understand rainfall excess. Consider as variables the volume of precipitation P, rainfall excess R, infiltration F, evaporation E, transpiration T, and initial abstraction I_A. Initial abstraction is water intercepted by vegetation and stored in surface depressions. A mass balance of a simplified water budget for a fixed time period, considering negligible boundary transfers, is written as

$$\text{Rainfall excess} = \text{precipitation} - \text{storage change}$$

$$R = P - E - T - F - I_A \tag{2.7}$$

Equation 2.7 is illustrated by the schematic in Figure 2.7.

In many locations it is difficult to separate evaporation and transpiration. Thus, the variables are considered together and most likely can be estimated as one value, identified as evapotranspiration (ET). For a short time period (hours-day) each of the above variables can be considered constant, and since

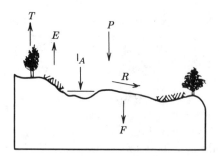

FIGURE 2.7 Water budget schematic.

evapotranspiration (ET) is negligible, Equation 2.7 is rewritten as

$$R = P - F - I_A \qquad (2.8)$$

If the volume of infiltration and initial abstraction is proportional to the precipitation volume, the quantity of rainfall excess can be expressed as a fraction of precipitation:

$$R = CP \qquad (2.9)$$

where C = runoff coefficient (dimensionless) such that $0 \leq C \leq 1$

The runoff coefficient, as defined here, is the ratio of rainfall excess to precipitation. The runoff coefficient can be determined from extensive rainfall and runoff studies, or from published values. In later chapters, the relationship of runoff (flow rate) to precipitation intensity and the runoff coefficient is developed.

☐ **EXAMPLE PROBLEM 2.1**

Over a two-month period of time, a catchment in the Pontypridd area of Wales is expected to receive 254 mm of rain with an expected evapotranspiration estimated at 85 mm and that lost to groundwater storage of 20 mm. There is no other significant storage in the watershed. What is the expected rainfall excess to a reservoir storage area if the catchment area is 65 km²? Express your answer in cubic meters and liters. Also, determine how many people can be serviced by this water if the per person per day water use rate is 160 liters.

Solution

Solving for rainfall excess using a mass balance:

$$R = P - ET - F$$

$$R = 254 - 85 - 20 = 149 \text{ mm (over the catchment)}$$

or in m³

$$R = \frac{149 \text{ mm}}{1000 \text{ mm/m}} \times 65 \text{ km}^2 \times 10^6 \text{m}^2/\text{km}^2 = 9.685 \,(10^6) \text{ m}^3$$

or in liters

$$R = 9.685(10^6)\text{m}^3 \times 10^3 \text{L/m}^3 = 9.685(10^9) \text{ liters}$$

Solving for the per person use rate:

$$\text{Usage}/2 \text{ mo} = 160 \text{ liters/person-day} \times 30 \text{ d/mo} \times 2 \text{ mo}$$
$$= 9600 \text{ liters/person}$$

and people
$$= \frac{9.685(10^9) \text{ liters}}{9.6(10^3) \text{ liters/person}} = 10^6 \text{ people} \quad \square$$

2.4

SUMMARY

The science of meteorology aids in the explanation of the hydrologic cycle and its variables. Some of the concepts, ideas, and formulas that form the basis for continued study are as follows:

- Since meteorology is the study of the atmosphere, it helps to explain precipitation, evaporation, and transpiration.
- Solar energy initiates the hydrologic cycle.
- Gases in the atmosphere can affect temperature.
- Temperature, water vapor, and winds are important factors in the determination of precipitation.
- Average daily temperature can be calculated using hourly values (Equation 2.3) or maximum and minimum values (Equation 2.4).
- Rainfall excess can be assumed to be directly related to precipitation, resulting in a coefficient relating both. This coefficient is called the runoff coefficient and can be defined as the ratio of rainfall excess to precipitation. In later chapters, the runoff coefficient will be used in another formula for estimating runoff.
- A mass balance of the hydrologic cycle results in useful equations for estimating one of the parameters of the hydrologic cycle.

2.5

PROBLEMS

1. What is the hydrologic cycle? Explain in your own words how it is related to the study of meteorology.
2. What are differences between cyclonic and tropical cyclone weather systems?
3. What is the dew-point temperature? How is it related to relative humidity?

4. Calculate the average minimum daily temperature for the month of March using the data of Table 2.3.

5. Pick any four days from Table 2.3 and show how the value of average temperature was calculated.

6. Given the following 24 hourly values of temperature, calculate the average using two methods.

HOUR	TEMP.,°C	HOUR	TEMP.,°C	HOUR	TEMP.,°C
1 am	20	9	15	5	20
2	19	10	16	6	20
3	17	11	17	7	19
4	16	12	18	8	18
5	14	1 pm	19	9	17
6	13	2	20	10	17
7	14	3	21	11	16
8	15	4	21	MN	16

7. For the total monthly rainfall of Table 2.3, calculate the monthly rainfall excess assuming the runoff coefficient is .6.

8. If the runoff coefficient of the previous problem changed to .8 for daily rainfall greater than .5 inches, what is the daily and monthly sum for rainfall excess?

9. If the rainfall on a watershed is 3 in., and the rainfall excess is 21,780 ft^3, what is an estimate of the runoff coefficient if the watershed area is 4 acres?

10. For the hydrologic cycle of Figure 2.5, write the equation for estimating the ending storage after 12 one-month periods considering monthly hydrologic data that are available for evaporation, transpiration, infiltration, subsurface runoff, boundary output, precipitation, and initial storage.

11. Estimate the amount of depression storage (inches and cubic feet) in a 6-acre parking lot using the following rainfall and discharge data. The discharge data were measured at the only inlet in the parking lot. Rainfall = 0.88 in. Rainfall excess = 5 cfs average for one hour. Also list assumptions for the other variables of the hydrology cycle.

12. It rains 3.0 in. on a 20.0-acre watershed. What is the volume of rainfall excess if 30% of the watershed area is a lake and infiltration on the soil is estimated at 1.0 in.? What is the total volume of runoff? Express your answer in cubic feet. Assume that the lake level is low and does not contribute to rainfall excess. Hint: Lakes are initial abstraction.

2.6

REFERENCES

Hansen, J., Johnson, D., Lacis, A., Lebedeff, S., Lee, P., Rind, D., and Russell, G. 1981. "Climate Impact of Increasing Atmospheric Carbon Dioxide," *Science* **213**, p. 4511.

Petterssen, S. 1964. "Meteorology" in Chow, Ven Te, *Handbook of Applied Hydrology*. McGraw-Hill, New York.

Wanielista, M.P., Yousef, Y.A., Taylor, J.S., and Cooper, C.D. 1984. *Engineering and the Environment*. Brooks/Cole Engineering, Monterey, CA, p. 21.

....
....
....

3

PRECIPITATION

Some moisture is always present in the atmosphere. It is stored in the atmosphere awaiting forces that can cause precipitation. As moisture content increases, the chances of precipitation increase. This chapter discusses the formation, classification, and measurement of precipitation. Once the data on precipitation depth and rate (intensity) are available, interpretation of data and various methods for presentation are developed. These presentations form some of the input data required in latter chapters to assess the probability of specific precipitation volumes and to predict runoff quantities.

3.1

THE FORMATION OF PRECIPITATION

In general, there are four conditions that must be present for the production of precipitation: (1) condensation onto nuclei, (2) cooling of the atmosphere, (3) growth of water droplets, and (4) mechanisms to cause a sufficient density of the droplets. These conditions can occur in a relatively short time period and may be observed simultaneously.

Vapors are present in the atmosphere and can change to a liquid. The process by which vapor changes to a liquid or solid form is called condensation. In the atmosphere, cloud droplets form on condensation nuclei. These nuclei are usually sea salts and combustion by-products. The size of the nuclei are generally less than 1 micron in diameter. Prior to precipitation, most water droplets and ice crystals in clouds are less than 10 microns. During the condensation process, the water droplets and ice crystals will tend to enlarge because of vapor pressure differences. However, without any other factors present, it takes about one or two days for the particles of water and ice to reach the size of a small raindrop, which is about 3000 microns (3 mm). Thus, other factors are more important if precipitation is to occur.

One of these factors is the collision of particles. Collisions occur because of differences in rising and falling velocities. Particles that collide usually coalesce to form larger particles. Gravity acts on the particle to increase its falling velocity, but the friction drag causes a terminal velocity that depends on temperature, pressure, and size of the raindrop. At around 7 mm in diameter, the raindrop travels at about 10 m/sec (30 feet/sec) and usually breaks up into smaller drops.

Another factor is the ice crystal growth process. When ice elements form a vapor pressure imbalance with the water, larger water drops are created. The equilibrium vapor pressure over the water droplets is higher than over the ice elements. This causes the water vapor to evaporate and condense on the ice. Larger particles are formed and precipitation may result.

Precipitation formation can be modified using cloud seeding. Dry ice and silver iodide deposited in clouds can increase the possibility of rainfall from that cloud formation. The effectiveness depends on many factors, but the idea is to increase the number of condensation nuclei and promote ice crystal growth.

3.2

CLASSIFICATION OF PRECIPITATION

A meteor is a small particle of matter in the atmosphere. Any formation that results from the condensation process is called a hydrometeor. Fog, haze, frost, and blowing snow are hydrometeors of some concern in the science of hydrology. Related to the hydrologic cycle are hydrometeors that fall to the earth, which are important for the study and application of hydrology. The general classes of precipitation are:

- Snow is complex ice crystals. A snowflake consists of agglomerated ice crystals. The average water content of snow is assumed to be about 10% of an equal volume of water.
- Hailstones are balls of ice that are about 5 to over 125 mm in diameter. Their specific gravity is about 0.7 to 0.9. Thus, hailstones have the potential for agricultural and other property damage.

- Sleet results from the freezing of raindrops and is usually a combination of snow and rain.
- Rain consists of liquid water drops of a size 0.5 mm to about 7 mm in diameter. Drizzle refers to small water drops less than 0.5 mm in diameter. The settling velocity is slow, with the intensity rarely exceeding 1 mm/hr (0.04 in./hr).

3.3

MEASUREMENT INSTRUMENTATION

Precipitation is measured as the vertical depth of water (or water equivalent in the case of snow) that would accumulate on a flat level surface if all the precipitation remained where it had fallen. The units for reporting the depth are inches and hundredths of an inch in the customary U.S. units and millimeters and tenths of a millimeter in the SI system. There are at least three types of gages commonly in use to record depth: tipping bucket, weighing, and float. Gages with standard 8-in. diameter collectors have been used but are, in general, not recording types. The depth of water has to be manually read from a storage reservoir.

The tipping-bucket gage (shown in Figure 3.1) works on the principle that water accumulated in the collector is funneled into a two-compartment bucket. Each bucket is designed to collect the equivalent of 0.01 in. or 0.1 mm of water over either an 8-in. or 10-in. diameter collector. Once one of the buckets is filled, the filled bucket will tip and empty its contents. The bucket on the other side is now in position to collect water from the funnel. When the bucket tips, an electrical signal for each 0.01 in. or 0.1 mm of precipitation is sent to a recording unit. As the buckets alternately fill and tip, a momentary closure of an electrical switch (mercury) is completed, causing the electrical signal. This type of gage is used primarily for the measurement of rainfall, and not for ice or snow measurements. The snow or ice must melt to be recorded.

The weighing-type gage measures the weight of rain or snow that accumulates in a bucket. The bucket sits on a scale that is calibrated to read an equivalent depth of water for a weight of precipitation. In remote areas, weighing-type gages have been known to operate for up to three months.

A float can be used to record the depth of water. The float is placed in the collector area or in a special reservoir of mercury or oil. As the depth of rainfall increases, the float increases and records the changes in depth with time. This type of gage can be easily damaged by freezing conditions.

3.3.1 Errors in Gage Measuring

Errors in measuring precipitation are usually small but tend to result in lower-than-expected readings. Instrument errors, however, must be protected

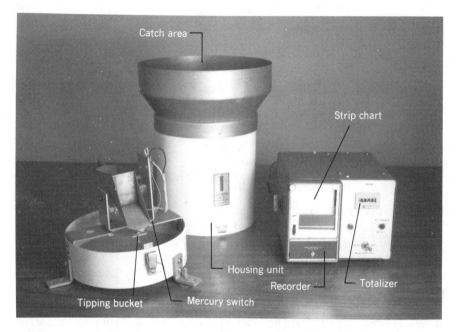

FIGURE 3.1   Tipping bucket housing unit mercury switch recorder strip chart totalizer.

against. Reduction of the collector area by damage to the collector, or covering of part of the collector, is probably the greatest source of error. If the collector area is reduced, the depth of water recorded will be reduced. Other errors with the instruments are related to the weighing mechanism calibration, recording drive friction problems, and electrical current failures. All gages and recorders should be calibrated and serviced at least once per year.

☐   *EXAMPLE PROBLEM 3.1*
_____

Part of a rain gage collector is covered during a storm event by debris. The debris reflected rain from the collector. Upon examination of the collector, it was found that 30% of the collector area was covered during rainfall. If the total amount of rain recorded was 0.51 in., what would be an estimate of the actual amount assuming a standard 8 inch diameter collector?

Solution

The collector diameter is 8 in, thus its area is $(\pi(8)^2/4) = 50.3$ in.^{2} The volume of rainfall recorded was 0.51 in. from a 35.2-in.^{2} area. The total volume of rainfall that should have been recorded is proportional to the total collector area of 50.3 in.^{2}, and is

$$(35.2 \text{ in.}^2)/(0.51 \text{ in.}) = (50.3 \text{ in}^2)/[X(\text{in.})]$$

Actual estimate = 0.73 in. □

The positioning of the gage is also important in order to reduce errors in collecting precipitation. Obstacles that block precipitation from a collector must be avoided, and the collector must be positioned in a vertical plane. If a gage is inclined towards the wind, a greater amount of precipitation will be collected. Conversely, an incline away from the wind will reduce the collected volume.

Wind speed at the collector will reduce the estimate of precipitation because air is reflected upwards at the collector and precipitation is diverted. The error is greatest for light, or less dense precipitation, such as mist and snow. At a wind velocity of 20 mph (8.9 mps) Larson and Peck (1974) estimated about a 20% reduction in the volume of rainfall collected. For snow measurements, the reduction in volume was about 70%. The higher the gage is off the ground, the greater the error because of increased wind velocities. Trees, fences, and buildings have been used as windbreaks. Their height should be no higher than about one to two times the distance from the gage to the windbreak.

3.3.2 Network of Gages

The areal, or spatial, distribution of precipitation is related to meteorological and topographical factors. The number of precipitation gage stations per unit area (precipitation gage density) is generally less for flat regions than for mountainous regions in temperate climate. The use of daily, hourly, or more frequently measured precipitation data from a site is generally only relevant for that site. Using data from another site may produce errors. If data from one site are to be used at another site, less error is introduced if monthly or yearly precipitation data are used rather than daily or hourly data.

Comparing the areal distribution of total rainfall resulting from convective and cyclonic (frontal) storms, the convective storms tend to produce greater variability. For example, the two types of storms were compared for a precipitation network of six gages over an area of 600 km^2 (10 × 60 km) in central Florida. The convective storm had an average rainfall of 30.7 mm (1.21 in.) and a range of 12.5 to 63.5 mm, while the cold front produced an average of 21.6 mm (0.85 in.) and a range of 15.5 to 28 mm (Wanielista, 1977).

In St. Louis, Missouri, a network of 225 recording gages were distributed over a 2100 mi^2 urban area (Huff, 1974). Evidence available from these records indicates that the urban area was modifying rainfall intensities. It is

TABLE 3.1   Annual Areal Rainfall in 1977 Compared with the 1941–1970 Long-Term Annual Average by Water Authority Areas in England and Wales, and by River Purification board Areas in Scotland and in Northern Ireland

	1977 RAINFALL IN MM	LONG-TERM ANNUAL AVERAGE IN MM	1977 RAINFALL AS PERCENTAGE OF LONG-TERM AVERAGE
United Kingdom	1101	1090	101
England and Wales	925	912	101
Water authority areas			
North West	1206	1217	99
Northumbrian	847	879	96
Severn-Trent	839	773	109
Yorkshire	856	833	103
Anglian	583	611	95
Thames	744	704	106
Southern	797	794	100
Wessex	934	869	107
South West	1179	1194	99
Welsh	1403	1334	105
Scotland	1457	1431	102
Western Isles, Orkney and Shetland Islands Area	1316	1296	102
River purification board areas			
Highland	1642	1722	95
North East	1022	1023	100
Tay	1299	1255	104
Forth	1167	1117	104
Clyde	1802	1665	108
Tweed	1023	1003	102
Solway	1542	1425	108
Northern Ireland	1026	1095	94

Source: United Kingdom Meteorological Office, 1982. Surface Water: UK 1974–1976. Wallingford, U.K.

generally believed that the climate in La Porte, Indiana, has changed primarily because of the large industrial complex in the Chicago area (Masters, 1974). Over 40 years, a 30 to 40% increase in precipitation has been noted.

Annual rainfall volumes for 1977 are compared in Table 3.1 to long-term averages over 30 years for various locations in Great Britain. These yearly data are important for regional water needs determination. Of equal importance is the yearly residual rainfall defined by Equation 3.1:

$$RR = RAIN - EVAP \tag{3.1}$$

where

    RR = residual rainfall (cm or in.)

RAIN = long-term average rainfall (cm or in.)

EVAP = long-term average evaporation (cm or in.)

The residual rainfall would be that which has the potential to recharge groundwaters and surface water reservoirs. In southern Wales, United Kingdom, yearly rainfall varies from 90 to 250 cm with residual rainfall varying from 50 to 200 cm.

Any network of precipitation gages should be planned to consider the intended use of the data and the economic impact. In more developed and densely populated regions that depend on the availability of scarce waters, the precipitation network operated by government groups is usually dense. For example, in the United Kingdom and Hawaii, there are about five to six stations per 100 mi^2, while in Alaska there is less than one per 2000 mi^2. In flat regions of temperate climate, one station per 200 mi^2 is recommended. In temperate mountainous regions, however, one station per 40 mi^2 is recommended. In polar regions, only one gage per 600 mi^2 is recommended (World Meteorological Organization, 1974).

The networks operated by the government of a country is believed to be responsive to large-scale, large-area projects. Specific related precipitation from convective storms need a greater density of gages. If a government network of gages is supplemented by other gages operated by private groups, the area density of gages is higher than expected and more useful for specific storm related data.

3.3.3 Radar Measurement of Rainfall

Radar can detect any type of hydrometeors in the atmosphere. A radar pulse for electromagnetic energy is used to determine the reflection of the hydrometeors. The reflection appears on a power display and is termed an echo. In general, the intensity (brightness) of the echo is a measure of the precipitation intensity. The distance from the radar site to the precipitation area can be measured by the time between emission of the radar pulse and receipt of the echo. The radar has an antenna that has to be orientated in the direction of the reflection. Thus, the spatial coordinates of the precipitation can be determined from the direction and distance measurements.

There can be a significant amount of ground clutter (interference from trees and buildings) when measuring hydrometeors in the atmosphere. To minimize the interference, a radar beam is directed upward at a slight angle. However, the height of the beam increases and accuracy decreases. Other factors affecting radar measurements are wind drift of particles, type of storm, distance from the radar to the storm, and the classification of the precipitation. However, radar can cover a complete area rather than relying on a single point measurement by a gage on the ground. Possibly, the joint use of radar and gage can lead to more accurate estimates of rainfall.

3.4

MISSING DATA

Precipitation measuring stations sometimes fail in providing a continuous record of precipitation. Instruments do malfunction and back-up systems may not always provide accurate data. A tipping-bucket gage may not function for a short period of time and the back-up volume gage may not provide time-related data. For a nonautomatic recording gage, an individual may fail to record the data or miss a visit to the site. Thus, there are generally missing data, the values of which must be estimated. There are two commonly used procedures for estimating daily precipitation depths, however, none are in common use for estimating hourly data (Paulhus and Kohler, 1952). The two procedures for estimating daily totals rely on the data from three adjacent stations. The locations of the adjacent stations are such that they are close to and approximately evenly spaced around the site with the missing data. Both procedures use the average annual precipitation (arithmetic average) at the three sites.

If the average annual precipitation at each of the three adjacent stations differs from the average at the missing data station by less than 10%, the following formula is used to estimate the missing daily data:

$$\bar{P}_X = \frac{(P_A + P_B + P_C)}{3} \tag{3.2}$$

where

$\bar{P}_X$ = estimated daily precipitation volume at the missing data site, X (depth)

P_A, P_B, P_C = estimated daily precipitation volume at the adjacent stations, A, B, and C (depth)

A simple arithmetic averaging of the data is used.

If the difference between the average annual precipitation at any of the adjacent stations and the missing data station is greater than 10%, a normal-ratio method is used. Normal is used as it refers to the arithmetic average. The method consists of weighting each adjacent station daily value by a ratio of the normal annual precipitation values and then average the numbers, or

$$\bar{P}_X = \tfrac{1}{3}[(N_X/N_A)P_A + (N_X/N_B)P_B + (N_X/N_C)P_C] \tag{3.3}$$

where

N_X = average annual precipitation at the missing data site X (cm)

N_i = average annual precipitation at the adjacent sites (cm)

3.5

INTERPRETATION AND QUANTIFICATION OF PRECIPITATION

To size water transport and storage systems, quantitative data for rainfall events must be provided. In some areas, these data are specified by regulations, however, it may be advantageous to update these data and certainly it is important to understand how these data were developed. These data can be defined in terms of:

1. Intensity (rate of rainfall)
2. Duration of storm
3. Time distribution of rainfall
4. Return period and associated depth of rain.

All of these measures are required to adequately define a rainfall storm event.

3.5.1 Intensity

Intensity, or depth of rainfall per unit time, is commonly reported in the units of millimeters per hour (inches per hour). Weather stations utilizing gages that provide continuous records of rainfall can be used to obtain intensity data. These data are typically reported in either tabular form or graphical form (hyetograph).

Another way of reporting intensity data is the use of different time intervals. Figure 3.2 illustrates a hyetograph using a 15-min time interval for 6 in. of rain over 6 h. It corresponds to a rainfall volume occurring once every 25 years for a specific region.

3.5.2 Cumulative Rainfall Diagram

A cumulative rainfall diagram that is a plot of cumulative rainfall versus time also is useful in runoff studies. At any given time during a storm, the intensity is the slope of the cumulative rainfall curve at that point in time. A graph of the cumulative rainfall diagram is shown in Figure 3.3. It can be used to determine the cumulative rainfall at any point during the duration of the storm event. The data of Figure 3.3 are obtained from Figure 3.2.

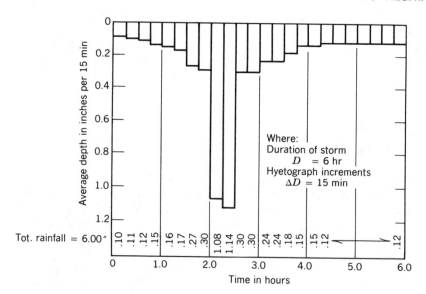

FIGURE 3.2   Hyetograph of 25-year design rainfall.

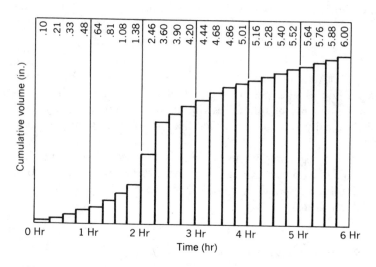

FIGURE 3.3   Cumulative rainfall diagram using the data of Figure 3.2.

TABLE 3.2   Storm Rainfall Variability (Maximum Events)

LOCATION	APPROXIMATE DEPTH		AVERAGE INTENSITIES		DURATION
	mm	in.	mm/hr	in./hr	
Funkiko, Formosa	1670	65.8	35	1.37	2 days
Cherrapunji, India	3330	131.1	20	0.78	7 days
Taylor, Texas, USA	585	23.0	24	0.96	24 hr
Hatteras, NC, USA	140	5.5	140	5.50	1 hr
Pensacola, FL, USA	60	2.4	720	28.80	5 min
Unionville, MD, USA	31	1.2	1860	72	1 min

☐   **EXAMPLE PROBLEM 3.2**

The maximum time it takes water to drain from a watershed under heavy rainfall is 45 min. Determine the maximum intensity (in./hr) in a 45-min. increment, assuming the cumulative rainfall diagram of Figure 3.3 is representative of the area where the watershed is located.

Solution

One must select from the diagram the maximum intensity associated with a 45-min period. Since Figure 3.3 was derived from Figure 3.2, either one can be used. Note, if one were to consider this intensity as being used to generate runoff rates or volumes, the watershed storage and infiltration capacity has to be considered. The maximum intensity of rainfall does not necessarily generate the maximum runoff condition. The maximum 45-min volume of rainfall from Figure 3.2 is 2.52 in. or 3.36 in./hr.   ☐

Some indication of the variability of maximum ranfall storm volumes and intensities recorded at a location is shown in Table 3.2. As the storm duration decreases the average intensity increases.

3.5.3   Duration of Precipitation

The duration of a storm is the time from the beginning of rainfall to the point where the mass curve becomes horizontal indicating no further accumulation of precipitation within a certain time after the rain stops. In Figure 3.2, the storm duration is simply the width (time base) of the hyetograph. There may be frequent short time periods of no rainfall in a storm. Using simple empirical probability calculations, one can determine what the probability is for rain starting after a time interval of no rainfall. This time interval will vary with the type of storm (convective, cyclonic, etc.). But, in general, if the probability of rain starting after a specified time period of no rainfall (say 5 hr) is very small relative to other time periods (e.g., 0.001 vs 0.08), then the start of rainfall after the specific time (5 hr) would indicate a new storm.

Storm durations are usually reported over a range of a few minutes through hours, and days up to about 5 days. A 5-day storm may have time intervals of no rainfall greater than 5 to 10 hr. However, the use of daily durations up to about 3 or possibly 5 days is based more on total rainfall volume over that time period and time periods of 4 or 5 hr of no rain are not considered. Relative to longer duration storms with lower average intensities, higher intensities for short durations on fast responding watersheds where storm durations are about equal to travel time produce higher flow rates.

The choice of storm duration and thus intensities depends on the use of the rainfall data. The peak flow rates from an area require estimates of intensities associated with short time intervals while volume storage estimates for a watershed require long duration storms.

3.5.4 Dimensionless Cumulative Rainfall Diagrams

Since maximum rainfall volumes vary for different regions or for different locations in an area, a dimensionless volume axis for the cumulative rainfall diagram would be helpful for the time distribution of any rainfall volume. Also, duration of a storm may not always equal the duration used to construct the cumulative rainfall diagram. Therefore, the time distribution of the rainfall is normally given in a dimensionless cumulative rainfall diagram (also called a dimensionless mass diagram). This is a plot of the fraction of rainfall from a given volume of total rainfall as a function of the fraction of time for a given duration of a storm (Figure 3.4). The diagrams are generally specific to a region. Procedures for developing these dimensional diagrams can generally be classified as (Pilgrim and Cordery, 1975):

1. Based on a large storm (usually one that produced a particular volume for an approximate duration)
2. Statistical averaging at each hour (usually many storms of similar duration)
3. Regression analysis (uses either same duration or mixed duration data)
4. The maximum intensities for selected durations

For a specified storm duration, some form of statistical analysis (regression or other curve fitting analysis) tends to produce the most realistic results. Usually, the larger volume storms are used.

Probably the most widely used diagrams among hydrologists were developed by the Soil Conservation Service (SCS) and were named Type I, Type

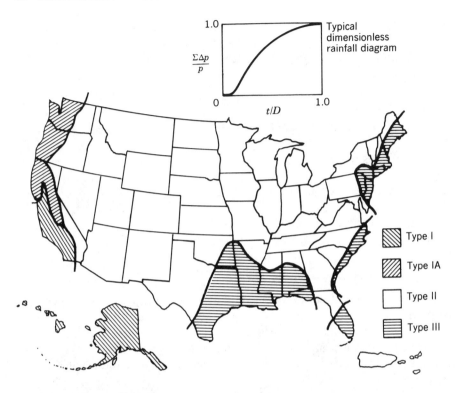

FIGURE 3.4 Approximate areas for SCS dimensionless rainfall diagrams and a typical plot (*Source:* United State Department of Agriculture Soil Conservation Service, 1986. *Technical Release #55*, Urban Hydrology, U.S. Department of Agriculture, SCS, Washington DC.).

1A, Type II, and type III. Type II is widely used in the United States because of its geographic coverage. The approximate areas for these distributions and an example diagram are shown in Figure 3.4. The numerical values associated with Types II and III are shown in Appendix C. Other dimensionless rainfall diagrams have been quantified by local and regional water management agencies. One such is the SCS Type II Florida Modified. These sources should be consulted because of the local nature and variability of storms. The Army Corps of Engineers also developed a dimensionless cumulative diagram and the numerical values are given in Appendix C. These values correspond to half hour intervals.

Given a known volume of rain for a given duration storm, the volume of rain at any time can be determined from the dimensionless cumulative rainfall diagram hyetograph. This time variation with watershed conditions directly determine the corresponding volume and flow rates of the surface runoff. High intensity rainfall at the beginning of a storm may result in a rapid rise in the runoff followed by a long recession of the flow. Conversely, if the more intense rainfall occurs toward the end of the storm, there will be a slow rise in runoff followed by a rapidly falling recession.

3.6

EXTRAPOLATION OF POINT MEASURES TO WATERSHEDS

The point measure of rainfall depth and intensity from a gage is of value for estimating volume and runoff for larger areas. To accomplish this, the depth and intensity measured at a point must be considered as constant over an area or two or more point measures must be averaged. In this section, equations are presented to convert point measures to area measures. In the next section, methods to estimate average values are presented.

3.6.1   Depth and Watershed Volumes

The depth of rainfall or equivalent rainfall (if snow measures) recorded on a gage can be related to a watershed area if one can assume that the point estimate is reasonable and constant for the watershed area. Because of the great area variability of precipitation, the point estimate is usually used for small areas (few acres to square mile). To convert from depth to volume, one simply follows:

$$V = PA(3630) \tag{3.4}$$

where

V = volume of rainfall (CF)
P = rainfall (in.)
A = watershed area (acres)
3630 = conversion factor (43,560 ft^2/acre divided by 12 in./foot)

3.6.2   Intensity and Watershed Discharge

The intensity measure at a gage also can be useful for scaling up to a watershed. From a basic mass per unit time balance of inputs and outputs, the rate of precipitation onto a watershed—if held constant—would equal the runoff from the watershed. The critical assumption is one of time to achieve steady-state conditions. If the intensity remains constant over the time it would take for the total contributing area to drain the rainfall excess to the output site, then precipitation intensity must equal runoff or:

Runoff (outflow) = precipitation intensity

and to balance units, intensity must be multiplied by area, or

$$Q = iCA(1.008) \tag{3.5}$$

where

Q = runoff rate (CFS)
i = precipitation intensity (in./hr)
CA = contributing area (acres)
1.008 = conversion factor (CFS-hr/acre-in.)

It is important to note the contributing area is the area from which precipitation will result in runoff. An impervious area (pavement, roofs, etc.) with a discharge point is an example of a contributing area. The constant (1.008) may be dropped from the equation.

3.7

AVERAGE WATERSHED PRECIPITATION

Precipitation levels are variable over large geographical areas, such as the United States or Europe. Air mass movements, topography, and water/land locations are a few more important reasons for differences. In addition, specific locations have seasonal and yearly variations. All these factors complicate the scientific and engineering processes of design and operation of water resources systems. An indication of the geographical variability of mean average yearly rainfall is illustrated in Figure 3.5. These are only approximate values for a particular region, but geographical variability of yearly rainfall is clearly seen.

For smaller geographical areas, such as towns, cities, and water basins, rainfall volumes per storm event are most likely variable over the area. To illustrate this, consider raincells that are imaginary lines of equal precipitation (isohyets) over an area (Figure 3.6). Raincells for the St. Louis area have been reported in the literature (Huff, 1974).

There are, in common use, three methods for estimating average precipitation for an area: isohyetal, Theissen, and arithmetic average. The calculation of isohyets is a reliable method of estimating average precipitation for a watershed, but the average is difficult to reproduce by another investigator because of the subjective nature (knowledge of storm morphology) of drawing isohyets. However, if precipitation values between precipitation station locations are determined by linear interpolation, the differences in average values should be reduced. The isohyetal calculations are well adapted for visual display (Figure 3.6 and 3.7). The area between each isohyet within the watershed is determined, and an average precipitation value is calculated. The isohyetal average is calculated as

$$\overline{P} = \sum_{i=1}^{n} W_i P_i \qquad (3.6)$$

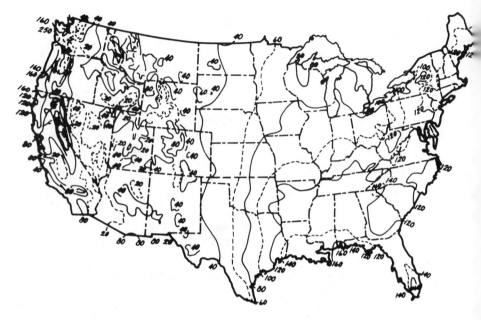

FIGURE 3.5   Mean annual precipitation (centimeters, converted from inches) (U.S. Department of Commerce, 1961).

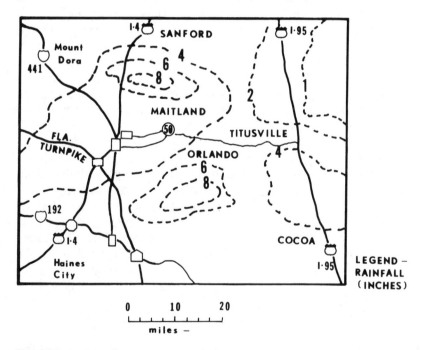

FIGURE 3.6   Raincells.

where

$\bar{P}$ = isohyetal average precipitation (mm)
P_i = isohyetal cell average precipitation (mm)
$W_i = A_i/A$; A_i − area of cell (km^2)
A = total area (km^2)
n = total number of cells

It should be noted that A_i is the area of the cell within the topographical drainage boundaries.

Other methods for calculating average precipitation are the Thiessen method and the arithmetic average method. The Thiessen method adjusts for the nonuniform location of gaging stations by attempting to determine the area of influence. The ratio of the area of influence of a station in the topographic basin to the total area in the topographic basin is a weighting factor to be applied for the calculation of the average value. If the procedure for calculating the weighting factors is followed, investigators are better able to duplicate the results of other investigators. The procedure is illustrated in Figure 3.7 and essentially involves connecting each precipitation station with straight lines, constructing perpendicular bisectors of the connecting lines and forming polygons with these bisectors. The area of the polygon is determined, and a weighted area is calculated using

$$W_i = A_p/A \tag{3.7}$$

where

W_i = weighted area, dimensionless
A_p = area of the polygon withing the tographic basic (km^2)
A = total area (km^2)

The average precipitation using the Thiessen method is

$$\bar{P} = \sum_{i=1}^{n} W_i P_i \tag{3.8}$$

where

$\bar{P}$ = average precipitation (mm)
P_i = gage precipitation for polygon i
n = total number of polygons

The arithmetic average method (Figure 3.7) uses only those gaging stations within the topographic basin and is calculated using

$$\bar{P} = \sum_{i=1}^{n} P_i/n. \tag{3.9}$$

where

$\bar{P}$ = average precipitation depth (mm or in.)

P_i = precipitation depth at gage (i) within the topographic basin, (mm or in.)

n = total number of gaging stations within the topographic basin

□ **EXAMPLE PROBLEM 3.3**

For the following watershed, estimate using three methods the average precipitation. The watershed is shown in Figure 3.7.

Solution

a. Isohyetal method

$$\bar{P} = \sum_i W_i P_i$$

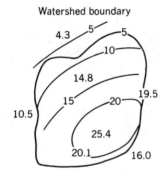

Watershed boundary

ISOHYTE (mm)	WEIGHTED AREA (W_i)	AVERAGE PRECIPITATION (P_i)	$W_i P_i$ (mm)
> 20	0.30	22.7*	6.8
10	0.58	15.0	8.7
5	0.12	7.5	0.9
			$\bar{P}$ = 16.4 mm

*(25.4 + 20)/2 = 22.7.

b. Thiessen method

$$\bar{P} = \sum_i W_i P_i$$

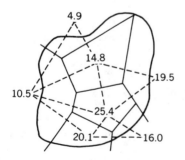

OBSERVED PRECIPITATION (P_i)	WEIGHTED AREA (W_i)	$W_i P_i$ (mm)
14.8	0.29	4.3
19.5	0.16	3.1
4.9	0.07	0.3
10.5	0.19	2.0
25.4	0.15	3.8
20.1	0.12	2.4
16.0	0.02	0.3
		$\bar{P}$ = 16.2 mm

c. Arithmetic average (add those within the watershed)

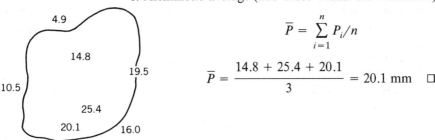

$$\overline{P} = \sum_{i=1}^{n} P_i/n$$

$$\overline{P} = \frac{14.8 + 25.4 + 20.1}{3} = 20.1 \text{ mm} \quad \square$$

FIGURE 3.7 Average precipitation (station location identified by the decimal point ex 4.9).

As the area increases, the average precipitation for that area decreases. Using selected data from the U.K. Meteorological Office (1982), Table 3.3 was developed to illustrate the decrease (areal reduction) with increasing areas for various storm durations. The areal reduction factor is calculated as a ratio of area average precipitation to maximum precipitation measured at a point within the area.

3.8

SNOW

Snow can cause significant problems both by accumulation and by melting thus creating potential floods. Deep accumulations can cause transportation and structural failures.

TABLE 3.3 Relation of Areal Reduction Factor with Duration (D) and Area (A) for the U.K.

DURATION D	\multicolumn{10}{c}{WATERSHED AREA (km²)}
	1	5	10	30	100	300	1000	3000	10,000	30,000
5 min	0.90	0.82	0.76	0.65	0.51	0.38	—	—	—	—
10 min	0.93	0.87	0.83	0.73	0.59	0.47	0.32	—	—	—
15 min	0.94	0.89	0.85	0.77	0.64	0.53	0.39	0.29	—	—
30 min	0.95	0.91	0.89	0.82	0.72	0.62	0.51	0.41	0.31	—
60 min	0.96	0.93	0.91	0.86	0.79	0.71	0.62	0.53	0.44	0.35
2 hr	0.97	0.95	0.93	0.90	0.84	0.79	0.73	0.65	0.55	0.47
3 hr	0.97	0.96	0.94	0.91	0.87	0.83	0.78	0.71	0.62	0.54
6 hr	0.98	0.97	0.96	0.93	0.90	0.87	0.83	0.79	0.73	0.67
24 hr	0.99	0.98	0.97	0.96	0.94	0.92	0.89	0.86	0.83	0.80
48 hr	—	0.99	0.98	0.97	0.96	0.94	0.91	0.88	0.86	0.82

Source: Flood Studies Report, 1975.

The density of snowpack varies with the time since initial accumulation and other meteorological conditions. Newly fallen snow may have as little as 5% water while long accumulated snowpack (close to ice) may have over 80% water.

Snow depth is measured by rain gages, snow stakes, and density determinations. Wind affects the accuracy of the measurement devices, thus shields are frequently used to protect gages from wind. Snow stakes are calibrated and driven into the ground. The height of the stake must be longer than most expected accumulations, or additional stakes must be added during the snow accumulation periods. Generally, many stakes are used for an area because of local variations in snow depth caused by wind. The stakes outline a snow course and are usually spaced out 15 to 30 m (50–100 ft) apart.

Stream gaging stations are useful for the measurement of water equivalents and density of the snowpack. By measuring the runoff volume, the equivalent depth of water over the watershed can be estimated. By knowing the average depth of snow, the density can be calculated.

3.8.1   Physical Nature and Thermal Properties

Snowflakes are crystals with a dendritic structure that form a low density snowpack immediately after falling. However, over time the density increases. The density increases because of many factors:

1. Surface heat exchange at the snow-air interface due to radiation, convection, and condensation.
2. A conduction process at the ground surface.
3. compaction due to its own weight.
4. Percolation of liquid (from melt or rain) through the snowpack.
5. Movement of air at the snow–air interface.
6. Air and snow temperature variations.

Of all these factors, the ones that have been primarily related to snowflake density are near-surface air temperature and wind speed. As near-surface air temperature increases, the snowflake density increases. The U.S. Army corps of Engineers (1956) illustrated this increase of snowflake density as air temperature increases to follow a nonlinear relationship. An average density value for calculating average water quaivalents is 0.10 g/cm^3. Also, as wind velocity increases, density increases.

Average snowpack density increases with time, and a settlement of depth of snowpack can be seen. On a daily basis, snowfall depth is recorded; however, the cumulative snowfall is greater than the cumulative snowpack depth over time (except on the very first day, the snowpack depth may equal the snowfall depth). Density of the snowpack will increase with depth into a snowpack. For one location, the U.S. Army Corps of Engineers (1956) reported a variation from 0.08 g/cm^3 at the surface to about 0.35 g/cm^3 at about 8 to 12 ft below the surface. The average density was about 0.27 g/cm^3 for this particular snowpack. At any particular time and depth into snowpack, ice may form and thus density may vary considerably. Ice forms when snow melts at the surface, percolates into the snow, and then freezes.

The depth of snowmelt (d_m) can be calculated if representative values for depth of snowpack and density of snowpack are available with the density of water at 0°C equal to 1 g/cm^3.

$$d_m = \rho_s d_s \qquad (3.10)$$

where
d_m = depth of melt (cm)
ρ_s = snowpack density (g/cm^3)
d_s = depth of snowpack (cm)

The depth of snowpack water (d_w) in a depth of snowpack (d_s) can be estimated by an indirect measure of average snowpack temperature (T_s) in degrees Celsius below zero (a positive value) and the snowpack density (ρ_s). The depth of snowpack water can be derived by knowing the heat capacity (H_c) of the snowpack, which depends on the snowpack specific heat, its density, and average snowpack column temperature. Investigations by the U.S. Army Corps of Engineers (1956) and knowledge that specific heat has a constant value of 0.5 calories per gram per degree Celsius for a range of snowpack density of 0.05 to 0.90, lead to Equation 3.11. The heat required per unit area to raise the temperature of the snowpack to 0°C is

$$H_c = \int_0^{d_s} \rho_s c_s T_s \, dz \qquad (3.11)$$

where
H_c = heat capacity (calories/cm^2)
c_s = snowpack specific heat (calories/gram °C)
T_s = snowpack temperature (°C)
z = depth for integration (cm)

Upon integration and assuming average values with depth

$$H_c \cong \rho_s c_s T_s d_s \qquad (3.12)$$

Before significant melt can occur, an additional latent heat of fusion must be supplied and is written as

$$H_c = L_f \rho_w d_w \tag{3.13}$$

where

H_c = heat content (cal/cm^2)
L_f = latent heat of fusion = 80 calories per gram
ρ_w = density of liquid water = 1 g/cm^3
d_w = water depth equivalent of the cold snowpack (cm)

For water, the latent heat of fusion is a quantity of heat required to convert one gram of ice to water. Equating Equations 3.12 and 3.13:

$$d_w = (\rho_s c_s T_s d_s)/(\rho_w L_f) = (\rho_s d_s T_s)/160 \tag{3.14}$$

The depth of water of the cold snowpack compared to the depth of snowmelt is usually less for the same snowpack density and snowpack depth.

The collection of accurate snowpack density data are not always possible for large areas. Furthermore, terrain features, wind velocities, and near surface air temperatures must be used to determine the rate of melt. Equations 3.10 and 3.14 provide estimates of potential quantities, but the rate of melt (depth per day) is not available. To accomplish this, energy budget methods are useful.

☐   **EXAMPLE PROBLEM 3.4**

Data on newly fallen snow density and air temperature are available from the U.S. Army Corps of Engineers (1956). Using a computer program, develop a best-fit linear and power equation relating density as a dependent (Y) variable to surface air temperature as an independent (X) variable. The partial data listing is:

DENSITY (g/cm^3)	AIR TEMPERATURE (°F)	DENSITY (g/cm^3)	AIR TEMPERATURE (°F)
0.04	14	0.09	22
0.06	17	0.10	23
0.08	18	0.09	24
0.08	19	0.11	25
0.09	20	0.12	30
0.08	20.5	0.13	31
0.08	21	0.18	32

Solution

Using the linear regression option of your computer program or solving by hand computation a linear regression model (see Chapter 9), the equations are:

linear: $\rho = -0.036 + 0.0058T$ $14 \leq T \leq 32$

power: $\rho = 0.0013T^{1.41}$ $14 \leq T \leq 32$

where
ρ = density of snowfall (g/cm^3)
T = degrees Fahrenheit (°F) □

3.8.2 Energy Budget

There exist at least six heat effects on a snowpack, which accounts for a change in heat stored in a pack during a time interval (Δt). In equation form, these are (units of calories):

$$\Delta H = H_S + H_L + H_C + H_{CS} + H_G + H_P \qquad (3.15)$$

where
ΔH = heat storage change
H_S = short-wave solar radiation
H_L = net long-wave radiation exchange
H_C = convective from the air
H_{CS} = condensation or sublimation
H_G = conduction from the ground
H_P = advection from precipitation

If heat is added to the snowpack column, it is a positive value, removed heat has a negative value. When ΔH exceeds the cold content H_C, melt will occur. Since it requires 80 cal/g for each square centimeter or 80 cal/cm (density of water is 1 g/cm^3) the depth of melt in centimeters is

$$d_m = \Delta H/80 \qquad (3.16)$$

where ΔH = energy change in calories.
The calculation of each heat effect requires extensive time related data. Thus, the Corps of Engineers (1956) developed other statistical measures to estimate the rate as a function of daily meteorological data. They completed extensive studies in the western portion of the United States. These studies are detailed sufficiently to separate rainy and rain-free periods of melt. During rainfall, heat transfer by convection and condensation is important. During rain-free periods, radiation becomes significant. During rainfall conditions, estimation equations in the U.S. system of units are:
For partial forest cover (< 60% of the area)

$$\text{SNM} = 0.09 + (0.029 + 0.0084kU + 0.007i)(T_a - 32) \qquad (3.17)$$

and for heavily forested cover (> 60% of the area)

$$SNM = 0.05 + (0.074 + 0.007i)(T_a - 32) \qquad (3.18)$$

where

SNM = daily snowmelt (in./day)

k = watershed constant (0.3 for dense areas to 1.0 for clear plains)

U = average wind velocity at 50 feet above snow (mph)

i = average rainfall intensity (in./day)

T_a = temperature of saturated air measured 10 ft above the snow (°F)

During rain-free conditions, a variety of equations exist as a function of percent forest area. The equation for heavy forested areas is

$$SNM = 0.074(0.53T_a' + 0.47T_d') \qquad (3.19)$$

where

T_a' = temperature difference between that at 10 ft and the snow surface (°F)

T_d' = temperature difference between the 10-ft dewpoint and snow surface temperature (°F)

3.9

FREQUENCY – INTENSITY-DURATION CURVES

Precipitation depths and intensities are useless by themselves unless they can be related to a frequency of occurrence. The frequency of occurrence establishes the risk of failure. An example is a storm volume that occurs once every 5 yr. If a water system is sized (designed) for the 5-yr storm volume, it should be sufficient for all storms up to that volume. However, if the 50-yr storm volume appears, the water system will be undersized. Precipitation data are used for the design and operation of closed or open conduits, reservoirs, groundwater pumps, pollution control structures, assimilative capacity studies, etc. It is frequently convenient to reduce intensities and volumes to more usable forms. Transmission systems are designed to transport a particular rate of flow resulting from a storm of a particular magnitude. Magnitude is specified by the intensity and duration of rainfall and frequency of occurrence of the storm. Soil Conservation Service technical paper No. 40 (1961) has frequency–intensity and durations reductions of rainfall data for the United States. An example is shown in Figure 3.8. As is shown in this figure, the intensities may vary from one geographic region to another. Typical examples

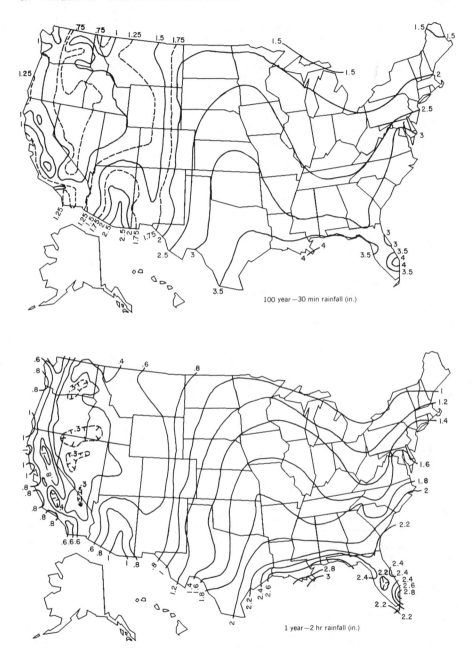

FIGURE 3.8 Example frequency – duration data (U.S. Department of Commerce, 1961).

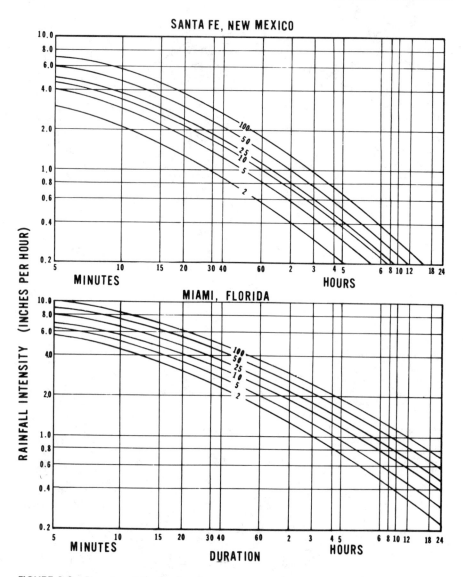

FIGURE 3.9 Frequency-intensity-duration curves.

of another reduction of precipitation data are illustrated for two different geographical areas in Figure 3.9 (Chow, 1964). Using rainfall data from many individual storm records, the generalized intensity–duration–frequency curves of Figure 3.9 can be computed. When using computers, calculators, or hand calculations, it may be more convenient to use equations rather than graphs. The observed data, in general, can usually fit an equation of the following form:

$$i = \frac{at^m}{(b + D)^n} \tag{3.20}$$

where

i = rainfall intensity (cm/hr or in./hr)
t = frequency of occurrence (return period) (yr)
D = duration of storm (min or hr)
a, b, m, n = coefficients and exponents varying from one region to another

The common form of Equation 3.20 used for hydrologic analysis is one that fixes the frequency of occurrence, thus we eliminate t and m from the

TABLE 3.4 Rainfall Quantities and Intensities

RAINFALL DURATION (D)	QUANTITY FOR GIVEN FREQUENCIES						
	1	2	5	10	25	50	100
5 min	0.56[a]	0.64	0.78	0.87	0.98	1.11	1.18
	(6.72)[b]	(7.68)	(9.36)	(10.44)	(11.76)	(13.30)	(14.2)
10 min	0.86	0.99	1.20	1.34	1.51	1.71	1.82
	(5.16)	(5.94)	(7.20)	(8.04)	(9.06)	(10.30)	(10.9)
15 min	1.09	1.25	1.51	1.69	1.91	2.16	2.30
	(4.26)	(5.00)	(6.04)	(6.76)	(7.64)	(8.64)	(9.2)
30 min	1.51	1.73	2.10	2.50	2.65	3.00	3.20
	(3.02)	(3.46)	(4.20)	(4.80)	(5.30)	(6.00)	(6.4)
60 min	1.95	2.25	2.70	3.10	3.40	3.80	4.20
	(1.95)	(2.25)	(2.70)	(3.10)	(3.40)	(3.80)	(4.20)
2 hr	2.30	2.70	3.30	3.80	4.30	4.80	5.30
	(1.15)	(1.35)	(1.65)	(1.90)	(2.15)	(2.40)	(2.65)
3 hr	2.50	2.90	3.70	4.30	4.80	5.30	5.90
	(0.833)	(0.967)	(1.23)	(1.43)	(1.60)	(1.77)	(1.97)
6 hr	2.90	3.40	4.40	5.20	5.80	6.50	7.20
	(0.483)	(0.567)	(0.733)	(0.867)	(0.967)	(1.08)	(1.20)
12 hr	3.30	4.00	5.20	6.20	7.00	7.80	8.70
	(0.275)	(0.333)	(0.433)	(0.517)	(0.583)	(0.650)	(0.72)
24 hr	3.90	4.70	6.20	7.20	8.40	9.30	10.50
	(0.163)	(0.196)	(0.258)	(0.300)	(0.350)	(0.388)	(0.43)

[a] Denotes inches of rainfall.
[b] Parentheses denote intensity (in./hr).

equation and assume the exponent n to equal unity, resulting in

$$i = \frac{a}{b + D} \qquad (3.21)$$

Standard statistical bivariate regression procedures are then used to solve for the coefficients a and b. Additional examples of these equations in graphical form are found in Appendix C.

□   ***EXAMPLE PROBLEM 3.5***

To illustrate the development of the above equation, rainfall storms of various return periods (frequencies) and durations are shown in Table 3.4. These data are obtained from local climatological reports. A graph relating intensity to duration of storm is illustrated in Figure 3.10 for a frequency of occurrence of 10 years.

Solution

Develop "best" fit equations using the least squares criteria. By our using bivariate regression techniques, equations are developed relating intensities and duration. These equations are listed in Table 3.5 (Golding, 1977).

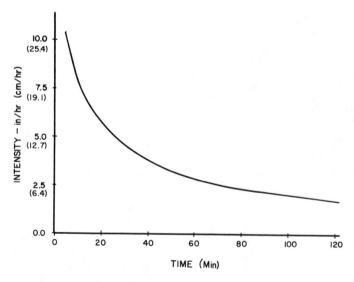

FIGURE 3.10   Intensity-duration curve for a 10-year return period (Golding, 1977).

TABLE 3.5 Best-Fit Intensity/Duration Curves

FREQUENCY (yr)	EQUATION	CORRELATION COEFFICIENT
1	$i^b = \dfrac{167.08}{23.210 + D^c}$	$r^2 = .999$
2	$i = \dfrac{195.29}{23.885 + D}$	$r^2 = .999$
5	$i = \dfrac{247.36}{26.185 + D}$	$r^2 = .996$
10	$i = \dfrac{289.07}{27.736 + D}$	$r^2 = .996$
25	$i = \dfrac{324.23}{27.969 + D}$	$r^2 = .996$
50	$i = \dfrac{357.76}{26.864 + D}$	$r^2 = .996$
100	$i = \dfrac{401.78}{28.864 + D}$	$r^2 = .995$

[a] Good only for durations less than 180 min.
[b] i = rainfall intensity (in./hr).
[c] D = duration (min). □

3.10

SUMMARY

- Precipitation forms when nuclei are present, onto which water attaches and grows to over 0.5 mm in diameter.
- Hydrometeor is the general term for the various forms of rain, snow, and other classifications of precipitation.
- A hyetograph is a plot of intensity versus time.
- A dimensionless mass diagram is a plot of the fraction of rainfall from a given volume of total rainfall as a function of the fraction of time for a given storm duration.
- Precipitation is measured both as depth and intensity at a point on the ground.

- Depth of precipitation can be converted to a watershed volume by assuming the depth is constant over the watershed area.
- The intensity of runoff is related to the intensity of rainfall. The rainfall intensity must remain constant over the time it would take the total contributing area to drain the rainfall excess.
- The network of gages provides precipitation data for points on the ground. For a wider regional estimate, averaging techniques must be used. Commonly used ones are the arithmetic average, isohyetal, and Theissen.
- Daily snowmelt can be estimated using an energy-budget method and for specific conditions, Equations 3.17, 3.18, and 3.19 can be used.
- Intensity–duration–frequency curves reflect the rainfall history of an area. By specifying the risk (frequency), an intensity can be estimated for a specific watershed.

3.11

PROBLEMS

1. A rain gage is located in a 2.5-acre impervious watershed with no initial abstraction. The gage records 1.0 in. of rainfall in one hour. The maximum intensity was 2.4 in. of rainfall/hour for 10 min. Assume that 10 min is a time during which all parts of the watershed can contribute to a discharge point. What is the volume of rainfall in cubic feet and the maximum runoff rate?

2. Develop a hyetograph (graphical presentation) for the following rainfall data. Plot the intensity (inches/hour) for 30 minute intervals.

TIME (min)	CUMULATIVE RAIN (in.)
30	0.04
60	0.38
90	1.07
120	1.44
150	1.62
180	1.70

3. What is the average rainfall intensity for a 1-hr and 6-hr rain event with a return period of 100 years for the Orlando, Florida, area? Use the frequency–intensity–duration (FID) Curves of Appendix C.

4. What is the total rain volume for the storms of Problem 3?

5. If 55 mm of rain is recorded for a 6-hr storm by one rain gage for a watershed area of 10 km^2, but the runoff from the watershed indicates only 45 mm of rain has fallen on the entire area, what is the areal reduction factor? How does this compare to the results reported in the U.K. (Table 3.3)?

6. Using Figures 3.2 and 3.3, determine the average rainfall intensities in inches/hour for the following time periods.
   a. From 3:00 hour to the 4:00 hour
   b. For the first half of the 6-hr storm
   c. The maximum in any one hour
   d. The maximum in any 15-min period
   e. The last half hour

7. Obtain hourly rainfall data from a local climatological report and develop a hyetograph and a cumulative rainfall curve.

8. For the cumulative rainfall curve of Figure 3.11, develop a 1-hr listing of rainfall intensities for a storm of 24-hr duration. The maximum storm volume is for a 100-yr storm event. To obtain the volume, use any frequency–intensity–duration (FID) curve or the ones in Appendix C. State your references.

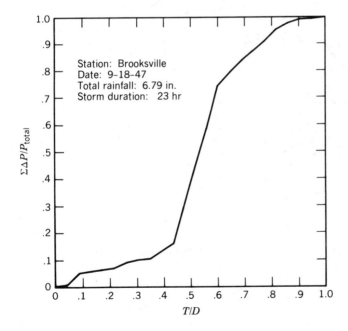

FIGURE 3.11 Actual cumulative rainfall curve.

9. Using the SCS Type II dimensionless cumulative rainfall curve of Appendix C, develop cumulative rainfall depths on an hourly basis for a total rainfall of 203 mm (8 in.). Do the same for the Corps of Engineers standard distribution. Compare results.

10. Develop for each half-hour increment the cumulative rainfall for a 24-hr storm using the SCS Type III curve of Appendix C and a 254-mm (10 in.) rainfall.

11. Describe the drainage area that is defined by the USGS Station #1 in Figure 3.12 by drawing on the map the appropriate boundaries and compute the area of the drainage basin in square miles.

    Now, from the precipitation stations, identified by (4.00 in.) calculate the average precipitation by three methods: (1) arithmetic mean, (2) Thiessen, and (3) isohyetal.

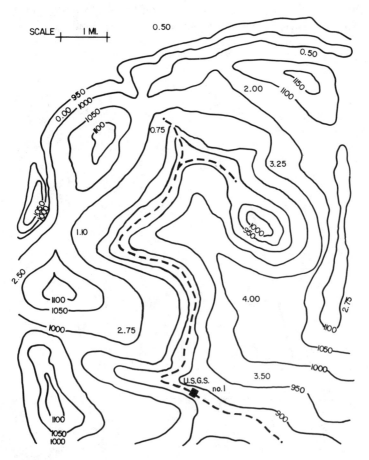

FIGURE 3.12   USGS No. 1 drainage area.

12. Plot the intensity duration data of this problem and fit by "graphical" (eye) technique the best line.

DURATION (min)	INTENSITY (in./hr)
10	4
15	3.2
20	2.7
30	1.9
60	1.2
120	0.8
180	0.6

13. Using two dimensionless cumulative rainfall diagrams as applied to a rural watershed with sandy type soils (high infiltration), which hyetograph would produce the maximum peak discharge if soil saturation occurs at about half of the rainfall volume?

14. Develop a dimensionless rainfall diagram using the following incremental precipitation data from a 24-hr storm.

TIME (hr)	ΔP(in) (in 4-hr increments)
0	0
4	1.00
8	2.00
12	3.00
16	2.00
20	1.00
24	1.00

Using one of the FID curves in Appendix C and a 24-hr–50-yr event, estimate the rainfall volume during the first 12 hr of the 24-hr storm using the dimensionless rainfall diagram just developed.

15. Using the FID curve for Baltimore, Maryland (Figure 3.9), answer the following questions.
   a. What is the rainfall intensity for a 50-yr storm event with a duration of 60 min?
   b. If the duration were 5 hr for the 50-yr storm event, what is the total rainfall?
   c. If the watershed response were only 30 min, what is the maximum 30-min intensity using the 50-yr storm event? Compare this to a storm with a frequency of once every 2 yr.

d. If the time of concentration for an impervious 20-acre watershed were 30 min, what is an estimate of the peak discharge for the 50-hr storm event? Express your answer in CFS Units. What assumptions did you make?

e. What is an estimate of rainfall excess for the same storm as used in part (d)? Express your answer in cubic feet.

16. Using Figure 3.9 and a 50-yr storm event over 24 hr provide a listing using 1-hr intervals of a dimensionless cumulative rainfall diagram. Assume the maximum intensity occurs in hour 12, the next in hour 11, the next in hour 13, and so forth.

17. Use an FID curve of your choice, possibly for your region, and provide a 1-hr listing of a dimensionless cumulative rainfall diagram. Also state your assumptions for the ranking of each value.

18. Snow is sampled for density and depth over a watershed approximately 4 mi^2 in area. The average density of water in the 27-in. snowpack was estimated to be 40%. What is the expected volume of runoff in acre-feet from this area if no additional evaporation occurs and all the snow melting goes to rainfall excess?

19. Using the U.S. Army snowmelt equation for a partial forest covered 160 acre area with a watershed constant of 0.5, average wind speed of 10 mph (50 ft above snow), temperature of 40°F, and an average rainfall of 0.4 in./day, what is the expected daily snowmelt in acre-feet/day?

20. For the following 10hr hyetograph measured at Baltimore, Maryland:
    a. What is the average intensity in cm/hr?
    b. What is the volume of rainfall in m^3 and liters if the watershed is 4000 m^2?
    c. What is the approximate return period?

TIME (min)	INTENSITY (cm/hr)
0–10	2.0
10–20	6.0
20–30	12.0
30–40	8.0
40–50	6.0
50–60	3.0

21. Using the SCS nondimensional Type II rainfall distribution and a 10-in., 24-hr storm event, list the cumulative and interval rainfall volumes for every 2-hr time interval.

22. A 12-hr duration, one in 25-yr storm, occurs in zone seven, Florida. What is the average intensity of rainfall for the first 3 hr? Use the SCS Type II rainfall distribution. State all assumptions.

3.12

COMPUTER-ASSISTED PROBLEMS

1. Using first computer program on your diskette, create two rainfall data files using the rainfall data of this chapter and Appendix C or other files for your local area.

2. Develop, using the "L" option (least squares), a mathematical equation to estimate the dimensionless cumulative rainfall curve for the following data:

TIME (hr)	P/P_{total}	TIME (hr)	P/P_{total}
0	0	13	0.453
2	0.01	14	0.585
3	0.05	15	0.74
4	0.065	16	0.79
5	0.07	17	0.835
6	0.075	18	0.87
7	0.09	19	0.91
8	0.10	20	0.95
9	0.11	21	0.975
10	0.135	22	0.985
11	0.17	23	0.99
12	0.29	24	1.00

3. Using the least squares computer program "L" option, estimate the "best" equation for one of the cumulative rainfall diagrams you have used in the past. What is the next best equation? How did you determine the best? For purposes of this problem, if a polynomial equation fit is used, do not exceed a 3 degree equation.

4. Develop your own computer program to calculate the average of any type of precipitation data (i.e., rainfall depth, snow equivalent depth, or intensities). The program must relate the units of the problem to the program user.

5.   Using the least squares computer program "L" option estimate a "best"
     fit line for the following rainfall intensity and duration data. Postulate at
     least three different relationships.

DURATION (min)	INTENSITY (in./hr)
10	4.0
15	3.2
20	2.7
30	1.9
60	1.2
120	0.8
180	0.6

6.   For Example Problem 3.4, execute the computer program (linear regres-
     sion) to obtain the solution. Also present a graphical display of both
     equations and estimates of density for a temperature of 28°F.

3.13

REFERENCES

Chow, V.T. 1964. *Handbook of Applied Hydrology.* McGraw-Hill, New York.

Golding, B.L. 1977. "Volusia County 208 Comprehensive Rainfall Analysis,"
Howard, Needles, Tammen, and Bergendoff, Orlando, FL, February.

Huff, F.A. 1974. "The Distribution of Heavy Rainfall in a Major Urban Area."
*Proceedings of the National Symposium on Urban Rainfall and Runoff and Sediment
Control*, D.T.Y. Kao, Ed., University of Kentucky, Lexington, July, pp. 53–59.

Larson, L.W. and Peck, E.L. 1974. "Accuracy of Measurements for Hydrologic
Modeling," *Water Resources Research*, **10**(4), pp. 857–863, August.

Masters, G.M. 1974. *Introduction to Environmental Science and Technology.* Wiley,
New York, p. 218.

Meteorological Office. 1982. Surface Water: United Kingdom 1974–76, HMSO
Water Data Unit, Wallingford, U.K.

National Environmental Research Council. 1975. U.K. Institute of Hydrology
Flood Studies Report, Volume II, Wallingford, U.K.

Paulhus, J.L.H. and Kohler, M.A. 1952. "Interpretation of Missing Precipitation
Records," *Monthly Weather Review*, **80**, pp. 129–133, August.

Pilgrim, D.H. and Cordery, I. 1975. "Rainfall Temporal Patterns for Design
Floods," *Journal of the Hydraulics Division, ASCE*, NYI, January, pp. 81–95.

U.S. Army Corps of Engineers. 1956. *Snow Hydrology*, North Pacific Division, Portland, Oregon, June 30.

U.S. Department of Commerce. 1961. "Rainfall Frequency Atlas of the United States," Tech. Paper #40, Soil Conservation Service, U.S. Department of Agriculture, Washington, DC, May.

Wanielista, M.P. 1977 *Orlando Area 208 Study*, Report to Black Crow & Eidesness and the East Central Florida Regional Planning Council," (January 31, 1977). Winter Park, Florida.

World Meteorological Organization. 1974. *Guide to Hydrometeorological Practices*, 3rd Ed. WMO Tech. Paper No. 82, pp. 3.8–3.10, Geneva.

············
············
············

4

INFILTRATION AND EVAPOTRANSPIRATION

In the previous chapters, precipitation and watershed storage were shown to vary with time and thus are hydrologic processes. Infiltration and evapotranspiration also change with time. Instrumentation to measure and methods to estimate infiltration, evaporation, and transpiration are presented in this chapter. Besides theoretical and empirical methods, other processes of a water budget can be measured to indirectly calculate infiltration and evapotranspiration. For predicting and describing potential infiltration rates and soil saturation levels, the hydrologic classification schemes for soils are important watershed factors.

4.1.

SOIL AND HYDROLOGIC CLASSIFICATIONS

Soil types and degree of soil saturation partly determine infiltration and evapotranspiration rates. Infiltration has been related to soil texture by Rawls et al. (1982). Minimum infiltration rates are shown in Table 4.1 and in general are related to texture class, water capacity, and the Soil Conservation Service

TABLE 4.1   Hydrologic Soil Properties Classified by Soil Texture

TEXTURE CLASS	EFFECTIVE WATER CAPACITY (in./in)	MINIMUM INFILTRATION RATE (f_c) (in./hr)	SCS HYDROLOGIC SOIL GROUPING[a]
Sand	0.35	8.27	A
Loamy sand	0.31	2.41	A
Sandy loam	0.25	1.02	B
Loam	0.19	0.52	B
Silt loam	0.17	0.27	C
Sandy clay loam	0.14	0.17	C
Clay loam	0.14	0.09	D
Silty clay loam	0.11	0.06	D
Sandy clay	0.09	0.05	D
Silty clay	0.09	0.04	D
Clay	0.08	0.02	D

Source: Rawls et al., 1982.
[a]Specific named soil types may have a different SCS soil classification than the general one of this column for a texture class.

TABLE 4.2   SCS Hydrologic Soil Groups

SOIL GROUP[a]	DESCRIPTION
A	Lowest runoff potential. Includes deep sands with very little silt and clay; also, deep, rapidly permeable gravel.
B	Moderately low runoff potential. Mostly sandy soils less deep and less aggregated than A, but the group as a whole has above average infiltration after thorough wetting.
C	Moderately high runoff potential. Comprises shallow soils and soils containing considerable clay and colloids, though less than those of group D. The group has below average infiltration after saturation.
D	Highest runoff potential. Includes mostly clays of high swelling percentage, but the group also includes some shallow soils with nearly impermeable subhorizons near the surface.

Source: U.S. Department of Agriculture, Soil Survey Manual #18, Washington DC, 1951.
[a]A mixed designation, (i.e., B/D) refers to drained/undrained natural situation.

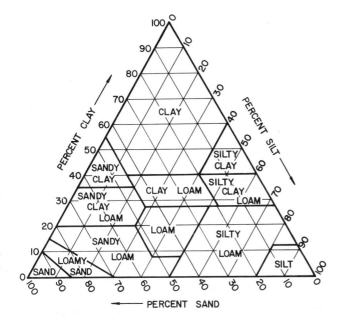

FIGURE 4.1   Textural soil classification. (Department of Agriculture, 1951).

(SCS) hydrologic soil grouping (Table 4.2). Also, evaporation rates from the soil have been shown to be related to texture class and water remaining in the soil (Holtan, 1975).

Sand, silt, clay, and decaying materials are the primary particles of soil. The U.S. Department of Agriculture defines soil in terms of percentage sand, silt and clay as shown in Figure 4.1 (U.S. Department of Agriculture, 1951). Soil is generally classified by five factors: climate, slope, biological activity, parent material, and age. These factors determine the soil type drainage characteristics. Using more than 3000 specifically named soil types, the SCS divided each into four hydrologic groups (Table 4.2).

Some sands, such as Leon Fine and the Intermixed Plummer and Rutledge Fine, are given a dual classification as A/D and B/D, respectively. The first letter applies to the drained condition while the second letter applies to the undrained natural condition. The drained condition can only occur if a closely spaced underdrain system or open ditch drainage system is installed to lower the natural high groundwater. This is expensive and in general not done in urban areas except if water problems exist. However, urbanization will lower the groundwater table because of open ditches and the construction of underground utilities, which cut the bonded organic pan layers. An extensive listing or classification of many soils has been completed by the SCS (U.S. Department of Agriculture, 1975). A partial listing is shown in Appendix H.

<hr>

4.2

INFILTRATION AS A HYDROLOGIC PROCESS

In the hydrologic cycle, infiltration is the entry of waters into the ground. The rate and quantity of water that infiltrates into the ground is a function of soil type, soil moisture, soil permeability, ground cover, drainage conditions, depth of water table, and intensity and volume of precipitation. The soil type helps to identify the number and size of the capillaries through which water must flow, while moisture content helps identify capillary potential and relative conductivity. Capillary potential is high and conductivity low for a low moisture content. Capillary potential is the hydraulic head due to capillary forces usually expressed as centimeters of equivalent water depth. As rainfall commences on a dry soil, the moisture level must increase before water will move into the soil mass or relative conductivity must increase. A distinct wetting front develops and, as more precipitation infiltrates into the soil, the thickness of the wet zone increases and the potential for infiltration decreases. It is this infiltration rate as a hydrologic process that is of concern in relation to infiltration storage rate and volume.

Four methods for prediction of infiltration will be presented: (1) theoretical, (2) empirical using curve numbers (CN), (3) water budget, and (4) direct field measurements using a double-ring infiltrometer.

4.2.1 Infiltration Using Theoretical Methods

Experiments with unsaturated soil media as reported by Todd (1980) and others, showed that velocity of flow through unsaturated media is proportional to hydraulic conductivity (K), pressure head, and volumetric moisture content (θ). The capillary suction (Ψ) plus the depth of percolating water (L_p) add to produce the pressure head (Δh) for flow in the vertical (z) direction through unsaturated media. A solution procedure was first proposed by Green and Ampt (1911). The rate of movement follows Darcy's law (see Chapter 10) and assuming a hydraulic conductivity equals K_s at saturation, the velocity of infiltration, $f(t)$, is:

$$f(t) = K_s(\Delta h/\Delta z) = K_s(L_p + \Psi)/L_p \qquad (4.1)$$

The infiltrated water is assumed to percolate through the dry soil as a "slug flow." The volume of water ($F(t)$) in the slug is equal to the difference between the saturated moisture content (θ_s) and the initial content (θ_i) times the depth of percolating water (L_p). The border between the slug of percolating water and the unsaturated soil is the wetted front. At the front, there is an average capillary suction head Ψ_{av}. Direct measurement for Ψ_{av}, K_s, and θ_s are generally difficult, but Skaggs and Khaleel (1982) outlined some estimation procedures. Substituting into Equation 4.1 for L_p as related to F and θ, the following infiltration capacity equation results:

$$f(t) = K_s + \left[K_s(\theta_s - \theta_i)\Psi_{av} \right]/F(t) \qquad (4.2)$$

where

$f(t) =$ infiltration rate, in./hr

$K_s =$ saturation conductivity, in./hr

$\theta_s =$ saturation soil water content which is usually less than soil porosity, fraction of total volume

$\theta_i =$ initial soil water content, fraction of total volume

$\Psi_{av} =$ average capillary suction (in.)

$F(t) =$ volume of infiltration (in.) at time t.

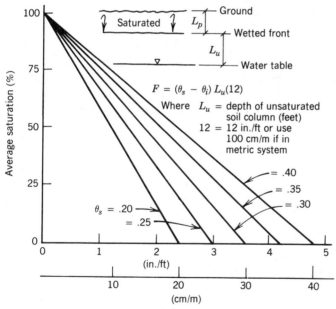

FIGURE 4.2   Theoretical available soil water storage per foot (or meter) of soil for various moisture content and saturated soil water content.

At the moment the ground surface becomes saturated, $F(t) = F_s$. Until F_s is obtained, the rate of infiltration equals the rainfall rate.

The theoretically available soil moisture storage in an unsaturated soil, expressed as the volume of available water storage (depth of water/unit depth of soil), is related to the average saturation usually expressed as a percentage, the average water content of the soil, and the depth of the soil from the soil surface to the zone of saturation in meters (feet). Figure 4.2 is a graphic representation of soil water storage capacity. The relation is plotted for soils having average soil water content from 20 to 40%. This concept is applicable to homogeneous soils that are not broken by layers of relatively impermeable soils.

☐   **EXAMPLE PROBLEM 4.1**

In some planning and design situations, Figure 4.2 will be all that is required to estimate soil storage or infiltration volume. As an example, consider the construction of a retention pond to hold water for a short period of time. If the depth to water table is 3 m, the soil has moderately slow permeability (0.3 m/day) and a $\theta_s = 0.20$, estimate the available soil water storage, the average velocity of infiltration and the time to reach saturation. At first, the 3 m of soil are unsaturated.

Solution

The available soil water storage is 20 cm/m from Figure 4.2; thus, for 3 m, 60 cm of water can be stored, assuming no groundwater outflow of waters that infiltrated into the soil. The velocity of infiltration is proportional to the permeability and inversely proportional to porosity and can be estimated from (Todd, 1980):

$$f = K \left(\frac{1}{n_p + 1} \right) \tag{4.3}$$

where
  f = infiltration rate (m/day)
  K = permeability (m/day)
  n_p = porosity, decimal

Thus, $f = 0.3 \, (1/0.2 + 1) = 1.8$ m/day. Knowing the velocity and storage depth, the time for saturation is estimated from $t = $ depth/velocity $= 0.6$ m/1.8 $= 0.3$ days. This problem assumes uniform soil and saturation conditions, which rarely exist in field situations; thus, experimental field methods are sometimes used to incorporate the time variability and variation in soil and moisture conditions.   ☐

4.2.2 Curve Number, Infiltration, and Rainfall Excess

There are many interrelated factors that influence infiltration volumes and rainfall excess. In general terms, these are climatic and watershed related. Infiltration and thus rainfall excess will vary during a storm event. One empirical description for infiltration and rainfall excess is the curve number method. At the start of precipitation, the intensity of rainfall is usually less than the rate at which water is stored. As depression storage becomes filled, and the soil and vegetative cover becomes saturated, rainfall excess increases. When soil, depression area, and vegetation storage approach ultimate saturation, storage will approach a potential saturation value (S') and infiltration rate approaches zero. Then the rainfall excess rate will equal the precipitation rate. Rainfall excess (R) and watershed storage (S) are derived from precipitation and the soil type. A possible relationship over time is shown in Figure 4.3 and rainfall excess (R) is expressed as

$$R = P - S \qquad (4.4)$$

where

R = rainfall excess

P = rainfall volume

S = storage volume on and within the soil (initial abstraction plus infiltration)

At saturation, the rate of rainfall excess is equal to the intensity of precipitation. A proportional relationship can be developed as

$$\frac{S}{S'} = \frac{R}{P} \qquad (4.5)$$

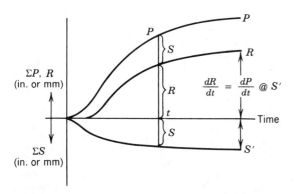

FIGURE 4.3 Time variability of hydrologic events.

where

S = storage at any time (mm, in.)

S' = storage at saturation (mm, in.)

R = rainfall excess at any time (mm, in.)

P = precipitation at any time (mm, in.)

TABLE 4.3   Saturation Values and Start of Rainfall Excess for Initial Abstraction of 20% for Given Curve Number[a]

CN FOR CONDITION	S' VALUES[a] (in.)	EXCESS CURVE STARTS WHERE $P =$ (in.)	CN FOR CONDITION	S' VALUES[a] (in.)	EXCESS CURVE STARTS WHERE $P =$ (in.)	CN FOR CONDITION	S' VALUES[a] (in.)	EXCESS CURVE STARTS WHERE $P =$ (in.)
100	0	0	76	3.16	0.63	52	9.23	1.85
99	0.101	0.02	75	3.33	0.67	51	9.61	1.92
98	0.204	0.04	74	3.51	0.70	50	10.0	2.00
97	0.309	0.06	73	3.70	0.74	49	10.4	2.08
96	0.417	0.08	72	3.89	0.78	48	10.8	2.16
95	0.526	0.11	71	4.08	0.82	47	11.3	2.26
94	0.638	0.13	70	4.28	0.86	46	11.7	2.34
93	0.753	0.15	69	4.49	0.90	45	12.2	2.44
92	0.870	0.17	68	4.70	0.94	44	12.7	2.54
91	0.989	0.20	67	4.92	0.98	43	13.2	2.64
90	1.11	0.22	66	5.15	1.03	42	13.8	2.76
89	1.24	0.25	65	5.38	1.08	41	14.4	2.88
88	1.36	0.27	64	5.62	1.12	40	15.0	3.00
87	1.49	0.30	63	5.87	1.17	39	15.6	3.12
86	1.63	0.33	62	6.13	1.23	38	16.3	3.26
85	1.76	0.35	61	6.39	1.28	37	17.0	3.40
84	1.90	0.38	60	6.67	1.33	36	17.8	3.56
83	2.05	0.41	59	6.95	1.39	35	18.6	3.72
82	2.20	0.44	58	7.24	1.45	34	19.4	3.88
81	2.34	0.47	57	7.54	1.51	33	20.3	4.06
80	2.50	0.50	56	7.86	1.57	32	21.2	4.24
79	2.66	0.53	55	8.18	1.64	31	22.2	4.44
78	2.82	0.56	54	8.52	1.70	30	23.3	4.66
77	2.99	0.60	53	8.87	1.77	0	infinity	infinity

[a] Watershed area is considered to have the same ground cover and soils. If directly connected impervious areas (discharge point hydraulically connected to watershed) exist, then calculate excess for the directly connected area separately from the remaining area. Rainfall excess from the directly connected areas will appear earlier in a storm event than excess from soils not directly connected. The curve number for the areas and initial abstraction are different.

TABLE 4.4 Curve Numbers for Urban Land Uses[a]

COVER DESCRIPTION		CURVE NUMBERS FOR HYDROLOGIC SOIL GROUP			
COVER TYPE AND HYDROLOGIC CONDITION	AVERAGE % IMPERVIOUS AREA[b]	A	B	C	D
Fully developed urban areas (vegetation established)					
Open space (lawns, parks, golf courses, cemeteries, etc.)[c]					
Poor condition (grass cover < 50%		68	79	86	89
Fair condition (grass cover 50 to 75%)		49	69	79	84
Good condition (grass cover > 75%)		39	61	74	80
Impervious areas:					
Paved parking lots, roof, driveways, etc. (excluding right-of-way)[d]		98	98	98	98
Streets and roads:					
Paved; curbs and storm sewers (excluding right-of-way)		98	98	98	98
Paved: open ditches (including right-of-way)		83	89	92	93
Gravel (including right-of-way)		76	85	89	91
Dirt (including right-of-way)		72	82	87	89
Western desert urban areas:					
Natural desert landscaping (pervious areas only)		63	77	85	88
Artificial desert landscaping (impervious weed barrier, desert shrub with 1–2-in. sand or gravel mulch and basin borders)		96	96	96	96
Urban districts:					
Commercial and business	85	89	92	94	95
Industrial	72	81	88	91	93
Residential districts by average lot size:					
$\frac{1}{8}$ acre or less (town houses)	65	77	85	90	92
$\frac{1}{4}$ acre	38	61	75	83	87
$\frac{1}{3}$ acre	30	57	72	81	86
$\frac{1}{2}$ acre	25	54	70	80	85
1 acre	20	51	68	79	84
2 acres	12	46	65	77	82
Developing urban areas					
Newly graded areas (pervious areas only, no vegetation)		77	86	91	94
Idle lands (*CN*s are determined using cover types similar to those in Table 4.5).					

Source: Reproduced from U.S. Department of Agriculture,–SCS (1986).
[a]Average runoff condition, Antecendent Moisture Condition (AMC) II, and Ia = 0.2S'.
[b]The average percent impervious area shown was used to develop the composite *CN*s. Other assumptions are as follows: impervious areas are directly connected to the drainage system, impervious areas have a *CN* of 98, and pervious areas are considered equivalent to open space in good hydrologic condition.
[c]*CN*s shown are equivalent to those of pasture. Composite *CN*s may be computed for other combinations of open space cover type.
[d]In some warmer climates, a curve number of 95 may be used.

TABLE 4.5 Runoff Curve Numbers for Hydrologic Soil-Cover Complexes (Antecedent Moisture Condition II)

LAND USE	TREATMENT OR PRACTICE	HYDROLOGIC CONDITION	A	B	C	D
Fallow	Straight row	—	77	86	91	94
Row crops	Straight row	Poor	72	81	88	91
	Straight row	Good	67	78	85	89
	Contoured	Poor	70	79	84	88
	Contoured	Good	65	75	82	86
	Contoured and terraced	Poor	66	74	80	82
	Contoured and terraced	Good	62	71	78	81
Small grain	Straight row	Poor	65	76	84	88
		Good	63	75	83	87
	Contoured	Poor	63	74	82	85
		Good	61	73	81	84
	Contoured and terraced	Poor	61	72	79	82
		Good	59	70	78	81
Close-seeded	Straight row	Poor	66	77	85	89
legumes[a]	Straight row	Good	58	72	81	85
or	Contoured	Poor	64	75	83	85
rotation	Contoured	Good	55	69	78	83
meadow	Contoured and terraced	Poor	63	73	80	83
	Contoured and terraced	Good	51	67	76	80
Pasture or range		Poor	68	79	86	89
		Fair	49	69	79	84
		Good	39	61	74	80
	Contoured	Poor	47	67	81	88
	Contoured	Fair	25	59	75	83
	Contoured	Good	6	35	70	79
Meadow		Good	30	58	71	78
Woods		Poor	45	66	77	83
		Fair	36	60	73	79
		Good	25	55	70	77
Farmsteads		—	59	74	82	86
Roads (dirt)[b]		—	72	82	87	89
(hard surface)[b]		—	74	84	90	92

Source: U.S. Department of Agriculature *National Engineering Handbook*, Soil Conservation Service U.S. Department of Agriculture Section 4, Chapter 9, Hydrologic Soil Cover Complexes, 1972. Washington, DC.

[a] Close drilled or broadcast.

[b] Including right-of-way.

Since $S = P - R$, substituting into Equation 4.5 yields:

$$\frac{(P - R)}{S'} = \frac{R}{P}$$

or

$$R = \frac{P^2}{(P + S')} \qquad \text{for } I_A = 0 \qquad (4.6)$$

Additional work done by the SCS and reported in various publications (Kent, 1973) identified an empirical relationship between the initial abstraction and storage and, thus, developed an equation where the initial abstraction was assumed equal to $0.2S'$. However, abstraction values for urban areas were shown to be less if the soil types were A or B, and, in fact, Golding (1986)

TABLE 4.6 *CN* Adjustments

CN CONDITION 2	CORRESPONDING CN	
	CONDITION 1	CONDITION 3
100	100	100
95	87	98
90	78	96
85	70	94
80	63	91
75	57	88
70	51	85
65	45	82
60	40	78
55	35	74
50	31	70
45	26	65
40	22	60
35	18	55
30	15	50

Source: U.S. Department of Agriculture, 1972.

recommends values of $0.075S'$ and $0.10S'$ for A and B type urban soils, respectively. Using more than 3000 soil types divided into four hydrologic groups, the SCS developed runoff curve numbers (CN) to estimate S' in Equation 4.6. The maximum storage of water is estimated in mm and inches using the following:

Metric (mm)   English (in.)

$$S' = (25,400/CN) - 254 \quad \text{and} \quad S' = (1000/CN) - 10 \quad (4.7)$$

and rainfall excess using

$$R = (P - 0.2S')^2/(P + 0.8S') \quad \text{if } P > 0.2S'$$

$$\text{and} \quad R = 0 \quad \text{if } P \leq 0.2S'. \quad (4.8)$$

A table for S' and the starting values of rainfall excess with time is shown in Table 4.3.

Runoff curve numbers can be estimated if the soil classification and the cover crop (land use) are known. In Tables 4.4 and 4.5, runoff curve numbers (CN) are shown for areas with the same ground cover and soils.

The SCS has established three antecedent moisture conditions for use with CN:

CONDITION	DESCRIPTION	ANTECEDENT RAINFALL
1	A condition of drainage basin soils where the soils are dry but not to wilting point	Five day antecedent rainfall is less than 0.50 in.
2	The average case	Five day antecedent rainfall varies from 0.5 to 1.5 in.
3	When heavy rainfall or light rainfall with low temps have occurred producing high runoff potential	Five day antecedent rainfall greater than 1.5 in.

To adjust the curve number (CN) for wet (condition 3) and dry (condition 1) moisture soils, if condition 2 is available, Table 4.6 can be used.

Miller and Veissman (1972) modified the SCS curve number procedure for urban drainage basins. The residential land use in Table 4.4 assumes an average percent impervious area. If this percentage were changed, the curve number would be changed. Runoff curve numbers for the unpaved (pervious) portions of urban basins are shown in Table 4.7.

TABLE 4.7 Runoff Curve Numbers (*CN*): Pervious Areas — Urban Watersheds (Moisture Condition 2)

LAND USE	HYDROLOGIC SOIL CLASS			
	A	B	C	D
Bare ground	77	86	91	94
Gardens or row crop	72	81	88	91
Good grass (cover on greater than 75% of the pervious area)	39	61	74	80
Fair grass (cover on 50–75% of the pervious area)	49	69	79	84
Poor grass (cover on less than 50% of the pervious area)	68	79	86	89
Fair woods	36	60	73	79

Source: U.S. Department of Agriculture, 1972.

For an urbanized area, if the unpaved (previous) area had a grass cover on 80% of that area and was in class B soil, the *CN* would be 61 (Table 4.7). If the grass cover were considered poor (grass on 40% of the area), the *CN* would be 79 in class B soil. This is contrasted to a *CN* of 86 on bare ground cover in class B soil.

☐ **EXAMPLE PROBLEM 4.2**

Consider a watershed for which the specification of curve numbers (*CN*'s), is desired and 75% is directly connected impervious and 25% is pervious (equally divided among poor and good grass cover) and in Class C Soil. Also calculate the composite *CN*.

Solution

Using Tables 4.4 and 4.7:

Calculations for each land use		Calculation for
COVER	CN	COMPOSITE CN
Impervious (directly connected)	98 (Table 4.4)	98(.75) + 80(.25) = 94
Pervious (Good grass) on 50%	74 (Table 4.7)	
Pervious (Poor grass) on 50%	86 (Table 4.7)	

Average of pervious area = .50(74) + .50(86) = 80. ☐

TABLE 4.8 Rainfall Excess (in.) Using Curve Numbers (CN)

RAINFALL	CURVE NUMBER (CN)[a]								
(in.)	60	65	70	75	80	85	90	95	98
1.0	0	0	0	0.03	0.08	0.17	0.32	0.56	0.79
1.2	0	0	0.30	0.07	0.15	0.28	0.46	0.74	0.99
1.4	0	0.02	0.06	0.13	0.24	0.39	0.61	0.92	1.18
1.6	0.01	0.05	0.11	0.20	0.34	0.52	0.76	1.11	1.38
1.8	0.03	0.09	0.17	0.29	0.44	0.65	0.93	1.29	1.58
2.0	0.06	0.14	0.24	0.38	0.56	0.80	1.09	1.48	1.77
2.5	0.17	0.30	0.46	0.65	0.89	1.18	1.53	1.96	2.27
3.0	0.33	0.51	0.72	0.96	1.25	1.59	1.98	2.45	2.78
4.0	0.76	1.03	1.33	1.67	2.04	2.46	2.92	3.43	3.77
5.0	1.30	1.65	2.04	2.45	2.89	3.37	3.88	4.42	4.76
6.0	1.92	2.35	2.80	3.28	3.78	4.31	4.85	5.41	5.76
7.0	2.60	3.10	3.62	4.15	4.69	5.26	5.82	6.41	6.76
8.0	3.33	3.90	4.47	5.04	5.62	6.22	6.81	7.40	7.76
9.0	4.10	4.72	5.34	5.95	6.57	7.19	7.79	8.40	8.76
10.0	4.90	5.57	6.23	6.88	7.52	8.16	8.78	9.40	9.76
11.0	5.72	6.44	7.13	7.82	8.48	9.14	9.77	10.39	10.76
12.0	6.56	7.32	8.05	8.76	9.45	10.12	10.76	11.39	11.76

Source: Reproduced from U.S. Department of Agriculture, SCS, 1986.
[a] To obtain rainfall excess for CNs and other rainfall amounts not shown in this table, use an arithmetic interpolation.

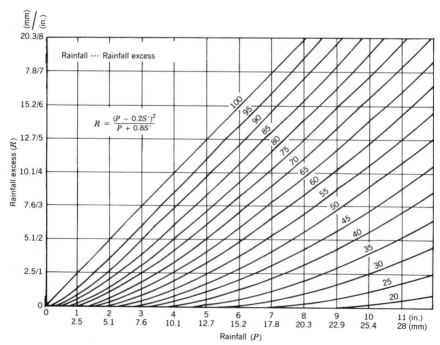

FIGURE 4.4 Rainfall excess — CN curves.

Calculations for maximum soil storage and curve numbers were completed for the Kissimmee River Basin in Florida (Huber et al., 1976). Results illustrated the validity of Table 4.4 and some changes due to local groundwater conditions.

If the appropriate curve number is known, the rainfall excess can be calculated. In fact, the SCS has developed a chart (Table 4.8) and a plot (Figure 4.4) of these relationships. The investigator must determine the land use and soil type. Then, assuming a soil moisture condition, he must calculate a curve number. Using Table 4.8 or Figure 4.4, read directly the volume of runoff, given a volume of rainfall. When rainfall excess is calculated as an intensity, it is called instantaneous rainfall excess, $r(t)$.

☐ **EXAMPLE PROBLEM 4.3**

Estimate infiltration volumes (inches) and rainfall excess (inches and CFS) from a 10-acre area on an hourly basis using the SCS/CN method and the following data:

$$CN = 90$$

$$P = 2.5''$$

$$D = 4 \text{ hours}$$

Solution

$$S' = \frac{1000}{CN} - 10 = 1.11''$$

GIVEN: →		CALCULATED: →			
TIME (hr)	P (in.)	R^a (in.)	$r(t)$ (in./hr)	(CFS)[b]	ΣF^c (in.)
0	0	0	0	0	0
1	0.7	0.14	0.14	1.5	0.56
2	1.6	0.76	0.62	6.2	0.84
3	2.1	1.18	0.42	4.2	0.92
4	2.5	1.53	0.35	3.5	0.97

[a] Calculated from $R = \dfrac{(P - 0.2S')^2}{(P + 0.8S')}$.

[b] $r(t)(\text{CFS}) = \dfrac{(\text{in./hr})(\text{acres})(43{,}560 \text{ ft}^2/\text{ac})}{12 \text{ in./ft} \times 3600 \text{ sec/hr}}$

$= (\text{in./hr})(\text{acres})(1.008)$.

[c] $\Sigma F = P - R$. ☐

4.2.3 Water Budget

If infiltration is the only unknown in a water budget and the variables can be easily measured, then a water budget would produce accurate results. But it is usually difficult to measure depression area and interception storage. Water held on the ground forming ponds or water films is referred to as water in depression storage. This water may eventually evaporate and infiltrate depending on ground cover. For small impervious watersheds, 1.0 to 3.0 mm of depression storage is possible. This storage generally decreases as the slope of the watershed increases. For pervious areas, depression storage is greater, ranging from 2.5 mm (0.1 in.) for clay to 5 mm (0.2 in.) for sandy soils (Hicks, 1944).

Intercepted water is that which adheres to the surface of plants. In urban areas with 10% foliage, Overton and Meadows (1976) estimated that approximately 2.5 mm (0.1 in.) of water is intercepted during the first hour of a storm. For more dense foliage areas, Schomaker (1966) estimated 24% of annual precipitation was intercepted by trees. In areas where the precipitation volume is light (less than 2–3 mm) and there is considerable ground cover, the intercepted water can be significant and potential evaporation high. Thus, precipitation volumes reaching the ground may be near zero.

The sum of depression and interception storage is initial abstraction, so named because the initial precipitation will not result in runoff if depression and interception storage are not saturated. Initial abstraction can be measured by knowing the volume of rainfall, runoff, and infiltration. Generally, initial abstraction is estimated from field observations included with infiltration estimates or directly measured from other known quantities. The measurement of runoff and rainfall on near totally impervious areas (parking lots) results in estimating initial abstraction at 1 mm (0.04 in.) (Wanielista and Shannon, 1977). For dense vegetative areas or flat urban areas, initial abstraction as high as 3 or 4 mm (0.12–0.16 in.) was used (Wanielista and Shannon, 1977).

4.2.4 Site-Specific Infiltration

Permeabilities and rates of soil infiltration, will fluctuate with time and location. Laboratory and field experiments are performed to determine rates. Since permeabilities can vary over a range from 10^{-7} cm/sec for sandy clays to 10^{-2} cm/sec for loose sands, the designer is confronted with many decisions. Laboratory testing using constant or falling head parameters usually are of limited value since there is usually too much soil disturbance and the laboratory boundary conditions and gradients are often different from those in the field. Field testing using borehole or percolation tests is more reliable than laboratory testing for small (< 2000 m^2 areas), but care must be taken to ensure representative testing locations.

For large percolation/recharge basins or areas, considerably more geotechnical surveying and analysis are necessary. Factors involved in such

TABLE 4.9 Double-Ring[a] Infiltrometer Results for Horton Infiltration Parameters

SITE	TEST NO.	INITIAL WATER DEPTH IN DRUM (in.)	f_0 (in./hr)	f_c (in./hr)	K (hr^{-1})	USDA[b] PERMEABILITY (in./hr)
Wimbledon Park	1	2.0	20	6.3	49.1	$10 \rightarrow 20 +$
(Lakeland-blanton)	2	3.7	32	7.8	36.9	in./hr
	3	5.9	60	13	48.8	
	4	8.3	29	13	25.1	
	5	10.2	40	16	16.6	
	6	11.0	55	19.4	15.4	
Cross Creek	1	3.1	1.25	0.19	8.0	< 10
(Lakeland-Blanton	2	3.5	0.84	0.26	5.3	in./hr
with some organics)	3	3.5	0.65	0.08	2.3	
	4	3.6	1.57	0.19	4.1	
	5	3.6	2.6	0.42	8.4	
	6	5.0	1.2	0.26	0.8	
	7	5.9	1.05	0.13	6.0	
Lake Nan	1	3.9	3.4	0.57	4.0	$5 \rightarrow 10$
(Blanton-	2	5.9	2.3	0.73	6.0	in./hr
Pomello-	3	9.1	2.4	0.56	8.4	
Plummer)	4	9.8	5.1	0.83	6.8	

Source: Beaver, 1977.
[a]ASTM D3385-75 Procedure.
[b]From Seminole County, florida Soil Survey Supplement, Soil Conservation Service, U.S. Department of Agriculture, September 1975.

works are discussed by Walton (1970). A fairly reliable percolation test for use in small retention/detention pond design is the double-ring infiltrometer (Chow, 1964). A double-ring infiltrometer is simply a 55-gal drum as an outer ring with a 10 in. or 12 in. inner ring. Example results of these percolation tests are shown in Table 4.9.

Beaver (1977) found using an infiltrometer, that infiltration can be represented by Horton's equation (Horton, 1939, 1940). This method gives an expression for time-varying infiltration. The Horton equation is shown as Equation 4.9 and drawn as shown in Figure 4.5. Also, in Figure 4.5, the rate of precipitation is compared to the rate of infiltration. The volume of infiltration is the area under the infiltration curve and the volume of rainfall is the area

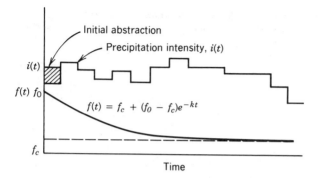

FIGURE 4.5   Infiltration (exponential decay).

under the rainfall intensity curve.

$$f(t) = f_c + (f_0 - f_c)e^{-Kt} \qquad (4.9)$$

where

$f(t)$ = infiltration rate as a function of time cm/hr (in./hr) or other consistent ones

f_c = final, or ultimate, infiltration rate—for a hydraulic gradient of unity, this is analogous to the soil permeability

f_0 = initial infiltration rate

K = recession constant (hr^{-1}) or other consistent units

t = time-units compatible with K

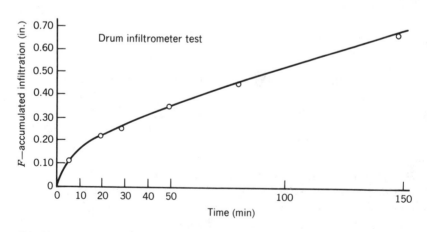

FIGURE 4.6   Example site-specific accumulated infiltration.

The total volume of infiltrate using Horton's equation is determined by integrating the area under the curve, or

$$F = \int_0^t f(t) = f_c t + \frac{(f_0 - f_c)}{K}(1 - e^{-Kt}) \tag{4.10}$$

where F = total infiltration volume, cm (in.) or other consistent units.

During a rainfall event, the application of Equation 4.10 has to be adjusted because rainfall intensity may be lower than the rate of water infiltration potential. Also, another empirical formulation by Holtan et al. (1975) or the theoretical equations of Green and Ampt (1911) also may provide a more accurate fit to the field observed data.

Figures 4.6 and 4.7 illustrate the results of one specific infiltrometer test on a pond floor at Cross Creek in Maitland, Florida (Beaver 1977). The Cross Creek basin has an approximate 280-m³ (10,000-ft³) volume capacity, and the site covers less than 0.25 ac. The bottom soils would be classified as Lakeland–Blanton fine sands using USDA criteria. There were slight organics in the surface soils. Field samples indicates a porosity of 33 to 35%, a coefficient of uniformity of 2 to 3 and an effective grain size (D_{10}) of 0.10 to 0.13 mm. Figure 4.6 is plotted from field infiltrometer tests while Figure 4.7 is derived by differentiating the infiltration curve of Figure 4.6.

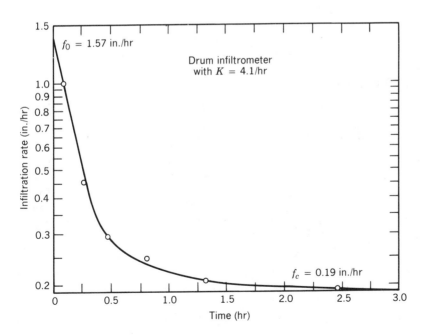

FIGURE 4.7 Example Horton infiltration illustrating the shape of the curve.

Results of infiltrometer testing at three central Florida sites are tabulated in Table 4.9 (Beaver, 1977). All tests were in the bottom of existing retention/detention ponds and the soils were relatively permeable. However, investigation of these data indicates that the Wimbledon Park site gave consistently higher Horton infiltration equation parameters than the other two sites. Some recommended Soil Conservation Service Permeabilities are also included in the table. The Horton parameters generally cannot be obtained without some field testing.

☐ **EXAMPLE PROBLEM 4.4**

Consider as an example problem the design of a stormwater percolation pond. A percolation pond is designed, and field data from a ring infiltrometer are used to estimate the time variability and total volume of infiltrate over a specified time period. The soil in the pond is a silty clay loam with a grass cover. If the initial rate of infiltration and the final rate of infiltration are 4.5 cm/hr and 1.0 cm/hr respectively, estimate the volume of filtrate after 45 min. The recession constant is 5/hr.

Solution

Using Equation 4.10:

$$F = f_c t + \frac{(f_0 - f_0)}{K}(1 - e^{-Kt})$$

$$F = 1.0(0.75) + \frac{(4.5 - 1.0)}{5}(1 - e^{-(5)(0.75)})$$

$$F = 0.75 + 0.68 = 1.43 \text{ cm} \quad \square$$

4.2.5 Phi (Φ) Index

It may be time consuming or costly to obtain all parameters for the Horton equation. The difficulty is primarily in the estimation of an initial rate (f_0). However, the initial rate can be ignored for infiltration over a long period of time. A simpler index for infiltration, namely Φ, assumes that an infiltration rate over time is constant. To calculate Φ, the surface runoff volume is measured and compared to rainfall volume over time. The difference between rainfall volume and runoff volume divided by the duration of the storm is the Φ rate (in./hr). Adjustments to the Φ rate can be made for initial abstraction.

4.3

EVAPOTRANSPIRATION

Evapotranspiration is the sum total of water returned to the atmosphere from surface and ground (soil) water, ice, snow, and vegetation. Evapotranspiration is the sum of evaporation and transpiration. Evaporation is water vapor from all but vegetation. Water movement through a plant that is lost to the ~~atmos~~phere is called transpiration. Transpiration is related to the type of ~~plant~~ and the quantity of sunlight. Transpiration rates are similar to evapora- ~~tion rat~~es when the stomata of plants are open, and appear to be controlled by ~~the dia~~meter of the stomata openings. When the stomata are closed, transpira- ~~tion ra~~tes continue but at a very slow rate (Daubernmire, 1959).

Evaporation

Evaporation is understood to be a cooling process because heat is removed from the surface where evaporation has taken place. Energy must be available for the vaporization process and are chiefly solar and advective. Advective winds carry heat into a watershed from other heated surfaces. In addition, vapor pressures at the surface and the overlying air must be different to allow for evaporation. If the overlying air is saturated, evaporation rates will be reduced to near zero. Also, on some lakes vapor blankets form; thus, evapora- tion is near zero during these times.

There are three general methods commonly in use for measuring evapora- tion, which are mainly indirect methods: (1) measurements from evaporation pans, such as a class A pan and the British Pan, (2) water budgets, and (3) correlations with climatic data.

Evaporation pans

To estimate evaporation, the class A evaporation pan is the most widely used method in the United States. The pan is an unpainted, galvanized iron 4-ft (122 cm) diameter circular container. It is usually filled to a depth of 20 cm and refilled when the depth has fallen to ≤ 18 cm. The water surface is measured daily with a hook gage. Precipitation is measured by the standard rain gage. A class A evaporation station would also include an anemometer.

Pan evaporation is used to estimate lake evaporation. The lake evapora- tion (E_L) is usually calculated for yearly time periods using a pan coefficient (p_c) or

$$E_L = p_c E_p \qquad (4.11)$$

The pan coefficient on an annual basis has been reported to vary between 0.65 and 0.82 (Kohler et al., 1955). For short time periods, the coefficient has been reported for well-watered grass to vary between 0.35 and 0.85 (Shih et al. 1983).

Some selected values of pan evaporation data are given in Table 4.10. These yearly averages are shown to vary within a country and certainly the method of measurement also would be variable. Hot, humid areas like Arizona have high readings. These evaporation rates also vary with the time of the year, the greatest usually being during the periods of intense sunlight (solar

TABLE 4.10   Selected Pan Evaporation Data[a] in (mm/y)

BRITISH PAN		CLASS A PAN	
AREA	YEARLY AVERAGES	AREA	YEARLY AVERAGES
Brecon, Wales	508	Bartlett Dam, Arizona	3089
Cardiff, Wales	652	Lincoln, Nebraska	1290[b]
Bath, England	625	Seattle, Washington	810[b]
Birmingham, England	490	Vicksburg, Mississippi	1311
London, England	650	Newark, California	1478
Belfast, N. Ireland	550	West Palm, Florida	1546
Yorkshire, England	400	Vero Beach, Florida	1580
Edinburgh, Scotland	590	Hoaeae, Hawaii	1589
Wick, Scotland	500	Norris, Tennessee	1059

[a]Approximate values based on Meteorological Data in the Country (Wallingford, 1977, and U.S. Weather Bureau, 1958.
[b]Ice cover on pan, thus inoperative during part of the year.

energy) and least during cold cloud-covered days. In the northern hemisphere, evaporation potential is greatest in the summer, while the winter months have the greatest evaporation potential for the southern hemisphere. This variability is shown in Table 4.11. The data are very useful to indicate regional rates. However, if evaporation is necessary for long-term studies of local regions then more specific estimates are necessary. In an area of about 200 mi^2, local yearly rates may vary among each location as shown in Table 4.12. However, note that the variability is less than a comparison among regional or country yearly rates (Table 4.10). Monthly variability for specific local areas are shown

TABLE 4.11   Average Evaporation Rates from Water Surfaces (cm/mo and in./mo)

LOCATION	JANUARY	APRIL	JULY	OCTOBER	ANNUAL
Columbia, SC	4.0 (1.6)	11 (4.4)	16 (6.5)	11 (4.4)	130 (51)
Eastport, ME	2.0 (0.8)	3 (1.1)	5 (2.0)	4 (1.6)	40 (16)
Galveston, TX	2.3 (0.9)	6.6 (2.6)	16 (6.3)	11 (4.4)	109 (43)
Miami, FL	7.6 (3.0)	13 (5.0)	13 (5.3)	10 (4.0)	127 (50)
Oklahoma City, OK	4.0 (1.6)	12 (4.7)	26 (10.2)	16 (6.3)	167 (66)
Salt Lake City, UT	2.0 (0.8)	8.9 (3.5)	27 (10.6)	10 (4.0)	140 (55)
Yuma, AZ	9.9 (3.9)	20 (8.0)	34 (13.4)	20 (8.0)	254 (100)

TABLE 4.12 South Florida Average Annual Evaporation

STATION	ANNUAL EVAPORATION, mm (in.)
Vero Beach	1240 (49)
Belle Glade	1120 (44)
Hialeah	1195 (47)
Loxahatchee	1175 (46)
Okeechobee	1060 (42)
Tamiami Trail	1165 (46)
Miami Metro area	1270 (50)

in Table 4.13. This variability must be expected and can be roughly explained by solar energy changes reflected in temperature and other weather condition changes.

The National Oceanic and Atmospheric Administration (NOAA) in the United States reports daily data on pan evaporation, wind movement above the pan and temperature of the water at the surface in the pan. Using these

TABLE 4.13 Monthly Evaporation Losses

MONTH	SOUTHEAST COAST, FL		SOUTHWEST COAST, FL	
	in.	mm	in.	mm
January	2.2	55	2.03	52
February	2.9	74	2.67	68
March	4.3	110	3.77	96
April	5.2	123	4.63	118
May	5.7	144	5.64	143
June	5.3	134	4.84	123
July	5.3	135	4.82	122
August	4.9	124	4.28	109
September	4.4	110	3.62	92
October	3.8	96	3.40	86
November	2.7	68	2.42	61
December	2.1	53	1.88	48
Annual total	48.5	1234	44.00	1118

Source: Partly from Boyd, 1986.

data, one can estimate empirical relationships for pan evaporation or predict surface water (lake) evaporation.

Water budget

Another estimate depends on an accurate water budget in which evaporation is the only unknown variable. As an example, assume a lake that has accurate measures on inflow and outflow. Using the surface inventory equations of earlier chapters.

$$\text{Change in storage} = \text{inputs} - \text{outputs}$$
$$\Delta S = P + R + BI - BO - T - E - O \tag{4.12}$$

where

ΔS = change in reservoir storage (mm)
P = precipitation (mm)
R = surface water inflow (mm)
BI = groundwater inflow (mm)
BO = groundwater outflow (mm)
T = transpiration (mm)
E = evaporation (mm)
O = surface water releases (mm)

Assuming a reservoir with little vegetation and lined to prevent groundwater additions or depletions, evaporation can be measured as accurately as precipitation and surface water discharge measurements using:

$$E = P + R - O \pm \Delta S \tag{4.13}$$

In some areas, the water budget has been used successfully to estimate lake evaporation. Perhaps, the best known study was done on Lake Hefner, Oklahoma (U.S. Geological Survey, 1952, 1954).

Correlations to climatic data

Empirical formulas have been developed to relate either pan or actual lake evaporation to atmospheric measures. The form of the equations are similar and in general are related to vapor pressure and wind speed.

$$E = f(\Delta e, U) \tag{4.14}$$

where

Δe = changes in vapor pressure from the water to the air
U = wind speed

The correlation was further defined by Kohler et al. (1955) and others as:

$$E_p = (e_0 - e_a)^n (m + bU) \tag{4.15}$$

where

E_p = daily pan evaporation (in./day)

e_0 = saturation vapor pressure at water surface temperature (in. of mercury)

e_a = saturation vapor pressure at air temperature (in. of mercury)

U = wind movement (mph)

n, m, and b = constants

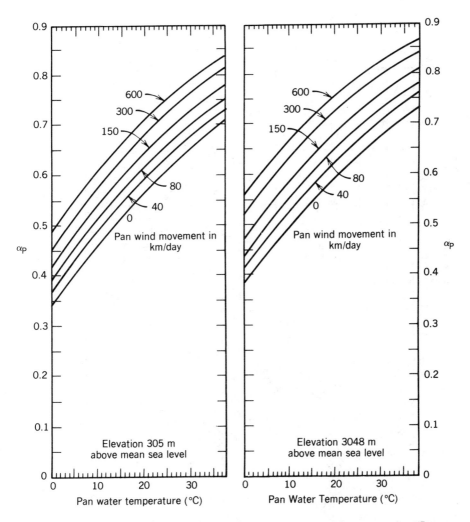

FIGURE 4.8 Portion of advected energy (into a class A pan) used for evaporation. (From Kohler, 1955).

Using data from many sites, Kohler et al. (1955) estimated these constants to be 0.88, 0.37, and 0.0041, respectively, using English system units for wind speed (mph), vapor pressure (in. of mercury) and evaporation (in./day). Additional correlations were performed to estimate pan evaporation for those areas not serviced by a class A pan station.

Other important climatic variables are mean daily air and water temperature, wind movement (advective energy), and solar radiation (solar energy). Not all the advective energy is used for evaporation. That portion used, designated by α_p, can be estimated using the data from Kohler et al. (1955), as shown in Figure 4.8 for class A pans.

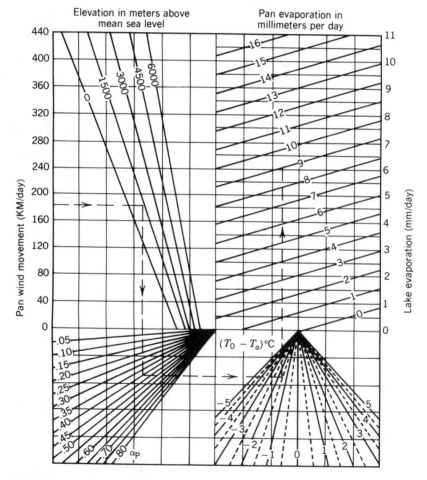

FIGURE 4.9   Shallow Lake evaporation (from Kohler, 1955).

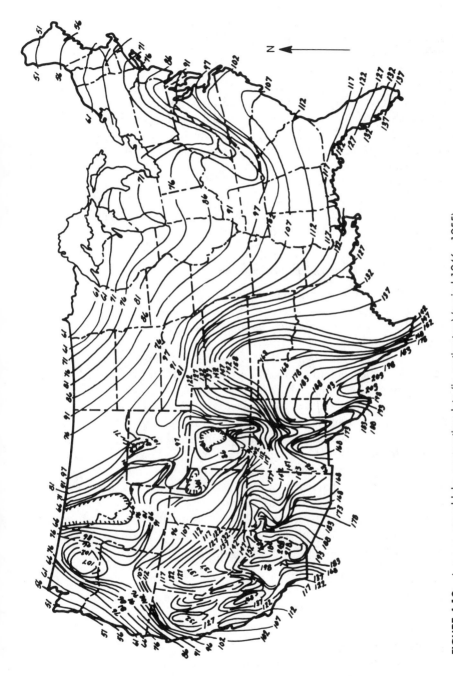

FIGURE 4.10 Average annual lake evaporation data (in centimeters) (period 1946–1955). (From Kohler, 1959).

To estimate lake evaporation, a general formula can be used with differences in temperature, mean daily air speed and elevation above sea level. Kohler developed such a formula, which was reduced to a coaxial graph and is shown in Figure 4.9. Knowing the elevation above mean sea level, wind speed, and differences in water (T_0) and air (T_a) temperatures, estimates can be made for α_p, then given pan evaporation, lake evaporation is obtained.

For generalized values of average annual lake evaporation in the United States, Kohler et al. (1959) presented data, which have been converted to the metric system of units and are shown in Figure 4.10. These evaporation rates are for shallow lakes that are not severely polluted. Changes in evaporation from lakes due to depth and water quality are minor. Thus, the evaporation data in Figure 4.9 are applicable as a first estimate and, if significant, more detailed studies at the site may be necessary. Sometimes, these correlation equations require data that are costly to obtain, thus their use may be limited.

4.3.2 Transpiration and Evapotranspiration

Factors affecting transpiration are similar to those affecting evaporation plus plant physiological factors, such as leaf structure, plant diseases and behavior of stomata. Soil moisture content is also important and perhaps one of the more important limiting factors.

Transpiration for small plant areas can be determined by a closed container in which humidity changes are measured. The soil can be sealed to prevent evaporation from soil. These experiments are performed onsite or by use of a phytometer, which is a container with a particular plant rooted in it. Precise determinations of transpiration are difficult, and extrapolations to other areas can be misleading. Exact environmental and physiological conditions should be reported when measuring transpiration. Water budgets are valuable but again require estimates of other variables, and, thus, the transpiration estimates are frequently only as accurate as the measurements of the other variables.

If total monthly consumptive use (evapotranspiration) can be measured for a vegetative area, and the monthly evaporation is known, the transpiration rate per time period can be estimated by using

$$T = ET - E \qquad (4.16)$$

where

T = transpiration rate (mm/time)
ET = evapotranspiration rate (mm/time)
E = evaporation rate (mm/time)

Estimates for evapotranspiration are made by measuring losses of water using soil sampling tubes and lysimeters (pervious bottom tubes). Field measures are in general very costly or difficult; thus, empirical equations have been developed using generally available climatic data. Some typical equations are:

1. Thornthwaite's (1944):

$$ET = 1.6\left(\frac{10t}{TE}\right)^{a} \tag{4.17}$$

where

$a = 0.49239 + 0.01792TE$
ET = monthly evapotranspiration (cm)
t = mean monthly temperature (°C)
TE = Thornthwaite's temperature efficiency

$$\text{index} = \sum_{i=1}^{12} (t_i/5)^{1.514}$$

[This equation usually has to be adjusted for time of year (month) and latitude.]

TABLE 4.14 Seasonal Potential Consumptive-Use Coefficients, k

CROP	LENGTH OF GROWING SEASON OR PERIOD	k	GRAM OF WATER PER GRAM DRY MATTER GROWN
Alfalfa	Between frosts	0.80–0.85	700–1000
Beans	3 months	0.60–0.70	350–600
Corn	4 months	0.75–0.85	250–350
Cotton	7 months	0.65–0.75	500–700
Orchard, Citrus	7 months	0.50–0.65	300–600
Walnuts	Between frosts	0.70	250–400
Deciduous	Between frosts	0.60–0.70	300–700
Pasture, grass	Between frosts	0.60–0.75	300–600
Ladino clover	Between frosts	0.80–0.85	300–800
Potatoes	$3\frac{1}{2}$ months	0.65–0.75	300–600
Rice	3–5 months	1.00–1.20	600–900
Suger beets	6 months	0.65–0.75	300–500
Tomatoes	4 months	0.70	500–800
Vegetables, small	3 months	0.60	400–800

Source: Criddle, 1958; Blaney, 1959.

TABLE 4.15 Daytime Hours Percentages, p

LATITUDE (DEG)	JAN.	FEB.	MAR.	APR.	MAY	JUNE	JULY	AUG.	SEPT.	OCT.	NOV.	DEC.
North
60	4.67	5.65	8.08	9.65	11.74	12.39	12.31	10.70	8.57	6.98	5.04	4.22
50	5.98	6.30	8.24	9.24	10.68	10.91	10.99	10.00	8.46	7.45	6.10	5.65
40	6.76	6.72	8.33	8.95	10.02	10.08	10.22	9.54	8.39	7.75	6.72	6.52
35	7.05	6.88	8.35	8.83	9.76	9.77	9.93	9.37	8.36	7.87	6.97	6.86
30	7.30	7.03	8.38	8.72	9.53	9.49	9.67	9.22	8.33	7.99	7.19	7.15
25	7.53	7.14	8.39	8.61	9.33	9.23	9.45	9.09	8.32	8.09	7.40	7.42
20	7.74	7.25	8.41	8.52	9.15	9.00	9.25	8.96	8.30	8.18	7.58	7.66
15	7.94	7.36	8.43	8.44	8.98	8.80	9.05	8.83	8.28	8.26	7.75	7.88
10	8.13	7.47	8.45	8.37	8.81	8.60	8.86	8.71	8.25	8.34	7.91	8.10
0	8.50	7.66	8.49	8.21	8.50	8.22	8.50	8.49	8.21	8.50	8.22	8.50
South
10	8.86	7.87	8.53	8.09	8.18	7.86	8.14	8.27	8.17	8.62	8.53	8.88
20	9.24	8.09	8.57	7.94	7.85	7.43	7.76	8.03	8.13	8.76	8.87	9.33
30	9.70	8.33	8.62	7.73	7.45	6.96	7.31	7.76	8.07	8.97	9.24	9.85
40	10.27	8.63	8.67	7.49	6.97	6.37	6.76	7.41	8.02	9.21	9.71	10.49

Source: From Criddle, 1959.

2. Blaney and Criddle (1950):

$$ET = kpt/100 \qquad (4.18)$$

where

k = consumptive use coefficient
p = percent of daytime hours per year in the study month
t = mean monthly temperature (°F)
ET = monthly evapotranspiration (in.)

Values for k and p are found in Tables 4.14 and 4.15. When a range of k values is presented, the lower values are for coastal areas with the higher values for arid lands. Also shown in Table 4.15 are a range of water transpired during the growing season per equal weight of dry matter grown.

The above equations estimate potential evapotranspiration. It is that quantity of water vapor that is not constrained by adequate moisture supply. When soil moisture is a constraint, potential evapotranspiration is never attained. The water budget method is one way of estimating evapotranspiration rather than potential evapotranspiration. The water budget method is more appropriate for monthly, seasonal or yearly time intervals. The calculation of starting and ending watershed storage can reduce the error of estimation, but over a longer period of time the difference in storage can be assumed equal to zero.

☐   **EXAMPLE PROBLEM 4.5**

Assume the following situations for a small watershed in northern Indiana. The six-month seasonal precipitation is 70 cm, runoff is 20 cm, and the change in groundwater storage is 15 cm. What are the monthly evapotranspiration rates, assuming no initial abstraction?

Solution

$$\Delta S = P - Q - ET$$

or

$$15 = 70 - 20 - ET: \ ET = 35 \text{ cm}/6 \text{ mo}$$

or

$$ET = 5.83 \text{ cm}/\text{mo} \quad \square$$

TABLE 4.16   North Florida Evapotranspiration Data (Latitude 28°N, Longitude 80°W)

MONTH	EVAPOTRANSPIRATION (cm/mo)	MONTH	EVAPOTRANSPIRATION (cm/mo)
January	3.05	July	12.95
February	4.88	August	11.40
March	6.86	September	9.15
April	10.29	October	6.60
May	12.20	November	4.55
June	12.95	December	3.00

TABLE 4.17   Ratio Between Evapotranspiration from Well-Watered Grass and Evaporation from Class A Pan

WIND (km/day)	CASE 1: PAN SURROUNDED BY SHORT GREEN CROP				CASE 2: PAN SURROUNDED BY DRY-SURFACE GROUND			
	UPWIND FETCH OF GREEN CROP (m)	RELATIVE HUMIDITY PERCENT			UPWIND FETCH OF DRY FALLOW (m)	RELATIVE HUMIDITY PERCENT		
		LOW 20–40	MED 40–70	HIGH > 70		LOW 20–40	MED 40–70	HIGH > 70
Light	0	0.55	0.65	0.75	0	0.7	0.8	0.85
	10	0.65	0.75	0.85	10	0.6	0.7	0.8
< 170 km/day	100	0.7	0.8	0.85	100	0.55	0.65	0.75
	1000	0.75	0.85	0.85	1000	0.5	0.6	0.7
Moderate	0	0.5	0.6	0.65	0	0.65	0.75	0.8
	10	0.6	0.7	0.75	10	0.55	0.65	0.7
170–425 km/day	100	0.65	0.75	0.8	100	0.5	0.6	0.65
	1000	0.7	0.8	0.8	1000	0.45	0.55	0.6
Strong	0	0.45	0.5	0.6	0	0.6	0.65	0.7
	10	0.55	0.6	0.65	10	0.5	0.55	0.65
425–700 km/day	100	0.6	0.65	0.7	100	0.45	0.5	0.6
	1000	0.65	0.7	0.75	1000	0.4	0.45	0.55
Very strong	0	0.4	0.45	0.5	0	0.5	0.6	0.65
	10	0.45	0.55	0.6	10	0.45	0.5	0.55
> 700 km/day	100	0.5	0.6	0.65	100	0.4	0.45	0.5
	1000	0.55	0.6	0.65	1000	0.35	0.4	0.45

Source: From Doorenbos and Pruitt (1974).

With the above example problem, it is assumed that evapotranspiration does not vary from month to month. This is a poor assumption because over a 6-month period, vegetation and climate changes are most probable. Using data from a north Florida watershed, the following evapotranspiration data (Table 4.16) were calculated assuming storage changes were negligible. Average monthly data were used.

Evapotranspiration data are applicable to a specific place with certain climatic and vegetative conditions. Investigators must examine the water resources data for a region to determine available data or to develop new data. Another indirect method for estimating evapotranspiration is to use the evaporation from a class A pan and convert the pan evaporation to evapotranspiration using results from other studies or developing ratios of evapotranspiration using a controlled mass balance and evaporation from a class A pan.

Doorenbos and Pruitt (1974) developed ratios of evapotranspiration and evaporation from a class A pan (Table 4.17). Their coefficients apply to conditions of initially dry soil. These results indicate that ET from grasses can vary from 0.35 to 0.85 of that from a class A pan. The range depends on the surrounding soil/plant conditions, wind speed, relative humidity, and upwind fetch.

4.3.3 Evaporation from Snow

The depth of evaporation (E_s) from snow surfaces can be estimated using a form of Dalton's law, when atmospheric vapor pressure is less than snowpack surface vapor pressure.

$$E_s = k_e \bar{u}_a (e_s - e_a)(z_a z_b)^{-1/3}(\Delta t) \qquad (4.19)$$

where

E_s = depth of evaporation (in.)
$\bar{u}_a$ = average wind speed in miles per hour at elevation A above the snowpack
e_a = atmospheric vapor pressure in millibars (mbar) at elevation A (note $e_a < e_s$)
e_s = saturated vapor pressure in millibars at the snowpack
z_a, z_b = height above snowpack (ft)

and for Δt in days, the constant (k_e) is estimated as (U.S. Army Corps of Engineers, 1956):

$$k_e = 0.00635 \text{ in. ft}^{1/3} \text{ hr per day mbar mile}$$

The vapor pressure of the surface film of melting snow is 6.11 mbar. For the same wind conditions, evaporation from snow is about one-fourth that from water at 30°C and dewpoint at 15°C. This and other data lead to the assumption that maximum evaporation from a snow surface is about 0.2 in. of water per day.

The direct transform of ice to a vapor or the reverse is called sublimation. The heat released during sublimation is 600 cal/cm³. The snowpack depth (Δd_e) should be reduced by an amount indirectly proportioned to the density of the snowpack or

$$\Delta d_e = (\rho_w/\rho_s)(E_s) \tag{4.20}$$

where

ρ_w = density of water = 1 g/cm³

ρ_s = snowpack density (g/cm³)

Δd_e = snowpack depth change due to evaporation (in.)

when E_s units are inches.

4.4

CASE STUDIES

1. A watershed in San Francisco, California, is considered highly urbanized with 187 ha of impervious area and 240 ha of pervious area with $CN = 90$. Two precipitation gage stations are located within the watershed. What is the predicted runoff from the watershed if the gage stations record 26 and 22 mm of rain, respectively? State all assumptions.

Using average moisture conditions and Table 4.4, the composite CN value is calculated assuming CN for impervious area = 98.

$$\text{percent impervious} = \frac{187}{427} = 44\%, \text{ therefore } CN = 93$$

Average precipitation is calculated using the arithmetic average (mean value) formula since the weighted areas are unknown:

$$\bar{P} = (26 + 22)/2 = 24 \text{ mm}$$

The runoff from a 24-mm precipitation event is calculated from Equations 4.7 and 4.8.

and

$$S' = 25,400/93 - 254 = 19.12 \text{ mm}$$

$$R = (24 - 0.2(19.12))^2/(24 + 0.8(19.12))$$

$$= 10.36 \text{ mm}$$

2. Using a water budget method, calculate the runoff coefficient for a planning area in Florida. How well do these compare to literature values? State all assusmptions and present a professional description of the environmental engineering aspects of the area. This section relates to comprehensive planning for point source facilities. This example was part of a larger facilities report (Dawkins and Associates, 1977).

A professional description with calculations for the runoff coefficients may be similar to the following. The area lies within the Middle Gulf Hydrologic system. This system is characterized by an overall flow of surface and groundwaters in a southwesterly direction toward coastal saltwaters. The rate of this flow is controlled by rainfall, evapotranspiration, runoff characteristics of the land, infiltration of the surface soils and percolation of subsurface soils. Water shed development causes a change in many of these variables and may, therefore, affect the relative availability of both groundwaters and surface waters. Because of the high population density of this area, plus its proximity to saltwaters, the region's freshwater hydrology has been viewed with considerable concern. Two agencies, the Water Management District (WMD) and the Coast Regional Water Supply Authority (CRWSA), bear the responsibility of regulating and assessing freshwater resources in this area.

One of the major considerations of this facility plan is to assess the impacts of various wastewater management alternatives on the water budget of the study area. Selection of a plan that helps preserve the hydrologic cycle of the area is certainly desirable, since significant disruption of this cycle could eventuate the loss of freshwater, which may be considered one of the more valuable resources to natural and technological systems within the area.

Development of a water budget involves quantification of several variables—precipitation, evapotranspiration, runoff, seepage, pumpage, and inflow. These variables are related by the following equation for a fixed period of time, possibly one year:

$$P + I = ET + O + \Delta S \qquad (4.21)$$

where

P = direct rainfall (mm)
I = inflow from surrounding areas (mm)
ET = evapotranspiration (mm)
O = losses from runoff and groundwater outflow (mm)
ΔS = change in storage (mm)

Outflow is a primary control variable as it is a function of recharge, groundwater withdrawal, runoff rates and aquifer characteristics. Storage serves as a buffer to maintain a usable supply. Depletion of storage can jeopardize the hydrological integrity of the area.

Rainfall in the planning area averages 1346 mm/yr (53 in./yr), with the summer months representing the rainy season. Surface water evaporation in the planning area has been shown to be about 1270 mm/yr (50 in./yr). Evapotranspiration from land surfaces depends on the proximity of the water table to the surface and the type of vegetation. Measured losses from evapotranspiration in marshes are 1524 mm/yr (60 in./yr). Higher topographical areas, such as flatwoods, show lower losses of around 889 mm/yr (35 in./yr). Using evapotranspiration rates of 1321 mm/yr (52 in./yr) for natural wetlands, 1270 mm/yr (50 in./yr) evaporation from surface waters and 889 mm/yr (35 in./yr) for developed areas and upland regions, an estimation may be made for the overall rates for each drainage area. These drainage areas shown in Table 4.18 with predicted evapotranspiration are those delineated by the Planning Council. The land uses utilized in predicting these evapotranspiration rates are those delineated by the Comprehensive Land Use Plan. The rate of evapotranspiration declines as development encroaches on some of the natural lands within the planning area.

Water may enter the boundaries of the planning area either as surface water or groundwater. Water movement is from northeast to southwest, with most of the water entering the area from the northeastern border of the planning area.

The Big River represents the major surface water contributor. It enters the planning area just northeast of the Big City. A U.S. Geologic Survey gaging station located just upstream of the point of entrance into the planning area, shows a long-term average flow of 2.5 m³/sec (87.9 ft³/sec). Another surface water inflow is from "B" Creek, which enters the planning area in the northeast section. The long-term average flow from this creek as it enters the Country as measured by the U.S. Geologic Survey is 0.21 m³/sec (7.5 ft³/sec). The total surface water contribution is estimated then at 2.7 m³/sec (95.4 ft³/sec or 61.7 mgd). For the total planning area, 238 km² (58,760 ac), this represents about 355 mm (14 in.) of water annually.

3. For the same planning area, estimate the groundwater storage depletion in the years 1980 and 2000.

Presently, 36.7 mgd of water is removed from the lower aquifer. Of this volume, 35.2 mgd, or 96%, comes from the 57 county wells. Increases in groundwater withdrawals are expected. By 1980 withdrawals will be approximately 217,050 m³/day (57.3 mgd or 13.2 in.) over the entire area. The only water possibly to be returned to the ground is that utilized for domestic purposes. Using a per capita usage of 0.53 m³/c-d (140 gpcd), and population projections of 94,409 for 1980 and 210,040 for 2000, it may be calculated that the average demand will be 50,000 m³/day (13.2 mgd) and 110,230 m³/day (29.1 mgd) for 1980 and 2000, respectively. This means that in 1980 about 44.1 mgd (57.3–13.2) of groundwater will be transported from the area for uses in other areas. In 2000, 28.2 mgd will be exported. These are considered to be 100% losses.

TABLE 4.18 Estimated Evapotranspiration Rates for the Planning Area

DRAINAGE BASIN	TOTAL ACREAGE[a]	ET = 52 in. PERCENT WETLAND		ET = 35 in. PERCENT URBAN AND UPLANDS[b]		E = 50 in. PERCENT OPEN WATER[c]		ESTIMATED EVAPOTRANSPIRATION YEARLY (in.)	
		1980	2000	1980	2000	1980	2000	1980	2000
Big River	11,476	43	09	46	79	11	12	44	38
"K" Bayou	2,144	0	0	99	98	01	20	35	35
Lake	9,400	20	10	53	61	27	29	42	41
"B" Creek	10,664	61	16	37	80	02	04	46	38
Old Creek	7,294	68	11	30	85	02	04	47	37
South Creek	2,787	32	14	62	77	06	09	43	39
South Bayou	2,331	28	10	68	84	04	06	40	38
Smith Creek	1,939	10	07	89	90	01	03	39	37
"C" Bayou	1,176	10	07	89	90	01	03	39	37
"C" Creek	5,942	05	03	90	90	05	07	37	37
Coastal Bayou	1,879	10	09	89	89	01	02	37	37
Spring Creek	2,028	02	01	97	97	01	02	35	35

Source: Dawkins and Associates, 1977.
[a] Determined by planimeter work.
[b] Includes pasture.
[c] Assumed that for every 24 ac of new land developed 1 ac is used for retention basin.

Of the predicted water demand of 13.2 mgd and the 20.1 mgd in 1980 and 2000, 71% is projected to become wastewater. The remaining is assumed to be lost either through consumption, evapotranspiration or runoff. The losses, therefore, from groundwater withdrawals in 1980 are estimated at 47.9 mgd, or 10.8 in., while in 2000 this is reduced to 36.6 mgd, or 8.4 in. The wastewater flows of 9.4 mgd and 20.1 mgd for 1980 and 2000, respectively, represent that variable which the Facility Plan can affect. These flows represent 2.2 in. for 1980 and 4.7 in. for 2000. If this wastewater is 100% wasted, the losses become 13.2 in. for both 1980 and 2000.

The total outflow for the area is estimated as the sum of groundwater outflow, groundwater withdrawals, runoff and stream outflow. This amounts to 1,120 mm (44 in.) for 1980 and 2000. If wastewater flows are lost the outflow is increased to 1,170 mm (46.2 in.) for 1980 and 1240 mm (48.7 in.) for the year 2000.

Using the water budget equation, and considering loss of all wastewater flows, it is possible to calculate storage by $S = P + F - ET - O$. For the year 1980, $P = 1350$ mm (53 in.), $ET = 1070$ mm (42 in.), $F = 430$ mm (17 in.), and $O = 1170$ mm (46.2 in.). Therefore, storage depletion for 1980 is estimated at the rate of 460 mm/yr (18.1 in./yr). For the year 2000, storage depletion is 500 mm/yr (19.7 in./yr).

While this analysis does account for the various homeostatic capabilities of the hydrologic cycle, such as regulation of recharge rates as stores are depleted, it does show that a stress is being placed upon freshwater supply of the area and conservation of potable water as a natural resource in the planning area is of prime importance. In addition, it may be shown that wastewater effluent disposal can be considered critical to the hydrology of the area, and is a major consideration for any water resource management plan (Wanielista and Shannon, 1977).

4.5

SUMMARY

Infiltration is the movement of water into the ground. Percolation relates to groundwater and refers to the movement of water in the ground. For the prediction of rainfall excess, infiltration and evapotranspiration rates are necessary for a specified time period.

- The SCS–CN method requires an estimate of the land use and the hydrologic soil types to determine an empirically derived curve number that is used to estimate storage. If the initial abstraction portion of saturated storage is assumed to be equal to 20%, then Equation 4.8 can be used to estimate rainfall excess. If initial abstraction is assumed to be zero, then Equation 4.6 can be used. The common formula is Equation 4.8: $R = (P - 0.2S')^2/(P + 0.8S')$.

- Table 4.4 is used frequently and it should be emphasized that the curve number is a composite value.
- Table 4.8 and Figure 4.4 can be used to aid in calculating rainfall excess using the SCS–CN method. However, the formulas are easy to use and should be used and then checked against values obtained from tables and figures.
- Infiltration rates and volumes can be estimated using data from a double-ring infiltrometer. Site conditions do vary requiring a number of tests depending on soil types and groundwater levels. An exponential equation usually can be used to reproduce the experimental data.
- Evaporation and transpiration estimates are necessary for long-term water budgets, especially those used for irrigation and reservoir capacity studies. The usual time periods are weeks to months.
- Experimental estimates of evaporation are made using evaporimeters or an evaporation pan. These estimates are higher than what can be expected from an open water body. Adjustment factors have been developed to convert "instrument" values to true lake evaporation.
- Evaporation rates vary with the weather conditions (see Tables 4.10 and 4.11). Cloud cover, wind speed, and temperature are three of the meteorological parameters commonly used to estimate evaporation.
- To estimate evapotranspiration, there are two equations in general use — Thornthwaite and Blaney and Criddle. Otherwise, a mass balance to estimate evapotranspiration can be used.

4.6

PROBLEMS

1. Estimate the volume of water that will infiltrate into a soil before surface saturation occurs using the Green–Ampt equation. The following data are known: (1) saturated moisture content is 0.25, (2) the initial moisture content is zero, (3) the average rainfall rate is 2 in./hr, (4) the average capillary suction head is 4 in., and (5) $K_s = 1$ in./hr. What is the maximum soil storage volume if the soil is homogeneous to a water table depth of 5 ft?

2. Assuming an average soil moisture condition on hydrologic soils group C, calculate the runoff volume (inches) for a 100-ac suburban development with the following land use if rainfall is 4 in. You must use the SCS–CN method.

LAND USE	PERCENTAGE OF LAND
$\frac{1}{4}$-ac residential lots	40
$\frac{1}{8}$-ac condominiums	20
Commercial area with curbs	25
Open space, gras cover = 85%	15

What is the area of retention (no outlet) or percolation basin in square feet and acres to store the runoff water (rainfall excess) if the maximum depth of storage is 5 ft, excluding debris storage and freeboard? Assume a rectangular pond with vertical sides.

3. Consider a proposed development in class B soil of 1000 ac of which 400 ac will be impervious, 50 ac will be water surfaces (lakes, detention and canals), 200 ac will be open space in good condition, and the remaining acres will be in fair grass cover on 50 to 75% of the land area. What *CN*

Experimental setup:

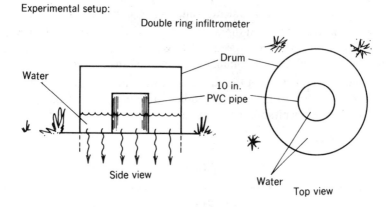

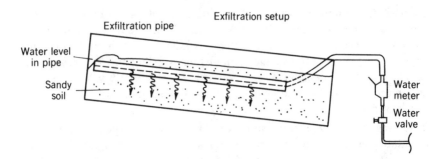

FIGURE 4.11 Double ring infiltrometer and exfiltration experimental apparatus.

number (weighted) would you use? Discuss results if the water surface were not contributory to the drainage system.

4. How much water is needed in acre-feet for 100 ac of corn growing at North latitude 27.5 during the month of May if precipitation is assumed at zero and 150% of the water must be provided?

5. For the experimental setups of Figure 4.11, determine equations to predict infiltration rates and exfiltration rates. The double-ring infiltrometer is used for infiltration. Exfiltration is to be performed on a previously constructed pipe underground. The recorded data and observations for discussion and analysis are shown.

	Exfiltration Data				Infiltration Data	
ELAPSED TIME (min)	INCREMENTAL TIME (min)	METER READING (gal)	INCREMENT VOL. (gal)	ELAPSED TIME	VOLUME H_2O ADDED $(in.^3)^a$	VOLUME H_2O ADDED (LITERS)
1	1	218.5	1.7	17 sec	76.7	1.25
2	1	220.1	1.6	1 min	82.9	1.35
3	1	221.5	1.4	2 min	41.5	0.68
4	1	223.1	1.6	3 min	16.5	0.27
5	1	224.5	1.4	4 min	8.3	0.136
6	1	225.9	1.4	5 min	8.3	0.136

^{a}To maintain a constant head.

Exfiltration Pipe Data:
Length—4.0 ft
Diameter—1.75 in
Total volume—115.5 in³

Head—2.0 in. (5.08 cm)
Inside pipe dia.—10 in. (25.4 cm)
Inside pipe area—78.5 in² (506.7 cm²)

6. Using the relationship of Figure 4.12 with D_{10} equal to 0.5, 1, and 2 with the data of Problem 1, provide a sensitivity analysis plot for volume as a function of D_{10}.

7. A hydrologist designing a stormwater drainage system requires an infiltration experiment for a new pond area to evaluate the infiltration characteristics of the clay loam soil. A ring infiltrometer test was made on the soil. The results of the test are given in the data table below. The inside diameter of infiltrometer is 35 cm and the area is 962 cm².
   a. Determine the infiltration capacity for the time intervals in the experiment.
   b. What is the initial infiltration, f_0, in Horton's equation?
   c. What is the ultimate infiltration, f_c, in Horton's equation?

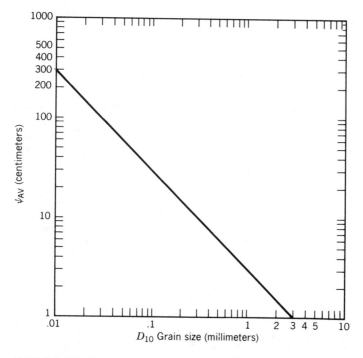

FIGURE 4.12 Suction potential versus grain size for well-graded cohesionless soils (after Weaver, R.J. Research Report 69-2, 1971. New York State Department of Transportation).

ELAPSED TIME (min) (1)	Δt (hr) (2) $\Delta(1) \div 60$	VOLUME OF WATER ADDED SINCE START (cc) (3)	f (cm) (4) $(3) \div$ AREA	ΔF (cm) (5) $\Delta(4)$	$f(t)$ (cm/hr) (6) $(5) \div (2)$
0		0			
2		300			
5		650			
10		1190			
20		1950			
30		2500			
60		3350			
90		3900			
150		4600			

8. A River Basin Regulatory Person must release water from a reservoir to satisfy a downstream need of 48,000 m³/day during the month of July.

The average daily class A pan evaporation is 5 mm and the pan coefficient is 0.70. Estimate how much water must be released from the reservoir to satisfy the 48,000 m³ need if the average river width is 61 m and the distance down the center of the river from the reservoir to point of need is 78 km. Express your answer in terms of both m³ and ac-ft. Neglect or assume that net infiltration into and out of the river from groundwater sources is negligible and there is no transpiration.

9. Estimate the mean monthly evaporation rate for the O'Hare International Airport watershed. Local climatological data supplied by NOAA for the Airport are shown for months in the year 1974.

MONTH	PRECIPITATION (in.)	OUTLET WATER (in.)
March	2.40	1.42
April	4.27	3.05
May	5.09	3.60
June	4.69	3.50
July	2.96	1.65

The water leaving the watershed is estimated form a U.S. Geologic Survey gaging station and is also shown. Comment on your answers by explaining why the results are low relative to the annual average values given in Figure 4.10. What assumptions have you made? Assume storage changes are minimal and no transpiration or infiltration.

10. For Example Problem 4.3, change the precipitation to 0, 1.4, 3.2, 4.2, and 5.0 in. over 20 ac of area and calculate the instantaneous rainfall excess in CFS.

11. What are the precipitation increments in 30-min intervals and the cumulative precipitation resulting from a 4.2-in. storm using the SCS Rainfall Distribution Type II? Assume a 6-hr-duration storm. Now, what shapes do the rainfall excess hydrographs have (draw cumulative rainfall excess graphs) for the rainfall distribution if the CN values were 60 and 80?

12. a. Use the SCS–CN method to estimate rainfall excess for an area before and after development. The rainfall is estimated at 6 in. The hydrologic soil type is A. The predevelopment condition is open space with grass on about 50% of the area. The postdevelopment condition is residential with a 38% impervious cover.
   b. If the watershed were 25 ac, how many acre-feet of ponding is necessary to store all the rainfall excess from the postdevelopment?

13. a. Compute the weekly evaporation from a class A pan if the precipitation and water added to bring the level of water in the pan to a fixed level are as follows.

WEEK	1	2	3	4
Rainfall (in.)	0.00	1.04	1.84	0.42
Water added (in.)	0.90	0.04	−0.70[a]	0.93

[a] Water taken from pan.

b. If the pan evaporation coefficient for this period of time is 0.8 and an adjacent lake has a surface area of 150 ac, what is the evaporation from the lake expressed in inches and cubic feet for the 4-week period of time?

c. How can evaporation volume of this lake be reduced?

14. a. Using empirical formula (4.15) for evaporation with a water temperature of 60°F, an air temperature of 80°F and a wind speed of 10 mph, what is the daily pan evaporation? Relative humidity is 40%.

b. if this is considered the average daily evaporation, what region of the United States is this characteristic of (use Figure 4.10 as comparison)?

15. The runoff coefficient and the curve number are important parameters for the design of stormwater holding ponds. A water management district specifies the 25-yr return period storm and a duration of 6 hr for all rainfall data. During this storm event, the volume of rainfall excess for a 100-ac urban watershed was measured at 725,000 ft^3. For this area, what is the runoff coefficient and curve number? Assume (from field measurements) that there is no initial abstraction.

16. For a 50-ac watershed, estimate the volume (millimeters and acre-feet) of infiltration in 3 hr from a rainfall with maximum intensity of 50 mm/hr if the initial infiltration rate is 100 mm/hr and the final rate is 40 mm/hr. The recession constant is 30/hr. What assumptions did you make to validate your answer?

17. Estimate the maximum evapotranspiration of corn grown at 27° north latitude over April and May. The average monthly temperatures are 70°F and 75°F, respectively. How much water must be added (irrigated) if rainfall for these 2 months is 3 in. and we loose 2 in. to infiltration and initial abstraction?

18. A 300-rural-acre watershed with initial abstraction is known to have a curve number of 61. If the precipitation on the watershed is as follows, What is the runoff at each time increment in cubic feet per second using the SCS/CN rainfall excess procedure?

TIME (min)	ΔP (in.)
0	0
5	0.07
10	0.90
15	0.32
20	0.04

19. One month of rainfall and pan evaporation data have been collected and a correlation to a mass balance for lake evaporation is attempted to determine the pan coefficient. The lake evaporation was 6.4 inches and the pan evaporation was 9.3. What is the pan coefficient?

4.7

COMPUTER-ASSISTED PROBLEMS

1. Using the first computer program (SMADA) and a rainfall volume and time distribution for a 25-yr-2-hr storm of your choice (for your area) develop the infiltration volume (watershed storage) for the following watershed condition using the SCS–CN procedure to estimate rainfall excess and infiltration for the pervious area. Use the Santa Barbara Urban Hydrograph Generation routine to get a printout.

$$\text{Area} = 200 \text{ ac}$$
$$t_c = 120 \text{ min}$$
$$\% \text{ Impervious} = 40$$
$$\% \text{ DCIA} = 70$$
$$CN = 60 \text{ (pervious area)}$$

2. Using the Santa Barbara Hydrograph Generation Procedure, provide a plot of infiltration volume (inches) versus percent impervious values for percent impervious values of 20, 40, 60, 80, and 90 using the same watershed conditions as in Problem 1 (except variable percent imperviousness). Also, construct a plot of peak discharge versus percent imperviousn.ess. Note the time of concentration is held constant. Comment on your results.

3. On the graph of Problem 2, also change the pervious area curve number to 85 and plot the resulting peak discharge and infiltration volumes as a function of percent imperviousness. Comment on your results.

4. It is more reasonable to expect the time of concentration to decrease as the percent impervious area which is directly connected increases. Develop the peak discharge versus the percent impervious relationship (graphical plot) using the data of Problem 1 except for the following changes:

T_c (min)	% IMPERVIOUS
150	20
120	40
90	60
70	80
60	90

4.8

REFERENCES

Beaver, R.D. 1977. "Infiltration in Stormwater Detention/Percolation Basin Design," Res. Report, College of Engineering, Florida Technological University, Orlando, FL.

Beaver, R.D., Hartman, J.P., and Wanielista, M.P. 1977. "Infiltration and Stormwater Retention/Detention Ponds," Stormwater Retention/Detention Basin Seminar, Y.A. Yousef, Ed., Florida Technological University, Orlando, FL.

Blaney, H.F. 1959. "Monthly Consumptive Use Requirements for Irrigated Crops," Proceedings of the American Society of Civil Engineers Journal, Irrigation and Drainge Division 85:1–12, March.

Blaney, H.F., and Criddle, W.D. 1950, "Determining Water Requirements in Irrigated Areas from Climatological and Irrigated Data," SCS, TP-96, August.

Boyd, C.E. 1986. "Influence of Evaporation Excess on Water Requirements for Fish Farming," *Conference on Climate and Water Management, A Critical Era*, American Meteorological Society, Asheville, NC, August.

Chow, V.T. 1964. *Handbook of Applied Hydrology*. McGraw-Hill Book Co., New York p. 12.7.

Criddle, W.D. 1959. "Methods of Computing Consumptive Use of Water," Proceedings of the American Society of Civil Engineers Journal, Irrigation and Drainage Division, 84 : 1–27, January.

Dawkins, E. and Associates. 1977. "North Pinellas County 201 Facility Plan," City of Orlando, FL.

Daubernmire, R.F. 1959. *Plants and Environment, 2nd Ed*. New York, Wiley.

Doorenbos, J. and Pruitt, W.O. 1974. *Guidelines for Prediction of Crop Water Requirements*. Foreign Agricultural Organization, Rome, Italy, Irrigation and Drainage Paper No. 25.

Golding, B.C. 1986. DABRO-Drainage Basin Runoff Model—A Computer Program, Hieldebrand Software, 8992 Islesworth Court, Orlando, FL 32819.

Green, W.H. and Ampt, G.A. 1911. "Studies on Soil Physics I, The Flow of Air and Water Through Soils," *Journal of Agricultural Science*, 4, 1–24.

Hicks, W.I. 1944. "A Method of Computing Urban Runoff," *Transactions of the American Society of Civil Engineers*, vol. 125, pg 1217–1253.

Holtan, H.N., Stitner, G.J., Henson, W.H., and Lopez, N.C. 1975. *USDAHL-74 Revised Model of Watershed Hydrology Technical Bulletin No. 1518*, Agricultural Research Service, U.S. Department of Agriculture, Washington, DC.

Horton, R.E. 1939. "An Approach Toward A Physical Interpretation of Infiltration Capacity," *Transations of the American Geophysics Union*, 20, 693–711.

Horton, R.E. 1940. "An Approach Toward a Physical Interpretation of Infiltration Capacity," *Proceedings of Soil Science Society of America*, 5, 399–317.

Huber, W.C., Heaney, J.P., Bedient, P.B., and Bowden, J.P. 1976. *Environmental Resources Management Studies in the Kissimmee River Basin*, University of Florida, Gainesville, May.

Kent, K.M. 1973. "A Method for Estimating Volume and Rate of Runoff in Small Watersheds," U.S. Department of Agriculture, Soil Conservation Service, TP-149, April.

Kohler, M.A., Nordenson, T.J., and Fox, W.E. 1955. "Evaporation from Pans and Lakes," Research Paper No. 38, U.S. Weather Bureau, Washington, DC.

Kohler, M.A., Nordenson, T.J., and Baker, D.R. 1959. "Evaporation Maps for the United States," U.S. Weather Bureau Technical Paper #37, Washington, DC.

Overton, D.E. and Meadows, M.E. 1976. *Stormwater Modeling*. New York, Academic Press.

Rawls, W.J., Brakensiek, D.L., and Saxton, K.E. 1982, "Estimation of Soil Properties," *Transactions of the American Society of Agricultural Engineers*, 25(5), 1316–1320.

Schomaker, C.E. 1966. "The Effect of Forest and Pasture on the Disposition of Precipitation," *Marine Farm Research*, July.

Seminole County, Florida. 1975. Soil Conservation Service, U.S. Department of Agriculture. Sanford, Florida, pp. 73–125.

Skaggs, R.W. and Khaleel, R. 1982. "Infiltration," in *Hydrologic Modeling of Small Watersheds*. C.T. Haan, Ed. American Society of Agricultural Engineers, St. Joseph, MI, 121–166.

Thornthwaite, C.W. et al. 1944. "Report of the Committee on Transpiration and Evaporation, 1943–44," *Transactions of the American Geophysics Union*, 25, Part V, 683–693.

Todd, D.K. 1980. *Ground Water Hydrology*. Wiley, New York.

U.S. Department of Agriculture. 1972. Soil Conservation Service. *National Engineering Handbook*, Section 4, Washington, DC.

U.S. Department of Agriculture. 1951. *Soil Survey Manual #18*, Washington, DC.

U.S. Department of Agriculture. 1986. Soil Conservation Service. "Urban Hydrology for Small Watersheds," Technical Release No. 55, Washington, DC.

U.S. Geological Survey. 1952. Quadrangle Size Map (Eastern U.S.) USGS Distribution Section, 1200 South Eads Street, Arlington, VA 22202, or (Western U.S.) Distribution Section, Federal Center, Denver, CO 80225.

U.S. Geological Survey. 1954. "Water-Loss Investigations: Vol. 1-Lake Hefner Studies," Paper No. 269 (Reprint of USGS Circular No. 229, 1952).

U.S. Geological Survey. 1954. "Water-Loss Investigations: Lake Hefner Studies, Base Data Report," Paper No. 270.

U.S. Army Corps of Engineers. 1956. *Snow Hydrology*, North Pacific Division, Portland, Oregon, June 30.

U.S. Weather Bureau. 1958 and 1980. Technical Paper 13, U.S. Government Printing Office, Washington, DC, with updates.

Wallingford. 1977. *Surface Water: United Kingdom, 1974–76*, Her Majesties Surface Water Office, Water Data Unit, 1982. Wallingford, U.K.

Walton, W.C. 1970. *Groundwater Resource Evaluation*. McGraw-Hill, New York.

Wanielista, M.P. and Shannon, E. 1977. *An Evaluation of Best Management Practices for Stormwater*, East Central Florida Regional Planning Council, July, Winter Park, Florida.

....
....
....
....

5

STREAMFLOW
MEASUREMENTS

Streamflow measurements provide needed data for estimating volumes and flow rates from a particular precipitation event or over an extended period of time. Methods exist that directly measure volumes over time or indirectly measure surrogate variables. These surrogates are then used to estimate streamflow rates. Streamflow is a general term used to represent volumes or rates of flow, while discharge is used primarily for rate measurements and applied to waters that flow from a specific watershed or pond area. In this chapter, the more common methods for estimating flow rates are presented. Examples of their use in measuring streamflow in rivers and discharge from stormwater control facilities (ponds) are presented. The actual sizing of reservoirs and stormwater ponds are dependent on discharge measurements.

5.1

METHODS OF MEASUREMENT

The accuracy with which one can estimate flow rates over time (a hydrograph) for a stream location depends on the method used for estimation. This

TABLE 5.1   Classification of Flow
Measurement Methods

A. Stage (water surface elevation)
   1. Visual observation
   2. Float
   3. Pressure sensor
   4. Electrical resistance
B. Discharge (nonstructural)
   1. Current meter
   2. Dilution
   3. Float
   4. Indirect via Manning's equation
C. Discharge (structural)
   1. Direct volume collection
   2. Weirs
   3. Flumes
   4. Orifices

assumes an appropriate application of the procedures for measuring and interpreting the data. If the proper procedures are followed, the accuracy of the estimates of discharge will be limited only by the range of the instrument and human error.

Some methods for discharge estimation are classified as shown in Table 5.1.

5.1.1 Stage

Stage is the water surface elevation recorded relative to some horizontal datum elevation, frequently mean sea level. Stage is a reflection of all the hydrologic processes and water transport characteristics of the watershed. Historical records of high water levels exist, and are either man-made or indirectly identified using the presence of water-related vegetation or stain marks on trees and structures.

Stage records are valuable for the definition of high and low water levels. Areal extent of flooding, history of the rate of fluctuation, and watershed hydrologic characteristics can be documented. The record of stage is called the stage hydrograph, primarily because it can be translated into flow rate (discharge) units.

A stage recorder can be as simple as a ruler along a bridge or other structure. It can be read periodically but is usually automatically recorded.

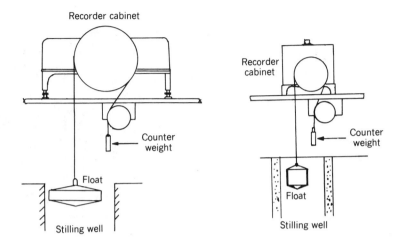

FIGURE 5.1 Typical guide pulley.

The automation is achieved using a water float, pressure sensor, or change in electrical resistance caused by water contact. The float and sensors are attached by wire or chain to a chart that records all water level changes. Typical guide pulley assemblies for a recording device with a counterweight are illustrated in Figure 5.1. The float and the counterweight should not encounter interference. All systems must be maintained and calibrated to ensure accurate results. Since rapid flow rates may move or destroy the float and sensors, protection from potentially damaging forces must be provided. In addition, waves or short-period water surface disturbances caused by boating or man-made events are not generally desired and certainly not reflective of natural conditions. Thus, for stage-level recorders, some type of structure that damps out man-made surface disturbances is needed. The structure is placed adjacent to the watercourse and connected in such a way as to minimize friction losses. Since short-period water surface disturbances inside the structure are minimal, it is called a stilling well, shown in Figure 5.2. The well should be checked frequently for debris and other obstructions.

In rough terrain with limited access and where silt is a problem, a stilling well in a stream may not be feasible. Also, for short-period measurement, construction of a stilling well may not be economical. For these cases a bubble or manometer-servo water-level sensor is used. It uses dry nitrogen (116 ft^3 cyclinder) (Figure 5.3) and battery power. The pressure measured corresponds to the water head. A servo motor adjusts a recorder, such as the Stevens Type A also shown in Figure 5.3. Another picture of the recorder is shown in Figure 5.4. The bubbler and recorder can be located several hundred feet from the measuring point. Only tubing is required for connection to the stream.

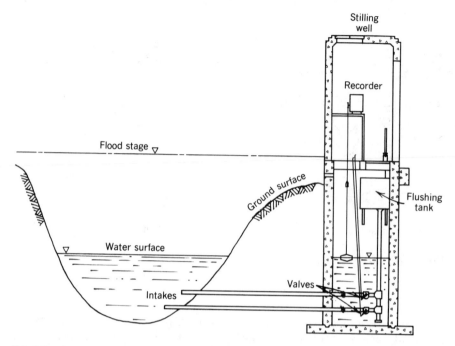

FIGURE 5.2 Typical stilling well installation for water stage recorder (from *Stevens Water Resource Data Book,* 4th Ed., Leapold and Stevens, January 1987).

There are other "stage detectors" available for use today. One device recognizes that water is a good conductor of electrical current. However, all systems must be maintained and calibrated to ensure accurate results.

5.1.2   Current Meter

A current meter is a device for sensing velocity. Older systems were revolution counting meters that converted angular velocity to linear velocity and consisted of a propeller or cup wheel, a revolution counter, shaft, earphones, weights, and rudder (see Figure 5.5). The meter with balancing weights has to be of sufficient weight so as not to be displaced during strong flow rates or must be anchored to a support. Normal propellers are designed to operate over a very wide range of velocities (0.03–10 m/s). The propeller reacts to flow velocity components in the axial direction only. Newer, electromagnetic meters remain hydrodynamically stable and function on an electromotive force (voltage) principle. The water, as a conductor, flows through a magnetic field.

Since velocity varies with location and time in a flowing stream or river, various areas and depths have to be used to estimate flow rates. Velocities near

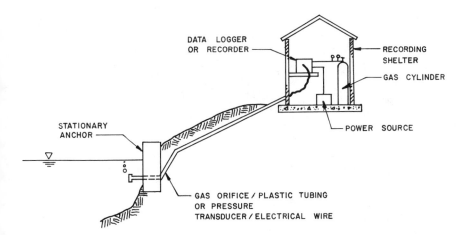

FIGURE 5.3 A gaging station with both a pressure transducer and nitrogen-gas-purge water-level sensing system.

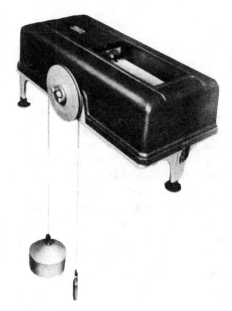

FIGURE 5.4 Stevens type A strip chart recorder (from Stevens, op. cit.).

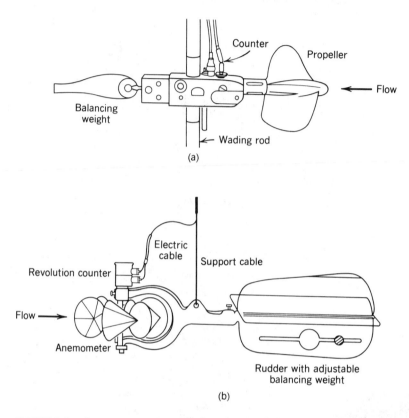

FIGURE 5.5   Current meters: (*a*) Propeller meter, and (*b*) price current meter.

the bottom will be lower because of stream bed friction and higher velocities at other depths. When the depth of the watercourse is greater than 2 ft (0.6 m) the average velocity for the section can be estimated as the average of the velocities measured at depths equal to 0.2 and 0.8 times the total depth of the watercourse. If the depth of flow is less than 2 ft (0.6 m), the velocity meter is set at 0.6 times the depth of the watercourse. The velocity at this depth is presumed to represent the average velocity for that section of stream. Guidelines for velocity measures with depth are shown in Table 5.2. A typical velocity profile with lines of equal velocity (isovels) is shown in Figure 5.6 and for pipe flow changing velocities perpendicular to the flow stream are shown. The number of sections across the channel must be sufficient enough to maintain desired accuracy. Usually, four measures are taken in a pipe.

    Once the average velocity for a section is determined, the cross-sectional area is estimated and the flow rate can be determined using the deterministic

TABLE 5.2   Depth Measure Points for Velocity and Averaging Equations

NUMBER OF MEASURES	DEPTH OF WATERCOURSE (ft)	OBSERVATION POINTS (MEASURED FROM WATER SURFACE)	AVERAGE VELOCITY ($\overline{V}$)
One	1–2	0.6D	$\overline{V} = V_{0.6}$
Two	2–10	0.2 and 0.8D	$\overline{V} = 0.5(V_{0.2} + V_{0.8})$
Three	10–20	0.2, 0.6, and 0.8D	$\overline{V} = 0.25(V_{0.2} + 2V_{0.6} + V_{0.8})$
Five	+20	1 foot, 0.2, 0.6, 0.8, and 1 ft above bottom	$\overline{V} = 0.10(V_1 + 3V_{0.2} + 2V_{0.6} + 3V_{0.8} + V_B)$

where D = depth of water

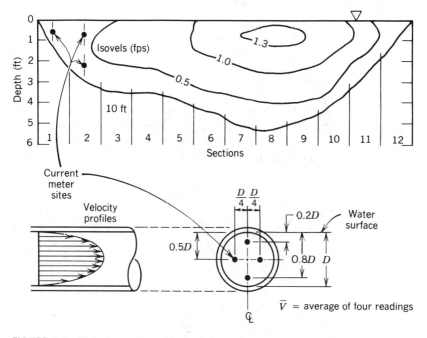

FIGURE 5.6   Velocity profiles with depth/area/velocity measurement points.

form of the continuity equation, or

$$Q_i = A_i \overline{V}_i \tag{5.1}$$

where

Q_i = volume flow rate for section i (cfs, cms)
A_i = cross-section area normal to the flow velocity in section i (ft^2, m^2)
$\overline{V}_i$ = average velocity for section i (fps, m/s)

The total flow rate is the sum of the flow rates of all sections across the stream. Sections are chosen to represent stream depths; thus, the number and the width of each section depend on the changes in stream depth and the degree of precision required. The depth of the stream is sounded and plotted as shown in Figure 5.6. The number of sections are determined (usually greater than 5 and less than 20). The velocity is measured at the center of each section and at depths recommended in Table 5.2. This method is frequently called the velocity–area method.

$$Q = \sum_i Q_i = \sum_i A_i \overline{V}_i \tag{5.2}$$

where Q = total streamflow (cfs).

   Since the measurements for flow rates take time, changes in depth (stage) may occur. These changes must be documented. Steady-state (constant discharge and depth) conditions should exist for best results. Schutz (1980) presents other details and expands this discussion.

◻ **EXAMPLE PROBLEM 5.1**

For a particular stream, estimate the flow rate (runoff for this case) using the following data for velocities measured at two depths (0.2 and 0.8 of the total) and the cross-sectional area corresponding to the velocity measures.

SECTION	SAMPLE DEPTHS	1	2	3	4	5
Velocity (m/s)	0.2 D	0.4	0.8	1.2	1.0	0.6
	0.8 D	0.3	0.6	1.3	1.2	0.6
Area (m^2)		3	6	10	8	4

Solution

$$Q = \sum_i Q_i = \sum_i A_i \bar{V}_i = \sum_i A_i (V_{0.2} + V_{0.8})_i/2$$

$$= 3(0.35) + 6(0.70) + 10(1.25) + 8(1.1) + 4(0.6)$$

$$= 1.05 + 4.20 + 12.50 + 8.8 + 2.4 = 29.00 \text{ m}^3/\text{s} \quad \square$$

Since it takes considerable time to measure flow rates using a current-meter, it is best to estimate flow rates at various stages and then develop a graphical plot of flow rate versus stage, called a stage-discharge relationship. Discharges can then be estimated from stage measurements, which are easier to obtain than flow rates. The relationship also is referred to as the rating curve for the stream. Frequently, equations of best fit can be determined and computer aided solutions found. The value of the stage-discharge relationship is evident during high flow times where complete velocity measures are difficult. Extrapolation of the rating curve beyond the points of measurement is practiced but the adequacy of the estimate should be verified by other measures.

5.1.3 Dilution

In situations where conventional current meters are not useful (shallow flows, high velocities, inaccessible areas), the dilution method is used to estimate flow rates over a reach of stream. A known quantity of a substance can be injected at a point and water samples containing the substance withdrawn downstream. Ideally, the substance should be conservative, nonpolluting, and able to be detected in minute quantities. Materials that have been used in the past are common salt, sodium dichromate, oxygen 18 (^{18}O), deuterium (^{2}H), Rhodamine B, and Rhodamine W. The downstream sampling point must be chosen so that the substance has become nearly uniformly distributed across the stream cross section. An estimate for the downstream sampling point location is

$$L = 0.13 C_Z [(0.7 C_Z + b)/g] [b^2/d] \qquad (5.3)$$

where

L = length from point of injection (m)
C_Z = Chezy's roughness coefficient
b = average width of stream (m)
g = gravity constant (9.81 m/s^2)
d = average depth of flow (m)

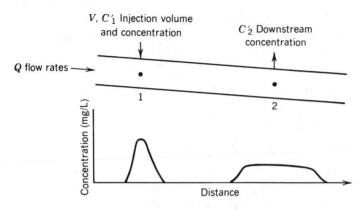

FIGURE 5.7   Chemical mass balance.

Writing a mass-balance between the injection point and the downstream point as shown in Figure 5.7, one obtains the following (C_1' and C_2' are known and Q is unknown):

$$\text{Mass in} - \text{mass out} \pm \text{generation} = \text{accumulation}$$

For a conservative substance with no generation:

$$\text{Mass in} = \text{mass out}$$

$$C_1'V = Q\sum_0^{t_2} C_2' \, \Delta t \quad \text{and} \quad Q = (C_1'V)\bigg/\left(\sum_0^{t_2} C_2' \, \Delta t\right) \qquad (5.4)$$

where
Q = unknown stream flow rate (L/s)
V = known injection volume (L)
C_1' = injection concentration (mg/L)
C_2' = downstream concentration (mg/L)
t_2 = time during which substance appears at location 2 (sec)

☐ **EXAMPLE PROBLEM 5.2**

At 07:00 hr, 400 kg of a tracer was injected immediately into a river. Two sampling points were used downstream at 14 km and 25 km. Tracer concentrations obtained from a sampling program are shown below. What is the flow rate downstream using the measurements at 14 km?

TIME	CONCENTRATION (mg/L)	
(hr)	14 km	25 km
0700	0	0
0800	0	0
0900	3	0
1000	10	0
1100	20	2
1200	15	9
1300	14	18
1400	7	15
1500	2	11
1600	2	7
1700	1	4
1800	1	3
1900		2
2000		1
2100		1

Solution

Using the mass balance approach and Equation 5.4, at the 14 km mark, the cumulative concentration is 75 mg-hr/L and

$$Q = (400 \text{ kg} \times 10^6 \text{ mg/kg})/(75 \text{ mg-hr/L} \times 3600 \text{ sec/hr}) = 1480 \text{ L/s}$$

Note that the mass has decreased to 73 mg-hr/L at the 25-km marker. The flow rate estimate at 25 km would thus be greater than that at 14 km. The greater the loss of concentration, the greater the flow rate estimate.   □

5.1.4   Float

There are dangers to human life and inaccuracies in measuring velocities during floods. In these situations, specially prepared floats have been used to measure velocity. Two stations along the stream are marked and the distance between the points are recorded. The distance measured must be parallel to the centerline of the stream. The time it takes for the float to pass through the marked distance is recorded. For wide streams, additional floats are used. Generally, a boat or structure across the stream is used to place the floats in the stream upgradient from the first station.

The surface of the stream is at greater than average velocity. Thus, the float velocity is usually reduced by 20% to estimate the average section velocity. However, for shallow flows, the float may be submerged in the water deep enough to almost hit the stream bottom. In this situation, the average velocity is the velocity of the float.

5.1.5   Indirect Method Using Manning's Equation

This method uses equations to estimate velocities and flow rates given a measure of the physical characteristics of the stream. The most popular equation is Manning's:

$$\overline{V} = \frac{1.486}{n} R^{2/3} S^{1/2} \tag{5.5}$$

where

V = average section velocity (fps)
n = roughness coefficient for deep flow (see Table 5.3)
R = hydraulic radius = flow area divided by wetted perimeter, (ft)
S = energy gradient, slope (ft/ft)

The metric equivalent of Equation 5.5 is

$$\overline{V} = \frac{1}{n} R^{2/3} S^{1/2} \tag{5.6}$$

where
$\overline{V}$ = m/s
R = m
S = m/m

Note that depth, width, stream profiles, and energy gradient estimates are needed. During an actual flow condition, this is time consuming. However, if the cross-sectional area is known, the use of Manning's equation is considerably easy. For newly constructed open channels, this physical characteristic is usually known. The roughness coefficient used for newly constructed channels is the lower value of Table 5.3. For old operational channels, the higher value is generally more appropriate.

5.1.6   Direct Measure

A direct measure of flow rates is done by the complete capture of a volume of water passing a point of reference. The time for the capture is known. Thus, the flow rate is the volume divided by time. Care must be exercised to capture

TABLE 5.3 Values of the Roughness Coefficient, n

TYPE OF CHANNEL AND DESCRIPTION	MINIMUM	NORMAL	MAXIMUM
A. Closed conduits flowing partly full			
a. Brass, smooth	0.009	0.010	0.013
b. Steel			
1. Lockbar and welded	0.010	0.012	0.014
2. Riveted and spiral	0.013	0.016	0.017
c. Cast iron			
1. Coated	0.010	0.013	0.014
2. Uncoated	0.011	0.014	0.016
d. Wrought iron			
1. Black	0.012	0.014	0.015
2. Galvanized	0.013	0.016	0.017
e. Corrugated metal			
1. 6 by 1 in. corrugations	0.020	0.022	0.025
2. 6 by 2 in. corrugations	0.030	0.032	0.035
3. Smooth wall spiral aluminum	0.010	0.012	0.014
f. Concrete			
1. Culvert, straight	0.010	0.012	0.013
2. Culvert with bends	0.011	0.013	0.014
3. Sewer with manholes, inlet, etc.,			
straight	0.013	0.015	0.017
g. Sanitary sewers	0.012	0.013	0.016

B. Channel conditions $n = (n_0 + n_1 + n_2 + n_3)m$ Values

			Values
a. Material involved	Earth		0.020
	Rock cut	n_0	0.025
	Fine gravel		0.024
	Coarse gravel		0.028
b. Degree of irregularity	Smooth		0.000
	Minor		0.005
	Moderate	n_1	0.010
	Severe		0.020
c. Relative effect of obstruction	Negligible		0.000
	Minor		0.010–0.015
	Appreciable	n_2	0.020–0.030
	Severe		0.040–0.060
d. Vegetation	Low		0.005–0.010
	Medium		0.010–0.025
	High	n_3	0.025–0.050
	Very high		0.050–0.100
e. Degree of meandering	Minor		1.000
	Appreciable	m	1.150
	Severe		1.300

Source: U.S. Department of Transportation, 1985, and W.L. Cowan, 1956.

the total volume of water. This limits the application of the direct measure to small flow rates found in some street inlets or laboratory models.

If the capture tank is used with some structural device for measuring depth or indirectly measuring flow rates, calibration of the structural device results. There are many structural devices used in practice. Some of the more common ones are presented here.

5.1.7 Weirs and Flumes

For measurements over a long period of time or for controlling discharges from a stormwater detention pond, a more permanent structural device is required. A detention pond attenuates (reduces) stormwater peak flows using an outflow control device. There are three main structures for gaging flow rates: thin-plate weirs, broad-crested weirs, and flumes. Generally, all barriers on the bottom of any channel that cause flow to accelerate while passing over are called weirs, whereas flumes are open conduits built such that the sides narrow the flow.

The thickness of the weir determines the type; narrow ones are called sharp crested, whereas thick weirs are called broad crested. The volume of the structure that is in the flow path determines the type of structure while the geometric profile determines the specific name of the structure (Figure 5.8). Table 5.6 lists weir-related terms. A schematic of a sharp-crested weir with staff gages is shown in Figure 5.9.

For all weirs, the bottom edge of the opening is called the crest. For a sharp-crested weir, an energy balance can be developed to determine a general equation for flow rates. When water passes over the weir and is not obstructed, an energy balance can be written. The total available energy upstream is expressed as

$$E_{\text{upstream}} = y + V_1^2/2g \qquad (5.7)$$

where y is the variable to represent changing "head" on the crest of the weir. It is measured upstream of the drawdown curve and V_1 is the approach velocity of the stream (again measured upstream of the drawdown). In some cases, the height P_1 is significant so that the approach velocity is near zero. This is also true for pond controlling weirs. The limits on y are zero to some depth H. The downstream energy is the velocity of flow. Equating energy up and downstream, one obtains by using the Bernoulli theorem with no losses:

$$0 + \left(V_1^2/2g\right) + y - \text{zero losses} = 0 + \left(V_{\text{jet}}^2/2g\right) + 0 \qquad (5.8)$$

Thus, rearranging for the ideal no-loss case;

$$V_{\text{jet}} = \sqrt{2g\left(y + V_1^2/2g\right)} \qquad (5.9)$$

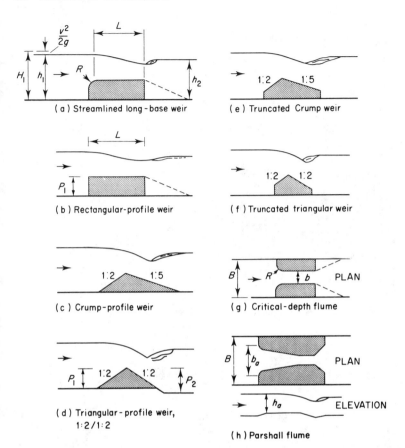

FIGURE 5.8 Comparison of volumes of gaging structures in lined rectangular channel: layout diagram (reproduced from Ackers et al., 1978, *Weirs and Flumes for Flow Measurement*).

an ideal

$$dQ = dA\,V_{jet} = (B\,dy)\,V_{jet} \tag{5.10}$$

and integrating between $y = 0$ to H with $C_f =$ friction loss coefficient;

$$Q = BC_f\sqrt{2g}\int_0^H \left(y + V_1^2/2g\right)^{1/2} dy$$

$$= 2/3 BC_f\sqrt{2g}\left[\left(H + V_1^2/2g\right)^{3/2} - \left(V_1^2/2g\right)^{3/2}\right] \tag{5.11}$$

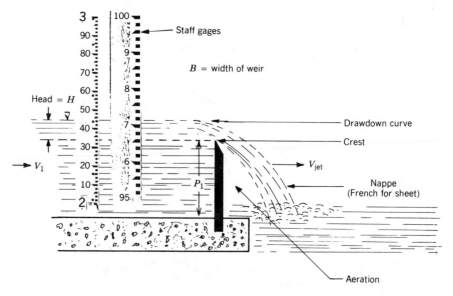

FIGURE 5.9 Sharp crested weir with two different style staff gages.

and if V_1 approaches zero, with $C_w = \frac{2}{3}C_f$ (approximately)

$$Q = C_w\sqrt{2g}\,BH^{3/2} \qquad (5.12)$$

where

Q = flow rate (L^3/T)
B = width of weir (L)
H = head or depth of flow above weir crest (L)
g = gravitation acceleration constant (L/T^2)
C_w = discharge coefficient for a weir

As noted by the air under the nappe of the discharge in Figure 5.9, there can be no downstream backwater effects on the weir. Also, note that the upstream water profile decreases as it approaches the crest, thus the head is measured at a point upstream equal to at least five times the weir width. This assumes an accuracy of measurement equal to ±1 percent.

For a rectangular weir extending the width of the channel, Equation 5.12 is rewritten as

$$Q = C_w BH^{3/2} \qquad (5.13)$$

where

Q = discharge (cfs, m³/s)

C_w = 3.33 (U.S.), 1.84 (SI) and is dependent on P_1/H, L/H, N_R, shape, roughness

B = width of weir (ft, m)

H = head (ft, m)

The coefficient C_w has been related to other flow depths and can change by as much as 10% when the head varies (see Figure 5.13) For a rectangular weir not extended across the channel or one that has its ends contracted and negligible velocity head:

$$Q = C_w H^{3/2}(B - 0.2H) \qquad (5.14)$$

Other types are also used and are listed as follows.

For low flows: 60° V-notch

$$Q = C_{60} H^{5/2} \qquad (5.15)$$

where C_{60} = 1.43 (U.S.), 0.80 (SI), (See Figure 5.14 for coefficient values as a function of head) and 90° V-notch

$$Q = C_{90} H^{5/2} \qquad (5.16)$$

where C_{90} = 2.50 (U.S.), 1.38 (SI) (Brater and King, 1980).

◻ **EXAMPLE PROBLEM 5.3**

A channel is known to produce a peak flow rate of 0.45 m³/s. The upstream depth must not exceed 2.25 m. If you have a 1.5-m wide end contracted rectangular weir, how high should it be placed in the channel so as not to exceed the 2.25 m upstream depth?

Solution

Using the end-contracted weir formula and solving for the upstream depth (H):

$$Q = 1.84H^{3/2}(B - 0.2H) \qquad 0.45 = 1.84H^{3/2}(1.5 - 0.2H)$$

$$0.45 = (2.76H^{3/2}) - (0.368H^{5/2})$$

by trial and error, H = 0.31 m. Thus, the weir height above the bottom of the channel is

$$P_1 = 2.25 - 0.31 = 1.94 \text{ m or less} \quad ◻$$

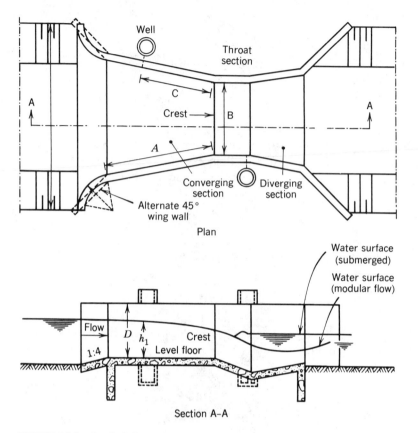

FIGURE 5.10   Parshall flume diagram.

One of the oldest flumes and most widely used to estimate flow rate in irrigation and water treatment is the Parshall flume (Parshall, 1950). It is constructed to converge water through critical depth near the end of the convergence. The geometry of the flume is shown in Figure 5.10. The flume has the advantages of less head loss and solids deposition relative to a weir. There are 22 standard designs that estimate flow rates within ±3% accuracy. Tne dimensions of Figure 5.10 (A, B, C, and D) change with the overall flume size and the constants in Equation 5.12.

$$Q = 4Bh_1^{1.522B^{0.026}}$$ (5.17)

where

Q = flow rate (m^3/s, fps)
h_1 = upstream depth (m, ft)
B = width of throat section (m, ft)

☐ *EXAMPLE PROBLEM 5.4*
_____

A Parshall flume of throat width equal to 2.0 ft will be used to measure peak discharge. The expected peak stage at the flume well is 2.5 ft. What is the peak discharge which this flume can estimate?

Solution

All one has to do is calculate the flow rate using Equation 5.17.

$$Q = 4Bh_1^{1.522 B^{0.026}}$$

or

$$Q = 4(2)(2.5)^{1.522(2)^{0.026}}$$

$$= 33.1 \text{ cfs} \quad \square$$

The type and size of weir or flume that is chosen for a particular application depends on the water quality (chemical composition and debris) and the range of discharge expected. Metals susceptible to corrosion should not be used for a weir or flume conveying water with a high corrosion potential. For very small discharges, V-notch weirs are used; for medium discharges, full-width thin plates and long-base weirs and flumes are used; and for large discharges, long-base structures are used. A comparison of discharge range, size, and geometry is shown for the different types of weirs and flumes in Table 5.4.

5.1.8 Other Gaging and Outlet Controls

With the growing use of stormwater storage facilities (detention ponds) to reduce peak flow rates, a wide range of flows must be considered in design and gaging. Rectangular weirs are commonly used to discharge and measure high flows and orifices are used to discharge and measure smaller flows. An orifice is an opening usually circular in shape. Typical outlet controls from a detention pond are shown in Figure 5.11. The side orifice in the riser pipe is used to slowly drain detained water, whereas the overflow weir and emergency spillway operate as weirs. Once the riser pipe is submerged, its discharge will be governed by the orifice equation rather than the weir equations. The equation for orifice flow is

$$Q = C_d A_0 \sqrt{2gH} \tag{5.18}$$

where

Q = flow rate (cfs, m³/s)
C_d = discharge coefficient
A_0 = orifice area (ft², m²)
H = head (measured from center line of orifice) (ft, m)
g = gravitational constant (32.2 ft/sec², 9.81 m/s²)

TABLE 5.4 Comparison of Size and Flow Rate Range (Reproduced in part from Ackers et al., 1978)

TYPE	SIZE AND GEOMETRY			DISCHARGE RANGE
Thin-plate,	B	P_1		
full-width weir	0.15 m	0.2 m		0.8 L/s–100 L/s
	1.0 m	0.5 m		5.4 L/s–2.7 m³/s
	10 m[a]	1 m		50 L/s–77 m³/s
	B	P_1		
Thin-plate,	0.15 m	0.2 m		1.4 L/s–67 L/s
side-	1.0 m	0.5 m		9.5 L/s–1.7 m³/s
contracted weir	10 m[a]	1 m		90 L/s–49 m³/s
V-notch weir	$\theta = 20$[a]			0.2 L/s–330 L/s
	$\theta = 90$[a]			1.1 L/s–1.8 m³/s
	B	P_1		
Triangular-	0.3 m[b]	0.2 m		3 L/s–350 L/s
profile				
(Crump) weir,	1.0 m[b]	0.5 m		10 L/s–4.6 m³/s
1 : 2/1 : 5				
	10 m[c]	1 m		0.3 m³/s–130 m³/s
	100 m[a,c]	1 m		3 m³/s–1300 m³/s
Triangular-	B	P_1		
profile weir,	0.3 m[b]	0.2 m		3 L/s–300 L/s
1 : 2/1 : 2	1.0 m[b]	0.5 m		11 L/s–3.9 m³/s
	10 m[c]	1 m		0.3 m³/s–110 m³/s
	100 m[a,c]	1 m		3 m³/s–1100 m³/s
Flat-V weir,	P_1, P_2, P_v	Slope	B	
1 : 2/1 : 5	0.2 m	1 : 10	4 m	14 L/s–5.0 m³/s
	0.5 m	1 : 20	20 m	27 L/2–180 m³/s
	1 m[a]	1 : 40	80 m	55 L/s–630 m³/s

continued

TABLE 5.4 *(Continued)*

TYPE	SIZE AND GEOMETRY			DISCHARGE RANGE
Flat-V weir,	$P_1, P_2, P_{l'}$	Slope	B	
$1:2/1:2$	0.2 m	1 : 10	4 m	15 L/s–2.5 m³/s
	0.5 m	1 : 20	20 m	30 L/s–65 m³/s
	1 m[a]	1 : 20	40 m	30 L/s–330 m³/s
Rectangular-	B	P_1	L	
profile weir	0.3 m	0.2 m	0.8 m	8 L/s–180 L/s
	1 m	0.5 m	2 m	90 L/s–2.3 m³/s
	10 m[a]	1 m	2 m	1.5 m³/s–65 m³/s
	B	P_1	L	
Round-nosed	0.3 m	0.15 m	0.6 m	8 L/s–34 L/s
horizontal-	1 m	0.15 m	1 m	25 L/s–740 L/s
crested weir	10 m	1 m	5 m	1 m³/s–82 m³/s
	100 m[a]	1 m	5 m	10 m³/s–820 m³/s
Long-throated	B		L	
flumes	0.5 m		1 m	9 L/s–300 L/s
	0.1 m		1 m	3 L/s–290 L/s
	1 m[a]		4 m	270 L/s–41 m³/s
Parshall	B			
flumes	25.4 mm			0.1 L/s–5 L/s
	0.305 m			3 L/s–450 L/s
	2.438 m			0.1 m³/s–3.9 m³/s
	15.24 m			0.75 m³/s–93 m³/s

Source:
[a] There is no upper limit specified for the size of these structures.
[b] Lower limit of head assumed to be 0.03 m for smooth crest section.
[c] Lower limit of head assumed to be 0.06 m for concrete crest.

The discharge coefficient will vary with the size, type of orifice (sharp edged, rounded, etc.), and the head. For a sharp-edged, 1-in. (25 mm) orifice, the coefficient varies in U.S. units between 0.609 and 0.594 for heads varying between 1 and 60 ft. For most applications, a discharge coefficient of 0.6 is used.

☐ **EXAMPLE PROBLEM 5.5**

For a 4-in. orifice with a discharge coefficient of 0.60, what head results when measuring a discharge of 0.87 cfs?

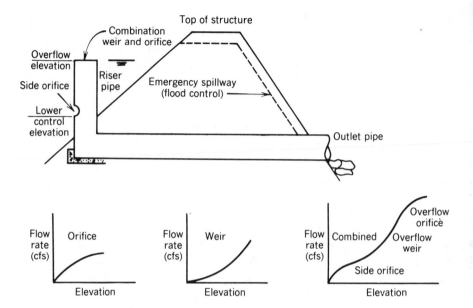

FIGURE 5.11   Stormwater pond outlet controls with generalized performance curves.

Solution

Using Equation 5.18, the head can be calculated as follows.

$$Q = C_d A_0 \sqrt{2gH}$$

$$0.87 = 0.60(0.087)\sqrt{2(32.2)(H)}$$

$$H = 4.3 \text{ ft} \quad \square$$

5.2

NETWORK OF GAGES

Surface and groundwater gaging systems are costly and time consuming but affect many social activities. Gaging is therefore usually the responsibility of a government body such as the U.S. Geologic Survey in the United States or the regional water authority in Great Britain. The density of gaging stations depends on the nature of the terrain and the purpose of the station. In countries conducting streamflow measurements, there are:

1. Primary or principal stations defined as permanent stations to measure most ranges of discharges with records as accurate and complete as possible.
2. Secondary stations operating for short periods of time to obtain a satisfactory correlation with the record of a primary station; their function is usually to provide hydrological knowledge of streams likely to be used for future studies.
3. Special stations serving particular needs, such as reservoir sizing, determining runoff volumes from a small urban watershed, and dry weather flow stations for estimating abstractions.

Some national, regional, and local agencies provide records of flow data from measurement programs. The U.S. Geological Survey (USGS) is one such agency. The USGS provides data for 16 major river watersheds in the United States, defined roughly as shown in Figure 5.12 and the accompanying legend. Each major watershed is divided into smaller ones and a vast quantity of data are available. In more recent history, smaller watersheds are being monitored and additional data are now available. Most of the streamflow records published by the USGS are found in two series of publications: the Water Resources Data and the Water Supply Papers.

Each structure for measuring flow is known as a gaging station. The printed records from the station are arranged in downstream order beginning with the main stream of the river. The record numbers are sequenced proceeding downstream until the main stream is joined by a tributary, which has a gaging station on it somewhere. The next record is then the most upstream gaging station on the tributary. The records of all the stations on the tributary are arranged in downstream order until the tributary joins the main stream. Other countries follow a similar ordering procedure.

Mean discharge at some gaging stations in Great Britain are shown in Table 5.5. These gaging stations were selected to include major river basins with complete flow records for 1977 and to give a representative assessment of the variability of 1977 runoff for Great Britain. The annual means are the monthly totals divided by the total number of days in 1977. In most cases, long-term mean gaged discharges are based on daily records of five years or more. These type of records are common for most developed countries.

Groundwater gaging is done primarily to determine storage volumes and the direction of groundwater movement. Generally, water levels are recorded. Groundwater monitoring is becoming more and more important as surface waters are depleted and polluted, and wells are overpumped.

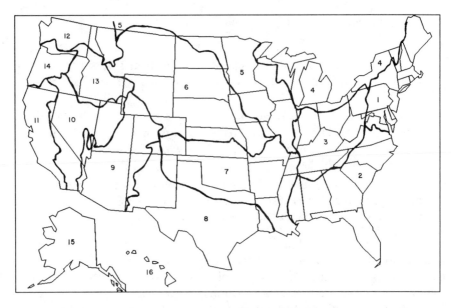

USGS Watersheds Corresponding to the Numbers
on the Map

WATERSHED	NAME	WATERSHED	NAME
1	North Atlantic	9	Colorado River
1	South Atlantic	10	The Great Basin
3	Ohio River	11	Pacific Slope California
4	St. Lawrence	12	Pacific Slope Washington
5	Hudson Bay and	13	Snake River
	Upper Mississippi	14	Pacific Slope Oregon
6	Missouri	15	Alaska
7	Lower Mississippi	16	Hawaii and Others
8	Western Gulf of Mexico		

FIGURE 5.12   Major river watersheds in the United States (from *U.S. Geological Survey*).

Major aquifers have been valuable sources of high quality water for many years with some areas relying totally on groundwater supplies. The lowering of regional water tables by the overdevelopment of the groundwater has led to a new appreciation of aquifers for water storage. When there are few measuring stations and data records are limited in length, then the analyses become more involved and statistical probabilities less assured.

TABLE 5.5 Mean Discharge (cubic meters/second) at Selected Gaging Stations for River Basins in 1977 in the United Kingdom

STATION NUMBER	LOCATION OF FLOW MEASUREMENT STATION	WATER AUTHORITY/RIVER PURIFICATION BOARD	GAGED FLOW													LONG-TERM MEAN GAGED DISCHARGE	CATCHMENT AREA (SQUARE) (km²)
			JAN	FEB	MARCH	APRIL	MAY	JUNE	JULY	AUG	SEPT	OCT	NOV	DEC	ANNUAL MEAN		
006007	Ness at Ness Side	Highlands	60.91	52.75	106.14	109.24	82.42	18.63	34.50	35.54	67.80	101.98	202.80	77.51	70.09	73.14	1,839.1
019001	Almond at Craigiehall	Fourth	10.13	13.74	5.42	4.11	3.72	3.58	1.10	1.68	4.34	11.64	14.32	5.85	6.58	5.06	369.0
025001	Tees at Broken Scar	Northumbrain	34.41	40.70	24.38	60.87	13.04	6.16	2.53	3.32	5.45	11.19	29.31	27.25	21.35	16.38	817.7
027001	Nidd at Hunsingore	Yorkshire	18.14	29.39	13.12	8.29	9.84	4.73	2.68	2.57	2.43	3.91	14.52	14.80	10.24	8.01	484.3
028009	Trent at Colwick	Severn-Trent	188.46	387.50	136.01	77.66	77.10	59.71	31.42	34.87	26.74	30.01	82.54	106.95	101.37	79.44	7,486.0
038005	Ash at Easneye	Thames	0.71	1.08	0.62	0.30	0.25	0.18	0.54	0.55	0.61	0.43	0.45	0.82	2.15	1.59	297.9
039001	Thames at Teddington	Thames	193.49	240.04	159.13	82.48	64.03	58.31	19.67	53.90	26.97	24.77	51.57	114.49	90.15	67.50	9,950.0
040011	Great Stour at Horton	Southern	8.06	7.29	6.29	4.32	3.29	2.31	1.78	2.01	1.65	1.53	2.61	4.44	3.28	3.30	345.0
052006	Yeo at Penn Mill	Wessex	6.56	7.55	5.40	2.05	1.84	1.095	0.68	0.85	0.61	0.61	1.62	6.10	2.88	2.46	213.1
045001	Seven at Bewdley	Severn-Trent	107.48	176.91	72.03	47.88	40.05	30.23	12.18	11.43	14.44	28.45	108.89	94.19	57.65	61.97	4,330.0
056001	Usk at Chain Bridge	Welsh	43.28	74.66	43.20	21.03	16.90	9.10	4.51	6.63	7.16	18.25	59.35	47.28	28.96	26.96	911.7
067015	Dee at Manley Hall	Welsh	43.37	83.99	34.81	26.54	19.34	13.83	10.66	9.50	11.39	23.23	76.62	43.70	32.67	27.66	1,019.0
079002	Nith a Friar's Carse	Solway	35.18	40.24	36.00	28.19	19.47	3.47	2.32	5.96	25.27	63.72	65.77	38.25	30.26	24.74	790.0
084013	Clyde at Daldowie	Clyde	56.18	74.81	57.79	49.77	39.12	15.62	13.36	17.46	50.01	101.51	108.99	50.72	52.73	36.90	1,903.0

Source: From United Kingdom Water Resources Data, 1979.

5.3

SUMMARY

Flow rate measurements provide data for an accounting of water in the hydrologic cycle. Accurate estimates are needed and there are at least three general methods: stage, nonstructural discharge, and structural discharge.

- The most widely used method for continuous data collection is stage recording. Stage is depth of flow and is converted to flow rate.
- Weirs, orifices, and flumes have been used to measure flow rate and equations developed which relate head (stage) to discharge. Weir related terms are shown in Table 5.6.

TABLE 5.6 Weir-Related Terms

BROAD CRESTED	A weir having a substantial length of crest parallel to the direction of flow of water over it, on which the nappe is supported for an appreciable length, and which produces no bottom contraction of the nappe.
CIPOLLETTE	A contracted weir of trapezoidal shape, in which the sides of the notch are given a slope of 1 horizontal to 4 vertical, in order to compensate as far as possible for the effect of end contractions.
CONTRACTED	A weir whose crest extends only part way across the channel in which it is installed, and is terminated by extensions in the same plane as the crest, these extensions rising above the water level on the upstream side of the weir, their effect being to produce a contraction in the width of the stream of water as it leaves the notch.
CRIB	A low diversion weir built of log cribs filled with rock.
DIVERTING	A weir placed in a sewer for the purpose of diverting storm flow. Also called an overflow, overfall, or side-flow weir in combined sewers.
DRAW-DOOR	A diversion weir fitted with doors or gates capable of being raised vertically so as to retain water when desired.
EFFLUENT	A weir at the outflow end of a hydraulic structure hydraulic structure.
FLAT CRESTED	A weir whose crest is horizontal in the direction of flow, and of appreciable length when compared with the depth of water passing over it.

continued

TABLE 5.6 *(Continued)*

FREE	A weir that is not submerged; a weir in which the tail water is below the crest or where the flow is not in any way affected by tail water.
INFLUENT	A weir at the inflow end of a hydraulic structure.
IRREGULAR	A weir whose crest is not of standard or regular shape.
LEAPING	An opening or gap in the invert of a combined sewer through which the dry-weather flow will fall to a sanitary sewer and over which a portion or all of the storm flow will leap.
LOG	A low weir, of triangular cross section, built of layers of logs placed side by side with butt ends downstream.
PARABOLIC	A weir with a notch parabolic in shape with the axis of the parabola vertical.
RECTANGULAR	A weir whose notch is rectangular in shape.
ROUNDED CREST	A weir whose crest is convex upward in the direction of flow over the weir. The term is also applied to weirs where the center of the crest may be flat, and the corners may be rounded.
SHARP CRESTED	A weir whose crest, usually consisting of a thin plate (generally of metal), is so sharp that the water in passing over it touches only a line.
SUBMERGED	A weir which, when in use, has the water level on the downstream side at an elevation equal to, or higher than, the weir crest; the rate of discharge is affected by the tailwater.
SUPPRESSED	A weir with one or both sides, flush with the channel of approach. This prevents contraction of the nappe adjacent to the flush side. The suppression may occur on one end, or both ends.
SUTRO	A weir with at least one curved side and horizontal crest, so formed that the head above the crest is directly proportional to the discharge.
TRAPEZOIDAL	A weir whose notch is trapezoidal in shape.
TRIANGULAR	A weir whose notch is triangular in shape, usually used to measure very small flows.
V-NOTCH	Another term for Triangular.
WIDE CRESTED	Another term for Broad Crested.

Source: Glossary—Water and Sewage Control Engineering, Joint Task Force. Published by American Society of Civil Engineers, New York, updated 1955.

- The Manning formula (Equation 5.5) is in general use for pipe and regular shaped open channels. Again, stage or depth of flow is needed along with other physical estimates of channel characteristics.
- Stormwater detention ponds have weir and orifice combination outlet control structures. Flow rate versus storage volume or depth curves can be developed that reflect an estimate for discharge rate as a function of pond depth and storage volume.
- All flow rate measurement methods should be calibrated on a periodic basis. The bed depth of a river changes and devices malfunction. The accuracy of the flow rate data is only as good as the calibration.
- There exists a network of streamflow gages, the data from which may be of some value for other sites.

5.4

PROBLEMS

1. Recalculate the discharge for Example Problem 5.1 if the area of Section 4 were doubled.

2. A 3-m-wide rectangular weir is placed across an open channel. There are end contractions. Graph a flow rate diagram for the catchment which drains into the channel, given the following data on time and the corresponding head on the weir (meters).

Time (min)	0	20	40	60	80	100	120	150	200
Head (meters)	0	0.4	0.9	1.2	1.0	0.8	0.6	0.3	0

3. For the catchment that produced the flow rate diagram for Problem 2, the land use was changed and a 1520-mm concrete pipe on a longitudinal slope of 0.05 replaced the open channel. Graph the flow rate for the storm event that produced the following pipe flow depth, area, and hydraulic radius. Assume that flow rate starts at time zero.

Time (min)	0	20	40	60	80	100
Flow depth (m)	0	0.76	1.52	0.91	0.46	0
Flow area (m^2)	0	0.90	1.81	1.13	0.46	0
Hydraulic radius (m)	0	0.38	0.38	0.42	0.26	0

4. Assume the storms that produced the flow rate graphs of Problems 2 and 3 were similar and in fact the rainfall volume was 100,000 m³ over the catchment. Estimate the runoff coefficient for each problem. Discuss the differences in hydrograph shapes and runoff coefficients.

5. a. A conservative chemical was added to an open channel to determine runoff in the channel. The chemical dosage rate was 6000 mg/L and 400 L were added as a slug. At a downstream station, the center of chemical mass was measured 4 min after release upstream and the average concentration was 10 mg/L. Estimate the runoff rate. State your assumptions.

   b. If the cross-sectional area at the measuring point downstream is 2 m² and the distance from the upstream injection point to the downstream point is 120 m. Estimate the runoff flow rate. The time of travel remains at 4 min.

6. Assume a 100-mm-diameter orifice is used to drain a 2-m² tank holding stormwater from the roof of a small building. The coefficient of discharge is 0.65. How long does it take to lower the tank from 2.5 m to 1.0 m above the center line of the orifice if the tank area varies as $A = 2 - (y/3)\,(\text{m}^2)$ where $y = $ depth? *Hint*:

$$qt = \frac{1}{C_d A_0 \sqrt{2g}} \int_{y_1}^{y_2} A y^{-1/2}\, dy$$

7. For the stream cross section shown in Figure 5.6, provide some reasonable velocity measures for each of the 12 sections and estimate the flow rate for the complete cross section.

8. For Example Problem 5.2, what is the discharge estimate at the 25-km marker? What percentage of the substance was lost between the two stations? Comment on how this loss affects your discharge estimate.

9. Specify the size of orifice in a riser pipe to measure a flow rate of 0.5 cfs from a storage reservoir when the head on the orifice is 3 ft and the coefficient of discharge is 0.60.

10. What depth of flow above a weir crest can be expected upstream of a sharp-crested rectangular weir extending the width of a rectangular channel if the channel width is 22 ft and the expected discharge is from an 8-acre impervious watershed located in Florida, Precipitation Zone 7, with time of concentration equal to 20 min. The storm used for the depth analysis is the 1-in-5-year event. Also, what is the depth of the channel if the design velocity is one foot per second?

11. A rectangular sharp crested weir with end contractions is 1.5 m wide. How high should it be placed in a channel to maintain an upstream depth of 2.25 m for 0.45 m³/s flow?

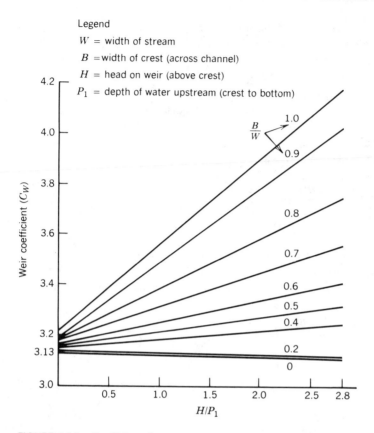

Legend
W = width of stream
B = width of crest (across channel)
H = head on weir (above crest)
P_1 = depth of water upstream (crest to bottom)

FIGURE 5.13 Coefficients for rectangular weirs (from Kindsvater and Carter, 1959).

12. Using Figures 5.13 and 5.14, what size and type of weir would you use to measure flows in a drainage ditch 3 ft wide and 2 ft deep if the expected flows were about 0.5 to 1.5 cfs? The flow depth in the channel cannot exceed 2 ft. Base your decision on the accuracy of measuring depth.

13. A 20-in. diameter pipe is placed in a vertical position at the end of a stormwater pond. The pipe acts as a weir for heads up to 1.5 ft. At heads of 0.1 ft and 1 ft, the flow rates are 0.52 cfs and 10.5 cfs, respectively. Using $Q = C_W B H^n$ as the general equation form for a weir, estimate the weir coefficients C_W and n.

14. a. What depth of flow can one expect using a 4-ft-wide contracted rectangular weir whose crest is 2 ft off the channel bottom and the discharge was 25 cfs?

    b. The maximum depth above the crest of a 60° V-notch weir is 2 ft. What is the maximum discharge that can be measured using this weir?

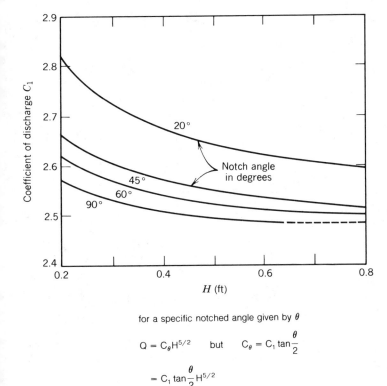

for a specific notched angle given by θ

$$Q = C_\theta H^{5/2} \quad \text{but} \quad C_\theta = C_1 \tan\frac{\theta}{2}$$

$$= C_1 \tan\frac{\theta}{2} H^{5/2}$$

FIGURE 5.14 Discharge coefficients for sharp-crested V-notch weirs (from Brater and King, 1980).

   c. How large of an impervious area (acres) can be measured for the 10-year storm if the design intensity is 8 in./hr using the 60° V-notch weir and the results of part (b)?

15. a. For an 8-in. concrete pipe ($n = 0.012$) carrying 1 cfs, what is the slope to maintain a velocity of 2 ft/sec? The pipe is flowing full.

   b. What is the invert downstream if the pipe length is 1000′ and the invert upstream is 80.0′?

16. Calculate the upstream invert of a 200-ft pipe flowing full at a design velocity of 2 fps if the downstream invert elevation is 10.5 ft. The pipe is discharging 10 cfs and is made of concrete. Also, what is the pipe diameter (best commercial size)?

17. If a smooth, straight, cut rock rectangular channel drops 3 ft for every mile in length, what is the flow (in cfs) in the channel if the normal depth is 2 ft? The width of the channel is 10 ft.

TABLE 5.7   Watershed Data 10B Lake Okeechobee and the Everglades Area 02264495 Shingle Creek at Campbell, FL

DISCHARGE (ft³/sec), WATER YEAR OCTOBER 1972 TO SEPTEMBER 1973

DAY	OCT	NOV	DEC	JAN	FEB	MAR	APR	MAY	JUN	JUL	AUG	SEP
1	53	39	71	76	298	115	88	41	36	97	293	319
2	63	35	65	72	281	105	101	41	36	128	366	384
3	78	32	65	73	359	94	101	30	36	75	332	389
4	84	42	62	69	297	94	121	41	33	134	301	369
5	71	73	62	69	256	89	124	41	30	237	279	386
6	70	66	62	65	233	78	108	40	30	217	278	401
7	60	49	65	65	214	84	85	37	36	281	305	403
8	60	49	59	54	196	73	136	33	33	220	332	396
9	60	42	59	75	189	79	120	49	30	168	330	406
10	66	39	55	67	445	30	111	53	33	151	303	417
11	73	39	52	80	352	80	90	41	30	127	281	414
12	73	39	55	189	291	73	81	37	30	119	274	428
13	63	39	52	161	270	72	75	33	27	139	260	440
14	56	43	41	130	274	60	83	36	27	128	251	404
15	56	49	41	112	286	60	82	32	30	125	241	391
16	53	42	63	108	274	54	81	38	36	103	208	387
17	53	45	49	112	252	58	72	31	30	91	184	354
18	53	42	50	121	239	62	62	27	24	82	164	306
19	53	39	44	121	246	68	65	33	33	115	149	284
20	65	42	44	118	214	62	64	32	36	118	150	264

21	63	49	37	115	193	50	55	32	47	88	157	240
22	53	45	106	154	178	53	51	31	97	82	183	240
23	49	45	97	397	163	54	50	28	131	100	381	231
24	49	42	86	476	157	59	38	28	144	91	375	219
25	46	43	86	412	147	49	34	37	97	88	313	220
26	46	64	82	337	142	80	38	31	81	85	285	415
27	35	61	82	360	136	79	27	25	70	97	280	890
28	25	57	83	436	126	73	41	22	59	112	276	791
29	28	68	79	501	—	78	41	24	51	112	271	681
30	32	69	83	426	—	73	37	33	70	117	263	624
31	35	—	80	347	—	78	—	36	—	149	277	—
Total	1,724	1,428	2,017	5,898	6,713	2,266	2,262	1,073	1,483	3,977	8,342	12,093
Mean	55.6	47.6	65.1	97.4	240	73.1	75.4	34.6	49.4	128	269	403
Max	84	73	106	501	445	115	136	53	144	281	381	890
Min	25	32	37	54	126	49	27	22	24	75	149	219
ac-ft	3,420	2,830	4,000	11,700	13,320	4,490	4,490	2,130	2,940	7,890	16,550	23,990

Cal yr 1972 Total 35,641 Mean 97.4 Max 472 Min 18 ac-ft 70,690

Wtr yr 1973 Total 49,276 Mean 135 Max 490 Min 22 ac-ft 97,740

Source: U.S. Geological Survey, 1973.

Location—Lat 28°16′01″, long 81°26′53″, in SE quarter sec. 31, T.25 S., R.29 F., Osccola County, near left bank at downstream side of bridge on county road, 100 ft (30 m) downstream from Atlantic Coast Line Railroad bridge, 0.8 mi (1.3 km) northeast of Campbell, and 2.5 (4.0 km) upstream from Lake Tohopekaliga.

Drainage Area—180 mi² (466 km²) approximately; includes part of watershed in Reedy Creek Swamp.

Period of Record—October 1968 to current year.

18. Develop a discharge–storage curve similar to the generalized performance curve of Figure 5.11 for a 3-in. diameter orifice 1 ft below the overflow elevation in a 2 ft diameter riser pipe. The discharge–storage curve starts at the control elevation and ends 2 ft above the overflow elevation.

5.5

COMPUTER-ASSISTED PROBLEMS

1. Using the least squares option L or the STAT program, estimate an equation for the coefficient of discharge for a weir with no end contractions as a function of H/P_1. Use Figure 5.13 and "pick off" at least 10 points to fit the equation. For the 60° V notch in Figure 5.14, estimate an equation for the coefficient of discharge as a function of head (H). Comment on how you determine the "best" equation.

2. Develop a computer program to solve for the volume of flow for any month given daily streamflow data. Data are available from Table 5.7 if not available elsewhere.

3. Write a computer program to develop a listing of cumulative mass flow or the mass curve (plot) for any rainfall data.

5.6

REFERENCES

Ackers, P. et al. 1978. *Weirs and Flumes for Flow Measurement*. Wiley, New York.

Brater, E.F. and King, H.W. 1980. *Handbook of Hydraulics*. McGraw-Hill, New York.

Cowan, W.L. 1956. "Estimating Hydraulic Roughness Coefficients," *Agricultural Engineering*, Vol. 37, No. 7, pp. 473–475, July.

Kindsvater, C.E. and Carter, R.W. 1959. "Discharge Characteristics of Rectangular Thin-Plate Weirs," *ASCE Transactions*, 772–822.

Parshall, R.L. 1950. Measuring Water in Irrigation Channels with Parshall Flumes and Small Weirs, *Soil Conservation Circular No. 843*, USDA, Washington, DC, May.

Schulz, E.F. 1980. *Problems in Applied Hydrology*, Water Resources Publications, Fort Collins, Colorado. USA pp. 280–286.

United Kingdom Water Resources Data. 1979. Her Magestic Surface Water Office, Water Data Unit, Wallingford, U.K.

U.S. Department of Transportation. 1985. *Hydraulic Design of Highway Culverts*, Report No. FHWA-IP-85-150 Federal Highway Administration, McLean, Virginia, September, p. 34.

U.S. Geological Survey. 1973. *Water Resources Data for Florida Water Year–1973*. Water Resources Division. Tallahasee, Florida.

6

HYDROGRAPHS

A hydrograph is a graph of flow rate versus time. It is also referenced as a listing of flow rate data versus time. It is one of the more useful concepts of hydrology and is used frequently in stormwater management. The hydrograph forms much of the ideas and concepts for later chapters of this book. The equations and concepts from this chapter plus those from Chapters 7, 8, and 11 form much of the practical knowledge needed for the control of stormwater volumes and flow rates.

This chapter develops mathematical descriptions for a hydrograph and explains how various shapes result from watershed conditions. A streamflow hydrograph is composed of both surface runoff and groundwater that has infiltrated into a stream. Groundwater flow is composed of interflow (fast responding from groundwater areas close to the stream) and base flow (relatively constant over longer time periods). Runoff hydrograph computation procedures are developed first using discrete flow values for specific times and then a continuous time, variable rainfall excess procedure.

6.1

HYDROGRAPH PROPERTIES

A hydrograph is typically a plot but can be a listing of flow rates versus time for a specific conduit. It consists of both surface (overland) and groundwater

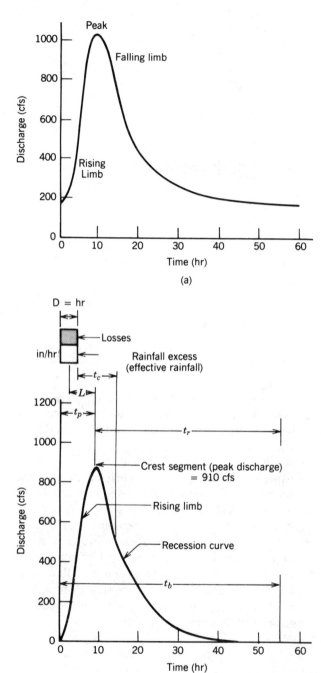

FIGURE 6.1   Hydrograph properties. (*a*) Streamflow (surface and groundwater) hydrograph. (*b*) Surface runoff.

flows that infiltrate from the ground to the surface conduit. Groundwater inflow that is relatively persistent over time is called base flow. Groundwater flows for shorter periods of time are sometimes called interflow. Many shapes for hydrographs are possible, one such is shown in Figure 6.1a. The groundwater flows are caused by many factors in the soil, some of which can be distinguished in analyzing the hydrograph recession curve (tail of the hydrograph). Thus ground and surface flow rates can be estimated from streamflow rates.

A typical surface runoff hydrograph is shown in Figure 6.1b. The hydrograph consists of three general parts: (1) rising limb or concentration curve, (2) crest segment or peak discharge, and (3) recession curve or falling limb. Note that the rainfall excess or effective rainfall volume is the same as the volume of runoff (area under the runoff hydrograph). From this effective rainfall and the watershed characteristics, a runoff hydrograph will have at least the following properties:

1. *Lag Time (L).* The time interval from the center of mass of the rainfall excess to the peak of the resulting hydrograph.

2. *Time to Peak (t_p).* The time interval from the start of rainfall excess to the peak of the resulting hydrograph.

3. *Time of Concentration (t_c).* The time interval from the end of rainfall excess to the inflection point (change of slope) on the recession curve. Also, the longest time for water to flow to a discharge point from any point in the watershed.

4. *Recession Time (t_r).* Time from the peak to the end of surface runoff.

5. *Time Base (t_b).* Time from the beginning to the end of surface runoff.

6.1.1 Hydrograph Records

Since most of the printed records report flow rates on a daily basis, most hydrographs for large watersheds are reported on a daily basis. However, if the rainfall excess passes from the watershed in less than a day, the hydrograph must reflect a time scale in hours or possibly minutes. One must be aware of the time frame over which flow rates occur and analyze accordingly.

The mean (arithmetic average) daily discharge is a representation of flow from midnight to midnight. A reasonable expectation of hydrograph variability for small and large watersheds is shown in Figure 6.2. Once the flow rates have been measured at time intervals which reflect hydrograph variability, a mathematical analysis can be done to describe the hydrograph shape and aid in predicting peak flow rates and volume discharge.

6.1.2 Stream Types by Streamflow Hydrograph Analysis

Hydrographs for a stream define the relative contributions of both surface and groundwaters. The magnitude of the hydrograph recession time will aid in

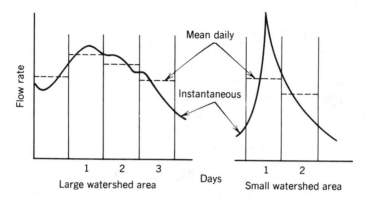

FIGURE 6.2   A comparison of instantaneous and mean daily flow rates for large and small watersheds.

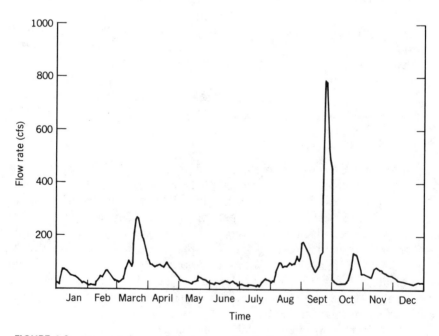

FIGURE 6.3   An example perennial stream — Reedy Creek, Florida.

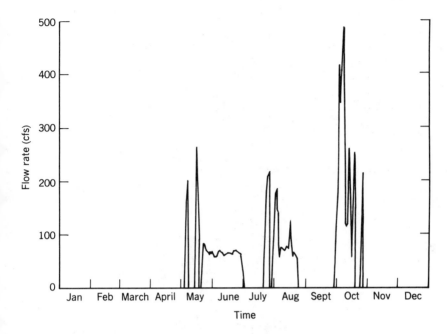

FIGURE 6.4 An example intermittent stream — Middle Creek, Florida.

determining the long term water yield of a stream. Annual hydrographs that have rarely zero flow (water yield) and relatively low recession times are characteristic of perennial streams, an example of which is shown in Figure 6.3. Perennial streams have dependable water yield potentials during the year. Water yield is maintained primarily because stored groundwater is released very slowly. The groundwater storage is always at a sufficiently high level to maintain the groundwater table above the bottom of the stream.

In contrast, intermittent streams have limited groundwater storage and release stored waters at a faster rate. The recession times are generally shorter than perennial streams, and stream flows fall to zero during extended dry period (Figure 6.4). Base flow or interflow exists only during and shortly after heavy rainfall periods, and the water yield is based primarily on surface runoff.

There are some streams that have no interflow and base flow because the soils forming the side walls and bed of the channel are relatively impervious materials. In other cases, the water table is always lower than the stream bottom and runoff waters actually recharge the groundwater from the stream bed. This stream is labeled an ephemeral one with a typical annual hydrograph shown in Figure 6.5. Note that most likely there is a single recession constant

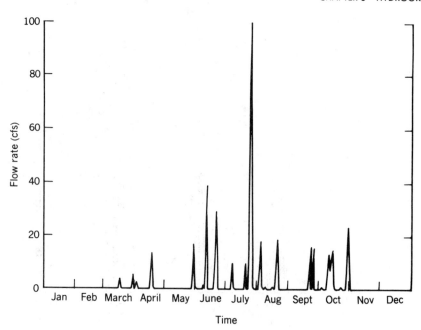

FIGURE 6.5 An example ephemeral stream — Colorado Springs, Colorado. (From F.F. Schuly, 1980).

that is higher in magnitude than the other two types of streams. This stream is not dependable for water yield.

6.2

WATERSHED CHARACTERISTICS

Watershed characteristics, such as watershed area, impervious area, directly connected impervious area, watershed slope, conduit roughness, surface (depression) storage, and soil storage affect runoff and rainfall excess. Determination of watershed area first requires an estimate of the watershed boundaries.

6.2.1   Watershed Boundaries

Watershed boundaries define a surface area that contributes drainage volumes and flow rates to a point of discharge. Generally, contours and man-made physical features, such as highways and other land improvements help define the boundaries. Open channels that intersect groundwater flow movement must also be considered in determining excess waters. Surface drainage patterns may not always produce expected streamflow. Groundwater flows into a surface stream must be added to obtain a streamflow hydrograph.

Maps with contours of a watershed will define most topographic and surface water conditions. U.S. Geological Survey (USGS) quadrangle sheets are generally available at scales of 1 : 24,000 and 1 : 250,000. These maps provide the basis for developing the surface area or topographic limits of watersheds. Essentially, one must determine the area that contributes runoff to surface storage. This area is defined by physical features, such as roadways, parking lots, and drainage conduits. Frequently, subwatersheds for a larger watershed are defined. Developed areas can significantly alter drainage requiring site determination of changed contours. If contours are correct, watershed boundaries can be determined by location of maximum elevation points. Water will always flow perpendicular to the contour lines (downhill) unless the contours are not representative of developed conditions. In natural areas, a stream can be identified by contours that bend upstream rather abruptly. For runoff studies, large depression storage areas should be located and not added to the contributing runoff area. If the depression storage areas are sufficiently pervious, then the infiltrated water can become part of the base flow of the drainage system.

Within the boundaries of the watershed, land use, and conduits (pipes, channels, rivers, streams) should be located and classified. Classifications are made in various ways to provide a base for the transfer of quantity and quality data from one watershed to another. Land uses are classified for runoff and pollution characteristics with common classifications being residential, commercial, industrial, woodland, etc.

6.2.2 Drainage System and Land Cover

Other watershed characteristics that affect hydrograph shapes and runoff volumes are details of the watershed soils and land cover. After initial abstraction, water flows over land to a natural or man-made drainage system. The conduit slope, hydraulic roughness, channel storage or length, impervious area, infiltration volume, and watershed shape affect the hydrograph shape from the watershed, known as the discharge hydrograph (Figure 6.6).

As shown in Figure 6.6, discharge hydrograph shapes and peak flow rates vary greatly from one location to another. The slope of the drainage affects the time it takes for water to flow to a discharge point. The greater the slope, the less the time of travel relative to a less steep slope. If the rainfall excess were the same for both slope conditions, the peak would occur at less time from the start of rainfall excess and be larger for steeper slope conditions. The same result would occur if the roughness of the transport system affected the travel

162

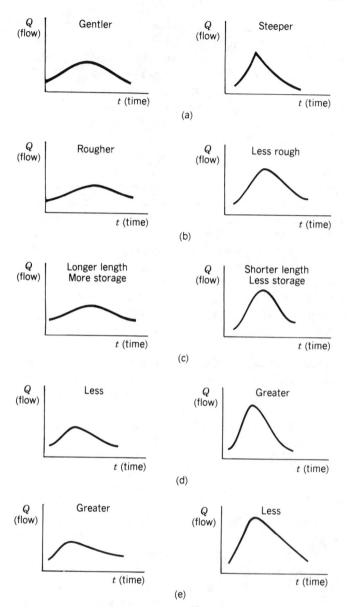

FIGURE 6.6   The effects of drainage characteristics on discharge hydrographs. (*a*) Slope. (*b*) Roughness. (*c*) Storage — length of time. (*d*) Directly connected impervious area. (*e*) Infiltration volume.

time. Watershed storage may result from natural depression areas, infiltration, and man-made storage. For similar rainfalls on watersheds of homogeneous (same) land use, the effect of storage on hydrograph shapes is shown in Figure 6.6c. The rising limbs of hydrographs for directly drained watersheds is steeper than that for watersheds with storage. For larger storage systems, the hydrograph starts well after the start of rainfall. The recession limb may be controlled partially by groundwater conditions, but if both watersheds have similar stream characteristics (bed depth, slope, area), the falling limbs will be similar. The area under the hydrographs (rainfall excess) will, however, be different, since the watershed with storage will produce a lower rainfall excess. Since infiltration can be considered watershed storage, hydrograph shapes should also reflect similar shapes as those for surface storage.

6.2.3 Area Storm Coverage

The area coverage of a storm on a watershed also affects the hydrograph shape. For a watershed with some directly connected impervious areas, a comparison of hydrograph shapes resulting from a localized storm and a storm over the entire watershed is shown in Figure 6.7. The location of the localized storm will affect the time of occurrence of the peak discharge. A rainfall near the outlet will result in a peak near the start of the storm and rapid passage of the streamflow. Rainfall in remote portions of the watershed will result in the runoff at the outlet being spread out over a longer time period. The peak will occur later in time and be lower than the peak resulting from localized rainfall near the outlet. Storm movement away from or towards a watershed also affects the time of occurrence of the peak discharge (Figure 6.8). Storms moving toward the gaging station generally produce a greater peak relative to movement in the opposite direction.

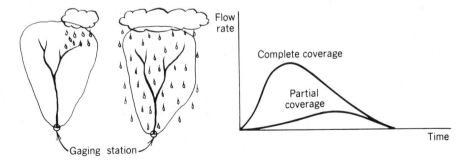

FIGURE 6.7 Area coverage effects on hydrographs.

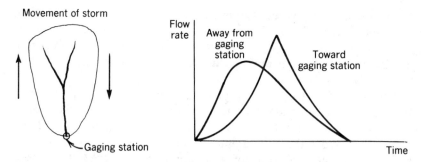

FIGURE 6.8 Storm direction effects on hydrographs.

6.2.4 Stream Order

To obtain a more accurate hydrograph shape, a watershed can be divided into individual streams and separate hydrographs computed for each. Then the separate hydrographs are routed using methods presented in Chapter 8. Stream order is a numbering system for the surface drainage segments which can assist in the identification of hydrographs. The smallest conduit or the only one for a watershed is designated order 1 (Figure 6.9). When two first-order conduits join, a conduit of order 2 is formed. Two conduits of the same order must join to increase the order of the new conduit. The order number is dimensionless; therefore, it is possible to compare corresponding order numbers from two dissimilar watersheds.

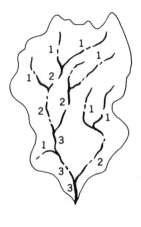
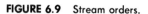
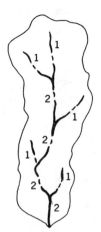

FIGURE 6.9 Stream orders.

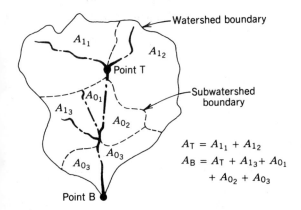

FIGURE 6.10 Subwatersheds.

The drainage area of a watershed or stream order will be that area contributing surface flow to the drainage conduit. The drainage area of a second-order basin consists of the sum of the drainage areas leading into the second-order conduit plus contributing areas (A_0) along the conduit. Figure 6.10 illustrates the areas and can be written as

$$A_u = \sum_{i=1}^{n} A_{1_i} + \cdots + \sum_{i=1}^{n} A_{i-1_i} + \sum_{i=1}^{n} A_{0_i} \qquad (6.1)$$

where

A_i = drainage area of the i stream order (km^2)
A_1 = drainage area of the stream order 1 (km^2)
A_0 = drainage area along the stream (km^2)
n = total number of contributary areas

Drainage area is used as input data in many mathematical models, and existing relationships to other hydrological data have been developed, for instance,

1. Drainage area versus order for a single large watershed:

$$\text{Log } A_u = KU \qquad (6.2)$$

where

A_u = watershed area (km^2)
K = proportionality constant (km^2)
U = stream order, dimensionless

2. Stream length versus watershed area for geographically similar areas:

$$L = k_1 A^{k_2} \tag{6.3}$$

where

L = conduit length (km)
A = watershed area (km^2)
k_1, k_2 = constants (consistent units)

3. Discharge versus watershed area for geographically similar areas:

$$Q = K_1 A^{K_2} \tag{6.4}$$

where

Q = discharge at specified return period (m^3/sec)
A = watershed area (km^2)
K_1, K_2 = constants (consistent units)

Empirical relationship three (Equation 6.4) can be found in basic hydrology texts. The exponent K_2 has been found to usually vary between 0.5 and 1.0 if discharge is expressed as ft^3/sec and drainage area as square miles.

The length of flow of a conduit can be scaled directly from development maps, from U.S. Geological Survey quadrangle sheets, or measured directly on the ground by field crews. The length of flow combined with slope, cross sections, and roughness characteristics of the conduit are used to determine velocities of flow, flow rates, depth of flow, and time of travel.

In general, a plot of slope vs. distance in a watershed will reveal higher gradients at the head of the watershed than at the end. Slope is a dimensionless number and is the vertical distance (drop) divided by the horizontal distance. In areas of steep slopes, erosion is higher than areas of flat slopes because velocity and discharges are higher.

6.3

MATHEMATICAL DESCRIPTION

One method of describing a hydrograph shape is to assume that watershed outflow rate is a linear function of storage. This method has been referred to as a single linear reservoir model (Pedersen et al., 1980). It appears to be appropriate for small watersheds and rainfall events of short duration.

6.3.1 Mathematical Description of the Rising Limb

For the rising limb of a hydrograph, a mathematical description can be developed using a mass balance equation with generation equal to zero:

$$\text{Input} - \text{output} \pm \text{generation} = \text{accumulation}$$

$$r - Q = dS/dt \tag{6.5}$$

where
r = rainfall excess rate (ft^3/sec)
Q = outflow rate (ft^3/sec)
S = storage for rainfall excess (ft^3)
t = time frame for analysis (sec)

Assuming an approximate linear relationship exists as shown in Figure 6.11 between outflow rate and storage

$$Q = KS \tag{6.6}$$

FIGURE 6.11   A linear storage relationship.

where
S = storage volume (ft^3)
K = storage coefficient (sec^{-1})
Q = outflow rate (ft^3/sec)

and in differential form:

$$dQ = K\,dS \tag{6.7}$$

Substituting for dS from Equation 6.7 into Equation 6.5 results in

$$r - Q = dQ/(K\,dt) \tag{6.8}$$

Integration of Equation 6.8 when $t = 0$ and $Q = 0$ results in

$$Q(t) = r(1 - e^{-Kt}) \tag{6.9}$$

Equation 6.9 is valid only for the rising limb of a hydrograph developed using a linear relationship between storage and outflow rate. As long as rainfall excess and stream flow data are available, the appropriate K (storage coefficient) can be estimated to "fit" the rising limb of the hydrograph. It is possible to use piecewise linear approximations of the storage–discharge relationship and thus have different K factors for different storage ranges, where K may vary with the watershed storage conditions. In this case, the runoff rate–storage relationship will be nonlinear and may be difficult to estimate. Other procedures for curve fitting including nonlinear responses are discussed in Chapter 9.

6.3.2 Hydrograph Groundwater Flow Separation (Recession Limb)

The recession limb of a streamflow hydrograph has been analyzed because it results from both surface runoff and groundwater flows. By subtracting groundwater flow rates from the stream hydrograph, an estimate of the runoff hydrograph and effective rainfall for the watershed and rainfall conditions is possible. Since groundwater flows are determined by both long-term and short-term groundwater storage, the groundwater portion of the recession limb is most likely a combination of groundwater flows resulting from many previous rainfall events.

Since both surface and groundwater flows will be directly related to surface and groundwater storage, assume the following differential relationship:

$$dQ = K' \, dS \qquad (6.10)$$

where

S = storage volume (L^3)

K' = storage coefficient, most likely a composite of 2 or 3 coefficients (t^{-1})

Q = outflow rate (L^3/t)

The mass balance with input equal to zero and no generation is

$$\text{Input} - \text{output} \pm \text{generation} = \text{accumulation}$$

$$Q = dS/dt \qquad (6.11)$$

Substituting for dS from Equation 6.10 into 6.11 and integrating with $Q = Q_p$ at $t_r = t - t_p$, where t_r is time from the peak (recession time), t_p is the time to peak, t is the time from start of rainfall excess, and Q_p is peak flow rate, yielding

$$Q_{t_r} = Q_p e^{-K' t_r} \qquad (6.12)$$

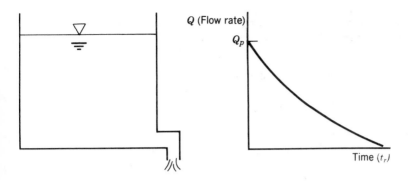

FIGURE 6.12   The recession curve analogy to a storage tank.

Equation 6.12 is analogous to a storage tank (watershed) losing its water at an exponential rate as shown in Figure 6.12.

The storage coefficient (recession coefficient) is rarely constant over the entire recession curve. Groundwater flows into a stream depend on the soil types at different locations. Still other flows depend on the elevation relationship (head) of the groundwater table to the stream surface over a very long period of time (base flow). Thus, it is more accurate to represent the recession curve by a composite exponential, or

$$Q = Q_i e^{-K_i' t_r} \tag{6.13}$$

where

Q_i = intercept for any segment "i" at $t_r = 0$ (cfs)
K_i' = slope for any segment i (1/time) (storage coefficient)

The Q_i's are the flow rate coefficients. Both the flow rate and storage coefficients can be estimated knowing the exponential form of Equations 6.12 and 6.13. Thus, by plotting the logarithm values of Q/Q_p versus time, lines of constant slope can be determined that result in estimates of the storage coefficients and the flow rate coefficients. This estimation procedure, which yields storage coefficients, inflection points, and estimates of base flow, is called the logarithm recession method.

☐   **EXAMPLE PROBLEM 6.1**

Estimate equations for the recession limb based on the following streamflow data. Assume that there are three types of flow that affect the recession limb: surface runoff, interflow, and base flow. The peak discharge occurred at 12:00 noon and was 200 cfs.

t_r (hr)	FLOW (cfs)	t_r (hr)	FLOW (cfs)
0 (noon)	200	10	20
1	142	11	19
2	96	12	18
3	60	13	17
4	42	14	16.5
5	35	15	16
6	31	16	15
7	28	17	14.5
8	25	18	14
9	22		

Solution

The data are plotted as shown in Figure 6.13 following the form of Equation 6.13. Thus the data plotted are

t_r	Q/Q_p	t_r	Q/Q_p
0	1.00	10	0.10
1	0.71	11	0.095
2	0.48	12	0.90
3	0.30	13	0.085
4	0.21	14	0.083
5	0.18	15	0.08
6	0.155	16	0.075
7	0.14	17	0.073
8	0.125	18	0.07
9	0.11		

The storage coefficients are the slopes from Figure 6.13. Note that the direct calculation yields a coefficient to the base "10," thus to convert to the base e logarithm, one must multiply by 2.3. The estimate of the slope is simplified if one considers a complete log cycle for the change in ordinate value; thus, each slope is calculated using

$$K' = [\log(1) - \log(0.1)]/\Delta t_r$$

or

$$K' = 1/\Delta t_r \qquad \text{base 10} \qquad (6.14)$$

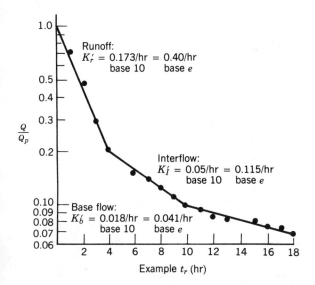

Runoff:
$K_r' = 0.173$/hr $= 0.40$/hr
base 10   base e

Interflow:
$K_i' = 0.05$/hr $= 0.115$/hr
base 10   base e

Base flow:
$K_b' = 0.018$/hr $= 0.041$/hr
base 10   base e

Example t_r (hr)

FIGURE 6.13   Example Problem 6.1, recession curves.

For a slope change (in this case $t_r \geq 10$ hr), the base flow rate coefficient is estimated from Figure 6.13 using the intercept of the exponential lines where the intercept ($t_r = 0$), which is 0.155.

$$Q_b = 0.155(200) = 31 \text{ cfs}$$

For $10 > t_r > 4$ hr, the interflow rate coefficient is

$$Q_I = 0.32(200) = 64 \text{ cfs}$$

The final equation forms are:

$$t_r \geq 10 \text{ hr} \qquad Q = 31e^{-0.041t_r}$$

$$4 \text{ hr} \leq t_r < 10 \text{ hr} \qquad Q = 64e^{-0.155t_r}$$

$$0 \leq t_r < 4 \text{ hr} \qquad Q = 200e^{-0.40t_r}$$

To illustrate the final curve fit by the equations for the original data, see Figure 6.14.   □

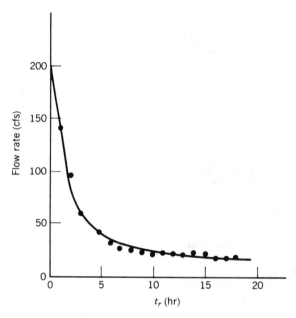

Selected Comparisons

t_r	STREAM FLOW	EQUATIONS
0	200	200
3	40	60
5	35	36
10	20	21
18	14	15

FIGURE 6.14   Example Problem 6.1, a hydrograph and equation comparison. The · denotes field data; the - denotes equation form.

Other methods for separating base flows from stream hydrographs exist. The fixed time method assumes that surface runoff always ends after a fixed time interval.

$$\tau = (DA)^n \tag{6.15}$$

where

τ = time from the peak to the end of the runoff hydrograph (days)

DA = drainage area (square miles)

n = recession constant

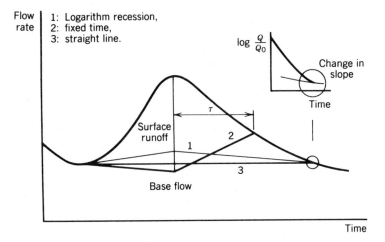

FIGURE 6.15 Base flow separation techniques.

Frequently the recession constant has a value of about 0.2 but must be derived for a particular location. The derivation is frequently dependent on the inflection point from a semilogarithm point of flows. The straight line and logarithm method also depend on inflection points. A comparison of methods is shown in Figure 6.15. The logarithm recession method is based on theory and is preferred. However the straight line and fixed time methods require less calculations and should be used when validated for a region. Other base flow separation methods illustrate reasonable separation but no standard procedures exist.

6.4

UNIT HYDROGRAPH FROM STREAMFLOW DATA

The area under the hydrograph represents the volume of runoff from a watershed. The area under a unit hydrograph represents the volume of runoff equivalent to a unit depth (1 in.) over the entire watershed. It is a description of the many watershed characteristics that affect the runoff process. The shape of the unit hydrograph expresses a set of characteristics of the land and soil that are assumed to be repeated for similar duration storms. If the duration changes, the time base of the hydrograph changes.

The method for determining unit hydrographs from streamflow data evolved from the work of Sherman (1932). Others (Clark, 1945) expanded on this work. It was originally assumed that the rainfall excess occurs over a fixed hydrograph time base, and consequently, for a given watershed, the hydrograph shape, time to peak, and recession time were constant. For a specific watershed, the unit hydrograph resulting from a given quantity of rainfall excess can be used to generate another hydrograph from a different quantity of rainfall excess if the storm durations are the same. For longer storm durations, the rainfall excess can be divided into smaller time periods, each of duration equal to that used for the unit hydrograph. This assumes that the unit hydrograph does not change with watershed conditions. If the soil becomes saturated or channel velocities increase with increasing cumulative rainfall excess, the shape of the unit hydrograph may change.

A unit hydrograph may be derived from streamflow data or by assuming a specific shape based on watershed conditions. Using streamflow records, the base flow (and other groundwater flows, if present) are subtracted from the streamflow. The resulting hydrograph is the runoff hydrograph. Thus, the hydrograph for the watershed can be specified. Next, the area under the hydrograph (rainfall excess) is calculated. The rainfall excess is in cubic feet if the streamflow is measured in cubic feet per second and the base of the hydrograph is converted to seconds. The volume of runoff is divided by the

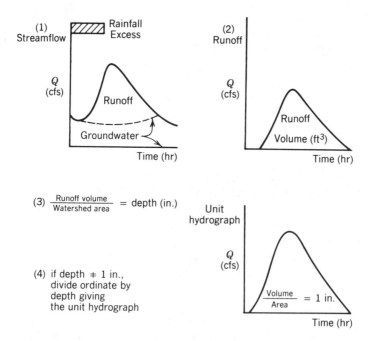

FIGURE 6.16 The steps for calculating a unit hydrograph.

watershed area obtaining a depth of rainfall excess. Frequently, it is called runoff depth. Since the duration of rainfall excess has been assumed to be constant and the base of the hydrograph is constant, the volume of runoff resulting from various rainfall excesses is proportional to the corresponding discharge (ordinate) values. Thus, the proportionality factor of a given runoff depth to the unit hydrograph runoff depth (1 in.) can be used to convert discharge values in any hydrograph to those resulting from a unit hydrograph. Steps for the calculation procedure are illustrated in Figure 6.16.

The following guidelines should be considered for developing the unit hydrograph if the procedures of Figure 6.16 are followed:

1. Independence in storm event and streamflow (one runoff event does not affect another).
2. For most situations, direct runoff should be greater than one-half inch (this improves the accuracy of the unit hydrograph).
3. Record many storms and average the ordinate values.

Since the assumption that two storms would have the same duration and area distribution is rarely true, there arose a need to improve and generalize the unit hydrograph method. Early studies (Clark, 1945) introduced the concept of instantaneous unit graphs: that rainfall intensities of short duration (minutes) produce instantaneous hydrographs. In the lagging procedure (Morgan and Hullinhors, 1939), each of these instantaneous hydrographs is added to produce a final hydrograph. Hydrographs from long duration storms are assumed to consist of several instantaneous unit hydrographs. For example, a 2-hr unit hydrograph is created from two 1-hr unit hydrographs, and two 4-hr

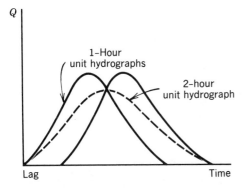

FIGURE 6.17 The example lagging procedure.

unit hydrographs form an 8-hr hydrograph, and so on. Also, a combination unit hydrograph can be formed by adding the ordinates of the two smaller duration storms and then dividing by 2 (see Figure 6.17). Note that the lagging procedure uses storms of equal duration.

6.4.1 A Convolution Computation Procedure Using Discrete Time Data

Rarely is there a constant rainfall excess over a single time increment. Usually, the rainfall excess varies with time. Consider a unit hydrograph method that divides a rainfall into successive shorter time events, each of constant rainfall excess and equal times. Each rainfall excess value is multiplied by the unit hydrograph to obtain the resulting ordinate values displaced in time by the start of each rainfall excess. This multiplication is defined in mathematical terms as a convolution. Then, the total runoff hydrograph is the superposition of each hydrograph as initiated by its rainfall excess.

The basic premise of the unit hydrograph method is that the individual hydrographs obtained by multiplying the ordinates of the unit hydrograph by the various successive rainfall excess increments, when properly arranged with

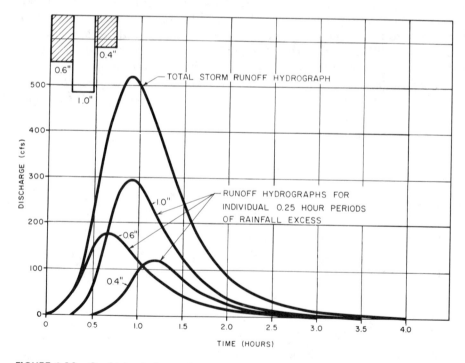

FIGURE 6.18 Combining hydrographs.

respect to time, can be added to give the total runoff hydrograph. Examine Figure 6.18, which illustrates a design hydrograph resulting from three successive 15-min rainfall excess increments (0.6, 1.0, and 0.4 in.). First, the individual hydrographs of runoff from each rainfall excess increment were computed by multiplying the ordinates of the 15-min unit hydrograph by the respective rainfall excess increment and plotted as shown in Figure 6.18. Note that each of the individual hydrographs start at the same time as the incremental rainfall excess producing it. The total storm runoff (design) hydrograph is then obtained by adding the ordinates of each of the individual incremental hydrographs. This procedure is very analogous to the influence line procedure in structural analysis, and the unit hydrograph could be considered as sort of an influence line of the contributary drainage watersheds. One should immediately recognize that the above procedure of computing the resulting, individual incremental hydrographs and then summing the ordinates is very time consuming and somewhat inaccurate if there are many rainfall excess increments involved. For example, if there are 15-min increments of a 6-hr rainfall, one may have to compute and add up the ordinates of as many as 24 individual hydrographs, each displaced by 15 min.

However, there is a relatively quick procedure, developed by the U.S. Bureau of Reclamation (BR) (1952), for applying rainfall excess increments to a unit hydrograph that can be used to compute the design hydrograph by the unit hydrograph method. This procedure is easily adopted to computation by a pocket calculator with a memory.

☐ ***EXAMPLE PROBLEM 6.2***
_____

Develop a composite hydrograph using the rainfall excess from a 25-yr, 6-hr rainfall.

Solution

The first step is to compute a unit hydrograph for the particular watershed. The ordinate values of the unit hydrograph are for an actual watershed and are shown in Table 6.1, column 2. To compute a 25-yr frequency design hydrograph, one applies to this unit hydrograph the rainfall excess increments resulting from a 25-yr frequency, 6-hr design rainfall. There are 23 increments of rainfall excess. Theoretically, no rainfall excess occurs during the first 15 min and very little up to hour 1.0, such that, for all practical purposes, rainfall prior to hour 1.0 can be ignored.

To demonstrate the BR procedure for applying these 20 rainfall excess increments to the unit hydrograph set up a standard form (Table 6.1). In the first column is the time in successive 0.25-hr increments. Second, write the rainfall excess increments in reverse order on a smaller piece of paper,

TABLE 6.1 Computation of Composite Flood Hydrographs (BR Procedure) Initial Matrix

MADE BY	DATE	JOB NO
CHECKED BY	DATE	SHEET NO

RAINFALL EXCESS
IN REVERSE ORDER

25-YR FREQUENCY — 6-HR DESIGN RAINFALL

OCP PHASE 6 — DRAINAGE BASIN (270.6 AC.), $CN = 95$

Rainfall excess in reverse order: 0.23, 0.23, 0.29, 0.29, 1.12, 1.03, 0.28, 0.20, 0.15, 0.13

TIME (hr)	ORDINATES OF 15-MINUTE UNIT U (ft³/sec)		DESIGN FLOOD HYDROGRAPH (ft³/sec)	TIME (hr)	ORDINATES OF 15-MINUTE UNIT U (ft³/sec)	RAINFALL-EXCESS (in.)	DESIGN FLOOD HYDROGRAPH (ft³/sec)
0	0	x 0.13 =	0	8.00			
0.25	68			8.25			
0.50	246			8.50			
0.75	293			8.75			
1.00	202			9.00			
1.25	121			9.25			
1.50	72			9.50			
1.75	41			9.75			
2.00	26			10.00			
2.25	15			10.25			
2.50	9			10.50			
2.75	6			10.75			
3.00	3			11.00			
3.25	1			11.25			
3.50	0			11.50			
3.75				11.75			
4.00				12.00			
4.25				12.25			
4.50				12.50			
4.75				12.75			
5.00				13.00			
5.25				13.25			
5.50				13.50			
5.75				13.75			

TABLE 6.2 Computation of Composite Flood Hydrographs (BR Procedure) First Calculation

		0.18				
		0.23		MADE BY	DATE	JOB NO
				CHECKED BY	DATE	SHEET NO
RAINFALL EXCESS		0.23	25-YR FREQUENCY — 6-HR DESIGN RAINFALL			
IN REVERSE ORDER		0.29	OCP PHASE 6 — DRAINAGE BASIN (270.6 AC.), $CN = 95$			
		0.29				
		1.12				

TIME (hr)	ORDINATES OF 15-MINUTE UNIT U (ft³/sec)			DESIGN FLOOD HYDROGRAPH (ft³/sec)	TIME (hr)	ORDINATES OF 15-MINUTE UNIT U (ft³/sec)	RAINFALL-EXCESS (in.)	DESIGN FLOOD HYDROGRAPH (ft³/sec)
		1.03						
		0.28						
		0.20						
0	0	x	0.15	= 0	8.00			
0.25	68	x	0.13	= 9	8.25			
0.50	246				8.50			
0.75	293				8.75			
1.00	202				9.00			
1.25	121				9.25			
1.50	72				9.50			
1.75	41				9.75			
2.00	26				10.00			
2.25	15				10.25			
2.50	9				10.50			
2.75	6				10.75			
3.00	3				11.00			
3.25	1				11.25			
3.50	0				11.50			
3.75					11.75			
4.00					12.00			
4.25					12.25			
4.50					12.50			
4.75					12.75			
5.00					13.00			
5.25					13.25			
5.50					13.50			
5.75					13.75			
6.00					14.00			

TABLE 6.3   Computation of Composite Flood Hydrographs (BR Procedure) Intermediate Calculatio

	MADE BY	DATE	JOB NO
	CHECKED BY	DATE	SHEET NO

RAINFALL EXCESS
IN REVERSE ORDER

0.15
0.18
0.23
0.23
0.29
0.29
1.12
1.03
0.28

25-YR FREQUENCY — 6-HR DESIGN RAINFALL

OCP PHASE 6 — DRAINAGE BASIN (270.6 AC.), $CN = 95$

TIME (hr)	ORDINATES OF 15-MINUTE UNIT U (ft^3/sec)		DESIGN FLOOD HYDROGRAPH (ft^3/sec)	TIME (hr)	ORDINATES OF 15-MINUTE UNIT U (ft^3/sec)	RAINFALL-EXCESS (in.)	DESIGN FLOOD HYDROGRAPH (ft^3/sec)
0	0	x 0.20	= 0	8.00			
0.25	68	x 0.15	= 9	8.25			
0.50	246	x 0.13	= 42	8.50			
0.75	293			8.75			
1.00	202			9.00			
1.25	121			9.25			
1.50	72			9.50			
1.75	41			9.75			
2.00	26			10.00			
2.25	15			10.25			
2.50	9			10.50			
2.75	6			10.75			
3.00	3			11.00			
3.25	1			11.25			
3.50	0			11.50			
3.75				11.75			
4.00				12.00			
4.25				12.25			
4.50				12.50			
4.75				12.75			
5.00				13.00			
5.25				13.25			
5.50				13.50			
5.75				13.75			
6.00				14.00			
6.25				14.25			

TABLE 6.4 Computation of Composite Flood Hydrographs (BR Procedure) Final Hydrograph

TIME (hr)	ORDINATES OF 15-MINUTE UNIT U (ft^3/sec)	RAINFALL-EXCESS (in.)	DESIGN FLOOD HYDROGRAPH (ft^3/sec)	TIME (hr)	ORDINATES OF 15-MINUTE UNIT U (ft^3/sec)	RAINFALL-EXCESS (in.)	DESIGN FLOOD HYDROGRAPH (ft^3/sec)
0	0		0				
0.25	68		9				
0.50	246		42				
0.75	293		89				
1.00	202		138				
1.25	121		244				
1.50	72		479				
1.75	41		694				
2.00	26		685				
2.25	15		557				
2.50	9		446				
2.75	6		365				
3.00	3		304				
3.25	1		256				
3.50	0		218				
3.75			189				
4.00			167				
4.25			152				
4.50			143				
4.75			138				
5.00			135				
5.25			126				
5.50			95				
5.75			60				
6.00			35				
6.25			21				
6.50			12				
6.75			7				
7.00			4				
7.25			2				
7.50			1				
			0				

place the smaller piece of paper at the top of the third column as shown in Table 6.1, and then start multiplying the unit hydrograph ordinates by the rainfall excess increments and summing up the total as you slide the small piece of paper down. Starting the small piece of paper (slide) on the first line, as shown on in Table 6.1, only multiply the first rainfall excess increment by 0, the first unit hydrograph ordinate. Moving the slide down an additional line, as shown in Table 6.2, multiply and sum up the first three lines as follows:

$$Q_1 = R_1U_1 = 0.13 \times 0 = 0$$

$$Q_2 = R_1U_2 + R_2U_1 = (0.13 \times 68) + (0.15 \times 0) = 9$$

which is the second value of the design hydrograph at time 0.25 hr. The slide is then moved down another line as shown in Table 6.3 with calculations as follows:

$$Q_3 = R_1U_3 + R_2U_2 + R_3U_1$$

$$Q_3 = (0.13 \times 246) + (0.15 \times 68) + (0.20 \times 0) = 42$$

with the result being placed in the third line of the design hydrograph (at time 0.50 hr). This process of summation and addition is continued until the computation of the design hydrograph is completed, as shown in Table 6.4. The design hydrograph as computed by this method is shown in Figure 6.19. □

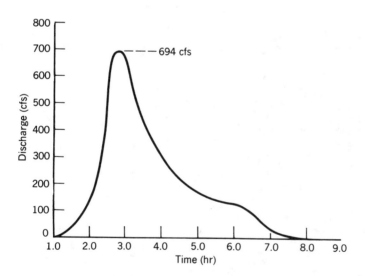

FIGURE 6.19 A design hydrograph, 25-yr frequency, 6-hr rainfall, unit hydrograph method.

The computation of a design hydrograph by the unit hydrograph method procedure requires much work if done manually. However, the various procedures outlined in this chapter can be programmed for computer or calculator computation. The unit hydrograph method has the advantage of acceptability in that it is universally understood and used in design. As previously mentioned, it does require a design rainfall with determination of rainfall excess and a unit hydrograph shape.

6.4.2   Matrix Procedure

A matrix is a set of numbers arranged in a rectangular array. From the calculations using the BR method, it was shown that a composite hydrograph is the result of multiplying rainfall excess by the unit hydrograph. It is a discrete convolution method. The rainfall excess is one rectangular array and the unit hydrograph is another. A streamflow record is always a combination of flows (composite) resulting from many rainfall events or increments of a single event; thus, one will rarely, if ever, have a hydrograph resulting from 1 in. of rainfall excess in one time increment. The challenge is to decompose a streamflow hydrograph into flows resulting from individual rainfall events and recognize that each of these flows results from a rainfall applied to the unit hydrograph. The unit hydrograph can then be identified using matrix methods. Thus, matrix and vector forms of the data are required.

Define the unit hydrograph as a vector of flows, that is, a column vector U, which has j unit hydrograph values. Also, define the rainfall excess R of i periods of time. Thus, the resulting hydrograph can be expressed in general matrix form as

$$Q = R \times U \qquad (6.16)$$

where

$$R = \begin{bmatrix} R_1 & 0 & 0 & \cdots & 0 \\ R_2 & R_1 & 0 & \cdots & 0 \\ R_3 & R_2 & R_1 & \cdots & 0 \\ R_i & R_{i-1} & & & R_1 \end{bmatrix} \qquad U = \begin{bmatrix} U_1 \\ U_2 \\ U_3 \\ U_j \end{bmatrix} \qquad Q = \begin{bmatrix} Q_1 \\ Q_2 \\ Q_3 \\ Q_k \end{bmatrix}$$

and the computations are expanded as

$$Q_1 = R_1 U_1$$

$$Q_2 = R_2 U_1 + R_1 U_2$$

$$Q_3 = R_3 U_1 + R_2 U_2 + R_1 U_3$$

etc.

where
the hydrograph has k values, $k = i + j - 1$
and i = number of rainfalls excess values
j = number of unit hydrograph values

6.4.3 Computation Procedure for Deriving a Unit Hydrograph

The most common streamflow hydrographs result from widely varying rainfall excesses. A constant rainfall excess usually cannot be assumed over the duration of the storm, and it is difficult to separate the streamflow hydrographs resulting from a particular rainfall excess. However, it is possible using matrix methods, to solve for the unit hydrograph. Rewriting Equation 6.16, one obtains

$$R^{-1} \times Q = R^{-1} \times R \times U$$

or

$$U = R^{-1} \times Q \tag{6.17}$$

Thus, knowing that the resulting streamflow (Q) vector and the rainfall excess inverse exists as a square matrix with a nonvanishing determinant, the unit hydrograph can be found. Since the rainfall excess is not a square matrix, a transformation must be done. Then the resulting equation is

$$R^{T} \times Q = R^{T} \times R \times U$$

and

$$U = \left(R^{T} \times R \right)^{-1} R^{T} \times Q \tag{6.18}$$

where R^{T} is the transpose of the matrix R. It is found by interchanging the rows for columns or in general notation:

$$R = \begin{bmatrix} R_1 & 0 \\ R_2 & R_1 \\ R_3 & R_2 \\ 0 & R_3 \end{bmatrix} \quad \text{and} \quad R^{T} = \begin{bmatrix} R_1 & R_2 & R_3 & 0 \\ 0 & R_1 & R_2 & R_3 \end{bmatrix}$$

☐ **EXAMPLE PROBLEM 6.3**

Derive a runoff hydrograph from streamflow data resulting from a storm of variable rainfall excess. Assume that the base flow record also is available. Runoff is not available.

Streamflow and Baseflow Data (cfs-hr)

TIME (hr)	EXCESS (in.)	STREAMFLOW (cfs)	BASEFLOW (cfs)	RUNOFF (cfs)
0	0	10	10	0
1	0.5	70	10	60
2	1.0	220	20	200
3	0	230	20	210
4	1.0	290	30	260
5	0	300	30	270
6		215	30	185
7		180	30	150
8		145	30	115
9		120	30	90
10		95	30	65
11		70	30	40
12		40	30	10
13		30	30	0

Solution

1. First calculate runoff as runoff = streamflow − baseflow.
2. Now arrange the values in a matrix form similar to Equation 6.16, or $Q = R \times U$ where $i = 4$, $k = 13$, and $j = k - i + 1 = 10$ nonzero values for the unit hydrograph.

Thus,

$$Q_1 = R_1 U_1$$

$$60 = 0.5(U_1) \quad \text{and} \quad U_1 = Q_1 R_1^{-1} = 60/0.5 = 120 \text{ cfs}$$

$$Q_2 = R_1 U_2 + R_2 U_1$$

$$200 = 0.5(U_2) + 1.0(120) \qquad\qquad U_2 = 160 \text{ cfs}$$

$$Q_3 = R_1 U_3 + R_2 U_2 + R_3 U_1$$

$$210 = 0.5(U_3) + 1.0(160) + 0.0(120) \qquad\qquad U_3 = 100 \text{ cfs}$$

$$Q_4 = R_1 U_4 + R_2 U_3 + R_3 U_2 + R_4 U_1$$

$$260 = 0.5(U_4) + 1.0(100) + 0.0(160) + 1.0(120) \qquad U_4 = 80 \text{ cfs}$$

$$Q_5 = R_1U_5 + R_2U_4 + R_3U_3 + R_4U_2 + R_5U_1$$

$$270 = 0.5(U_5) + 1.0(80) + 0.0(100) + 1.0(160) + 0.0(120)$$

$$U_5 = 60 \text{ cfs}$$

$$Q_6 = R_1U_6 + R_2U_5 + R_3U_4 + R_4U_3$$

$$185 = 0.5(U_6) + 1.0(60) + 0.0(80) + 1.0(100) \qquad U_6 = 50 \text{ cfs}$$

$$Q_7 = R_1U_7 + R_2U_6 + R_3U_5 + R_4U_4$$

$$150 = 0.5(U_7) + 1.0(50) + 0.0(60) + 1.0(80) \qquad U_7 = 40 \text{ cfs}$$

$$Q_8 = R_1U_8 + R_2U_7 + R_3U_6 + R_4U_5$$

$$115 = 0.5(U_8) + 1.0(40) + 0.0(50) + 1.0(60) \qquad U_8 = 30 \text{ cfs}$$

$$Q_9 = R_1U_9 + R_2U_8 + R_4U_6$$

$$90 = 0.5(U_9) + 1.0(30) + 1.0(50) \qquad U_9 = 20 \text{ cfs}$$

$$Q_{10} = R_1U_{10} + R_2U_9 + R_4U_7$$

$$65 = 0.5(U_{10}) + 1.0(20) + 1.0(40) \qquad U_{10} = 10 \text{ cfs}$$

$$Q_{11} = R_1U_{11} + R_2U_{10} + R_4U_8$$

$$40 = 0.5(U_{11}) + 1.0(10) + 1.0(30) \qquad U_{11} = 0 \text{ cfs}$$

Note that previous computed values are used in later computations therefore roundoff errors tend to build. Care must be used in the computations. □

6.5

CONVOLUTION WITH CONTINUOUS TIME FUNCTION FORM

Until this discussion, unit hydrograph generation procedures depended on using the same hydrograph shape and constant rainfall excess for equal time intervals. Now, using basic mass balances to develop a continuous functional form, rainfall excess and routing can be considered variable with time. In the analysis of streamflow data, three different situations can exist: (1) the streamflow hydrograph shapes do not change drastically with changing flows, thus the watershed acts as a linear time invariant system; (2) the streamflow hydrograph shapes change with time during a rainfall event; and (3) the past input elements of rainfall excess may affect the present hydrograph shape such that the sum of separate hydrographs do not directly add to form the total. The watershed then acts as a nonlinear time variant system. For situation 1, the synthetic hydrograph procedures of the next chapter are appropriate and are based on the concept of the unit hydrograph from this chapter. Situation 2 is solved by this convolution procedure which allows changing rainfall excess and routing functions over a continuous time interval. Situation 3 is not presented here.

In the historical development of unit hydrograph procedures, it was assumed that the watershed produces a series of rainfall excesses that can be multiplied by the same hydrograph shape and added together to form the final hydrograph. As long as the watershed continues to produce the same hydrograph shape, the unit hydrograph procedure is reasonable and acceptable. In watersheds that experience changing groundwater and surface storage conditions and whose drainage channels are such that velocities change drastically with flow rates, a given hydrograph shape will be valid only over a small range of rainfall excess values.

For example, consider a watershed with highly permeable soils, low water tables, and very little relief resulting in channels with low velocity gradients (similar to coastal regions). When rainfall occurs, infiltration will recharge the superficial water table causing it to rise. As rain continues, the ground will become saturated and runoff occurs at a higher intensity. At the beginning of rainfall, the hydrograph shape is relatively flat because it is primarily composed of groundwaters infiltrating into the drainage system. As the groundwater table rises towards the ground surface, the hydrograph shape will become steeper or flow rates will change faster with time. The change in flow rates appear gradually. Once the infiltrated waters enter a channel, velocities may change. Thus, the watershed storage conditions and drainage geometry can produce different hydrograph shapes.

Recall from unit hydrograph theory that the product of the unit hydrograph and rainfall excess is the estimate of the watershed hydrograph. Given any hydrograph shape and a rainfall excess, the product of the two results in a hydrograph for the given rainfall excess (watershed) and channel response (velocity of flow). Snyder et al. (1970) labeled the channel response or routing function as a state function because it describes the current translation state of the watershed drainage system. The rainfall excess is characteristic of the watershed soil and initial abstraction conditions, thus it is labeled as a characteristic function. A mathematical procedure which is basically the integration of the product of two functions is called convolution. The general form of the convolution integral is

$$Q_t = \int_0^t r(\tau) g(t - \tau) \, d\tau \qquad (6.19)$$

where

Q_t = hydrograph flow rate (ft^3/sec)

$r(\tau)$ = rainfall excess rate or characteristic function as a function of a time parameter (τ) for integration (ft^3/sec)

$g(t - \tau)$ = hydrograph or routing function offset in real time by τ

Convolution integrals can be solved by either discrete processes or by functional forms. Both methods are available for computer programming solution. The discrete forms allows one to specify any shape hydrograph without the necessity of a mathematical equation form, but fixed time intervals are used. The function forms however have the advantage of more efficient computer programming, variable time intervals, and numerical stability.

6.5.1   Convolution and Constant Rainfall Excess

A constant characteristic function represents a constant rate of rainfall excess. This is reasonable for short time periods and permits a detailed explanation of the convolution method including solution details. Rainfall excess that is constant over a time period can result from an impervious area with constant intensity rainfall. Thus, the characteristic function is a constant denoted by the parameter a. The state function will be assumed to be exponential because the exponential function can be used to estimate the shape of stream hydrographs. The resulting functional form derived from a mass balance (see Appendix G) results in the convolution form:

$$Q_t = \int_0^t a\left(ke^{-k(t-\tau)}\right) d\tau \qquad (6.20)$$

where

a = constant rainfall excess, flow rate units (ft^3/sec)

k = routing coefficient (1/t)

The value of the routing coefficient (k) will determine the particular form of the state (hydrograph routing) function and must be determined. Various forms are illustrated in Figure 6.20. The routing function reflects the drainage characteristics such as geometry, slope, channel transections, etc. The routing function with high recession $(0.5e^{-0.5t})$ reflects a rapidly responsive drainage watershed. A sluggish drainage watershed with an attenuated peak can be represented by a routing function with a low recession initially $(0.1e^{-0.1t})$. The choice of the routing function $(k$ value) and the characteristic function (a) determine the shape of the hydrograph.

Assuming end of rainfall occurs at time (D), the integration of Equation 6.20 produces

$$Q_t = a\left(1 - e^{-kt}\right) \qquad 0 \le t \le D \qquad (6.21)$$

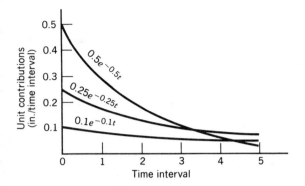

FIGURE 6.20 A routing function form.

and

$$Q_t = ae^{-kt}(e^{kD} - 1) \qquad t > D \tag{6.22}$$

There are two unknowns, a and k. However, from rainfall and streamflow data these unknowns can be determined. The peak is defined when time equals storm duration:

$$Q_p = a(1 - e^{-kD}) \tag{6.23}$$

Also, the area under the hydrograph must reflect the rainfall excess over the watershed, or

$$R = \int_0^D a(1 - e^{-kt})\, dt + \int_D^t ae^{-kt}(e^{kD} - 1)\, dt \tag{6.24}$$

with time in units of hours and k as per hour values, Equation 6.24 integrates to Equation 6.25 in units of cubic feet.

$$R = (60\ \text{s/m} \times 60\ \text{m/h})\left[aD + (a/k)e^{-kt}(1 - e^{kD})\right] \tag{6.25}$$

and if $t = \infty$, Equation 6.25 reduces to

$$R = 3600(aD) \tag{6.26}$$

where
a = peaking parameter (ft^3/sec)
D = duration of rainfall excess (hr)

Note that Equation 6.26 is the same result as will be shown by using the

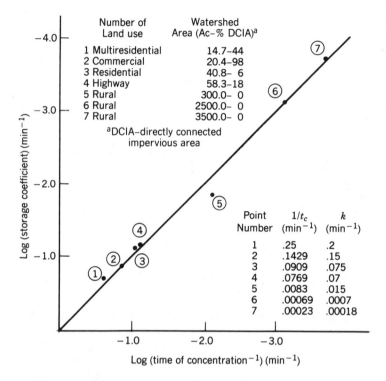

FIGURE 6.21   The relationship between the storage coefficient k and $1/$time of concentration for seven watersheds. The coefficient k was chosen as the one that best fits the runoff hydrograph whereas time of concentration was estimated from the watershed characteristics.

rational formula assumption of an isosceles triangle in Chapter 7. There results two equations and two unknowns: namely, a and k in Equation 6.23 and 6.25, and only one unknown in Equation 6.26: a.

The convolution parameters a and k generally have to be estimated from runoff or streamflow data by using a curve fit procedure. Curve fit procedures will be discussed in Chapter 9. However, in many situations, streamflow data are not available, and the parameters a and k are known from other sources. Also, the routing coefficient k is the inverse of the time it takes to drain the watershed—this relationship is shown in Figure 6.21. By knowing the time of concentration, the routing coefficient can be determined.

☐   *EXAMPLE PROBLEM 6.4*

Continuing with the above assumption of a constant rainfall excess and the hydrograph routing function shape assumed as an exponential, develop a hydrograph for a 10-acre area with a runoff coefficient of 0.5, and rainfall of 4 in. over 3 hr. The time to peak is assumed at 3 hr, which can be verified by stream measures.

Solution

The assumption of any hydrograph procedure can be used, but for simplicity, assume that the runoff given by Equation 3.5 is used:

$$Q_p = iCA(1.008) = 0.5(4/3)(10)(1.008) = 6.72 \text{ cfs}$$

and for rainfall excess (in cubic feet):

$$R = CPA \text{ (conversion factors)}$$

$$= 0.5(4 \text{ in.})(10 \text{ ac})(1/12 \text{ in./ft})(43,560 \text{ ft}^2/\text{ac})$$

$$= 72,600 \text{ ft}^3$$

First, solve Equations 6.23 and 6.25 by trial and error. Assume that $k = 0.50$ and solve for a from Equation 6.23, assuming peak discharge is 6.72 cfs.

$$a = Q_p/(1 - e^{-kD}) = 8.65 \text{ cfs}$$

Does Equation 6.25 have a value of 72,600 ft³? Solving for R with $t = 7$

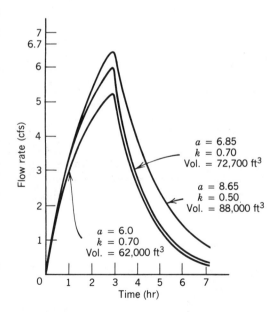

FIGURE 6.22 A hydrograph shape with rectangular rainfall excess. Note that 7 hr was considered the maximum hydrograph base time because of the small (10 ac) homogeneous area. Volumes were calculated over a 7-hr period by using Equation 6.25, and peak discharges were calculated by using Equation 6.23.

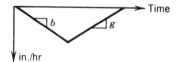

FIGURE 6.23   Rainfall excess.

hr and $D = 3$ hr yields $R = 88{,}000$ ft^3, thus the value is greater than 72,600 ft^3. The trial-and-error solution is very time consuming but, with the aid of a computer program and a reasonable hydrograph ending time, the equations can be solved, and the comparisons are shown in Figure 6.22. The rate of increase of the rising limb can be reduced if the contributing area was made a function of time. Thus, a more reasonable shape would result.   □

6.5.2   Convolution and Variable Rainfall Excess

A more reasonable distribution of rainfall excess is one that increases with time and decreases after the period of maximum rainfall intensity. Consider a straight line mathematical expression for the variable rainfall excess as shown in Figure 6.23. The equations for rainfall excess are

$$r(\tau) = d + b\tau \text{ for increasing excess}$$

and

$$r(\tau) = f - g\tau \text{ for decreasing excess} \tag{6.27}$$

the convolution integral for the increasing excess is

$$Q_t = k \int_0^t (d + b\tau) e^{-k(t-\tau)} \, d\tau \tag{6.28}$$

It is important to note that this equation is defined when rainfall excess starts. Thus, the function for different rainfall excesses may lag the other in time. The parameter (τ) is used rather than real "clock" time. Integration of Equation 6.28 by separation yields

$$Q_t = (d + b\tau)(1 - e^{-k\tau}) + \frac{b}{k}\big[(k\tau + 1)e^{-k\tau} - 1\big]$$

$$0 \le \tau \le D' \qquad \text{where } D' = \text{end of excess function} \tag{6.29}$$

and

$$Q_t = (d + b\tau)(e^{kD'} - 1)e^{-k\tau} + \frac{b}{k}\big[(k(\tau - D') + 1)e^{-k(\tau - D')} - (k\tau + 1)e^{-k\tau}\big]$$

$$\tau > D' \quad (6.30)$$

Note here that D' is defined as the end of the particular continuous rainfall excess function. If the rate of excess changes, a new function for rainfall excess has to be defined of length (D'). For decreasing excess, (f) is substituted for (d), and $(-g)$ is substituted for b. The equations are mathematically clear, but the constant k must be determined to "fit" the physical situation or streamflow data.

The use of a triangular shaped distribution of rainfall excess produces a more realistic hydrograph shape. The hydrograph is developed from the rainfall excess expressed in flow units. Conversion from inches per hour to a flow rate establishes an instantaneous rainfall excess in flow rate units (i.e., cfs).

☐ **EXAMPLE PROBLEM 6.5**
___

Determine the constants in the equations for rainfall excess assuming triangular shaped rainfall excess distributions. The watershed area is 10 ac, the runoff coefficient is 0.5, the storm duration is 3 hr, the rainfall excess is maximum (peaks) at $1\frac{1}{2}$ hr, and the total rainfall volume is 4 in. Also, draw the rainfall excess diagram in cfs units.

Solution

The triangular shaped rainfall excess equations are

$$\text{Increasing rainfall excess (in./hr): } d + bt \qquad 0 \le t \le \tfrac{3}{2}\,\text{hr}$$

$$\text{Falling rainfall excess (in./hr): } f - gt \qquad \tfrac{3}{2} < t \le 3\,\text{hr}$$

First, transpose time axis to use Equation 6.27:

$$d + b\tau \qquad 0 \le \tau \le \tfrac{3}{2}\,\text{hr}$$

$$f - g\tau \qquad 0 \le \tau \le \tfrac{3}{2}\,\text{hr}$$

The rainfall excess diagram is

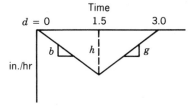

The volume of rainfall excess is $= 0.5(4) = 2$ in. Thus, the volume of the rainfall excess diagram is calculated by the area of a triangle; and the peak rainfall excess follows:

$$\text{Volume} = \text{in.} = \tfrac{1}{2}(b)(h) = \tfrac{1}{2}\,(\text{hr})(\text{in./hr})$$

$$2 \text{ in.} = \tfrac{1}{2}(3 \text{ hr})(h) \text{ or } h = \tfrac{4}{3} \text{ in./hr}$$

Determine the d and b coefficients for unit watershed area:

$$0 \le \tau \le \tfrac{3}{2} \qquad d + b\tau = 0 \qquad @ \qquad \tau = 0 \; d = 0$$

$$d + b\tau = \tfrac{4}{3} \qquad @ \qquad \tau = \tfrac{3}{2}$$

and $\qquad\qquad 0 + b\left(\tfrac{3}{2}\right) = \tfrac{4}{3} \qquad$ or $\qquad b = \tfrac{8}{9} \text{ in./hr}^2$

Determine the f and g coefficients for unit watershed area:

$$0 \le \tau \le \tfrac{3}{2} \qquad f - g(0) = \tfrac{4}{3} \qquad @ \qquad \tau = 0 \qquad \text{or} \qquad f = \tfrac{4}{3}$$

$$f - g\left(\tfrac{3}{2}\right) = 0 \qquad @ \qquad \tau = \tfrac{3}{2}$$

and $\qquad\qquad \tfrac{4}{3} - g\left(\tfrac{3}{2}\right) = 0 \qquad$ or $\qquad g = \tfrac{8}{9} \text{ in./hr}^2$

Now, translate the rainfall excess in units of inches/hour to units of cfs. For area in acres: (in./hr × acres × 1.008 = cfs):

Increasing excess $\left(0 + \tfrac{8}{9}\tau\right)10.08 = 0 + 9.0\tau$ (cfs) $\qquad 0 \le \tau \le \tfrac{3}{2}$

Falling excess $\qquad \left(\tfrac{4}{3} - \tfrac{8}{9}\tau\right)10.08 = 13.5 - 9.0\tau$ (cfs) $\qquad 0 \le \tau \le \tfrac{3}{2}$

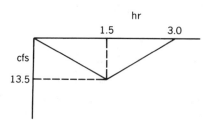

□

□   EXAMPLE PROBLEM 6.6

Assuming a hydrograph routing factor $k = 0.7$, and the rainfall excess of Example Problem 6.5, develop a graphical representation of the hydrograph. Compare the results by using a k of 0.5 and plot.

TABLE 6.5 Example Calculations — Example Problem 6.6

$k = 0.7$

t	τ	FIRST EXCESS $(0 + 9\tau)$		τ	SECOND EXCESS $(13.5 - 9\tau)$		TOTAL
		$\tau \le 3/2$	$\tau > 3/2$		$\tau \le 3/2$	$\tau > 3/2$	
0	0	0	0	—	0	0	0
1	1	2.53[a]	0	—	0	0	2.53
1.5	1.5	5.14	0	0	0	0	5.14
2.0	2.0	—	3.62[b]	0.5	3.28[a]	0	6.91
2.5	2.5	—	2.55	1.0	4.27	0	6.82
3.0	3.0	—	1.80	1.5	3.63	0	5.43
3.5	3.5	—	1.27	2.0	—	2.56[b]	3.83
4.0	4.0	—	0.89	2.5	—	1.80	2.69
5.0	5.0	—	0.44	3.5	—	0.90	1.34
6.0	6.0	—	0.22	4.5	—	0.45	0.67
7.0	7.0	—	0.11	5.5	—	0.22	0.33

[a] Use Equation 6.29.
[b] Use Equation 6.30.

$k = 0.5$

t	τ	FIRST EXCESS $(0 + 9\tau)$		τ	SECOND EXCESS $(13.5 - 9\tau)$		TOTAL
		$\tau \le 3/2$	$\tau > 3/2$		$\tau \le 3/2$	$\tau > 3/2$	
0	0	0	0	—	—	—	0
1.0	1.0	1.92	—	—	—	—	1.92
1.5	1.5	4.00	—	0	—	—	4.00
2.0	2.0	—	3.12	0.5	2.47	—	5.59
2.5	2.5	—	2.43	1.0	3.39	—	5.82
3.0	3.0	—	1.89	1.5	3.12	—	5.01
3.5	3.5	—	1.47	2.0	—	2.43	3.90
4.0	4.0	—	1.15	2.5	—	1.89	3.04
5.0	5.0	—	0.70	3.5	—	1.15	1.85
6.0	6.0	—	0.42	4.5	—	0.70	1.12
7.0	7.0	—	0.26	5.5	—	0.42	0.68

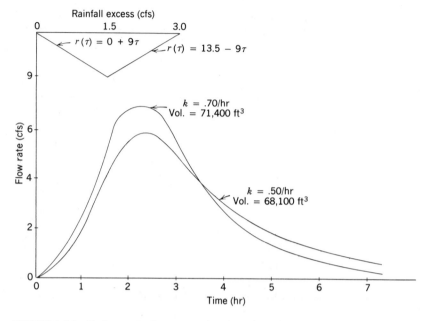

FIGURE 6.24   Hydrographs from triangular-shaped rainfall excess.

Solution

Calculations are done by using Equations 6.29 and 6.30. The results are shown in Table 6.5 and Figure 6.24.

☐   ***EXAMPLE PROBLEM 6.7***

The following rainfall excess is divided into five separated durations because the slope of the rainfall excess curve changes. It was developed from rainfall data and represents a typical rainfall hydrograph that has peak intensity near the middle of a storm. The rainfall excess also reflects a watershed with high initial storage.

TIME INTERVALS (hr)	RAINFALL EXCESS (cfs)	ROUTING COEFFICIENT k	COMMENTS
0–1	0		No excess
1–2	$0 + 8\tau$	0.3	Increasing
2–3	8	0.4	Constant excess
3–4	$8 - 2\tau$	0.5	Decreasing excess
4–5	$6 - 6\tau$	0.3	Decreasing excess

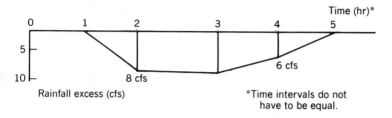

FIGURE 6.25 A rainfall excess diagram — Example Problem 6.7.

The rainfall excess diagram is shown in Figure 6.25:

Solution

Using the superposition of rainfall excess generated hydrographs and the convolution procedures for both constant and variable rainfall excess, Table 6.6 and Figure 6.26 are developed.

TABLE 6.6 Example Problem 6.7: Hydrograph Tabulation

EXCESS: t	$0 + 8\tau$ $k = 0.3$	8τ $k = 0.4$	$8 - 2\tau$ $k = 0.5$	$6 - 6\tau$ $k = 0.3$	TOTAL (cfs)
1	0	0	0	0	0
2	1.178[a]	0	0	0	1.178
3	0.8064[b]	2.64[c]	0	0	3.446
4	0.597	1.77[d]	2.722	0	5.089
5	0.443	1.185	1.651	0.739	4.018
6	0.328	0.794	1.001	0.547	2.6754
7	0.243	0.532	0.607	0.405	1.787
8	0.170	0.357	0.368	0.300	1.205
9	0.133	0.239	0.223	0.223	0.818
10	0.099	0.160	0.135	0.165	0.559

Example Calculations:

[a] $Q_2 = [0 + 8(1)](1 - e^{-0.3(1)}) + (8/0.3)[(0.3(1) + 1)e^{-0.3(1)} - 1]$ using (6.29)

[b] $Q_3 = [0 + 8(2)](e^{(0.3)1} - 1)e^{-0.3(2)} + (8/0.3)[(0.3(1) + 1)e^{-0.3(1)} - (0.3(2) + 1)e^{-0.3(2)}]$ (6.30)

[c] $Q_3 = 8(1 - e^{-0.4(1)})$ (6.21)

[d] $Q_4 = 8(e^{0.4(1)} - 1)e^{-0.4(2)}$ (6.22)

□

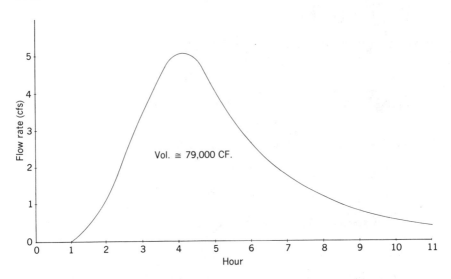

FIGURE 6.26   Example Problem 6.7, hydrograph.

6.6

SUMMARY

A hydrograph is a presentation of the time variable nature of flow rates. Usually the presentation is in graphical form. Streamflow is a combination of surface flow rates (runoff) and groundwater flow rates. The primary material of this chapter relates to a streamflow hydrograph and mathematical descriptions of hydrographs. The primary emphasis of Chapter 7 is on synthetic runoff hydrographs.

- Watershed characteristics are important for the determination of hydrograph shapes.
- A streamflow hydrograph can be composed of both surface runoff and groundwater infiltrating into a stream.
- Streamflow hydrograph analysis on a yearly basis is helpful in determining the type and yield of a stream.
- A linear model for the rising limb of a hydrograph was developed. It resulted in Equation 6.9. Its development assumes a linear relationship among storage and flow rate. This is a reasonable assumption for a range of data for most streamflow hydrographs.
- Two commonly used methods for separating base flow from runoff in a streamflow hydrograph are fixed time and logarithm. The logarithm method and equations are presented and developed.

- The unit hydrograph is for one unit (inch or centimeter) or rainfall excess (runoff). Groundwater flow must be estimated and subtracted from streamflow to determine the runoff. The unit of rainfall excess is assumed to be spread out over the entire watershed.
- A computation procedure using rainfall excess and a unit hydrograph developed from streamflow data is presented to generate a composite hydrograph.
- Matrix methods also can be used to generate a composite hydrograph from a unit hydrograph and rainfall excess. Computer programs are available to do this.
- A unit hydrograph can be derived from a streamflow hydrograph using matrix methods.
- The mathematical equations for the general case of changing rainfall excess and hydrograph shapes were developed using a convolution procedure. Formulas were developed that can be used for any routing and rainfall excess condition.

6.7

PROBLEMS

1. Determine the following from the hydrograph of Figure 6.27: L, t_p, t_r, t_B, and the volume of rainfall excess in cubic feet.
2. Comment on the peak discharge and rainfall excess changes resulting from the same volume and intensity of rainfall after converting a land

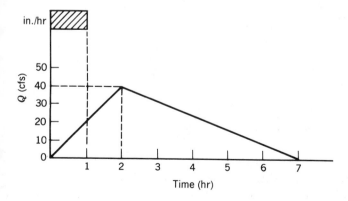

FIGURE 6.27 The hydrograph for Problem 1.

from:
a. Pervious to impervious
b. Directly drained (hydraulic connection) to indirectly drained
c. A high-water-table sandy soil to a low-water-table sandy soil
d. No surface storage to surface storage through which runoff waters must travel

3. Derive Equation 6.9 from Equation 6.5 and Equation 6.12 from Equation 6.11.

4. Given the following recession limb of a streamflow hydrograph, develop the recession equations for flow rate.

TIME (hr)	FLOW (cfs)	TIME (hr)	FLOW (cfs)
0	300 (peak)	6	30
1	208	7	28
2	144	8	26
3	91	10	24
4	63	14	20
5	45		

5. Pick any streamflow record and separate the base flow using the straight line and fixed time methods if τ in the fixed time method is equal to $1.5T_p$.

6. Consider the following runoff hydrograph. If the watershed area is 100 acres, what is the rainfall excess expressed in inches under the runoff hydrograph?

TIME (hr)	RUNOFF (cfs)	TIME (hr)	RUNOFF (cfs)
0	0	6	45
1	70	7	30
2	160	8	20
3	110	9	12
4	80	10	5
5	60	11	0

7. Develop a unit hydrograph for Problem 6. Also plot the results.

8. What size (acres) of watershed produced the following unit hydrograph? The flow rates are average hourly data. What is precipitation volume if the runoff coefficient were .5?

TIME (hr)	RUNOFF (cfs)
0	0
1	90
2	50
3	30
4	20
5	10
6	0

9. Given the unit runoff hydrograph of Problem 8, develop a composite runoff hydrograph given the following rainfall excess values. Set up the problem and complete it as if you were using the matrix method.

TIME (hr)	R (in.)
1	0.2
2	1.0
3	0.5

10. Assume that the surface runoff hydrograph of Figure 6.1(b) is a unit hydrograph resulting from a 5-hr storm event. The peak discharge occurs at hour 9 and is 910 cfs. A 10-h storm event is divided into two equal time intervals with 0.5 in. of rainfall excess in the first 5 hr and 1.0 in. of rainfall excess in the next 5 hr. What is the discharge at hours 9 and 14, assuming the unit hydrograph can be used?

11. Compute a design hydrograph resulting from the following rainfall excess increments using the following unit hydrograph, which is in 0.25-hr increments: 70, 182, 137, 68, 33, 16, 9, 5, 2, 1, 0 cfs @ 2.75 hr.

Time (hr)	0.25	0.50	0.75
Rainfall excess increment (in.)	0.50	1.25	0.75

12. For the convolution procedure and assuming a constant rainfall excess, derive Equation 6.21 from equation 6.20 (show all work).

13. Assume that rainfall excess for an 8-hr rainfall on a 40-ac watershed can be represented by a first rainfall excess,

$$r(t) = 0 + 25t \qquad 0 \le t \le 4 \, \text{hr}$$

and the next excess $r(t) = 100 - 25t \quad 4 \leq t \leq 8$ hr

where $r(t)$ = rainfall excess in cfs. Develop the hydrograph assuming that the routing factor is 0.25. *Hint*: Convert real time t to τ such that $r(\tau) = 100 - 25\tau$ between 4 and 8 hr real time.

14. For Problem 13, what is the runoff coefficient if the total rainfall volume used for design were 10 inches?

TABLE 6.7 Data Sheet for Watershed 2: Unit Hydrograph Determination

UPSTREAM NODE/ DOWNSTREAM NODE	SURFACE TYPE (RATIONAL C)	TOTAL CONTRIBUTING AREA (ac)	EFFECTIVE CONTRIBUTING AREA (ac)	TIME OF CONCENTRATION TO DOWNSTREAM NODE (min)	Σ T_c TO DOWNSTREAM NODE (min)
1/1	Residential (0.36)	7.9	2.84	6.1	6.1
2/1	Residential (0.36)	3.8	1.37	5.2	11.3
3/1	Residential (0.36)	4.2	1.51	5.2	11.3
5/1	Residential (0.36)	7.8	2.81	6.1	12.2
4/3	Residential (0.36)	2.1	0.76	5.2	16.5
6/5	Residential (0.36)	3.9	1.40	5.2	17.4
7/5	Commercial 50% Residential 50% (0.61)	4.3	2.60	5.2	17.4
9/5	Residential (0.36)	6.2	2.23	6.1	18.3
10/9	Residential (0.36)	2.0	0.72	4.2	22.5
8/7	Commercial (0.85)	5.4	4.59	5.2	22.6
11/9	Residential 20% Commercial 80% (0.75)	4.0	3.01	5.2	23.5
12/11	Commercial (0.85)	5.4	4.59	5.2	28.7
13/12	Commercial (0.85)	4.0	3.4	1.3	30.0

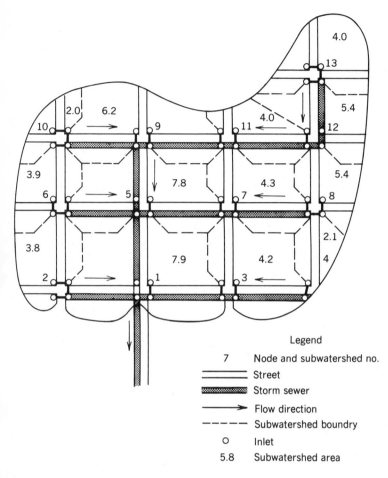

FIGURE 6.28 A plan view of watershed No. 2.

15. Do the detailed calculations for Example Problem 6.7. Change the rainfall excess and the routing coefficient in the first time interval to be a constant 2 cfs and 0.30, respectively, and in the second interval to $2 + 8(\tau)$. Compare results and comment on the peak as related to initial abstraction.

16. For the watershed of Table 6.7 and Figure 6.28 with a rainfall of 2 in./hr for 30 min and a discharge of 6 cfs at 2 hr, estimate the parameters using convolution (determine k and a).

17. For the following listing of a runoff hydrograph, determine an equation for the recession limb using an exponential decay function.

TIME (hr)	FLOW RATE (cfs)
6 (peak)	300
7	220
8	165
9	120
11	73
14	30
17	12

18. Obtain the stream flow rate data for one or more years and describe the type of stream it is.

6.8

COMPUTER-ASSISTED PROBLEMS

1. Using the matrix method computer program and the following data for rainfall excess and a unit hydrograph, develop a composite runoff hydrograph.

		UNIT HYDROGRAPH	
TIME (hr)	RAINFALL EXCESS (in.)	TIME (hr)	FLOW RATE (cfs)
0	0	0	0
0.25	0.13	0.25	68
0.50	0.15	0.50	246
0.75	0.20	0.75	293
1.00	0.28	1.00	202
1.25	1.03	1.25	121
1.50	1.12	1.50	72
1.75	0.29	1.75	41
2.00	0.29	2.00	26
2.25	0.23	2.25	15
2.50	0.23	2.50	9
2.75	0.18	2.75	6
3.00	0.15	3.00	3
3.25	0.15	3.25	1
3.50	0.12	3.50	0
3.75	0.12		
4.00	0.12		
4.25	0.12		
4.50	0.12		
4.75	0.12		
5.00	0.12		

2. Change the unit hydrograph shape to the following attenuated values and comment on the composite runoff hydrograph if the same rainfall excess were used.

TIME (hr)	ORDINATE (cfs)
0	0
0.25	68
0.50	200
0.75	250
1.00	240
1.25	172
1.50	72
1.75	41
2.00	26
2.25	15
2.50	9
2.75	6
3.00	3
3.25	1
3.50	0

3. If additional on-site retention by diversion of rainfall excess reduces the rainfall excess stated in Problem 1 to 0.00, 0.00, 0.00, 0.15, 1.03, 1.12, 0.29, 0.29, 0.23, and 0.23, what effect does this have on the peak discharge?

4. Using the regression program with the data of Problem 2, estimate the parameters for a straight line equation and a polynomial of degree 3. Comment and provide a graphic display of the results.

5. Using the continuous convolution program, develop a hydrograph (at 30-min increments) for the following situation.

Rainfall Conditions:

$$\text{Precipitation} = 2 \text{ in. in first hour}$$

$$= 3 \text{ in in second hour}$$

Watershed Conditions:

Time of concentration = 60 min
Drainage area = 100 ac

Shape of watershed is approximately triangular

% Impervious = 40

% of impervious directly drained = 75

SCS curve number for pervious area = 62

Routing coefficient = .5

6. For Problem 5, change the routing to ($k = .05$) and the time of concentration to 180 min, what is the hydrograph shape?

6.9

REFERENCES

Clark, C.O. 1945. "Storage and the Unit Hydrograph," *ASCE Transactions*, **110**, pp. 1419–1446.

Morgan, R. and Hullinhors, D.W. 1939. "Unit Hydrographs for Gauged and Ungauged Watersheds," U.S. Army Corps of Engineers, Engineers Office, Binghamton, NY.

Pedersen, J.T., Peters, J.C., and Helwey, O. 1980. "Hydrographs by Single Linear Reservoir Model," *Journal of the Hydraulics Division*, **HY5**, ASCE, New York, May, pp. 837–851.

Schulz, E.F. 1980. *Problems in Applied Hydrology*. Water Resources Publications, Fort Collins, CO, 5th Printing, pp. 280–286.

Sherman, L.K. 1932. "Stream-Flow from Rainfall by the Unit-Graph Method," *Engineering News Record*, **108**, April, pp. 501–505.

Snyder, W.M., Mills, W.C., and Stephens, J.C. 1970. "A Method of Derivation of Nonconstant Watershed Response Functions," *Water Resources Research*, **6**(1), February, pp. 261–274.

U.S. Bureau of Reclamation. 1952. Unitgraph Procedures, Division of Planning, Denver, CO.

....
....
....

7

SYNTHETIC
HYDROGRAPHS

A synthetic hydrograph is one developed with minimum use of streamflow data, a very common situation in practice. As an example, consider a pending land use change. Obviously, hydrographs must be synthesized for the anticipated postdevelopment conditions.

A runoff hydrograph is defined as an expression for surface water discharge over time. It is an expression of the watershed characteristics that invariably govern the relationship between rainfall and the resulting runoff. It represents the integrated effects of rainfall and watershed characteristics, such as area, shape, drainage patterns, land use, land and channel properties, land and drainage slopes, and the infiltration capacity of the soil. Thus, any synthetic hydrograph must be related to watershed and precipitation conditions. Some of the methods to achieve these relationships are presented in this chapter. The methods discussed are those in common use: rational, SCS hydrograph, unit-hydrograph, contributing area, Santa Barbara, and discrete unit-time hydrograph.

7.1

WATERSHED DATA

Before presenting various synthetic methods for estimating hydrograph peaks and shapes without streamflow data, a brief discussion of various watershed characteristics as affecting hydrograph shapes is beneficial. The following discussion assumes other factors are equal when discussing changes.

Area (A)	The total volume of runoff and peak discharge are proportional to the area of the watershed. As the area contributing to a point of discharge increases, the volume and peak increases. Also, the hydrograph base will increase with increasing area.
Overland Slope (S_1)	This is the average vertical elevation change per horizontal distance. In the general case, the time it takes water to get to a point of discharge is the sum of overland flow and channel (pipe) flow. In small watersheds, the time of overland flow may be an appreciable part of the total time. As watershed size increases, overland slope decreases in significance. The greater the overland flow time (less slope), the less the peak discharge.
Channel Slope (S_0)	The average vertical elevation change per horizontal distance along a watercourse bed. The steeper the channel slope, the greater the velocity and the peak discharge.
Channel Area (A_x)	The cross-sectional area has an effect on storage and thus attenuation of the hydrograph can be expected as storage increases. Attenuation is a term used to express a hydrograph shape with longer base time and less peak discharge.
Soil Type and Vegetation Cover	This affects the amount of rainfall excess and thus the peak of a hydrograph. The greater the initial abstraction and infiltration, the less the rainfall excess.
Basin Length (L)	The travel length associated with the longest time it takes for a particle of water to flow overland. The basin length and slope determines the watershed time of concentration.
Stream Pattern and Watershed Shapes	A fan-shaped area with streams radiating from the same point (similar to spokes of a wheel meeting

at the shaft) suggests contributing incremental areas increasing with time such that a late but high peak in the hydrograph is suggested, whereas an elongated area traversed by one major stream with some relatively uniformly spaced tributaries suggest a less pronounced rise and fall of the hydrograph.

Channel Roughness The lower the roughness, the higher the velocity and possibly the peak discharge.

Some of the above watershed characteristics have been used to directly or indirectly estimate the hydrograph shape and peak discharge. An example of an indirect use is in the calculation of travel time knowing watershed slope. Then the travel time is used in other equations to estimate hydrograph shape and peak discharge.

7.2

TIME OF CONCENTRATION

The time of concentration is the longest travel time it takes a particle of water to reach a discharge point in a watershed. There are three common ways that waters are transported: overland flow, pipe flow (storm sewer), and channel flow, including gutter flow. Each method has a separate formula for estimating time of concentration.

7.2.1 Izzard's Formula

The time of concentration for overland flow can be calculated using many different formulas. As the size of the watershed decreases, overland flow becomes dominant for the calculation of time of concentration. Izzard (1944) conducted experiments on pavements and turf. He developed a dimensionless hydrograph for surface flow laminar regions. When using Izzard's formula, well-defined channels should not be evident. The time of concentration is the same as time to equilibrium developed by Izzard and the maximum runoff value of flow is calculated by using

$$t_c = \frac{41KL^{1/3}}{i^{2/3}} \qquad \text{(for } i \times L < 500) \qquad (7.1)$$

where

t_c = time of concentration (min)
L = overland flow distance (ft)
i = rainfall intensity (in./hr)
$$K = \frac{0.007i + c_r}{s^{2/3}}$$

and

S = slope (ft/ft)
c_r = retardance coefficient, given as

Very smooth asphalt	0.007
Tar and sand pavement	0.0075
Crushed-slate roof	0.0082
Concrete	0.012
Tar and gravel pavement	0.017
Closely clipped sod	0.046
Dense bluegrass	0.060

7.2.2 Kerby's Equation

Kerby (1959) also developed an equation for overland flow:

$$t_c = c\left(Lns^{-0.5}\right)^{0.467} \qquad \text{for } L < 365 \text{ m (1000 ft)} \qquad (7.2)$$

where

t_c = time of concentration (min)
L = length of flow (ft) (generally less than 1000 feet)
s = slope (ft/ft)
c = 0.83 (when using feet) or 1.44 (when using meters)
n = retardance roughness coefficient

Smooth pavements	0.02
Poor grass, bare sod	0.30
Average grass	0.40
Dense grass	0.80

7.2.3 Kirpich's Equation

Kirpich (1940) developed an equation that can be used for rural areas to estimate t_c. The Kirpich equation (7.3) is based on data reported by Ramser

(1927) for six small agricultural watersheds near Jackson, Tennessee. The slope of these watersheds was steep with well-drained soils. Timber cover ranged from zero to 56%, and watershed areas ranged from 1.2 to 112 acres.

$$t_c = 0.0078(L^{0.77}/S^{0.385})\qquad(7.3)$$

where

t_c = time of concentration (min)
L = length of travel (ft)
S = slope (ft/ft)

7.2.4 Kinematic Wave

The kinematic wave equation (Ragan, 1971; Fleming, 1975) can be used to estimate time of concentration when there exists a kinematic wave (velocity not changing with distance but changing at a point). The time of concentration equation for these conditions is

$$t_c = \frac{0.93[L^{0.6}N^{0.6}]}{i^{0.4}S^{0.3}}\qquad(7.4)$$

where

t_c = time of concentration (min)
L = overland flow length (ft)
N = Manning's roughness coefficient for overland flow (see Table 7.1)
i = rainfall intensity (in./hr)
S = average slope of overland flow path (ft/ft)

The length of the overland flow segment generally should be limited to 300 ft. Manning's N values of Table 7.1 were determined specifically for overland flow conditions. Equation 7.4 generally involves a cumbersome trial and error process using the following steps.

1. Assume a trial value of rainfall intensity (i).
2. Find the overland travel time (t_c), using Equation 7.4.
3. Find the actual rainfall intensity for a storm duration of t_c from the appropriate intensity–duration–frequency (IDF) curve for your area. Also, record the intensity for t_c.
4. Compare rainfall intensities, if they are not the same, select a new trial rainfall intensity and repeat step 1.

An alternative way for evaluating overland flow using the kinematic wave

TABLE 7.1 Overland Flow Manning's N Values[a]

	RECOMMENDED VALUE	RANGE OF VALUES
Concrete	0.011	0.01–0.013
Asphalt	0.012	0.01–0.015
Bare sand	0.010	0.010–0.016
Graveled surface	0.012	0.012–0.030
Bare clay-loam (eroded)	0.012	0.012–0.033
Fallow (no residue)	0.05	0.006–0.16
Plow	0.06	0.02–0.10
Range (natural)	0.13	0.01–0.32
Range (clipped)	0.08	0.02–0.24
Grass (bluegrass sod)	0.45	0.39–0.63
Short grass praire	0.15	0.10–0.20
Dense grass	0.24	0.17–0.30
Bermuda grass	0.41	0.30–0.48
Woods	0.45	— —

Note: These values were determined specifically for overland flow conditions and are not appropriate for conventional open channel flow calculations.
[a]Values are from Engman (1983), with additions from the Florida Department of Transportation Drainage Manual (1986).

equation is to use a computer program that is included with this book. The computer program, entitled kinematic, will increase accuracy and save time.

7.2.5 Soil Conservation Service

The Soil Conservation Service (SCS) (USDA, 1975) used two techniques, which are essentially hydraulic wave equations. The simpler of the two estimation equations relates time of concentration to watershed lag, or

$$t_c = 1.67 t_L \qquad (7.5)$$

where

t_L = watershed lag time in hours (from the center of mass of rainfall excess to the time of peak runoff)

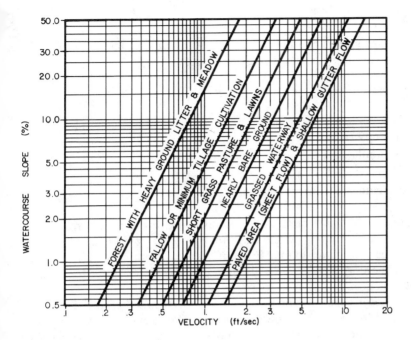

FIGURE 7.1 The average velocities for estimating travel time for overland flow (SCS method). (*Source*: SCS, 1975.)

and

$$t_L = L^{0.8} \frac{(S' + 1)^{0.7}}{1900 w_s^{0.5}} \tag{7.6}$$

where

L = watershed hydraulic length (ft)
S' = potential watershed storage (in.)
w_s = average watershed slope (percentage value)

Perhaps the most frequently used table to aid in calculating overflow velocities was presented by the Soil Conservation Service (SCS) (1975) and is reproduced as Figure 7.1. This alternate SCS method requires an estimate of overland slope and a description of the cover crop or land use. Thus, some engineering judgment must be exercised. Generally, estimates are made for each relatively constant slope area. Large areas of constantly varied slopes and ditches should be divided into smaller homogeneous areas with regard to slope and cover type.

7.2.6 Manning's Equation

In storm sewer gutters and open channels, Manning's equation (Chow, 1959) to calculate average velocities is frequently used:

$$v = (1.486/n)(R^{2/3})(S^{1/2}) \tag{7.7}$$

where

v = velocity (ft/sec)
R = hydraulic radius, ft = $D/4$ for pipes flowing full
S = slope (ft/ft)
n = roughness coefficient (see Table 5.3)

For gutters, an n value of 0.021 is recommended for a belted or broomed finish on a concrete pavement and 0.018 for a smooth, trowel-finished concrete gutter. A length of gutter to establish uniform flow depth may be in the order of 50 ft or more. Appendix F details additional calculation steps for computing time of concentration in storm sewer gutters.

The time of concentration is the longest travel time between a point on the watershed to the point of interest. The time of concentration will vary with the depth of rainfall excess in the watershed at any time. Deeper flows within a well-defined transport system (channel or pipe) will produce higher velocities and shorter times of concentration. Conversely, shallow flows will produce slower velocities and longer times of concentration. Very flat sloped lands have very shallow overland flow. Thus, the time of concentration will vary and produce different runoff hydrograph shapes. In some studies, it may be beneficial to spend extra time in developing these changing relationships with time. However, the more common way of generating hydrographs is to assume conditions which produce reasonable hydrograph shapes.

Other equations are also used. One such is that developed by Eagleson (1959) and includes the effects of conduit geometry, slope, and roughness. It relates to the general form of most equations for lag time, which is a function of travel distance (L), slope (S), pipe roughness, and hydraulic radius. Capice (1984) developed a regression equation for lag time in very flat large watersheds. The watershed areas were up to 3600 acres and include wetlands. Lag time was related to watershed area and percent wetlands. For other than very flat lands, a general equation was developed by the Soil Conservation Service, and related lag time to time of concentration using the following equation:

$$L = 0.6t_c \tag{7.8}$$

☐ **_EXAMPLE PROBLEM 7.1_**

Consider a watershed shown in Figure 7.2. Compute the time of concentration for the basin from points A through D.

Solution

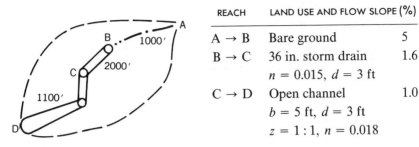

REACH	LAND USE AND FLOW SLOPE (%)	
A → B	Bare ground	5
B → C	36 in. storm drain	1.6
	$n = 0.015$, $d = 3$ ft	
C → D	Open channel	1.0
	$b = 5$ ft, $d = 3$ ft	
	$z = 1:1$, $n = 0.018$	

FIGURE 7.2 The example watershed for time of concentration.

From A → B

From Figure 7.1, $v = 2.2$ ft/sec,

$t_c = $ length/velocity $= 1000$ ft/2.2 ft/sec $= 455$ sec

From B → C

$v = (1.486/0.015)(3/4)^{2/3}(0.016)^{1/2} = 10$ ft/sec

(usually pipe flow velocity is between 3 and 10 feet/sec)

$t_c = $ length of B–C/velocity $= 2000$ ft/(10 ft)(sec) $= 200$ sec

From C → D

$v = (1.486/0.018)(1.78)^{2/3}(0.01)^{1/2} = 12.1$ ft/sec

$t_c = $ length of C–D/velocity $= 1100/12.1 = 91$ sec

Total $t_c = 455 + 200 + 91 = 746$ sec $\square$

The Manning equation is the most widely used to estimate velocity and time of concentration for sewer pipe, open channels, and gutters. Overland flow time of concentration requires more judgment and the comparison of results from a few equations. The time of concentration is an important description of a watershed because of its vital role in defining the shape of a runoff hydrograph.

7.3

RAINFALL EXCESS

Rainfall that produces the runoff hydrograph is represented by an estimate of rainfall excess. In hydrologic terminology, the hyetograph consists of two separate parts: the losses due to infiltration and initial abstraction, evapora-

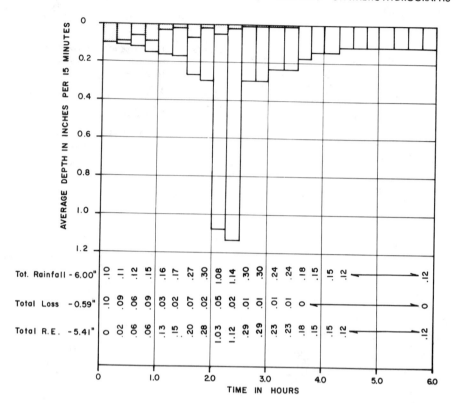

FIGURE 7.3   The hyetograph of 25-yr design rainfall curve No. 95. Note that rainfall excess values are adjusted to present a constantly increasing and then a decreasing rainfall excess. The actual computations produce no rainfall excess during the first hour.

tion, etc. and the rainfall excess that represents that portion of the rainfall that runs off (hence the term runoff) and produces the hydrograph. The ordinate of the hyetograph is in millimeters per hour or inches per hour and the abscissa has the same time scale as the hydrograph (see Figures 7.3 and 7.4). Thus, the rainfall excess hyetograph actually represents a volume of runoff; mm/hr × hr = mm over the watershed, which is a volume. If the drainage watershed is 5 km^2 in area, the volume of runoff from a rainfall excess of 30 mm is 150 km^2-mm, or 150,000 m^3, or 150 million liters. Rainfall excess can be expressed in units of depth over the watershed or in more familiar units of volume (cubic feet, cubic meters).

From a rainfall excess of 0.5 hr (30 min), the resultant hydrograph is referred to as a 30-min hydrograph, or a hydrograph resulting from a rainfall excess of 30-min duration. If the rainfall excess represents 1 in. of rainfall of 30-min duration, the resulting hydrograph is a 30-min unit hydrograph. A

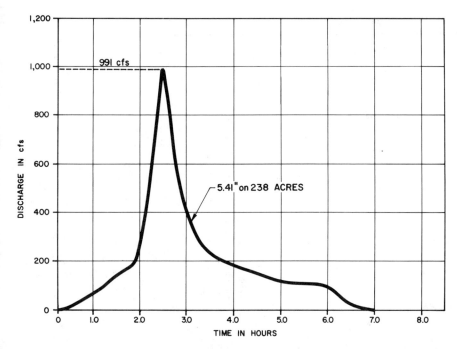

FIGURE 7.4 The 6-hr design storm hydrograph, curve No. 95.

hydrograph is always associated with the time duration of the rainfall excess producing it. The rainfall excess and the hydrograph must start at the same time. Also, note that the volume of rainfall excess must have the same volume as the area under the hydrograph—the area under the hydrograph represents the total volume of rainfall that fell on the watershed and appeared as runoff. Examining a hyetograph of a typical design rainfall (storm) shown on Figure 7.3, note that the rainfall excess does not start until hour 0.25, at which time the resulting hydrograph will start. This figure illustrates the rainfall excess as calculated by the SCS curve number or soil/cover complex method. A hydrograph of runoff from a particular watershed and rainfall hyetograph with the resulting rainfall excess shown on Figure 7.3 is given on Figure 7.4.

☐ _EXAMPLE PROBLEM 7.2_

What is the runoff in inches expressed by the runoff hydrograph of Figure 7.4?

Solution

The hydrograph represents the total volume of rainfall on that basin that appeared as discharge (rainfall excess). If one planimeters the area under

TABLE 7.2   Volumetric Calculations

TIME (hr:min)	AVERAGE (ft^3/sec)	(ft^3/sec/hr)	Σ (ft^3/sec/hr)	
0:15	0	0	0	
0:30	30	7.5	7.5	
0:45	45	11.3	18.8	
1:00	80	20.0	38.8	
1:15	90	22.5	61.3	
1:30	125	31.3	92.6	
1:45	160	40.0	132.6	
2:00	200	50.0	182.6	
2:15	310	77.5	260.1	
2:30	620	155.0	415.1	
2:45	900	225.0	640.1	
3:00	600	150.0	790.1	
3:15	260	65.0	855.1	
3:30	240	60.0	915.1	
3:45	220	55.0	970.1	
4:00	190	47.5	1017.6	
4:15	170	42.5	1060.1	
4:30	150	37.5	1097.6	
4:45	120	30.0	1127.6	
5:00	110	27.5	1155.1	
5:15	105	26.3	1181.4	
5:30	100	25.0	1206.4	
5:45	100	25.0	1231.4	
6:00	95	23.7	1255.1	
6:15	80	20.0	1275.1	
6:30	50	12.5	1287.6	
6:45	30	7.5	1295.1	
7:00	10	2.5	1297.6	call 1298

the hydrograph shown on Figure 7.4, which is a synthetic 15-yr hydrograph computed for a particular project, the volume of runoff from the watershed can be calculated. In this particular case, the volume amounted to 1298 ft^3/sec-hr. The calculations are illustrated in Table 7.2. If this value is divided by 12.1 (1 ac-ft/hr = 12.1 ft^3/sec), one can convert the volume to ac-ft (= 107.3 ac-ft). Dividing by the area of the basin in acres

(= 238 ac) and then multiplying by 12 in./ft, one can compute the rainfall excess in inches (= 5.41) that appeared as runoff from the contributory watershed area. □

7.4

RUNOFF HYDROGRAPHS AND WATERSHED SHAPES

Runoff hydrograph shapes resulting from a single storm event for different shaped watersheds are shown in Figure 7.5. The particular shape of the watershed and drainage patterns affect the shape of a hydrograph. The dotted lines on the watershed indicate the areas of constant time of concentration or isochrones. These areas are assumed to affect the hydrograph shape. The larger the area, the greater the rainfall excess and discharge rate. Also of importance is the amount of rainfall excess and the time it appears on the watershed. The comparisons shown in Figure 7.5 assume many of the other watershed hydrologic processes and meteorological processes are constant among the watersheds. These are rarely constant but can be assumed fixed for worst-case design conditions. As an example, rainfall volumes are fixed and related to worst-case volumes given a level of risk for which the design will protect against. Another example is the time of concentration. A shorter time of

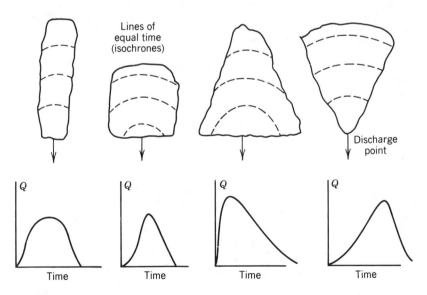

FIGURE 7.5 The possible time and area effects on runoff hydrograph shapes.

concentration is usually chosen if a worst-case (high) peak discharge must be assumed.

The shape of a runoff hydrograph can be estimated by assuming that the volume of rainfall excess for a period of time is directly proportional to the area contributing runoff during that particular time period. The area is effective in producing runoff, thus it is called effective area. The procedure assumes that the shape can be characterized by separable watersheds at various time periods and translation is proportional to the watershed areas.

The procedure requires that the watershed drainage system must be defined and the more accurately the system is defined, the more accurate the estimate of the time of concentration for each area. The physical descriptions of the watershed must include, at a minimum, the extent of the watershed area, tributary, and main stream locations (include sewer pipe and inlets); areas contributing to the inlets; and slopes from elevation changes. Cross sections for open channels, streams, rivers, and the like and pipe sizes with

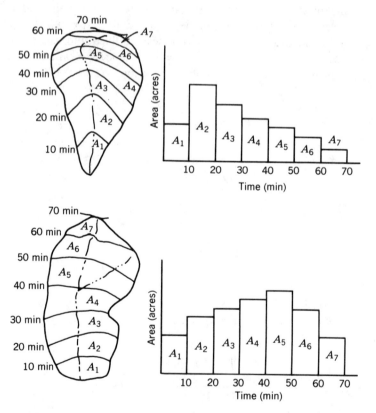

FIGURE 7.6 Area-time of concentration graphs. (Note that areas are effective areas.)

inverts are useful but not always required. When designing the drainage system, details on cross sections, slopes, and watershed areas are readily available and can be documented. The times of concentration calculated are based on more accurate data and can be computed for a number of alternate watershed configurations. Thus, area plots as related to time of concentration are relatively time consuming for the as-built land use conditions but are relatively easy for the design or planning conditions, which are frequently referred to as the postdevelopment conditions.

Isochrones, or lines of equal travel distance, are determined. The isochrones are defined so that at least seven areas are delineated. This will result in a histogram that indicates the shape of the hydrograph. In Figure 7.6 are illustrated two area-time shapes for two watersheds. The sizes of the areas (in acres) are calculated based on those areas which contribute runoff for a given rainfall (called effective areas). Thus, highly pervious areas (sandy soils) may not contribute runoff and would not be included in the area-time of concentration graphs. When rainfall intensities are multiplied by the effective areas, an instantaneous hydrograph results in standard units (acre-inch/hour $\times$ 1.008 = cubic feet/second).

7.5

PEAK DISCHARGE AND HYDROGRAPH SHAPE

There are at least four widely used methods for estimating peak discharge and hydrograph shapes: rational, SCS-hydrograph, Santa Barbara, and unit hydrograph. The rational method is one of the oldest and was originally used to only estimate the peak discharge. More recently, it has been used to develop a particular hydrograph shape. Also, the SCS method originally specified a common shape, but with minor modifications other shapes are possible. The Santa Barbara method also has a parameter that is used to vary the peak and shape. The unit hydrograph method refers to any hydrograph shape with a unit (1 in.) of rainfall excess. The rational method is presented first.

7.5.1 Rational Method Rainfall Intensity Runoff Relationship

If rainfall intensity remains constant over the time interval required to completely drain a watershed, then the runoff (intensity) would be equal to the rainfall intensity. A mass balance relating rainfall intensity to runoff intensity was developed in Chapter 3 (Equation 3.5), and both intensities can be equated and expressed in the following formula:

$$Q = K'iCA \qquad (7.9)$$

where

Q = runoff (cfs)

i = rainfall intensity (in./hr)

CA = contributing area (ac)

K' = conversion factor = 1.008 (cfs-hr/ac-in.) or in the metric system = 0.00278 m³/s/ha-mm/hr)

The assumptions for use of the formula requires a delineation of the contributing area and intensity remains constant over the time period required to drain the area (time of concentration). The contributing area can be related to the characteristics of the watershed that contribute runoff. For impervious areas that are hydraulically connected (water flow is continuous), runoff and rainfall excess must come from this area. However, other areas may contribute during heavy or additional rainfall conditions making the contributing area larger. The impervious area that contributes runoff is frequently called the directly connected impervious area (DCIA). In a residential area, roofs on homes may not directly drain to another impervious surface or a sewer, thus the roofs would not be directly (hydraulically) connected.

For watersheds that have long travel times, it is almost impossible to have a constant intensity over that time period. This limits the use of Equation 7.9 to short time of travel watersheds. Examples of such watersheds are paved areas with curb, gutter, and sewers. Thus, the contributing area, rainfall intensity, and hydraulic characteristics are constant or fixed. As presented by Mulvaney (1851) and used by Kuichling (1889), Equation 7.9 can be restated as the rational formula:

$$Q_p = CiA \qquad (7.10)$$

where

Q_p = peak discharge (cfs)

C = runoff coefficient (dimensionless)

i = rainfall intensity (in./hr)

A = watershed area (ac)

The conversion factor (1.008) was dropped from Equation 7.10. The form of Equation 7.10 is called the rational formula primarily because the units of the quantities are approximately numerically consistent. The runoff coefficient can be simply related to the contributing area by dividing the contributing area by the total area. For a contributing area that is well defined, the runoff coefficient also is well defined. However, if there is no well-defined contributing area, then the runoff coefficient must be determined from published data (Table 7.3) or from runoff studies that relate the volume of runoff to the volume of precipitation.

TABLE 7.3 Runoff Coefficients C Recurrence Interval $\leq$ 10 years[a]

DESCRIPTION OF AREA	RUNOFF COEFFICIENTS	CHARACTER OF SURFACE	RUNOFF COEFFICIENTS
Business		Pavement	
Downtown	0.70 to 0.95	Asphalt or concrete	0.70 to 0.95
Neighborhood	0.50 to 0.70	Brick	0.70 to 0.85
Residential		Roofs	0.70 to 0.95
Single family	0.30 to 0.50	Lawns, sandy soil	
Multiunits, detached	0.40 to 0.60	Flat, 2%	0.05 to 0.10
Multiunits, attached	0.60 to 0.75	Average, 2–7%	0.10 to 0.15
Residential, suburban	0.25 to 0.40	Steep, 7% or more	0.15 to 0.20
Apartment	0.50 to 0.70	Lawns, heavy soil	
Industrial		Flat, 2%	0.13 to 0.17
Light	0.50 to 0.80	Average, 2–7%	0.18 to 0.22
Heavy	0.60 to 0.90	Steep, 7% or more	0.25 to 0.35
Parks, cemeteries	0.10 to 0.25		
Railroad yard	0.20 to 0.35		
Unimproved	0.10 to 0.30		

Source: From *Design and Construction of Sanitary and Storm Sewers. ASCE Manual of Practice No. 37,* 1970. Revised by D. Earl Jones, Jr.
[a] For 25- to 100-yr recurrence intervals, multiply coefficient by 1.1 and 1.25, respectively, and the product cannot exceed 1.0.

The basic assumptions for using the rational formula are

1. The rainfall intensity must be constant for a time interval at least equal to the time of concentration.
2. The runoff is a maximum when the rainfall intensity lasts as long as the time of concentration.
3. The runoff coefficient is constant during the storm volume.
4. The watershed area does not change during the storm.

These assumptions appear reasonable for well-defined watersheds with a short time of concentration (less than 20 min). A rainfall intensity associated with the time of concentration and frequency of occurrence can be obtained from frequency–intensity–duration curves and the runoff coefficient from standard published results (Table 7.3). The calculations are simple and the numerical data easily obtained.

7.5.2   The Rational Hydrograph

As demonstrated by Williams (1950), Pagan (1972), Mitchi (1974) and others, the peak flow, Q_p, as computed by the rational method, $Q_p = CiA$, is actually the peak of a triangular hydrograph. Consider a rainfall of constant intensity i uniformly distributed over a particular drainage basin and of a duration, D, as shown on the hyetograph of Figure 7.7. The volume of runoff (rainfall excess), V_1, the lower (clear) portion of the hyetograph, is equal to $CiDA$, where C is the runoff coefficient in the rational method as normally used—a dimension-

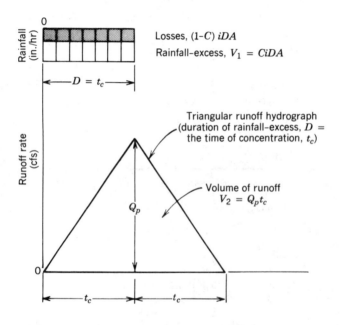

Assume: Contributing area varies linearly with time.

Since:
$$V_1 = V_2$$
$$CiDA = Q_p t_c$$

But:
$$t_c = D$$

Therefore:
$$Q_p = CiA$$

where
$$Q_p = \text{ft}^3 / \text{sec}$$
$$i = \text{in.} / \text{hr}$$
$$A = \text{ac}$$

FIGURE 7.7   A rational method hydrograph with derivation.

less ratio of the total volume of runoff to the total volume of rainfall; i is the intensity of rainfall in inches/hour; D is the rainfall duration in hours, and A is the area of the drainage basin in acres. The units of runoff are acre-in./hr or ft^3/sec (1.008 ac-in./hr = 1 ft^3/sec; however, ignore the 1.008) which, from previous discussion, are recognized as a volume. The upper portion of the hyetograph, again a volume, is equal to the fraction of rainfall remaining onsite $(1 - C)$ times rainfall volume (iAD). From Figure 7.7 the volume, V_2, of the triangular hydrograph is equal to $t_c Q_p$, where t_c is the time of concentration of the drainage area. Note that in this case we have assumed that the time to peak, t_p, previously defined as the time from the start of rainfall excess to the peak of the hydrograph, is equal to the time of

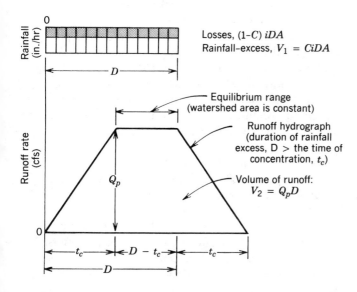

Assume: Contributing area varies linearly with time.

Since
$$V_1 = V_2$$

$$CiDA = Q_pD$$

Therefore,
$$Q_p = CiA$$

where
$Q_p = $ ft^3 / sec
$i = $ in./ hr
$A = $ acres

FIGURE 7.8 A rainfall hyetograph $D > t_c$ with resulting hydrograph and derivation.

concentration, t_c. Since the volume of runoff, V_1, as represented by the lower portion of the hyetograph, must equal the volume of the triangular hydrograph, V_2, and making the assumption that the duration of rainfall D is equal to the time of concentration, t_c, of the basin, the rational method equation is obtained. Thus, the peak flow, Q_p, as computed by the rational method, is shown to be the same as the height of an isosceles triangle with base equal to $2t_c$. Minor modifications to include curve lines can be made as long as the peak and rainfall excess remain the same. An exponential curve approximation also can be made.

From an examination of the isosceles triangular hydrograph shown in Figure 7.7, the shape is different from the typical hydrograph shown in Figures 7.4 and 7.5. For instance, the recession curve portion of this hydrograph is too short. However, the rational method hydrograph shape is approximately that shown in Figure 7.7. Curved rising and falling limbs are also possible as long as the peak and volume of runoff remain constant.

Rainfall intensity that continues past the time of concentration produces a constant runoff rate beyond the time of concentration. As before, consider that the rainfall is uniformly distributed over the watershed and of equal intensity, i, throughout its duration, D. Consider a situation in which the duration of the rainfall, D, is greater than the time of concentration, t_c, as shown in Figure 7.8. Again the volume of runoff, V_1, the lower portion of the hyetograph, is equal to $CiAD$. The volume, V_2, of the trapezoidal hydrograph is equal to Q_pD.

The rational method for calculating hydrograph peak runoff is used frequently by designers. Essentially, the users must estimate a runoff coefficient, rainfall intensity and watershed area. Using this runoff coefficient, the slope of the land, and the overland flow distance, overland time of travel can be computed using Figure 7.9 and the C factor of Table 7.3. Note the range of values for the runoff coefficient. Also, remember from previous chapters that the runoff coefficient can vary with soil moisture conditions and the period of time and volume of rainfall. Conservative designs producing higher runoff peaks require a higher value for the runoff coefficient. Also, the time of concentration must be consistent with the use of the data.

The coefficients in Table 7.3 are applicable for storms of 2- to 10-yr return frequencies and were originally developed when many streets were uncurbed and drainage was conveyed in roadside swales. For recurrence intervals longer than 10 yr, the indicated runoff coefficients should be increased, assuming that nearly all of the rainfall in excess of that expected from the 10-yr recurrence interval rainfall will become runoff and should be accommodated by an increased runoff coefficient.

The rational formula has been used to estimate the peak discharges from areas with a relatively low time of concentration, that is, a few minutes up to about 20 min. Thus, watershed areas are generally homogeneous in hydrologic processes (same runoff areas, similar soil storage, etc.) and usually less than 30

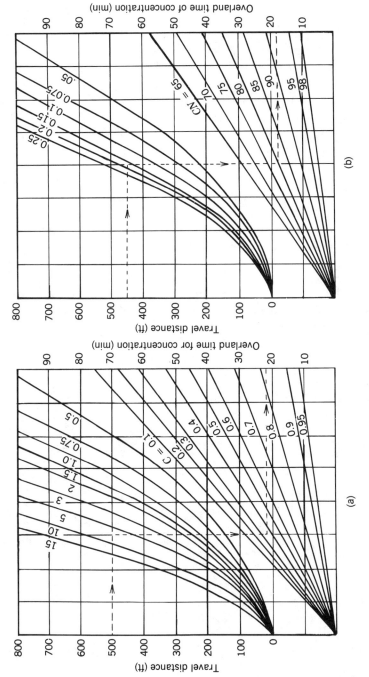

FIGURE 7.9 (a) The t_c for slopes, > 0.5%. (b) The t_c for slopes, < 0.25%.

227

to 50 ac in size. The larger areas generally have steeper drainage slopes. The lower time of concentration is more consistent with the assumption of constant rainfall intensity, or in other words, it is not probable to have constant rainfall intensity over longer periods of time. When designing for a peak discharge, the duration for the rainfall interval should approximate the time of concentration. The longer the time of concentration, the longer the rainfall interval and thus, there is less of a chance of constant rainfall intensity.

7.6

THE SCS HYDROGRAPH

The SCS hydrograph shape has a lesser peak and a longer recession time relative to the rational hydrograph. If the recession curve were longer to make the triangular hydrograph more nearly represent a more true-to-life situation, say of a length equal to $1.67t_c$, Figure 7.10 would result. Again setting V_1 equal to V_2, the peak Q_p of this hydrograph is computed to be equal to $0.75CiA$. This fact should immediately indicate that the rational method is a conservative design procedure because of existing hydrograph shapes. Since

$$V_1 = V_2$$

$$CiDA = 1.34Q_p t_c$$

But

$$t_c = D$$

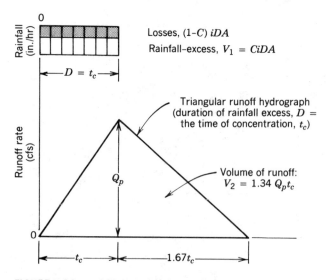

FIGURE 7.10 A SCS typical hydrograph.

Therefore,

$$Q_p = 0.75 \, CiA^* \tag{7.11}$$

where

Q_p = ft^3/sec
i = in./hr
A = ac

*If A = square miles, then Equation 7.11 is rewritten as $Q_p = 484CiA$.

Also consider a case in which the duration of the rainfall, D, is less than the time to peak, t_p, as shown in Figure 7.11. Again, the volume of runoff, V_1, the lower portion of the hyetograph, is equal to $CiAD$. The volume, V_2, of the triangular runoff hydrograph is equal to $\frac{1}{2}Q_p(t_p + t_r)$.

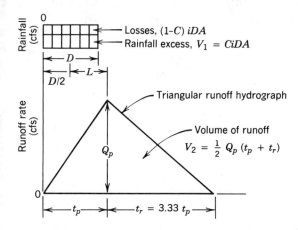

FIGURE 7.11 The rainfall hyetograph $D < t_p$.

Since

$$V_1 = V_2$$
$$CiAD = \tfrac{1}{2}Q_p(t_p + t_r)$$

However,

$$t_r = 3.33t_p$$

Therefore,

$$Q_p = \frac{2CiAD}{4.33t_p}$$

However,

$$t_p = D/2 + L$$

Therefore,

$$Q_p = \frac{0.46CiAD}{D/2 + L} \qquad (7.12)$$

Thus, from Equation 7.12, it is noted that the peak discharge is less than that calculated by Equation 7.11. The difference results because the recession limb time is 3.33 times longer than the time to peak, thus the hydrograph peak would have to be attenuated if rainfall excess were the same (volume of runoff is the same in Figures 7.10 and 7.11).

The specific shape of the hydrograph is important. Reasonable estimates of the recession time and the time to peak must be made. Some guidance is available from the SCS (USDA, 1975) and other researchers (Capice, 1984). However, the guidelines are general and rely on the judgment of the hydrologist, engineer, planner, and others. Given the watershed area (A) and a hydrograph, which is a triangular shape, guidance for the selection of K is given in Table 7.4. Equations 7.13 and 7.14 can be used to calculate the falling limb time and peak discharge.

$$t_f = x t_p \qquad (7.13)$$

and

$$Q_p = KCiA \qquad (7.14)$$

where

K = peak attenuation factor
A = watershed, square miles or acres
i = average intensity (in./hr)
x = falling limb factor, dimensionless
$x = (1291/K) - 1$ (with A in square miles)
$\quad = (2/K) - 1$ (with A in acres)
t_f = falling limb time (same units as t_p)

TABLE 7.4   Triangular Shaped Hydrograph Attenuation Factors

GENERAL DESCRIPTION	FALLING LIMB FACTOR (x)	PEAK ATTENUATION FACTOR (K)[a]	
		A = SQUARE MILES	A = ACRES
Rational formula	1	645	1.00
Urban, steep slopes	1.25	575	0.89
Typical SCS	1.67	484	0.75
Mixed urban/rural	2.25	400	0.62
Rural, rolling hills	3.33	300	0.46
Rural, slight slopes	5.5	200	0.31
Rural, very flat	12.0	100	0.16

[a] Includes 1.008 conversion factor.

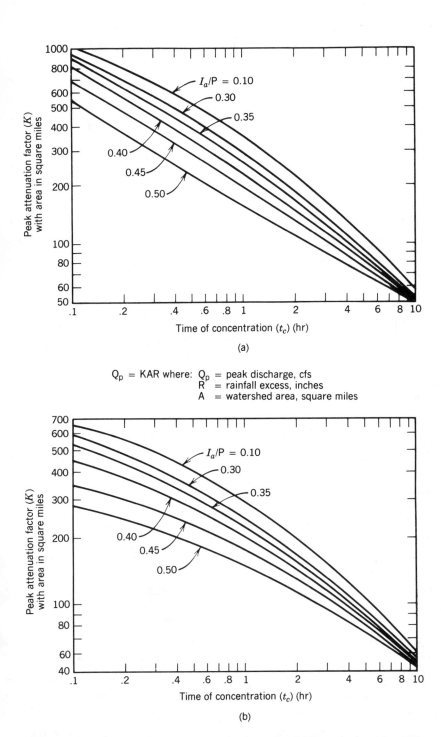

$Q_p = KAR$ where: Q_p = peak discharge, cfs
R = rainfall excess, inches
A = watershed area, square miles

FIGURE 7.12 The peak discharge factor for the updated SCS method. (*a*) For SCS type II rainfall distribution. (*b*) For SCS type III rainfall distribution. (Reproduced from U.S. Department of Agriculture-SCS, 1986.)

231

Again, the user of the factors in Table 7.4 should attempt with field data to justify the choice with the field-derived hydrographs for similar type areas. Table 7.4 assumes a hydrograph shape is available. However, for a nongaged area, time of concentration and composite curve number can be estimated. From the curve number (see Chapter 4), an initial abstraction can be calculated ($I_a = 0.2S'$: $S' = [1000/CN] - 10$) and using Figure 7.12 with a total rainfall (P), the peak attenuation factor is obtained.

Note: The peak discharge is calculated by using $Q_p = KAR$

where

Q_p = peak discharge (cfs)
R = rainfall excess (in.)
A = watershed area (mi^2)

The peak rate can be reduced if the watershed has lakes and swamps through which it flows (USDA-SCS, 1986). For a lake area of 1%, the peak discharge is reduced by the factor 0.87 and for 3%, the factor is 0.75.

7.7

SYNTHETIC UNIT HYDROGRAPH

The rational formula hydrograph shape, the SCS hydrograph shape with any peak attenuation factor, or any shape obtained from streamflow records can be used to develop a unit hydrograph. Once the unit hydrograph is specified, rainfall excess increments can be applied for each duration and a composite hydrograph obtained.

In Chapter 6, the unit hydrograph was defined and developed from streamflow data. It was shown that the unit hydrograph for a watershed is the runoff hydrograph resulting from a unit (1 in.) of rainfall excess from the watershed area during a specified rainfall period of time. The specified period of time is an interval that is brief enough so that natural fluctuations of rainfall intensity during that interval will not materially affect the shape of that hydrograph. Also, one can develop a synthetic unit hydrograph given watershed, rainfall excess, and hydrograph shape information, but no streamflow data.

The derivation and application of the unit hydrograph are based on the following assumptions:

1. For a particular point in a watershed, identical rainfalls with same antecedent conditions produce identical hydrographs.
2. For a particular point in a watershed, the time base of all hydrographs from rainfalls of the same duration with the same antecedent conditions are equal. A graphic example is shown in Figure 7.13a.

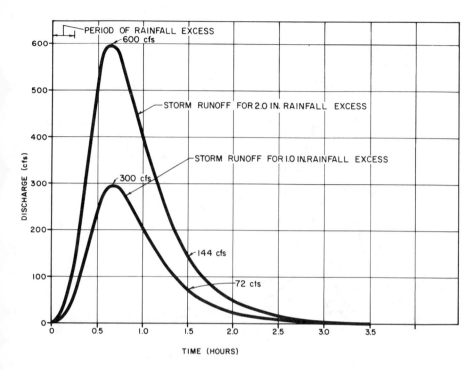

FIGURE 7.13a Hydrographs for different volumes of runoff.

3. For a particular point in a drainage basin, the ordinates of all hydrographs from rainfalls of the same duration with the same antecedent conditions are proportional to the volume of the rainfall excess. Therefore, if the ordinates of each hydrograph are divided by the volume of rainfall excess that produced it, the resulting unit graphs will be identical in shape.

4. The ordinates of several partial hydrographs obtained by multiplying the unit hydrograph by successive rainfall excess amounts of unit duration may be added to obtain the total hydrograph of runoff. A graphic example is shown in Figure 7.13b.

The basic premise of the unit hydrograph, therefore, is that individual hydrographs resulting from the successive increments of rainfall excess that occur throughout a storm period will be proportional in discharge throughout their length, and that when properly arranged with respect to time, the ordinates of the individual hydrographs can be added to give ordinates representing the

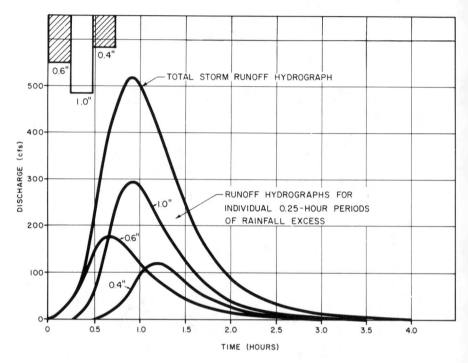

FIGURE 7.13b   Combining hydrographs.

total storm discharge. Constructing a hydrograph of storm discharge resulting from the 3 to 15-min increments of rainfall excess as shown in Figure 7.13b will illustrate calculation procedures. First, the individual hydrographs resulting from each 15-min increment of rainfall excess are computed by multiplying the ordinates of the 15-min unit hydrograph shown in Figure 7.13a by the increments of rainfall excess in inches, each individual hydrograph beginning at the same time as its respective rainfall excess. The hydrograph of total storm discharge is then obtained by summing the ordinates of the individual hydrographs as is shown in Figure 7.13b. To express total discharge, the ordinates of the storm discharge hydrograph must be increased by the amount of the estimated groundwater discharge.

The principles as mentioned above are not rigorously true for all channels. Channel storage varies with the stage, so that the unit hydrographs of large flows will differ from those of small flows. However, it has been found by experience that the unit hydrograph method gives results sufficiently accurate for most practical problems if reasonable judgment is used in its application.

<hr>

7.8

SCS SYNTHETIC UNIT HYDROGRAPH

A procedure commonly in use is the synthetic unit hydrograph procedure developed by the SCS of the U.S. Department of Agriculture (USDA-SCS, 1975). In this procedure, the peak discharge, q_p, of the synthetic unit hydrograph is computed by the following equation:

$$q_p = \frac{(484AR)}{t_p} \tag{7.15}$$

where

q_p = the peak discharge (ft^3/sec)
A = the area of the drainage basin (mi^2)
R = rainfall excess (in.) (1.0 in for unit hydrographs)
t_p = the time to peak (hr)
484 = peak attenuation factor, K

In the SCS procedure, the time to peak, t_p, in hours is computed by the following equation:

$$t_p = (D/2) + L \tag{7.16}$$

where

D = the duration of the rainfall excess
L = the lag time (hr) (time between the centroid of the rainfall excess and the peak of the unit hydrograph)

These are the same terms as previously defined and shown on Figure 6.1.

For the purposes of computing t_p, the lag time, L, is assumed equal to $0.6t_c$, where t_c is the time of concentration of the drainage basin in hours. Substituting into Equation 7.16

$$t_p = (D/2) + 0.6t_c \tag{7.17}$$

Substituting for peak flow (Equation 7.15), the peak of the SCS unit hydrograph can be calculated using the following equation:

$$q_p = \frac{484AR}{(D/2) + 0.6t_c} \tag{7.18}$$

In this procedure, the time of concentration of the drainage basin is computed using the conventional procedures of computing and then summarizing overland and channel flow time.

Dimensionless hydrograph ratios developed by the SCS from a study of many storms for use with Equation 7.18 are shown in Table 7.5. These dimensionless ratios for both a curvilinear and a triangular unit hydrograph give the relationship between q_p (the peak discharge) and any other Q and t_p and any other time, t. Actually, for plotting the triangular unit hydrograph only three points are necessary.

In Figure 7.10, Equation 7.19 was derived with $t_p = (D/2) + L$.

$$Q_p = \frac{0.75 C i A D}{(D/2) + L} \tag{7.19}$$

If we multiply by 640 to allow the drainage area A in acres to be given in square miles and multiply again by 1.008, with $CiAD = AR$ and $L = 0.6t_c$, Equation 7.19 is converted to

$$Q_p = \frac{484 A R}{(D/2) + 0.6t_c} \tag{7.20}$$

Equation 7.20 can be recognized as the equation for peak flow of the SCS synthetic unit hydrograph given as Equation 7.19. Therefore, in Figure 7.10 the Soil Conservation Service's synthetic unit hydrograph equation has been derived.

If one can consider the rainfall excess to be estimated by approximately the same rate (e.g., 0.1 in./hr, 2 mm/hr) over the duration of a storm event, then Equation 7.18 can be used to estimate the peak for the whole storm and the dimensionless hydrograph shapes of Table 7.5 can be used. It is important to note, however, that the attenuation factor (K, Table 7.4) for the dimensionless hydrographs of Table 7.5 is 484. One can develop dimensionless hydrographs for other peak attenuation factors. This has been done for any attenuation factor and has been incorporated into the stormwater management computer program, Stormwater Management and Design Aid (SMADA). In this computer program, the user is asked to specify any factor and unit hydrograph method.

If the rainfall excess were to vary with each rainfall increment throughout the storm event (typical design hyetograph), then the unit hydrograph shape can be applied to each rainfall excess increment and distributed with time. This is the more common application of the unit hydrograph theory. The method can assimilate different intensity–duration rainfall characteristics. This usually results in a more accurate simulation of runoff.

TABLE 7.5 Ratios for Dimensionless Hydrographs for $K = 484$

TIME $(t/t_p)^b$	CURVILINEAR HYDROGRAPH		TRIANGULAR HYDROGRAPH[a]	
	DISCHARGE $(q/q_p)^b$	MASS (Q_a/Q)	DISCHARGE[b] (q/q_p)	MASS (Q_a/Q)
0	0	0	0	0
0.1	0.015	0.001	0.1	0.004
0.2	0.075	0.006	0.2	0.015
0.3	0.16	0.018	0.3	0.034
0.4	0.28	0.037	0.4	0.060
0.5	0.43	0.068	0.5	0.094
0.6	0.60	0.110	0.6	0.135
0.7	0.77	0.163	0.7	0.184
0.8	0.89	0.223	0.8	0.240
1.0	1.00	0.375	1.0	0.375
1.1	0.98	0.450	0.94	0.448
1.2	0.92	0.517	0.88	0.516
1.3	0.84	0.577	0.82	0.579
1.4	0.75	0.634	0.76	0.639
1.5	0.65	0.683	0.70	0.694
1.6	0.57	0.727	0.64	0.744
1.8	0.43	0.796	0.52	0.831
2.0	0.32	0.848	0.40	0.900
2.2	0.24	0.888	0.28	0.951
2.4	0.18	0.916	0.16	0.984
2.6	0.13	0.938	0.04	0.999
2.8	0.098	0.954	0[c]	1[c]
3.5	0.036	0.984		
4.0	0.018	0.993		
4.5	0.009	0.997		
5.0	0.004	0.999		
Infinity	0	1		

Reproduced from USDA-SCS, 1986.
[a]To draw the triangular hydrograph, points only at $(t/t_p) = 0$, 1 and 2.67 are needed.
[b]Given q_p and t_p.
[c]At $(t/t_p) = 2.67$.

An example problem to illustrate the very basic calculations of the unit hydrograph procedure using the typical SCS hydrograph shape ($K = 484$) is developed for one rainfall time increment.

☐ **EXAMPLE PROBLEM 7.3**

For an actual drainage basin with data shown in Table 7.6, compute a unit hydrograph using the SCS procedure.

Solution

The first parameter to determine is the duration of the unit hydrograph which, to produce reasonable peak flow estimates, should be in the range of one-fifth to one-eighth of the time of concentration. However, a longer time, up to one-half of the lag time, can be used for planning or preliminary calculations. The lag time for a time of concentration of 55 min (0.92 hr) is

$$L = 0.6t_c = 0.6 \times 0.92 = 0.55 \text{ hr}$$

Assuming a duration of one-half the lag time, we compute the duration of our unit hydrograph as follows:

$$D = 0.50 \times 0.55 = 0.28 \text{ hr}$$

Round off to $D = 0.25$ hr for computation convenience.

The time to peak, t_p, and the peak discharge, q_p, of the 15-min (0.25 hr) unit hydrograph are then computed as follows by substituting in Equa-

TABLE 7.6 OCP-Phase Drainage Basin Physical and Topographical Characteristics

Drainage area, ac	270.6
Percent impervious (land area)	75
Percent pervious (land area)	25
Pervious area Makeup, %	
Good grass cover	12.5
Poor grass cover	12.5
time of concentration, min	55
Hydrologic soil group (SCS classification)	C

From Golding, 1974.

tions 7.15 and 7.16. Assume that $t_c = 0.92$ hr,

$$t_p = (D/2) + 0.6t_c = (0.25/2) + 0.6(0.92) = 0.68 \text{ hr}$$

$$q_p = \frac{484AR}{t_p} = \frac{(484)(0.42)(1)}{0.68} = 298.94 \text{ ft}^3/\text{sec}$$

As the drainage area is acutally slightly greater than 0.42 mi², use $q_p = 300$ ft³/sec.

The curvilinear unit hydrograph for 15-min intervals is computed by multiplying t_p and q_p by the dimensionless hydrograph ratios given in the first two columns of Table 7.5. This computation of the 15-min curvilinear unit hydrograph is shown in Table 7.7 and has been plotted on Figure 7.14. If we want to draw a triangular 15-min unit hydrograph to compute a design hydrograph, only the basic information must be known, the peak q_p (= 300.17 ft³/sec) occurs at a time t_p (= 0.68 hr) from the start of the hydrograph, and the base of the triangular hydrograph is equal to $2.67t_p$ (= 1.82 hr). The 15-min triangular unit hydrograph is also shown in Figure 7.14. Frequently, the "tail" of the hydrograph is not important,

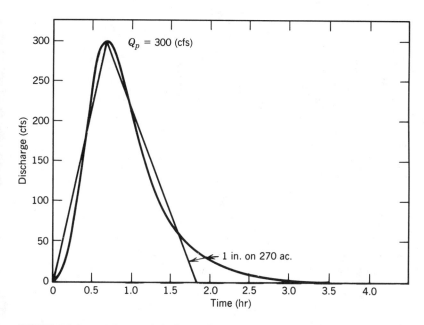

FIGURE 7.14 A 15-min unit hydrograph — the comparison of triangular and curvilinear dimensionless hydrographs.

TABLE 7.7   Calculation of Unit Hydrograph SCS Procedure
$(t_p = 0.68, q_p = 300)$

COMPUTATION OF UNIT HYDROGRAPH				CLOCK HOUR READINGS[a]	
TIME RATIO (t/t_p)	DISCHARGE RATIO (q/q_p)	TIME (T) (hr)	DISCHARGE (q) (ft^3/sec)	TIME (hr)	DISCHARGE (ft^3/sec)
0	0	0	0	0	0
0.1	0.015	0.07	5	0.25	73
0.2	0.075	0.14	23	0.50	246
0.3	0.16	0.20	48	0.75	293
0.4	0.28	0.27	84	1.00	202
0.5	0.43	0.34	129	1.25	121
0.6	0.60	0.41	180	1.50	72
0.7	0.77	0.48	231	1.75	41
0.8	0.89	0.54	267	2.00	26
0.9	0.97	0.61	291	2.25	15
1.0	1.00	0.68	300	2.50	9
1.1	0.98	0.75	294	2.75	6
1.2	0.92	0.82	276	3.00	3
1.3	0.84	0.88	252	3.25	1
1.4	0.75	0.95	225	3.50	0
1.5	0.65	1.02	195		
1.6	0.57	1.09	171		
1.8	0.43	1.22	129		
2.0	0.32	1.36	96		
2.2	0.24	1.50	72		
2.4	0.18	1.63	54		
2.6	0.13	1.77	39		
2.8	0.098	1.90	29		
3.0	0.075	2.04	23		
3.5	0.036	2.38	11		
4.0	0.018	2.72	5		
4.5	0.009	3.06	3		
5.0	0.004	3.40	1		

[a]Time from start of rainfall, rainfall excess assumed to start immediately after start of rainfall.

thus the triangular shape gives adequate results for the peak estimate and flows immediately adjacent to the peak.

To use the 15-min curvilinear unit hydrograph, or for that matter the triangular shape, one must determine the discharge, q, at time equal to 0.25-hr intervals (clock hour readings), which can be done by scaling the ordinates of the plotted 15-min unit hydrograph on Figure 7.14. The discharges at clock intervals of 0.25 hr for the 15-min curvilinear unit hydrograph have been scaled and area also given in Table 7.7. □

7.9

CONTRIBUTING AREA METHOD

When estimating hydrograph shapes for large mixed land use and mixed soil conditions, different hydrograph shapes will result from the different soil and ground cover. If an average soil and ground cover were used for an entire watershed, the estimated hydrograph may not adequately represent the mixed soil and ground cover. It is more accurate to generate the hydrograph shape for each land use with the same soil and ground cover system. All contributing area hydrograph estimates are then added (linearly) with respect to time to produce a final hydrograph shape. The Contributing Area Method must use some method of hydrograph generation; usually the equation ($Q = iCA$) as a hydrograph procedure is used. As in the Rational Method itself, the Contributing Area Method requires estimates for rainfall intensity, watershed areas, and a runoff coefficient (C) to translate precipitation to rainfall excess in addition to a more detailed description of the watershed. The Rational Method for calculating hydrographs assumes the watershed to have similar soils and ground cover for estimating a hydrograph at the discharge or other decision point (inlets). The duration of the storm must be divided into short time increments (ΔD). This is the same concept as used for the hyetograph time intervals.

The concept of directly or hydraulically connected impervious areas is important when using the Contributing Area Method. This method requires a knowledge of flows from one watershed to the next. Those impervious areas (i.e., pavements) that are directly connected to the outlet of the watershed either by overland flow by other impervious areas or by conduits are considered to be directly or hydraulically connected impervious areas.

Another important concept to consider is the proper selection of the boundary of the watershed for which the hydrograph is to be estimated. In general, the maximum watershed size is any one drained by a single principal drainage conduit or water course such as subbasins A, B, and C in Figure 7.15. This is partly because most synthetic hydrograph procedures were established by experiments on watersheds with single principal water courses. These

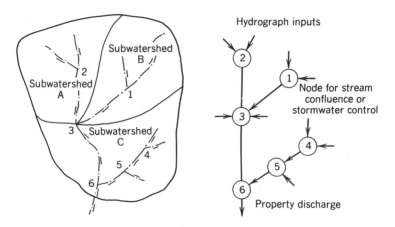

FIGURE 7.15   Subbasins and schematic (stick) diagrams.

watersheds are considered to be homogeneous. If, in Figure 7.15, watersheds A and B were considered as a single watershed, computation would be difficult because uniform rainfall would most likely produce a double-hump hydrograph and the rational method produces a single peak.

In addition to the same land use and soil conditions criteria, inlets can be used to define a subbasin. Generally, the more a major watershed is subdivided into smaller ones, the more accurate the final result. Of course, dividing a large watershed into many will create additional work, which may not be warranted and may not actually increase the accuracy because the accuracy of a hydrograph is directly dependent on how correct the basic information is that is used in the design.

Examining Figure 7.15, one would compute separate hydrographs for subbasins A, B, and C and combine them for each time calculation as follows:

1.   Combine the hydrograph for subbasins A and B by vertical addition of the flow hydrograph at each time.
2.   Route (by flood-routing procedures) the combined hydrograph of subbasins A and B through the length of the receiving channel of subbasin C.
3.   Add the hydrograph from subbasin C to the routed combined hydrograph from subbasins A and B.

If the principal water course draining subwatershed C entered the receiving channel at the upper end of C (node 3), one would combine all three hydrographs by vertical addition of flow and then route the combined hydrograph through the length of the receiving channel in subwatershed C.

Construction of a nodal (stick) diagram indicating flow direction would aid in describing the watersheds and keeping inventory of calculations. The computations are not complex but strict computation procedures must be followed. Thus, an example problem is beneficial.

☐ EXAMPLE PROBLEM 7.4

Consider the watershed of Figure 7.16. The minor system is the drain pipes underground. Overland flow in the streets, parking lots, and lawns is called the major system. The total watershed is defined as an urban

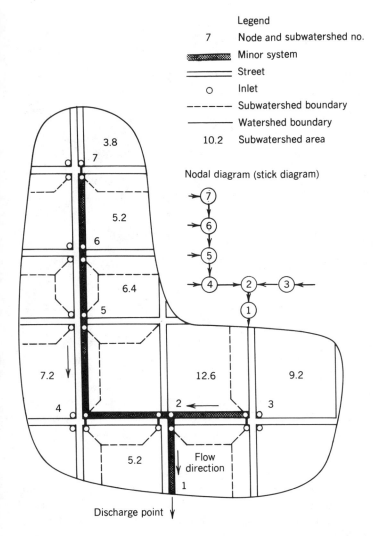

FIGURE 7.16 The contributing area watershed for Example Problem 7.4.

TABLE 7.8 Area, Equivalent Impervious Area, and Time of Concentration for Example Problem 7.4

UP STREAM NODE / DOWN-STREAM NODE	SURFACE TYPE (RATIONAL C)	TOTAL CONTRIBUTING AREA (ac)	EQUIVALENT IMPERVIOUS AREA (C × AREA) (ac)	TIME OF CONCENTRATION TO DOWNSTREAM NODE 1 (min)
1/1	Commercial (0.85)	5.2	4.42	5.0
2/1	Commercial (0.85)	12.6	10.71	13.2
3/2	Residential (0.36)	9.2	3.31	23.8
4/2	Commercial 12% Residential 88% (0.88 × 0.36) + (0.12 × 0.85) = 0.42	7.2	3.02	20.5
5/4	Commercial 42% Residential 58% (0.58 × 0.36)] + (0.42 × 0.85) = 0.565	6.4	3.62	27.8
6/5	Residential (0.36)	5.2	1.87	34.4
7/6	Residential (0.36)	3.8	1.37	40.0
Σ		49.6	28.32	

area. For better accuracy, the total area is subdivided into seven homogeneous contributing areas. The rational formula is used to estimate the runoff hydrograph shape. The time of concentration is estimated for each contributing area. This plus a list of contributing areas, the rational "C" for each area, and the equivalent impervious area (product of area and "C") are shown in Table 7.8.

Next, it is necessary to estimate the time of concentration from the furthest point in the watershed to the point of discharge. In doing this, the schematic nodal diagram in Figure 7.16 is helpful. The time of concentration is estimated along the flow path. The maximum flow rate will occur when the concentration is the smallest value because rainfall

TABLE 7.9 Cumulative Time of Concentration
Related to Effective Area

UPSTREAM NODE / DOWNSTREAM NODE	Σ t_c ALONG FLOW PATH	Σ EFFECTIVE AREA (ac)
1/1	5.0	4.42
2/1	13.2	15.13
3/2	23.8	21.46
4/2	20.5[a]	18.15[a]
5/4	27.8	25.08
6/5	34.4	26.95
7/6	40.0	28.32

[a] Flow path is from node 4 to 2, and area 4
contributes in time before area 3 contributes.

intensity is larger for shorter duration storms. Thus, the shortest time of
concentration is recorded in Table 7.9. By considering the time of
concentration equal to the incremental duration (ΔD) of rainfall, the
peak flows are estimated for that time increment. Thus, the peak flows
can be calculated for each subwatershed and each rainfall intensity if the
time of concentration is known for that subwatershed. Figure 7.17 illus-

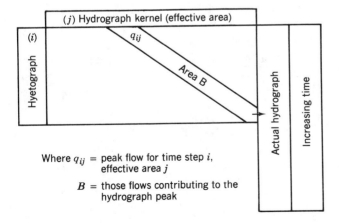

Where q_{ij} = peak flow for time step i, effective area j

B = those flows contributing to the hydrograph peak

FIGURE 7.17 The computation format — contributing area method.

TABLE 7.10 Calculation Sheet for Storm 1A

HYETOGRAPH		SUBWATERSHED HYDROGRAPH ESTIMATES FOR EACH TIME STEP								ROUTED HYDROGRAPH	
TIME (min)	PRECIP. (in./hr)	A_{40} 1.3	A_{35} 1.4	A_{30} 3.1	A_{25} 4.8	A_{20} 1.9	A_{15} 4.6	A_{10} 6.8[b]	A_5 4.4	DISCHARGE (cfs)	TIME (min)
5	0.6	0.78	0.84	1.86	2.88	1.14	2.76	4.08	2.64[a] →	2.64	5
10	0.3	0.39	0.42	0.93	1.44	0.57	1.38 ↗	2.04 ↗	1.32 →	5.40	10
15	0.2	0.26	0.28	0.62	0.96	0.38	0.92	1.36	0.88 →	5.68	15
20	0.1	0.13	0.14	0.31	0.48	0.19	0.46	0.68	0.44	4.32	20
25	0.1	0.13	0.14	0.31	0.48	0.19	0.46	0.68	0.44	5.49	25
30	0.1	0.13	0.14	0.31	0.48	0.19	0.46	0.68	0.44	5.26	30
										4.06	35
										2.95	40
										1.65	45
										1.19	50
										0.58	55
										0.27	60
										0.13	65
										0.00	70

[a] $Q = i(A)$ where $(A)_k = CA_k$ and k = hyetograph time step. $Q = 0.6(4.4) = 2.64$ cfs.

[b] $A_{10} = 11.2 - 4.4 = 6.8$ Ac

Note: CA is the incremental contributing area.

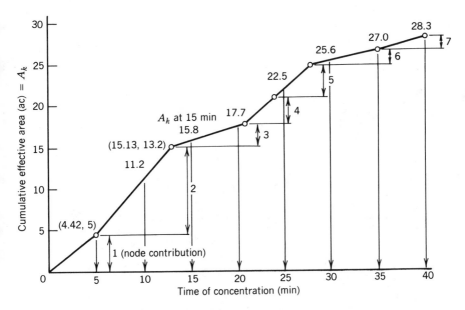

FIGURE 7.18 An S-curve plot of cumulative effective area versus time of concentration.

TABLE 7.11 Incremental Values for each 5-min Hyetograph Interval

HYETOGRAPH TIME (min)	CUMULATIVE EFFECTIVE AREA (ac)	INCREMENTAL EFFECTIVE AREA (ac)
0	0	0
5	4.4	4.4
10	11.2	6.8
15	15.8	4.6
20	17.7	1.9
25	22.5	4.8
30	25.6	3.1
35	27.0	1.4
40	28.3	1.3

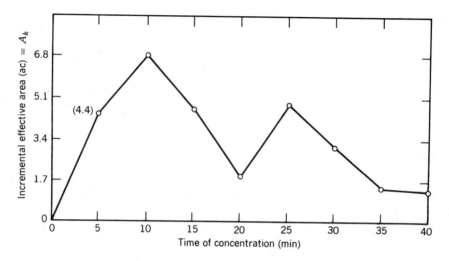

FIGURE 7.19   An incremental effective area — concentration curve ($\Delta t = 5$ min).

trates the format for computing peak flows at each subwatershed. Note that the discharge hydrograph must be calculated for each hyetograph time step (ΔD) and the hydrograph estimates for each time step must therefore be summed. The summation is done on a diagonal because of the time it takes to reach the discharge point. The time increments (steps) for the hyetograph must be specified. The time steps must be at most 20% of the watershed time of concentration or at least five steps must be specified. The effective area is then estimated for each time step and obtained from the time of concentration estimate. If the hyetograph time steps were every 5 min, the first 5 min has an equivalent impervious area of 4.42 ac. This is the "effective area" for contributing runoff.

Table 7.10 shows the calculations for a storm with higher intensity at the start of the storm and a decreasing intensity with time. The effective contributing areas were estimated from Figure 7.18. Since the hyetograph time step is 5 min, the effective area associated with each 5-min increment has to be determined. The cumulative area is estimated from Figure 7.18, the values of which are repeated in Table 7.11 to one-place accuracy since it was read from a graph. The incremental values of Table 7.11 are for each 5-min hyetograph interval. Figure 7.19 graphically represents the effective areas and illustrates the variable contribution of area as it affects runoff. If the incremental effective areas were about the same, the hyetograph would primarily determine the hydrograph shape. Note for the example problem that the effective areas of Figure 7.19 illustrate possibly two separate hydrograph peaks (there are two incremental effective area

TABLE 7.12 Calculation Sheet for Storm 2 (Denoted by ⊙ on Figure 7.20)

HYETOGRAPH		SUBWATERSHED HYDROGRAPH ESTIMATES FOR EACH TIME STEP								ROUTED HYDROGRAPH	
TIME (min)	PRECIP. (in./hr)	A_{40} 1.3	A_{35} 1.4	A_{30} 3.1	A_{25} 4.8	A_{20} 1.9	A_{15} 4.6	A_{10} 6.80	A_5 4.42	DISCHARGE (cfs)	TIME (min)
5	0.1	0.13	0.14	0.31	0.48	0.19	0.46	0.68	0.44	0.44	5
10	0.2	0.26	0.28	0.62	0.96	0.38	0.92	1.36	0.88	1.56	10
15	0.4	0.52	0.56	1.24	1.92	0.76	1.84	2.72	1.76	3.58	15
20	0.4	0.52	0.56	1.24	1.92	0.76	1.84	2.72	1.76	5.59	20
25	0.2	0.26	0.28	0.62	0.96	0.38	0.92	1.36	0.88	6.30	25
30	0.1	0.13	0.14	0.31	0.48	0.19	0.46	0.68	0.44	5.67	30
										5.04	35
										4.41	40
										3.21	45
										2.18	50
										1.11	55
										0.40	60
										0.13	65

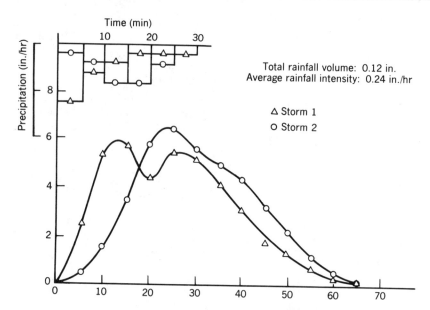

FIGURE 7.20   Hydrographs resulting from two different hyetographs.

"humps.") Example calculations for the incremental hydrograph values at 10 min are

AREA	RATIONAL Q_p
1	$Q_p = (CA)(i) = (4.4)(0.3) = 1.32$ cfs
2	$Q_p = (6.8)(0.3) = 2.04$ cfs
etc.	

and the discharge hydrograph at 10 min is $4.08 + 1.32 = 5.40$ cfs. The flow from area 2 takes 10 min to reach the discharge point; thus, the incremental hydrograph value from the first 5 min of the storm is used.

Table 7.12 shows calculations for a different hyetograph. The two resulting hydrographs are shown in Figure 7.20 (Walsh and Wanielista, 1982). Note the double "hump" on the first hydrograph and the differences between the two hydrographs. Because the rain volume is the same for both storms (about 0.12 in.), one would expect the same peak discharge if the rational formula were applied to the same area. Note, however, that the hyetographs are different. If a constant rainfall intensity were assumed (say 0.24 in./hr) then the rational formula estimate of the peak discharge is 0.24(28.3) = 6.8 cfs. □

7.10

THE SANTA BARBARA URBAN HYDROGRAPH METHOD

The Santa Barbara Urban Hydrograph Method (SBUH method) was developed by Mr. James M. Stubchaer of the Santa Barbara County (California) Flood Control and Water Conservation District and was first presented at the National Symposium on Urban Hydrology and Sediment Control held at the University of Kentucky (1975). One is immediately impressed by the SBUH method's ease of application as it computes a hydrograph directly without going through an intermediate process as the unit hydrograph method does. A comparison with other methods currently in use indicates the SBUH method's apparent accuracy and ease of application.

Although the SBUH method was originally programmed for a desk-size computer in the BASIC computer language, the computations can be done manually as will be demonstrated here. It is also easily handled by a programmable pocket-type calculator. With the SBUH method, a unit hydrograph shape can be specified by choice of the calculation time interval (Δt) and a time of concentration.

The SBUH method is similar to the contributing area procedure for hydrograph computation in which subwatershed hydrographs in a watershed are developed and then routed to determine an outflow hydrograph from the watershed. However, in the SBUH method, the final design (outflow) hydrograph is obtained by routing the instantaneous hydrograph for each time period (obtained by multiplying the various incremental rainfall excesses by the watershed area in acres) through an imaginary linear reservoir with a routing constant dependent on the time of concentration of the watershed. Therefore, the difficult and time-consuming process of preparing an effective area time of concentration curve for the watershed is eliminated.

A step-by-step description of the SBUH method is given as follows:

1. Runoff depths for each time period are calculated using the following equations.

Impervious area runoff, $R(I) = d'P(\Delta t)$(depth) $\qquad$ (7.21)

Pervious area runoff, $R(P) = (1 - d')[P(\Delta t) - F(\Delta t)]$ (depth) $\qquad$ (7.22)

Total runoff depth, $R(\Delta t) = R(I) + R(P)$(depth) $\qquad$ (7.23)

where

$P(\Delta t)$ = rainfall depth during time increment Δt (depth)

$F(\Delta t)$ = infiltration during time increment Δt (depth)

d' = directly connected impervious portion of drainage basin (fraction)

Δt = incremental time period (hr) (i.e., 0.25, 0.50, etc.)

2. The instantaneous hydrograph is then computed by multiplying the total runoff depth, $R(\Delta t)$ for each time period, Δt, by the watershed area, A, and dividing by the time increment, Δt, and converted to m^3/s or ft^3/s if necessary.

$$I(\Delta t) = \frac{R(\Delta t)A}{\Delta t} \qquad (m^3/s \text{ or } ft^3/s) \qquad (7.24)$$

(Note that as in the Rational Method, the conversion factor 1.008 is dropped when using inches and acres and the total watershed area is used rather than a contributing area at each time step.)

3. The final design (outflow) hydrograph, $Q(\Delta t)$, is then obtained by routing the instantaneous hydrograph, $I(\Delta t)$, through an imaginary reservoir with a time delay equal to the time of concentration, t_c, of the watershed. This flood routing may be done by use of the following equation to estimate routed flow Q.

$$Q(2) = Q(1) + K_r[I(1) + I(2) - 2Q(1)] \qquad (7.25)$$

where

$$K_r = \frac{\Delta t}{(2t_c + \Delta t)} \qquad (7.26)$$

I = inflow to imaginary reservoir

t_c = time of concentration

The shape of the discharge hydrograph is determined by the value of K_r (the routing constant). In Figure 7.21, the shapes of unit hydrograph are shown for various K_r values.

In the SBUH method, the impervious portion of the watershed is considered to be the directly (hydraulically) connected portion of the impervious area as previously discussed. All of the rain that falls on this impervious portion of the basin is considered rainfall excess. The equation for impervious area runoff can be modified for depression storage or evaporation if applicable by the following equation:

$$R(I) = d'[P(\Delta t) - D(\Delta t)]EVP \qquad (7.27)$$

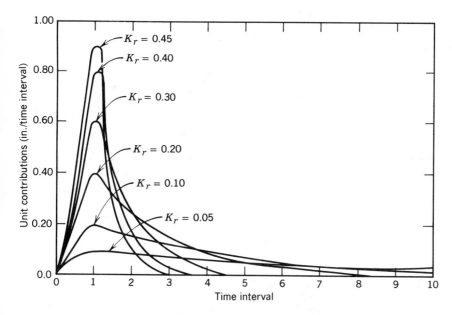

FIGURE 7.21   Normalized Santa Barbara unit hydrographs. (From Walsh and Wanielista, 1982.)

where

$R(I)$ = impervious area runoff (mm)

d' = impervious portion of the drainage basin (fraction)

$P(\Delta t)$ = rainfall depth during time increment (Δt) (mm)

$D(\Delta t)$ = depression storage during time increment (Δt) (mm)

EVP = portion of rainfall excess which is evaporated before runoff (fraction)

☐   **EXAMPLE PROBLEM 7.5**

To illustrate the SBUH method, and for purposes of comparison with other hydrograph methods, a design hydrograph by the SBUH method is required. A computer program included with this book is used for the 270.6-ac watershed basin as shown in Table 7.13. The results are also shown in Table 7.13 following exactly the step-by-step computation procedure for the SBUH method listed previously.

The rainfall increments given in column 3 are taken directly from the 25-yr frequency, 6-hr rainfall hyetograph (Figure 7.3). Because the pervious and impervious areas are considered separately in the SBUH method,

TABLE 7.13 Design Hydrograph[a]

Given: Area = 270.6 ac   Compute: 1. Routing Constant (K_r)

$d' = 0.75$

$\Delta t = 15$ min $= 0.25$ hr

$t_c = 55$ min $= 0.92$ hr

$$K_r = \frac{\Delta t}{2t_c + \Delta t} = \frac{0.25}{2(0.92) + 0.25} = 0.12$$

2. Design hydrograph (via computer output)

$CN = 54$ (pervious area)

Note: Rainfall excess for pervious area calculated assuming initial abstraction saturated, thus, $R = P^2/(P + S')$

TIME INCREMENT	TIME (min)	RAINFALL DEPTH (in.)	INFILTRATION % INIT ABST (in.)	RUNOFF DEPTH (in.)	INSTANT HYDROGRAPH (cfs)[b]	WATERSHED HYDROGRAPH (cfs)[c]
1	15	0.10	0.025	0.075	81.49	9.78
2	30	0.11	0.027	0.083	90.35	28.05
3	45	0.12	0.028	0.092	99.38	44.09
4	60	0.15	0.034	0.116	125.37	60.48
5	75	0.16	0.035	0.125	135.06	77.21
6	90	0.17	0.036	0.134	144.94	92.28
7	105	0.27	0.055	0.215	233.04	115.49
8	120	0.30	0.057	0.243	262.72	147.26
9	135	1.08	0.180	0.900	973.84	260.31
10	150	1.14	0.155	0.985	1065.68	442.58
11	165	0.32	0.039	0.281	304.68	500.80
12	180	0.28	0.032	0.248	268.32	449.37
13	195	0.24	0.026	0.214	231.18	401.46
14	210	0.24	0.025	0.215	232.22	360.72
15	225	0.18	0.018	0.162	174.82	322.99
16	240	0.16	0.016	0.144	155.84	285.15
17	255	0.14	0.014	0.126	136.69	251.82
18	270	0.13	0.012	0.118	127.20	223.05
19	295	0.13	0.012	0.118	127.45	200.07
20	300	0.12	0.011	0.109	117.86	181.49
21	315	0.12	0.011	0.109	118.07	166.25
22	330	0.12	0.011	0.109	118.27	154.71
23	345	0.11	0.010	0.100	108.58	144.80
24	360	0.11	0.010	0.100	108.74	136.13
25	375	0.00	0.000	0.000	0.00	116.50
26	390	0.00	0.000	0.000	0.00	88.54
27	405	0.00	0.000	0.000	0.00	67.29
28	420	0.00	0.000	0.000	0.00	51.14
29	435	0.00	0.000	0.000	0.00	38.87

continued

TABLE 7.13 *(Continued)*

Given: Area = 270.6 ac   Compute: 1. Routing Constant (K_r)

d' = 0.75

Δt = 15 min = 0.25 hr

$$K_r = \frac{\Delta t}{2t_c + \Delta t} = \frac{0.25}{2(0.92) + 0.25} = 0.12$$

t_c = 55 min = 0.92 hr

2. Design hydrograph (via computer output)

CN = 54 (pervious area)

Note: Rainfall excess for pervious area calculated assuming initial abstraction saturated, thus, $R = P^2/(P + S')$

TIME INCREMENT	TIME (min)	RAINFALL DEPTH (in.)	INFILTRATION % INIT ABST (in.)	RUNOFF DEPTH (in.)	INSTANT HYDROGRAPH (cfs)[b]	WATERSHED HYDROGRAPH (cfs)[c]
30	450	0.00	0.000	0.000	0.00	29.54
31	465	0.00	0.000	0.000	0.00	22.45
32	480	0.00	0.000	0.000	0.00	17.06
33	495	0.00	0.000	0.000	0.00	12.97
34	510	0.00	0.000	0.000	0.00	9.86
35	525	0.00	0.000	0.000	0.00	7.49
36	540	0.00	0.000	0.000	0.00	5.69
37	555	0.00	0.000	0.000	0.00	4.33
38	570	0.00	0.000	0.000	0.00	3.29
39	585	0.00	0.000	0.000	0.00	2.50
40	600	0.00	0.000	0.000	0.00	1.90

Total rain = 6.00 total infiltration & abstraction = 0.88 total runoff = 5.12

[a] Generated from a computer program, (i.e., SMADA).
[b] From Equation 7.24.
[c] From Equation 7.25.

it is easier to specify a curve number (*CN*) for the pervious area and estimate infiltration increments for the pervious area only. Using the methods previously outlined, a *CN* of 54 is used to compute the infiltration for the pervious area.

The design hydrograph as computed by the SBUH method is plotted on Figure 7.22. Note that the runoff hydrograph shape is different from that obtained by the rational formula (peak at 6 hr and equal to (0.8) (1) (270) = 216 cfs with c = 0.8, i = 1 in./hr. and area = 270 ac).   □

The basic equations for the SBUH Method are simple enough for computerization on even the smallest programmable pocket-type calculator, which

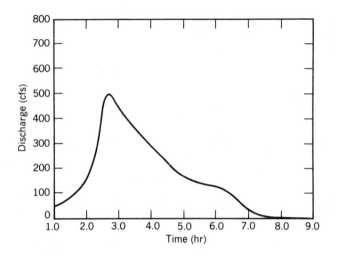

FIGURE 7.22   The design hydrograph, 25-hr frequency, 6-hr rainfall, SBUH method.

is a big advantage of the SBUH method. Another advantage of the SBUH method is that it does not have the tendency to overcompute the peak of the hydrograph. However, as in the unit hydrograph method, it does require the promulgation of a design rainfall, the determination of rainfall excess, and a hydrograph shape.

For purposes of comparison, the design hydrograph as computed by the SCS unit hydrograph and SBUH method resulting from the same 25-yr

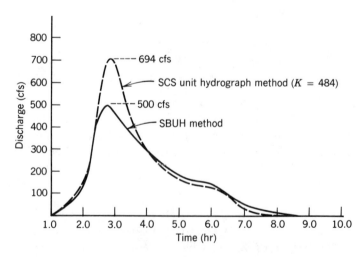

FIGURE 7.23   A hydrograph comparison, design hydrograph, 25-yr frequency, 6-hr rainfall.

frequency, 6-hr design rainfall have been plotted as shown in Figure 7.23. From an examination of these two hydrographs, one can immediately recognize that both methods produce similarly shaped hydrographs. However, the peak flow as computed by the unit hydrograph method is greater (approximately 40%). The runoff volume is less with the SBUH method illustrating a consideration of the pervious area runoff and soil moisture.

7.11

THE DISCRETE UNIT – TIME HYDROGRAPH METHOD

Since rainfall intensity is generally not constant with time and watersheds do not have equal retention capacity with time, rainfall excess is almost always variable with time. Thus, for Example Problem 7.3, there most likely are other rainfall excess increments, and the hydrograph discharges can be summed with time. This type of detail is very time consuming if done by hand calculations. However, computer programs, like DABRO (Drainage Basin Runoff Model) (Golding, 1986), SMADA, and SCSUNIT (Soil Conservation Service Unit Hydrograph) (Ghioto, 1986) are helpful and save time. DABRO and SMADA both allow for calculations of rainfall excess by the composite curve number (CN) or the directly connected impervious area plus pervious areas.

A general procedure for using any attenuation factor K is outlined here. The watershed is separated into directly connected impervious area and pervious area. Rainfall excess is calculated for both impervious and pervious areas and then added with time. The general procedure is to do the following:

1. Quantify watershed parameters, such as watershed area, time of concentration, curve number for pervious area (or other rainfall excess method), initial abstraction, and soil moisture.
2. Quantify hyetograph (intensity vs. time).
3. Pick a hyetograph unit time, as a guide $\Delta D = (\frac{1}{5}$ to $\frac{1}{8})t_c$.
4. Calculate peak discharge for 1 in. of rainfall excess

$$Q_p = \frac{[K(A)(R)]}{[(\Delta D/2) + 0.6t_c]}$$

where

$$K = \text{attenuation factor}$$
$$R = 1 \text{ in.}$$
$$A = \text{watershed area}$$

5. Choose a hydrograph shape that defines the attenuation factor.
6. Develop the complete unit hydrograph for all times consistent with the factors of Table 7.4, call this $U_1, U_2 \ldots U_n$.

7. a. Calculate the rainfall excess from the impervious area.
    b. Calculate the rainfall excess ($R_{\Delta D}$) for each (ΔD) time step and for the pervious area, use the curve number method.

$$R_{\Delta D} = \frac{(P - 0.2S')^2}{(P + 0.8S')} \quad \text{for } P \geq 0.2S'$$

where

$$R_{\Delta D} = \text{rainfall excess for all } \Delta Ds$$

$$S' = \text{maximum soil storage}$$

$$P = \text{cumulative rainfall}$$

    c. Add the rainfall excess from the pervious and impervious areas.
8. For each rainfall excess, calculate a watershed hydrograph (Q_t) by using the convolution procedure:

$$Q_1 = U_1 R_1$$
$$Q_2 = U_1 R_2 + U_2 R_1$$
$$Q_3 = U_1 R_3 + U_2 R_2 + U_3 R_1$$
$$Q_m = U_1 R_m + U_2 R_{m-1} + \cdots + U_n R_1$$
$$Q_{m+n-1} = U_n R_m$$

where
Q_i = discharge rate of the ith time interval
m = total number of storm intervals
n = total number of unit hydrograph intervals, which is a function of the hydrograph attenuation parameter

9. To facilitate the foregoing calculation, a matrix may be set as follows:

$$
\begin{array}{cccc}
U_1 R_m & U_2 R_m & \dots & U_n R_m \\
U_1 R_3 & U_2 R_3 & \dots & U_n R_3 \\
U_1 R_2 & U_2 R_2 & \dots & U_n R_2 \\
& \searrow & & \\
U_1 R_1 & U_2 R_1 & \dots & U_n R_1 \\
& \searrow & \searrow & \\
& Q_1 & Q_2 &
\end{array}
$$

Sum along a diagonal to compute the respective Q_i values. These discharge values are the final hydrograph.

This type of detailed hydrograph analysis is suited for both large and small watersheds with similar surface and soil characteristics. Nonhomogeneous watersheds can be divided into smaller units and hydrographs developed for each unit. The discrete unit time–unit hydrograph method is accurate if the hydrograph shape factor and hyetograph are well defined.

7.12

SUMMARY

The development of a synthetic hydrograph requires specific knowledge of watershed characteristics and rainfall excess. With this knowledge, hydrograph shape and peak discharge estimates can be made. Hydrograph procedures in common use were presented in this chapter. Some brief summary comments are as follows:

- Synthetic hydrograph procedures are useful for the generation of hydrographs when no streamflow data are available.
- Time of concentration is a necessary parameter for the generation of hydrographs using the procedures of this chapter. For gutter and sewer systems, the Manning equation is useful to estimate velocity and then time of concentration. For overland flow, at least two other equations have been frequently used.
- Watershed area-time curves can be used with intensity data to generate hydrographs. The method is a convolution procedure called Contributing Area.
- The rational method is used extensively for peak discharge estimation for small watersheds with well-defined contributing areas. The rainfall intensity is assumed constant for a time period equal to the longest travel time for the watershed.
- For larger mixed land use areas, the rational method can be considered simplistic, and like some time-tested methods, it generally produces an overestimate of the peak discharge.
- The SCS typical hydrograph shape ($K = 484$) estimates a peak discharge that is about 75% of that estimated using the rational formula, assuming all other factors are equal.
- The peak attenuation factor (K) in the general hydrograph formula ($Q_p = KCiA$) can be changed to develop other hydrograph shapes.

- The Santa Barbara hydrograph method is based on a formula to route rainfall excess. Directly connected impervious areas can be considered. A hydrograph shape factor is inherent in its use.
- Given rainfall intensities and rainfall excess that are different for fixed time periods with a unit-hydrograph for each time period, the convolution procedure can be used to generate a hydrograph shape. A discrete unit–time hydrograph method is outlined in the text and is available in some computer programs like the one (SMADA) included with this book.
- Computer programs can be used to generate hydrographs using the rational, Santa Barbara, SCS, or unit hydrograph shape.

7.13

PROBLEMS

1. For a 50-ac single-family residential area and a rainfall intensity of 3 in./hr for 1 hr, develop a hydrograph using an assumed average runoff coefficient from Table 7.3 and assume the rational triangular hydrograph shape. What is the peak discharge if a maximum runoff coefficient is assumed?

2. Calculate the time of concentration for overland flow on sandy soil of 5% slope for a distance of 500 ft by using the SCS method. The soil has a high water table resulting in a potential watershed storage of only 0.5 in. Compare these figures by using the data in Figure 7.9. Discuss the results.

3. Explain in your own words the meaning of rainfall excess as it affects time of concentration.

4. Calculate the peak runoff from a residential area with similar watershed soil and surface characteristics. The area is 20 ac in size with 40% imperviousness. Use a rainfall intensity of 3 in./hr for 1 hr. Do the calculations by using the rational formula and the SCS typical hydrograph procedure. Compare results and discuss assumptions. The pervious area does not contribute runoff.

5. Assume that the hydrograph of Problem 4 had an attenuation factor of 520. What is the peak discharge? Now, assume that only 50% of the impervious area is directly connected and the soil is very permeable and can store 6 in. of water before saturation. The duration of rainfall is 1 hr. What is your estimate of peak discharge? Again, state your reasoning.

6. Using longhand calculations, estimate the time of concentration using Izzard's formula and the kinematic equation. There is 300 ft of overland flow, the rain intensity is for a short duration storm, the flow slope is 0.05, and the area is sodded.

7. By using longhand calculations and the SCS unit–time discrete hydrograph procedure, develop the resulting triangular hydrograph for one time step using the watershed data of Table 7.6, a hydrograph attenuation factor of 250, and a constant rainfall of 2 in. over 4 hr. Use $\Delta D = 10$ min = duration of one rainfall increment; the curve number method for infiltration is used to estimate rainfall excess from the pervious area.

8. Increase the attenuation factor to 350 with the same input assumptions of Problem 7 and discuss your results. Now change the hyetograph to 0.25 in. for the first ΔD, 0.50 in. for the second ΔD, 1 in. for the third ΔD, and 0.25 in. for the fourth ΔD. How do the resulting peak discharges compare.

9. Prove mathematically one of the attenuation factors (other than 484) of Table 7.4.

10. Calculate the storage needed for the rainfall excess from a 30-ac, 40% directly connected impervious area, and a 0.5-in. rainstorm. State your assumptions. Develop a hydrograph if the time of concentration is 1 hr and the rain lasted 1 hr. Prove the area under the hydrograph equals your pond storage (by example calculations). The runoff coefficient is 0.72.

11. Develop two instantaneous hydrographs for the watershed of Table 7.6. Use the hyetograph of Figure 7.4. The percentage of the impervious area that is directly connected is 60 and should be used in the analysis. One hydrograph is estimated without any stormwater management. The second hydrograph is estimated considering 1 in. of initial abstraction over the total area (stormwater management). Compare the resulting hydrograph shapes and comment on your results.

12. Use the assumptions of the rational method (triangular hydrograph, constant rainfall intensity) and, by hand calculations, compute the peak discharge for the data of Problem 11. Compare and discuss your results. Why is the rational method not a reasonable approximation for the peak in this case?

13. An area of the county requires use of the 1 in 10-year storm frequency for detention basin design (use curves from Appendix C or other similar ones). What duration (1 or 6 hr) produces the largest detention basin, if the outpout hydrograph is 10 ft^3/sec, the watershed area is 50 ac, the rational coefficient is 0.8, the output hydrograph starts at 1 hr at a constant 10 ft^3/sec, and the time of concentration is 1 hr? Only compare the two duration storms and use the rational formula.

14. For Watershed No. 2 in Figure 7.24, and the data of Table 7.14, develop a discharge hydrograph by using the contributing area method. Compare your results to the peak discharge calculated using the rational formula. Use the hypothetical storm intensity of Figure 7.25 or make up your own

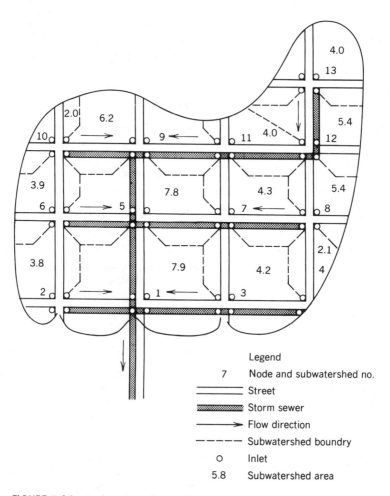

FIGURE 7.24   A plan view of watershed No. 2.

of similar complexity. Compare your results to a hydrograph by using the data of Example Problem 7.4 (Watershed No. 1).

15. Compare the two hydrographs of Figure 7.20 with the hydrograph resulting from the use of the Rational Formula applied to the total watershed of Figure 7.16.

16. A pre- versus post-development hydrograph analysis for a 100-ac watershed must be completed. The precondition watershed has a runoff coefficient of .2 and a hydrograph shape with a peak attenuation factor of .31. The postcondition is most likely to have a hydrograph shape similar to the standard SCS–peak attenuation factor and a runoff coefficient of .4. If

TABLE 7.14 Data Sheet for Watershed 2 Unit Hydrograph Determination

UPSTREAM NODE/ DOWNSTREAM NODE	SURFACE TYPE (RATIONAL C)	TOTAL CONTRIBUTING AREA (ac)	EFFECTIVE CONTRIBUTING AREA (ac)	TIME OF CONCENTRATION TO DOWNSTREAM NODE (min)	Σt_c to DOWNSTREAM NODE (min)
1/1	Residential (0.36)	7.9	2.84	6.1	6.1
2/1	Residential (0.36)	3.8	1.37	5.2	11.3
3/1	Residential (0.36)	4.2	1.51	5.2	11.3
5/1	Residential (0.36)	7.8	2.81	6.1	12.2
4/3	Residential (0.36)	2.1	0.76	5.2	16.5
6/5	Residential (0.36)	3.9	1.40	5.2	17.4
7/5	Commercial 50% Residential 50% (0.61)	4.3	2.60	5.2	17.4
9/5	Residential (0.36)	6.2	2.23	6.1	18.3
10/9	Residential (0.36)	2.0	0.72	4.2	22.5
8/7	Commercial (0.85)	5.4	4.59	5.2	22.6
11/9	Residential 20% Commercial 80% (0.75)	4.0	3.01	5.2	23.5
12/11	Commercial (0.85)	5.4	4.59	5.2	28.7
13/12	Commercial (0.85)	4.0	3.4	6.1	34.8

the time of concentration is one hour and the rainfall intensity is 5 in./hr, draw both hydrographs and estimate the peak discharge. Next, estimate the storage volume that approximates the condition of pre- versus post-peak discharge. Express storage in terms of cubic feet.

17. Using Example Problem 7.4, change the rainfall hyetograph to a constant intensity of 0.25 in./hr for 30 min and calculate the peak discharge using the other conditions of the example. Compare this to the peak discharge estimate using the rational formula.

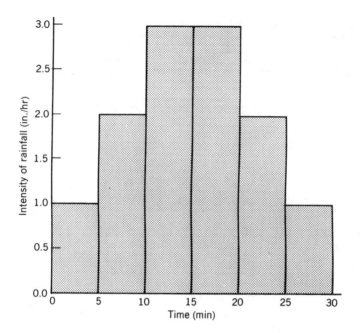

FIGURE 7.25 A hypothetical $\frac{1}{2}$-hr, 1-in. rainfall event.

18. Estimate the time and magnitude of a peak discharge from a 10-ac completely impervious smooth pavement area where the overland length is 1000 ft at a slope of 0.5 ft/100 ft. The geographic area is zone 7 in Florida and the design return period (frequency) is 1 in 10 yr. Regulations require the use of Kerby's equation.

19. Provide flow estimates for a synthetic unit hydrograph at times equal to half the peak flow time, at the peak flow time, 1.5 times the peak flow time, twice the peak flow time, and 5 times the peak flow time using the SCS curvilinear hydrograph shape. The watershed is a 40-ac commercial area with a percent impervious directly connected area of 32 ac and a 15-min time of concentration. Assume a rainfall duration of half the lag time. Also, what is the peak discharge if the attenuation factor were 400?

20. A 3-ft diameter storm sewer transports water to a discharge point. We are interested in the hydrograph shape at the discharge point. The sewer is 2000 ft long at a slope of 0.001 and $n = 0.012$.
    a. If the sewer is flowing full at peak discharge, estimate the routing constant for the Santa Barbara method. The computation interval is 2 min.
    b. What is the peak discharge?

c. If the resulting discharge hydrograph can be represented by a rational hydrograph shape, what is the volume discharge in cubic feet?

7.14

COMPUTER-ASSISTED PROBLEMS

1. For the watershed of Table 7.15, develop a hydrograph for a 25-yr, 24-hr storm using the Santa Barbara Urban Hydrograph procedure. At first, assume the impervious area is directly connected, then assuming only 50% directly connected impervious area. Note that the pervious curve number must be used if SMADA is being used. Comment on the changes in the hydrograph shape when all the impervious area is directly connected versus only partial connection.
2. Compare the resulting hydrographs of Problem 1 with a hydrograph generated using the SCS unit graph method with hydrograph attenuation of 350. Discuss your results.
3. Determine the hydrograph shape at a proposed river crossing of an interstate highway. The watershed is 300 ac with little impervious area, C type soils, and $\bar{t}_c = 3$ hr. State all your assumptions.
4. Increase by 50% the time of concentration in Problem 1 and compare peak discharges. Also, assume a 50% directly connected impervious area for the comparisons.
5. Using the SMADA computer program and a rainfall volume and time distribution for a 25 yr, 2 hr storm of your choice (for your area), develop a runoff hydrograph and the infiltration volume (watershed storage) for the following watershed condition (use Santa Barbara Hydrograph Routine).

$$\text{Area} = 200 \text{ ac}$$
$$t_c = 120 \text{ min}$$
$$\% \text{ Impervious} = 40$$
$$\% DCiA = 70$$
$$CN = 60 \text{ (pervious area)}$$

TABLE 7.15 Hypothetical Watershed

Watershed area = 250 ac
Time of concentration = 60 min
% Impervious = 60
% $DCiA$ = 100
CN for pervious area = 80

6. Provide a plot of infiltration volume (inches) versus percent impervious values for percent impervious values of 20, 40, 60, 80, and 90 using the same watershed conditions as in Problem 5 (except variable percent imperviousness). Also, construct a plot of peak discharge versus percent imperviousness. Note that the time of concentration is held constant. Comment on your results.

7. On the graph of Problem 6, also change the pervious area curve number to 85 and plot the resulting peak discharge and infiltration volumes as a function of percent imperviousness. Comment on your results.

8. For some watersheds, it is more reasonable to expect the time of concentration to decrease as the percent impervious area (which is directly connected) increases. Develop a peak discharge versus the percent impervious relationship (graphical plot) by using the data of Problem 1, except for the following changes:

t_c (min)	PERCENT IMPERVIOUS (DIRECTLY CONNECTED)
150	20
120	40
90	60
70	80
60	90

7.15

REFERENCES

Capice, J. 1984. *Estimating Runoff Rates and Volumes from Flat High-Water-Table Watersheds*, Master's Thesis, University of Florida, Gainesville.

Chow, V.T. 1959. *Open-Channel Hydraulics*, McGraw-Hill, New York, pp. 108–114.

Eagleson, Peter S. 1959. "Characteristics of Unit Hydrographs for Sewered Areas," American Society of Civil Engineers, Los Angeles, CA (unpublished).

Engman, E.T. 1983. "Roughness Coefficients for Routing Surface Runoff." *Proceedings of the Conference on Hydraulic Engineering*, American Society of Civil Engineers, pp. 560–565, New York.

Fleming, G. 1975. *Computer Simulation Techniques in Hydrology*. Elsevier, New York.

Florida Department of Transportation. 1986. *Drainage Manual*. Tallahassee, FL.

Golding, B.L. 1974. Area Water Control Plan, OCP Phase 6, Reynolds, Smith and Hills, Inc., Orlando, FL.

Golding, B.L. 1986, DABRO–Drainage Basin Runoff Model—A Computer Program, Hieldebrand Software, 8992 Islesworth Court, Orlando, FL 32819.

Ghioto, R. 1986. SCS Unit—A Computer Program. Advanced Engineering Technologies, 4558 Hoffner Avenue, Suite 301, Orlando, FL 32812.

Horton, R.E. 1938, "The Interpretation and Application of Runoff Plot Experiments with Reference to Soil Erosion Problems," *Proceedings of the Soil Science Society of America*, **3**, pp. 340–349.

Izzard, C.F. 1944. "The Surface–Profile of Overland Flow." *Transactions of the American Geophysics Union*, **25**, pp. 959–968.

Kerby, W.S. 1959. "Time of Concentration for Overland Flow," *Civil Engineering*, **29**(3), p. 174.

Kirpich, Z.P. 1940. "Time of Concentration of Small Agricultural Watersheds," *ASCE Civil Engineering*, **10**(6), p. 362, June.

Kuichling, E. 1889. "The Relation Between the Rainfall and the Discharge of Sewers in Populous Areas," *Transactions of the American Society of Civil Engineers*, **20**, pp. 1–56.

Mitchi, C. 1974. "Determine Urban Runoff the Simple Way," *Water Wastes Engineers*, **10**(1) January.

Mulvaney, T.J. 1851. "On the Use of Self-Registering Rain and Flood Gauges," *Institute of Civil Engineering Transactions* (Ireland), **4**(2), pp. 1–8.

Pagan, A.R. 1972. "Rational Formula Needs Change and Uniformity in Practical Applications," *Water and Sewage Works*.

Ragan, R.M. 1971. "A Nomograph Based on Kinematic Wave Theory for Determining Time of Concentration for Overland Flow," Report #44, College Park, MD, University of Maryland, December.

Ramser, C.E. 1927. "Runoff from Small Agricultural Areas," *Journal of Agricultural Research*, **34**(9), pp. 797–823.

Smisson, R.P.M. 1980. "The Single Pipe System for Stormwater Management," *Progressive Water Technology*, *Vol. 13*. International Air and Water Pollution Research/Pergamon Press, Oxford, England.

Stubchaer, J.M. 1975. "The Santa Barbara Urban Hydrograph Method," *Proceedings of the National Symposium of Hydrology and Sediment Control*, College of Engineering, University of Kentucky (Lexington, KY: ORES Publication).

U.S. Department of Agriculture, Soil Conservation Service (USDA-SCS). 1975. *National Engineering Handbook*, Section 4, Washington, DC.

U.S. Department of Agriculture, Soil Conservation Service. 1986. *Urban Hydrology for Small Watersheds*, Technical Release No. 55, Washington, DC, June.

Walsh, T.B. and Wanielista, M.P. 1982. *Low Flow Analysis in Stormwater Management*. University of Central Florida, Orlando, FL.

Wanielista, M.P. 1987. *KINEMAT, Kinematic Wave Equation*. STE Inc., 221 W. Trotters Drive, Maitland, FL 32751.

Williams, G.R. 1950. "Hydrology," in *Engineering Hydraulics*, H. Rouse, Ed. Wiley, New York.

C H A P T E R

....
....
....

8

FLOW
ROUTING

When we examine streamflow data from two points on the same stream, we see that hydrograph peaks are usually different. Without any additional tributary inputs between an upstream and downstream point, the upstream hydrograph peak is frequently larger than the downstream peak. The hydrograph peak reduction is called attenuation. The possible causes of attenuation relate to the transport characteristics including the storage volume between the upstream and downstream locations. Flow routing can be described as a procedure for predicting the temporal and spatial hydrograph.

Flow routing procedures route hydrographs over land, through conduits and through reservoirs. Flow routing methods are used to analyze the effects of conduit modifications, detention or reservoir storage, spillway sizing, a pumping station, changes in land use, and overtopping of highway embankments. Flood warning systems use some form of flood routing to predict flood stages before the actual stages are realized. Also, it should be noted that the models are useful for applications in stormwater detention pond design.

The theoretical basis for both hydrologic and hydraulic routing are presented. Hydrologic models have a closed-form solution equation. While hydraulic models usually require some form of numerical integration with a finite difference approach being illustrated. Hydrologic models are more commonly used and the most popular ones are presented.

8.1

THEORETICAL BASIS

Most of the hydrograph models of the previous chapters use a unit-graph approach, but frequently it is difficult to develop adequate relationships between physical watershed parameters and the unit-graph shape. Routing procedures may produce more accurate results.

Routing procedures are generally classified as hydrologic and hydraulic. Hydrologic procedures use the continuity equation and mathematical relationships between discharge and storage. Many investigators and most data suggest the discharge/storage relationship can be assumed to be linear, at least over a small storage differential volume. However, nonlinear relationships are also used. Hydraulic procedures use both the continuity and momentum equations.

The fundamental laws that govern and describe fluid flow are described by the momentum and continuity equations (Chow, 1959).

$$\frac{\partial y}{\partial x} + \frac{v}{g}\frac{\partial v}{\partial x} + \frac{1}{g}\frac{\partial v}{\partial t} = S_0 - S_f \qquad (8.1)$$

$$\frac{\partial A}{\partial t} + \frac{\partial Q}{\partial x} = q \qquad (8.2)$$

where

y = depth (ft)
v = velocity (ft/s)
x = longitudinal distance (ft)
t = time (sec)
g = gravitational acceleration (ft/sec^2)
S_0 = ground slope (ft/ft)
S_f = friction slope (ft/ft)
Q = flowrate (cfs)
A = flow area (ft^2)
q = discharge per unit length (cfs/ft)

Methods for solving the dynamic (Equation 8.1) and the continuity (Equation 8.2) relationships are approximate because generally more exact or closed-form solutions do not exist (Yevjevich, 1968 and Chow, 1959). Equations 8.1 and

8.2 have been approximated by the following equations (Manning's, Equation 8.3, and Continuity, Equation 8.4):

$$V = (1.486/n) R^{2/3} S_0^{1/2} \qquad (8.3)$$

$$Q = VA \qquad (8.4)$$

where

A = average area (ft^2)
R = hydraulic radius (ft)
V = velocity (ft/sec)
n = Manning's coefficient (Table 5.3)
S_0 = ground slope (ft/ft)
Q = flowrate (ft^3/sec)

One way to solve the continuity equation is to use finite difference equations to determine the depth of flow at each time period. The resulting depth of flow as a function of rainfall excess depth, $R(t)$, is:

$$R(t + \Delta t) = R(t) + \frac{[Q(t + \Delta t) - Q(t)]}{A}(\Delta t) \qquad (8.5)$$

Knowing the input flow rate to a drainage component, overland flow, gutter, sewer, etc., the output depth of flow or hydrograph can be calculated. Steady-state approximations can be made and hydrographs approximated, but the procedure is time consuming. Thus, computer programs were developed (Wanielista et al., 1986 and Hydrologic Engineering Center, 1979). These programs will aid in flow routing using either hydrologic or hydraulic routing procedures.

8.2

KINEMATIC WAVE

Hydrographs and flood waves can be described as either dynamic or kinematic. Dynamic waves are determined by mass, inertial forces, and pressure force while kinematic waves do not include mass and forces. Kinematic waves are determined by the weight of the fluid flowing downhill in response to gravity. Flows will remain approximately uniform along the channel, thus kinematic flows are classified as unsteady uniform flows. The flow is unsteady because velocity at a point can change with time. A uniform flow is one for which the velocity with respect to distance does not change for a given time period.

The equations used to express unsteady state flows were developed in 1870 by St. Venant. Derivations of the equations from the basic principles of mass momentum can be found in Chow (1959) or Henderson (1966). When the dynamic terms in the momentum equation (Equation 8.1) are minimal, this implies that the slope of the bed is about equivalent to the friction slope ($S_0 = S_f$) and with no backwater effects, the discharge can be described as a function of flow depth if one assumes the bed slope and bed material to remain constant.

$$Q = \alpha A^m \tag{8.6}$$

where

Q = flow rate (cfs)
α, m = kinematic wave constants
A = cross-sectional area (ft^2)

The momentum equation has been reduced to a functional relationship and what remains is the movement of flow using the continuity equation. Substituting Equation 8.6 into Equation 8.2, one obtains

$$\partial A / \partial t + \alpha m A^{(m-1)} \partial A / \partial x = q$$

and

$$\alpha m A^{(m-1)} \cong \alpha m (\bar{A}^{m-1}) \frac{\Delta A}{\Delta X} \tag{8.7}$$

This equation can now be solved for the only dependent variable (A) by using a numerical technique. There are several methods in use to solve the equation (Mahmood and Yevjevich, 1975). The finite difference method will be presented because of its general acceptability (Hydrologic Engineering Center, 1985).

The finite difference method is a "point approximation" to the partial differential equation. It uses simple difference equations to replace the partial differential equations for an array of space and time points (Figure 8.1). It is known as an explicit solution method. The discharge and water surface elevations are computed for each intersection point. Computations advance along the downstream direction for each time step (Δt) until all the flows and stages are calculated over the entire time. Substituting the area differences into Equation 8.7, one obtains

$$\frac{A_{i,j} - A_{i,j-1}}{\Delta t} + \alpha m \left[(A_{i,j-1} + A_{i-1,j-1})/2 \right]^{m-1}$$

$$* \left(\frac{A_{i,j-1} - A_{i-1,j-1}}{\Delta x} \right) = \bar{q} \tag{8.8}$$

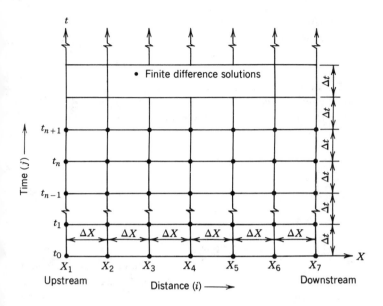

FIGURE 8.1 The characteristic curves on a fixed $X - t$ grid.

where

$$\bar{q} = (q_{i,j} + q_{i,j-1})/2 \qquad (8.9)$$

j = time step, and i = the space position. The only unknown is $A_{i,j}$, thus rearranging Equation 8.8 one obtains

$$A_{i,j} = A_{i,j-1} + \bar{q}(\Delta t) - \alpha m (\Delta t / \Delta x)\left[(A_{i,j-1} + A_{i-1,j-1})/2\right]^{m-1}$$
$$*\left[A_{i,j-1} - A_{i-1,j-1}\right] \qquad (8.10)$$

Once $A_{i,j}$ is known, $Q_{i,j}$ is calculated from

$$Q_{i,j} = \alpha\left(A_{i,j}\right)^{m} \qquad (8.11)$$

This standard form is used when the average wave celerity, $\bar{c}$, is less than the space-to-time ratio.

$$\bar{c} < \frac{\Delta x}{\Delta t} \qquad (8.12)$$

The average celerity for a reach is based on the average flow area for the time step and is calculated using

$$\bar{c} = \alpha m (\bar{A})^{m-1} \tag{8.13}$$

The choice of Δx and Δt should be done to identify the peak discharge and develop a convergence for the solution procedure. In general, the following guidelines should be used (Hydrologic Engineering Center, 1985).

$$\frac{L}{50} \leq \Delta x \leq \frac{L}{2} \tag{8.14}$$

where

$$L = \text{total length of flow}$$

The time step is the time interval at which the ordinates of the inflow hydrograph are represented. The time step should be sufficiently short to not only define the hydrograph and peak flow within the model accuracy but also provide for numerical stability of the mathematics involved in the routing procedure. A guideline for the selection of the time step is

$$\Delta t \leq t_p/5 \tag{8.15}$$

where

$$t_p = \text{time to peak}$$

However, sometimes Δt is controlled by the time interval during which precipitation data were collected.

If wave celerity $\geq \Delta x / \Delta t$, it is possible for a flood wave to propagate more rapidly through space and time than the numerical technique can estimate by the standard equations. Numerical stability can be gained by rewriting the continuity equation and solving for flow rate, or

$$\frac{(A_{i-1,j} - A_{i-1,j-1})}{\Delta t} + (Q_{i,j} - Q_{i-1,j})/\Delta x = \bar{q}$$

Solving for $Q_{i,j}$, the only unknown

$$Q_{i,j} = Q_{i-1,j} + \bar{q}\,\Delta x - \left(\frac{\Delta x}{\Delta t}\right)(A_{i-1,j} - A_{i-1,j-1}) \tag{8.16}$$

and the area is calculated from

$$A_{i,j} = (Q_{i,j}/\alpha)^{1/m} \tag{8.17}$$

Equations 8.16 and 8.17 are known as the conservative form of the kinematic equations.

8.2.1 Overland Flow

For an overland flow situation of unit width and using Manning's equation for shallow depth (y_0), the hydraulic radius is simply equal to depth and the area of flow is depth, thus, Equations 8.3 and 8.4 can be combined with $R = y_0$, and $A = y_0$ and q_0 as discharge per unit width:

$$q_0 = \frac{1.486}{N} S_0^{1/2} y_0^{5/3} \tag{8.18}$$

and

$$q_0 = \alpha_0 y_0^{m_0} \tag{8.19}$$

where the subscripts (0) refer to overland flow and the Manning's roughness parameter is defined as N because it usually has a larger value than the channel or pipe roughness factor n. Suggested values were shown in Table 7.1. If a section of overland flow is constant and the bed consists of the same surface material, α_0 and m_0 are defined by equating q_0 in equations 8.18 and 8.19 as (Hydrologic Engineering Center, 1979):

$$\alpha_0 = \frac{\left(1.486 S_0^{1/2}\right)}{N}$$

and

$$m_0 = \tfrac{5}{3} \tag{8.20}$$

The continuity equation 8.2 can be rewritten for shallow flows of unit width as

$$\frac{\partial y_0}{\partial t} + \frac{\partial q_0}{\partial x} = r \tag{8.21}$$

where

$$r = \text{rainfall excess rate } \left(\text{cfs/ft}^2\right)$$

Substituting Equation 8.19 into Equation 8.21 and considering overland flow:

$$\frac{\partial y_0}{\partial t} + \alpha_0 m_0 y_0^{(m-1)} \frac{\partial y_0}{\partial x} = r \tag{8.22}$$

which is an equation parallel in structure to Equation 8.7 and also can be solved by finite difference methods. For overland flow calculations, rainfall excess rate (ft/s or cfs/ft^2) is used and replaces $\bar{q}$.

8.2.2   Kinematic Parameters for Channel Shapes

The concept of hydrograph generation using the kinematic wave technique can be applied to overland and conduit flows as represented in Figure 8.2. Depicted are four basic elements of a flow system and their kinematic parameters. For a trapezoidal section, it is not possible to derive a simple formula for α and m, however, given a depth (y_c), the Manning equation can be solved as

$$Q_c = \frac{\left(1.486 S_c^{1/2}\right)}{n} \left(\bar{A}_c\right)^{5/3} \left\{ \frac{1}{\left[w + zy_c\left(1 + z^2\right)^{1/2}\right]} \right\}^{2/3} \tag{8.23}$$

and m is approximately $5/3$. An example problem is beneficial to display the calculations, however, computer solutions are more reasonable because of the time involved and the choice of Δx and Δt are not always known.

Overland Flow

$$\alpha_0 = \frac{\left(1.486 S_0^{1/2}\right)}{N}$$

$$m_0 = 5/3$$

Triangular Channel

$$\alpha_c = (0.94/n) S^{1/2} [Z/(1 + Z^2)]^{1/3}$$

$$m_c = 4/3$$

Pipe (Circular)

$$\alpha_c = (0.804/n) S^{1/2} D^{1/6}$$

$$m_c = 5/4$$

Rectangular

$$\alpha_c = (1.486/n) S^{1/2} w^{2/3}$$

$$m_c = 5/3$$

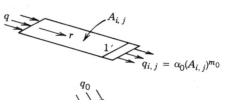

$$q_{i, j} = \alpha_0 (A_{i, j})^{m_0}$$

$$Q_c = \alpha_c (A_{i, j})^{m_c}$$

$$Q_c = \alpha_c (A_{i, j})^{m_c}$$

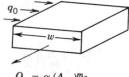

$$Q_c = \alpha_c (A_{i, j})^{m_c}$$

FIGURE 8.2   Elements and parameters.

□ **EXAMPLE PROBLEM 8.1**

A 1/5-acre parking lot is about 60 ft wide and 150 ft long with the lot sloping toward one side. It is completely impervious with no initial abstraction or infiltration. A rainfall of 1 in./hr is expected during the first 5 min, then 4 in./hr for the next 5 min and 2 in./hr for the last 5 min. There is a triangular ditch on one side of the lot that collects the overland flow of water (see Figure 8.3). A time step of 5 min (300 sec) is chosen because of the precipitation data interval. The space interval is set at 30 ft for overland flow and 50 ft for channel flow. Estimate the peak discharge and a hydrograph shape using the kinematic equations. Additional data are shown in Figure 8.3.

Solution

First calculate the parameters (α, m) for both the overland and channel flow equations. Next, calculate the flow to the side channel from overland flow, being careful to substitute rainfall excess (cfs/ft^2) for average unit

Size: $\frac{1}{5}$-Acre Parking Lot

Overland Flow

   Flow = 60 ft

  Slope = 0.05 ft/ft

    $n = 0.15$

   $\Delta x = 30$ ft

$\Delta t = 5$ min = 300 sec

   $m_0 = 1.67$

Triangular Channel

  Flow = 150 ft

Slope = 0.005 ft/ft

  $n = 0.025$

Side slope = 1 on 2

  $\Delta x = 50$ ft

  $m_c = 1.33$

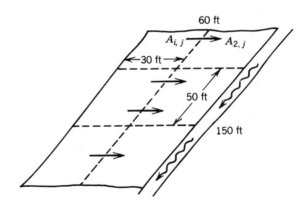

FIGURE 8.3 Example Problem 8.1 schematic.

TABLE 8.1   Overland Flow Calculations—Example Problem 8.1 (let $A_{i,i} = y_{i,i}$)

TIME		RAINFALL EXCESS RATE $\bar{r}$ (cfs/ft^2)	$A_{1,i}$ (ft^2)	$A_{2,i}$ (ft^2)	CHANNEL FLOW $q_{2,i}$(cfs/ft)
STEP (j)	(min)				
0	0	0	0	0	0
1	5	[a]2.31×10^{-5}	[b]0.006930	0.006930	0.000550
2	10	9.26×10^{-5}	[c]0.018130	[d]0.024001	0.004436
3	15	4.63×10^{-5}	0.011962	0.020450	0.003352
4	20	0	0	0.010935	0.001178
5	25	0	0	0	0

[a]1 in./hr $\times$ 1 ft/12 in. $\times$ 1 hr/3600 sec = 2.31(10^{-5}) ft/sec or cfs/ft^2
[b]Using Equation 8.10: for $\bar{c} < \Delta x/\Delta t$, and $\bar{r} = \bar{q}$

$$A_{1,1} = A_{1,0} + \bar{r}(\Delta t) - \alpha_0 m_0 \left(\frac{\Delta t}{\Delta x}\right)\left[\frac{(A_{1,0} + A_{0,0})}{2}\right][A_{1,0} - A_{0,0}]$$

$$= 0. + 2.31(10^{-5})(300) - 2.22(1.67)(300/30)[(0 + 0)/2](0 - 0)$$

$$= 0.00693 \text{ ft}^2$$

Check celerity:

$$\bar{c} = \alpha_0 m_0 (\bar{A})^{m_0 - 1} = 2.22(1.67)[(0 + 0.00693)/2]^{0.67}$$

$$= 0.08 \text{ ft/sec}$$

thus $\bar{c} < \Delta x/\Delta t$ or $0.08 < 0.10$ ft/s and using Equation 8.11,

$$q_{1,1} = \alpha_0 [A_{1,1}]^{m_0} = 2.22[0.00693]^{1.67}$$

$$= 0.000550 \text{ cfs/ft}$$

[c]$A_{1,2} = A_{1,1} + \bar{r}(\Delta t) - \alpha_0 m_0 (\Delta t/\Delta x)[(A_{1,1} + A_{0,1})/2]^{m_0 - 1}[A_{1,1} - A_{0,1}]$

$$= 0.00693 + 9.26 \times 10^{-5}(300) - 2.22(1.67)(300/30)[(0.00693 + 0)/2]^{0.67}$$

$$\times (0.00693 - 0)$$

$$= 0.00693 + .02778 - .005773 = 0.028937$$

Check celerity:

$$\bar{c} = 2.22(1.67)[(0.00693 + 0.028937)/2]^{0.67} = 0.25 \text{ ft/s}$$

continued

since $\bar{c} > \Delta x/\Delta t$, use conservative Equation 8.16.

$$q_{1,2} = Q_{0,2} + \bar{r}(\Delta x) - (\Delta x/\Delta t)[A_{0,2} - A_{0,1}]$$

$$= 0 + 9.26 \times 10^{-5}(30) - (30/300)(0 - 0)$$

$$= 0.002778 \text{ cfs/ft}$$

$$A_{1,2} = (0.0022778/2.22)^{0.6} = 0.01813 \text{ ft}^2$$

$$^d A_{2,2} = A_{2,1} + \bar{r}(\Delta t) - \alpha_0 m_0 (\Delta t/\Delta x)[(A_{2,1} + A_{1,1})/2]^{m_0-1}[A_{2,1} - A_{1,1}]$$

$$= 0.00693 + 9.26 \times 10^{-5}(300) - 2.22(1.67)(300/30)$$

$$\times [(0.00693 + 0.00693)/2]^{0.67}(0)$$

$$= 0.00693 + 0.02778 - 0 = 0.03471 \qquad \text{and} \qquad \bar{c} > \Delta x/\Delta t$$

$$q_{2,2} = Q_{1,2} + \bar{r}(\Delta x) - (\Delta x/\Delta t)[A_{1,2} - A_{1,1}]$$

$$= 0.002778 + 9.26 \times 10^{-5}(30) - (30/300)(0.018131 - 0.00693)$$

$$= 0.002778 + 0.002778 - 0.0011220 = 0.004436 \text{ cfs}$$

$$A_{2,2} = (0.004436/2.22)^{0.6} = 0.024001 \text{ ft}^2$$

width flow rate. Some of the calculations are detailed in Table 8.1. The standard formula is assumed to be accurate, however, celerity is checked and the formula adjusted. The celerity by time step is

$$\bar{c} = \frac{\Delta x}{\Delta t} = \frac{30}{300} = 0.10 \text{ ft/s}$$

Next, calculations for flow in the triangular ditch are completed and are shown in Table 8.2.

α Calculations

For Overland Flow

$$\alpha_0 = (1.486/N)S_0^{1/2}$$

$$= (1.486/0.15)(.05)^{1/2}$$

$$= 2.22$$

For Triangular Channel

$$\alpha_c = [(0.94S^{1/2})/n][Z/(1 + Z^2)]^{1/3}$$

$$= [(0.94(0.005)^{1/2})/0.025][2/(1 + 2^2)]^{1/3}$$

$$= 1.96$$

Rainfall

1 in./hr for first 5 min or 0.08 in. in 5 min
4 in./hr for next 5 min or 0.33 in. in 5 min
2 in./hr for last 5 min or 0.17 in. in 5 min
no rainfall past 15 min

TABLE 8.2   Kinematic Calculation Triangular Channel—Example Problem 8.1

i	t (min)	q (cfs/ft)	$A_{1,i}$ (ft²)	$A_{2,i}$ (ft²)	$Q_{3,i}$ (cfs/ft²)
0	0	0	0	0	0
1	5	0.000550	0.04077	0.06211	0.06535
2	10	0.004436	0.19511	0.31376	0.59863
3	15	0.003352	0.15813	0.28767	0.54415
4	20	0.001178	0.07218	0.13229	0.21696

The final shape of the hydrograph can be more accurately defined if the time step were made smaller, say $\Delta t = 2$ min. The time to peak is about 10 min and a guideline for the selection of Δt requires $\Delta t \leq t_P/5$.

□

8.3

ROUTING BY THE INVENTORY EQUATION

There exist in common use, at least two hydrologic flood-routing methods for routing an inflow hydrograph-through storage in a reservoir, river, or stormwater detention basin. Routing flows through channels or streams is considered to have storage between the inlet and outlet structures or mile markers and, thus, is similar to reservoir/detention basin storage. The inventory method and the Muskingum formula are two common ways of flood routing using the continuity equation. Both methods assume a relationship between the inflow and outflow hydrographs with the outflow being dependent on previous outflow and inflows. Consider the hydrographs of Figure 8.4 that show the primary characteristics of routing. The outflow hydrograph is determined from a given inflow hydrograph. The hydrograph shape is modified as water is stored. The maximum storage occurs when the inflow and outflow rates are equal. Up to this point in time, storage was increasing because the rate of inflow exceeded outflow rate. Beyond the time of maximum storage, the outflow rate exceeds inflow rate, thus storage decreases.

By using the continuity Equation 8.2 and considering $\partial Q/\partial x$ is the change in flow per unit channel length (ft²/sec) or inflow minus outflow, $\partial Q/\partial x$ is

$$\frac{\partial O}{\partial x} = \frac{I - O}{\Delta x} \tag{8.24}$$

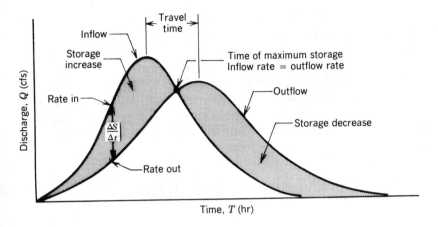

FIGURE 8.4 Inflow and outflow hydrographs.

where

I = inflow, L^3/T

O = outflow, L^3/T

The change of area per unit time, $\Delta A/\Delta t$ multiplied by channel length can be considered as a change in channel storage volume, or

$$\frac{\Delta A\, \Delta x}{\Delta t\, \Delta x} = \frac{\Delta S}{(\Delta x)(\Delta t)} \qquad (8.25)$$

where

ΔS = storage volume, L^3

Δt = time interval, t

Substituting Equations 8.24 and 8.25 into Equation 8.2 and multiplying by Δx and Δt yields a form of the inventory equation:

$$I(\Delta t) - O(\Delta t) = \Delta S \qquad (8.26)$$

recognizing that ΔS includes $q\, \Delta x\, \Delta t$ term. Dividing by Δt and using average values,

$$\bar{I} - \bar{O} = \frac{\Delta S}{\Delta t} \qquad (8.27)$$

and by taking the limit as $\Delta t \rightarrow O$

$$\bar{I} - \bar{O} = \frac{dS}{dt} \qquad (8.28)$$

Most of the more commonly used methods of flood routing are based solely on the solution of the inventory equation, which provides for conservation of mass. Typically, these methods employ a storage discharge relationship in a repetitive manner to solve the inventory equation to determine the ordinates of the outflow hydrograph for a given inflow hydrograph. The inventory equation as applied to a reservoir routing states that the " volume of inflow minus the volume of outflow over a given time interval is equal to the change in volume stored over that time interval." Therefore, the inventory equation can be written in the following form:

$$S_2 - S_1 = \bar{I}(\Delta t) - \bar{O}(\Delta t) = \Delta S = \left[\frac{(I_1 + I_2)}{2}\right](\Delta t) - \left[\frac{(O_1 + O_2)}{2}\right](\Delta t)$$

$$(8.29)$$

where

$\bar{I}$ = the average inflow during the time step, Δt, (L^3/T)
$\bar{O}$ = the average outflow during the time step, Δt, (L^3/T)
ΔS = the volume stored during the time step, Δt, (L^3)

Collecting the unknowns of Equation 8.29 on one side of the equation, letting $(I_1 + I_2)/2 = \bar{I}$ (average inflow), and letting N_2 be a variable defined as

$$N_2 = S_2 + \left(\frac{O_2}{2}\right)\Delta t = S_1 - \left(\frac{O_1}{2}\right)\Delta t + \bar{I}\Delta t \qquad (8.30)$$

To solve the problem one must find a relationship between outflow and storage, called an O–S relationship.
Thus, make

$$N = S + \left(\frac{O}{2}\right)\Delta t \qquad \text{(volume units)}$$

or in another form

$$N = \left(\frac{S}{\Delta t}\right) + \left(\frac{O}{2}\right) \qquad \text{(flow units)}$$

An N–O relationship can be developed from the O–S relationship, since N is a function of S and O.
Equation 8.30 can be written in another form if we add $(O_1 \Delta t)$ to both sides of the equation (letting $i - 1 = 1$; $i = 2$):

$$O_{i-1}\Delta t + S_i + \left(\frac{O_i}{2}\right)\Delta t = S_{i-1} + \left(\frac{O_{i-1}}{2}\right)\Delta t + \bar{I}\Delta t + O_{i-1}\Delta t$$

$$N_i = N_{i-1} + \bar{I}\Delta t - O_{i-1}\Delta t \qquad (8.31)$$

or

$$N = \bar{I}\Delta t - O_{i-1}\Delta t \qquad \text{(volume units)} \qquad (8.32)$$

Since Equation 8.29 is the basis of many hydrologic routing methods, its application in a particular routing method is demonstrated in Example Problem 8.2.

☐ **EXAMPLE PROBLEM 8.2**

Given an inflow hydrograph and a detention volume discharge relationship, determine the outflow hydrograph using an inventory equation.

INPUT HYDROGRAPH		BASIN DISCHARGE	
TIME (hr)	FLOW (cfs)	VOLUME (ft^3)	DISCHARGE
0	0	$\leq 10,000$	0
1	25	$> 10,000$	1 ft^3/sec/10,000 ft^3
2	20		
3	16		
4	12		
5	9		
6	6		
7	3		
8	0		

Solution

$S-O$ Relationship

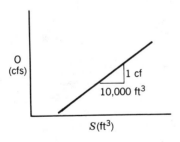

$$O = (S - 10,000)/10,000 \qquad \text{for } S > 10,000 \text{ cf and}$$

$$S = 10,000(O) + 10,000 \qquad \text{if } O \text{ is } > \text{zero}$$

TABLE 8.3 Calculations for Example Problem 8.2

ASSUME AT TIME ZERO, 10,000 ft³ OF WATER IS IN STORAGE.

SOLUTION: $t = 1$ hr $= 3600$ sec

FROM $N-O$ AND $S-O$ RELATIONSHIPS

TIME (hr)	I_{i-1} (cfs)	I_i (cfs)	i (cfs)	$i\Delta t$ (ft³)	S_{i-1} (ft³)	O_{i-1} (cfs)	$O_{i-1}\dfrac{\Delta t}{2}$ (ft³)	$N_i = i\Delta t + S_{i-1} - O_{i-1}\dfrac{\Delta t}{2}$ (ft³)	O_i (cfs)	S_i (ft³)
0	—	0	0	0	10,000	0	0	10,000	0	10,000
1	0	25	12.5	45,000	10,000	0	0	55,000	3.814	48,140
2	25	20	22.5	81,000	48,140	3.814	6,865	122,275	9.515	105,150
3	20	16	18.0	64,800	105,150	9.515	17,127	152,823	12.104	131,036
4	16	12	14.0	50,400	131,036	12.104	21,787	159,649	12.682	136,821
5	12	9	10.5	37,800	136,821	12.682	22,828	151,800	12.016	130,164
6	9	6	7.5	27,000	130,164	12.016	21,629	135,535	10.639	116,386
7	6	3	4.5	16,200	116,386	10.639	19,132	113,454	8.767	97,673
8	3	0	1.5	5,400	97,673	8.767	15,780	87,292	6.550	75,502
9	0	0	0	0	75,502	6.550	11,790	63,712	4.552	55,519
10	0	0	0	0	55,519	4.552	8,194	47,325	3.163	41,632
11	0	0	0	0	41,632	3.163	5,693	35,939	2.198	31,980
12	0	0	0	0	31,980	2.198	3,956	28,024	1.527	25,274
13	0	0	0	0	25,274	1.527	2,749	22,525	1.062	20,615
14	0	0	0	0	20,615	1.062	1,912	18,703	0.738	17,375
15	0	0	0	0	17,375	0.738	1,328	16,047	0.512	15,125
16	0	0	0	0	15,125	0.512	922	14,203	0.356	13,562
17	0	0	0	0	13,562	0.356	641	12,921	0.248	12,476
18	0	0	0	0	12,476	0.248	446	12,029	0.172	11,720
19	0	0	0	0	11,720	0.172	310	11,410	0.120	11,200
20	0	0	0	0	11,200	0.120	216	10,984	0.0834	10,834
21	0	0	0	0	10,834	0.0834	150	10,683	0.058	10,580
22	0	0	0	0	10,580	0.058	104	10,475	0.040	10,402
23	0	0	0	0	10,402	0.040	72	10,330	0.028	10,280
24	0	0	0	0	10,280	0.028	50	10,230	0.020	10,195
25	0	0	0	0	10,195	0.020	36	10,159	0.013	10,134
26	0	0	0	0	10,134	0.013	23	10,111	0.009	10,094
27	0	0	0	0	10,094	0.009	16	10,078	0.007	10,066
28	0	0	0	0	10,066	0.007	13	10,053	0.004	10,045

Checking: $\Sigma I \Delta t = 327,600$ ft³ $\Sigma O_{i-1}(\Delta t/2) = 327,538$ ft³.
< 5% error in acceptable.
The input and output hydrographs are shown in Figure 8.5.

$N-O$ Relationship:

$$N = S + \frac{O}{2}(\Delta t) = 10,000(O) + 10,000 + \left(\frac{O}{2}\right)(3600)$$

for $\Delta t = 1$ hr:

$$N = 11,800(O) + 10,000$$

and

$$N - 10,000 = 11,800(O)$$

$$O = \frac{(N - 10,000)}{11,800} \qquad \text{if } O \text{ is } > \text{zero}$$

The solution is tabulated in Table 8.3 and the graphs are shown in Figure 8.5. ☐

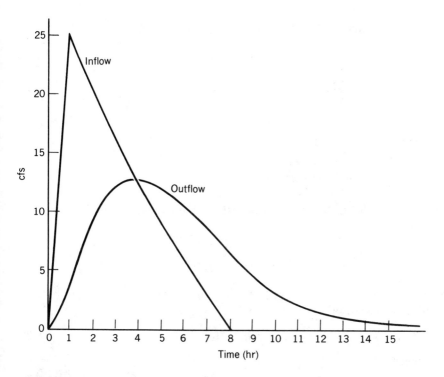

FIGURE 8.5 A graphical plot of input – output hydrograph.

8.4

ROUTING BY THE MUSKINGUM METHOD

The Muskingum method for flood routing was developed for the Muskingum Conservancy District flood control study in the 1930s. A discussion of the development with assumptions will illustrate its use. A stream length is chosen that has near constant geometric properties, and at the beginning of the reach, the inflow and storage are assumed to be related to depth by the following equation forms.

$$I = a y_u^n \tag{8.33}$$

and

$$S_I = b y_u^m \tag{8.34}$$

where

I = inflow rate, L^3/T
S_I = storage inflow, L^3
y_u depth of flow upstream, L
a, b, m, n = constants for the stream reach

Similar equations are developed for the downstream point, or

$$O = a y_d^n \tag{8.35}$$

and

$$S_0 = b y_d^m \tag{8.36}$$

where

O = outflow rate, L^3/T
S_0 = outflow storage, L^3
y_d = depth of flow downstream, L

Equating depths upstream and downstream, the following equations result.

$$S_I = (b/a^{m/n})(I^{m/n}) \tag{8.37}$$

$$S_0 = (b/a^{m/n})(O^{m/n}) \tag{8.38}$$

Now, postulate that the storage (S) within the reach is a weighting of both the input and output, or

$$S = cS_I + (1 - c)S_0 \tag{8.39}$$

where

c = weighting factor between 0 and 0.5

when $c = 0.0$, maximum attenuation is achieved and when $c = 0.5$, the input hydrograph is not attenuated.

Let $K = b/a^{m/n}$ and $x = m/n$, such that Equation 8.39 is rewritten as

$$S = K[cI^x + (1 - c)O^x] \tag{8.40}$$

where

K = storage time constant for the reach, units of time

For rectangular channels, $n = 5/3$, $m = 1$ and $x = 0.6$ have been used. For natural channels, x has been calculated to be larger and in most cases x is assumed equal to 1.0, as was done in the Muskingam method. Thus, the Muskingum formula is

$$S = K[cI + (1 - c)O] \tag{8.41}$$

The constants of Equation 8.41 must be determined for a reach of stream. Field streamflow data are generally used for gaged sites and the experiences of the investigators are used for ungaged sites. Applications using streamflow data generally show that K is reasonably close to the travel time in the reach. When field data are available, Equation 8.41 can be written in difference form over successive time periods of analysis, Δt, where Δt is chosen to be less than K and greater than $2Kc$ (Chow, 1964).

$$S_2 - S_1 = K[c(I_2 - I_1) + (1 - c)(O_2 - O_1)] \tag{8.42}$$

Combining the inventory equation (8.29) with Equation 8.42 to eliminate the storage variables and solving for the unknown O_2, given I_2, I_1, and O_1, the following equation (8.43) results

$$O_2 = c_0 I_2 + c_1 I_1 + c_2 O_1 \tag{8.43}$$

in which

$$c_0 = \frac{-Kc + 0.5(\Delta t)}{K - Kc + 0.5(\Delta t)}$$

$$c_1 = \frac{Kc + 0.5(\Delta t)}{K - Kc + 0.5(\Delta t)}$$

$$c_2 = \frac{K - Kc - 0.5(\Delta t)}{K - Kc + 0.5(\Delta t)}$$

and

$$c_0 + c_1 + c_2 = 1.0$$

Note that the time units for K and Δt must be the same. If K and c are known with an upstream hydrograph, routing can be accomplished.

8.4.1 Muskingum Routing Constants K and c

When no flow or streamflow data are available, it is common to use the travel time in the stream reach to approximate K and $c = 0.2$. If inflow and outflow hydrograph records are available, better estimates of K and c are possible. Since storage and outflow are assumed to be related by Equation 8.41, an acceptable value of c would be one that gives a linear relationship. After finding the linear relationship, K is the reciprocal of the slope or

$$K = \frac{\Delta S}{\Delta O} \tag{8.44}$$

Equating K values of Equation 8.44 and the Muskingum equation (Equation 8.41), one obtains a relationship

$$\frac{S}{cI + (1 - c)O} = \frac{\Delta S}{\Delta O} \tag{8.45}$$

☐ **EXAMPLE PROBLEM 8.3**

Determine an estimate for K and c for a river segment (reach) that is believed to have relatively constant cross-sectional area and slope, if inflow and outflow hydrographs are available as shown in Table 8.4.

TABLE 8.4 Calculations for Example Problem 8.3

Day	i (cfs)	$\overline{O}$ ($c = 0$) (cfs)	S^a (cfs-days)	WEIGHTED DISCHARGE (cfs)[b] $c = 0.1$	$c = 0.2$	$c = 0.3$
1	0.0	0.0	0.0	0.0	0.0	0.0
2	35.0	10.0	25.0	12.5	15.0	17.5
3	95.0	50.0	70.0	54.5	59.0	63.5
4	60.0	60.0	70.0	60.0	60.0	60.0
5	35.0	50.0	55.0	48.5	47.0	45.5
6	20.0	35.0	40.0	33.5	32.0	30.5
7	10.0	25.0	25.0	23.5	22.0	20.5
8	5.0	15.0	15.0	14.5	13.0	12.0
9	0.0	10.0	10.0	9.0	8.0	7.0
10	0.0	5.0	5.0	4.5	4.0	3.5
11	0.0	0.0	0.0	0.0	0.0	0.0

$^a S_i = S_{i-1} + (\overline{I}_i - \overline{O}_i)$.
$^b O_i = c\overline{I}_i + (1 - c)\overline{O}_i$.

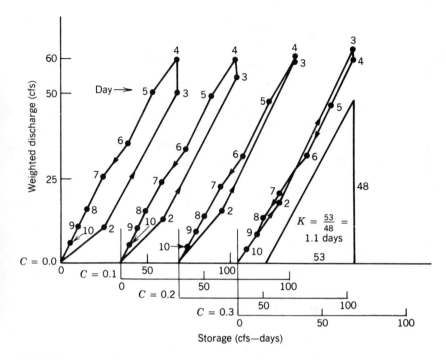

FIGURE 8.6 A discharge – storage curve — Example problem 8.3.

Solution

It is assumed that the water surface profile is uniform or unbroken. The inventory equation (Equation 8.29) is used to solve for the cumulative storage, and the denominator of Equation 8.45 is used to calculate the weighted discharge for various assumed values of c. Graphs are drawn for the rising and falling limbs of the outflow hydrograph, and the loop that best approximates a straight line is chosen (see Figure 8.6). A straight line results because of Equations 8.38 and 8.41. The estimates for K and c are 1.1 days and 0.3, respectively. □

8.4.2 Additional Methods for Estimating K and c

When streamflow data are available, a graphic display of the upstream and downstream hydrograph produces insight on the translation and by proportional analysis an estimate of K.

From Figure 8.7, a relationship between the inflow and outflow hydrographs can be developed. This empirical relationship is generally chosen in time units. Similar triangles result in a relationship to estimate K using inflow

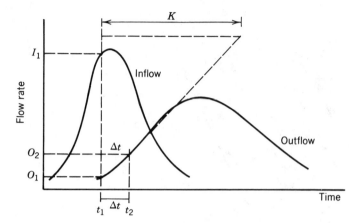

FIGURE 8.7 The graphical convex method.

and outflows at two consecutive periods of time.

$$\frac{O_2 - O_1}{\Delta t} = \frac{I_1 - O_1}{K} \qquad (8.46)$$

and

$$\frac{\Delta t}{K} = \frac{O_2 - O_1}{I_1 - O_1} \qquad (8.47)$$

The choice of Δt is made such that it is less than 20% of the time to peak. Thus, from stream flow data, the outflow and inflow hydrograph values are known, and K can be estimated.

Other equations for estimating the constants c and K have been developed from empirical equations, such as

$$K = \frac{LA}{3600} Q \qquad (8.48)$$

where
L = length between points (ft)
A = average cross-sectional area (ft^2)
Q = steady-state average discharge (ft^3/sec)

and

$$c = \frac{V}{V + 1.7} \qquad (8.49)$$

where

$$V = \text{steady-state velocity (ft/sec)}$$

☐ **EXAMPLE PROBLEM 8.4**

A flowrate of 5 ft^3/sec passes an upstream point in a stream and travels 5280 ft downstream in a rectangular channel and at the same time; the flowrate downstream is 3 ft^3/sec. Neglecting evaporation and infiltration, what is the next flowrate downstream if the channel is 8 ft wide with a channel slope of 0.001 and the roughness coefficient is 0.029?

Solution

Calculate the upstream conditions first using continuity and Manning's equation.

$$Q = AV = (1.486/0.029)(8d)[8d/(8 + 2d)]^{2/3}(0.001)^{1/2} = 5$$

$$d = 0.6 \text{ ft}; \quad \text{and} \quad A = bd = 8(0.6) = 4.8 \text{ ft}^2$$

$$V = \frac{Q}{A}$$

$$= \frac{5}{4.8} = 1.04 \text{ fps}$$

now

$$c = \frac{V}{(V + 1.7)} = \frac{1.04}{(1.04 + 1.70)} = 0.38$$

For the downstream conditions and the next time period:

$$O_2 = cI_1 + (1 - c)O_1$$

$$= (0.38)(5) + (0.62)(3)$$

$$= 3.76 \text{ cfs} \quad \square$$

☐ **EXAMPLE PROBLEM 8.5**

This problem was adopted from the U.S. Department of Transportation (FHWA, 1984) and is typical of highway design problems. A 6-mi reach of a channelized river is flooding and destroying homes. A channel

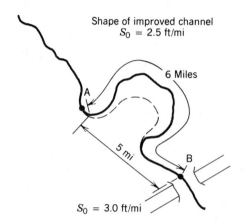

Shape of improved channel
$S_0 = 2.5$ ft/mi

6 Miles

A

5 mi

B

$S_0 = 3.0$ ft/mi

FIGURE 8.8 A proposed channel improvement.

improvement is proposed that will cut off the channelized river and reducing the length of channel to 5 mi (Figure 8.8). What effect will this channel improvement have on the peak discharge experienced at the roadway at point B? A synthetic hydrograph at point A is estimated for a 25-yr design discharge and is shown in Figure 8.9.

Solution

The average discharge for this hydrograph is 2200 cfs (71 cms). Using the cross-sectional data, the average travel time is computed by using a value of .025 for Manning's n and the following formulas.

$$V = \left(\frac{1.486}{.025}\right) R^{2/3} S_0^{1/2}$$

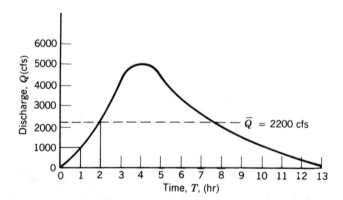

FIGURE 8.9 Hydrograph at point A.

In the original 6-mi reach, the average travel time is computed to be 0.70 hr. For the modified 5-mi reach, the average travel time is computed to be 0.55 hr. For the original reach, the coefficients c_0, c_1, and c_2 are first computed using $\Delta t = 1$ hr, an assumed value of $c = 0.2$, and $K = 0.70$ hr as follows:

$$c_0 = [-0.70(0.2) + 0.5(1)]/[0.70 - 0.70(0.2) + 0.5(1)] = 0.3396$$

$$c_1 = [0.70(0.2) + 0.5(1)]/[0.70 - 0.70(0.2) + 0.5(1)] = 0.6038$$

$$c_2 = [0.70 - 0.70(0.2) - 0.5(1)]/[0.70 - 0.70(0.2) + 0.5(1)] = 0.0566$$

These values can be checked as follows:

$$c_0 + c_1 + c_2 = 0.3396 + 0.6038 + 0.0566 = 1.0000$$

The outflow hydrograph ordinates can now be computed with Equation 8.43.

TABLE 8.5 Existing Reach—
Example Problem 8.5
Outflow Calculations

t (hr)	I (cfs)	O (cfs)
0	0	0
1	1000	340
2	2000	1303
3	4200	2707
4	5200	4455
5	4400	4886
6	3200	4020
7	2500	3009
8	2000	2359
9	1500	1851
10	1000	1350
11	700	918
12	400	610
13	0	276
14	0	16
15	0	1

Beginning at $t = 2$ hr:

$$O_2 = C_0 I_2 + C_1 I_1 + C_2 O_1 = 0.3396(1000) + 0.6038(0) + 0.0566(0)$$
$$= 340 \text{ cfs } (9.6 \text{ cms})$$

and

$$O_2 = 0.3396(2000) + 0.6038(1000) + 0.0566(340) = 1303 \text{ cfs } (36 \text{ cms})$$

These values along with the remaining calculations are tabulated in Table 8.5. The same procedure is used to route the hydrograph through the modified reach. The routing coefficients are recomputed using $K = .55$, the travel time through the modified reach. The new coefficients are

$$c_0 = 0.4149$$
$$c_1 = 0.6489$$
$$c_2 = -0.0638$$
$$c_0 + c_1 + c_2 = 1.0000$$

TABLE 8.6   Modified Reach—
Example Problem 8.5
Outflow Calculations

t (hr)	I (cfs)	O (cfs)
0	0	0
1	1000	415
2	2000	1452
3	4200	2948
4	5200	4695
5	4400	4900
6	3200	3870
7	2500	2867
8	2000	2269
9	1500	1775
10	1000	1275
11	700	858
12	400	565
13	0	223
14	0	0
15	0	0

The results of the hydrograph routing through the modified reach are summarized in Table 8.6. The peak discharge at the bridge for the original channel is 4886 cfs (138 cms) and for the shorter channel is 4900 cfs (139 cms). The difference is not significant and the channel modification will have minimal effect on the peak discharge experienced at the bridge. □

8.5

SUMMARY

Hydraulic routing procedures use both the momentum and continuity equations, while hydrologic routing procedures use the continuity equation. Included in this chapter are three commonly used routing procedures: the kinematic, inventory, and Muskingum equations.

- The kinematic procedure uses both momentum and continuity principles with solution by finite differences.
- The kinematic equations require a detailed description of the watershed physical parameters, such as slope and cross sections, but the hydrograph shape does not have to be specified as in the unit–graph methods.
- The time and distance steps selected for modeling should define hydrograph and peak discharge within the accuracy expected.
- The inventory method is based on the continuity equation, and must include an outflow–storage (O–S) relationship to route hydrographs.
- The Muskingum method uses the continuity principle and assumes a weighting of inflow and outflow for a stream reach. The parameters of the method should be estimated from existing data or past experiences.
- There are numerous calculations required for routing methods (see example problems). It is beneficial to do some calculations to learn the sensitivity of the methods and the details of the calculations.

8.6

PROBLEMS

1. Explain in your own words the theoretical basis for the development of hydrologic models and compare this to the development of hydraulic models. Give an example of a method which fits each classification.
2. For an overland flow situation, develop the finite difference equations to solve for unit width flow rates (similar to Equation 8.10).

3. In Table 8.1, show the calculations for $A_{1,3}$, $A_{2,3}$, and $q_{2,3}$.

4. What is the relative change (sensitivity) in the values of $Q_{3,1}$ (Table 8.2) if the channel roughness coefficient changed is to .015?

5. If rainfall excess of Example Problem 8.1 were constant at 4 in./hr, what is an estimate of peak discharge using kinematic equations? Compare this discharge with an estimate using the rational formula.

6. Using the input hydrograph of Example Problem 8.2, determine the size (volume) of a detention basin if the outflow hydrograph is

STORAGE (ft^3)	BASIN DISCHARGE (ft^3/sec)
$\leq$ 10,000	0
> 10,000	10 ft^3/sec (constant value)

Assume the detention basin is initially empty or the 10,000 ft^3 of initial storage will eventually percolate into the ground.

7. What are the rainfall excess increments in 30-min intervals and the inflow rates (cfs) for a 100-ac impervious area for the first 2 hr from a 4-in. storm over 6 hr by using the SCS Mass Curve Type II if the maximum soil storage (S') is 0.5 in.? Now route this rainfall excess through the new channel of Example Problem 8.5.

TIME	ΔP (in.)	INFLOW (cfs)	OUTFLOW (cfs)
0	0.00		
30	0.17		
60	0.20		
90	0.26		
120	1.89		
150	1.34		
180	0.34		
210	0.29		
240	0.30		
270	0.22		
300	0.15		
330	0.18		
360	0.10		

What is the "routed" flow (output hydrograph) at 120 minutes if $t_c = \Delta t$ = 30 min? No other information is available.

8. Using Manning's equation, calculate the discharge for a natural channel cut from rock that is severely irregular and no meandering or vegetation. The depth of flow is 4 ft, and the slope of the channel is 0.005.

9. Derive Equation 8.40 from Equations 8.37 and 8.38 being careful to state your assumptions and define all variables.

10. Using the coefficients in the Muskingum routing equation as developed in Example Problem 8.3, solve for the discharge hydrograph if the input hydrograph were

Time (days)	0	1	2	3	4	5	6	7	8	9	10	11	12
Average input (cfs)	0	100	250	380	300	200	130	80	50	30	15	5	0

11. If the outflow hydrograph of Example Problem 8.3 were attenuated further, or for the following average flow values (cfs) starting at Day 1, what are estimates of c and K?

Day	1	2	3	4	5	6	7	8	9	10	11	12
Outflow	0	10	40	50	45	35	30	20	15	10	5	0

12. Given the following inflow and outflow hydrographs for a stream reach with a relatively constant cross-sectional area and slope, determine the Muskingum routing constants K and c.

DAY	I (cfs)	O (cfs)
1	0	0
2	33	6
3	99	50
4	61	61
5	33	50
6	17	40
7	6	25
8	0	11
9	0	3
10	0	0

13. What is the discharge hydrograph for a 50-ac watershed with a rational coefficient of .4 and a storm intensity of 2 in./hr over 2 hr if the time of concentration is 60 min and the rational hydrograph is routed through a

reservoir with the following characteristics? (Assume that the pond level is at control elevation.)

Permanent pool (dead storage) = 43,560 ft^3 (at control elevation)
Discharge/storage = 4 ft^3/sec/20,000 ft^3
Show all work for a 3-hr time period.

8.7

COMPUTER-ASSISTED PROBLEMS

1.   Write a computer program to solve Example Problem 8.2 and generate a table similar to Table 8.3. Make the program as general as possible by having the capability of reading any input hydrograph and storage–discharge relationship as one linear piecewise approximation.

2.   Using the SMADA computer program (Wanielista et al., 1986) obtain a print out for an outflow hydrograph. The watershed and routing conditions are:

A = 100 ac
% impervious = 60
$DCiA$ = 50%
CN = 70 (pervious area)
Santa Barbara method
t_c = 200 min

The printout must illustrate about 55% reduction in the peak discharge. No pollution control should be done. Use a rainfall volume and time distribution of your choice. Use a storage–discharge relationship, which is estimated by two straight lines (start with 10,000 cf/cfs up to 16 cfs, and 9000 cf/cfs over 16 cfs; also assume an initial storage of 10,000 ft^3). This problem illustrates the sensitivity of discharge as related to a storage discharge relationship.

3.   For the previous problem, what duration storm would produce the largest detention volume? Use at least five different durations.

8.8

REFERENCES

Chow, V.T. 1959. *Open-Channel Hydraulics*. McGraw-Hill, New York.
Chow, V.T. (editor). 1964. *Handbook of Applied Hydrology*. McGraw-Hill, New York.

Federal Highway Administration (FHWA). 1984. *Hydrology*, Hydrologic Engineering Center Circular No. 19, McLean, VA.

Henderson, F.M. 1966. *Open Channel Flow*. Macmillan, New York.

Hydrologic Engineering Center. 1979. *Introduction and Application of Kinematic Wave Routing Techniques Using HEC-1*, McLean, VA.

Hydrologic Engineering Center. 1985. *Flood Hydrograph Package, Users Manual*, Training Document No. 10, Devries and MacArthur, U.S. Army Corps of Engineers, Davis, CA (May).

Mahmood, K. and Yevjevich, V. 1975. *Unsteady Flow in Open Channels*. Water Resources Publications, Fort Collins, CO.

Wanielista, M.P., 1977. *Manual of Stormwater Management Practices*. Report submitted to the East Central Florida Regional Planning Council, Winter Park, November.

Wanielista, M.P., Curran, T.C., and Cassogrol, C.C. 1986. Stormwater Management and Design Aid Computer Program, University of Central Florida, Orlando, January.

Yevjevich, V. 1968. "Computer and Observed Unsteady Water–Surface Profiles in a Circular Cross-Section," *American Society of Civil Engineers Hydraulics Division 16th Specialty Conference*, August.

PROBABILITY
AND STATISTICS
FOR HYDROLOGIC
DESCRIPTORS

When one accurately predicts future water flow rates and volumes with knowledge of the uncertainties of meteorologic, hydrologic, and watershed changes, design and operation of projects cost less and are more effective. However, a designer or planner is not certain of the future rate and volume that will affect a project. To reduce the uncertainty of hydrological processes, probability and statistics models can be designed and used. This chapter presents probability and statistics concepts for rainfall and runoff events, especially the extreme events of droughts and floods. The concepts of this chapter are used in many water resources-related areas.

Hydrologic and meteorologic information are sometimes available at a location where a change is anticipated. This availability of data is very helpful and statistical descriptions from the data can be developed. However, data information at a location is frequently incomplete or available for some other location. But statistics still can be used to correlate one location to another in hopes of determining "best" predictive and descriptive mathematical models.

9.1

TERMINOLOGY

Some hydrology and stormwater management terms that use concepts from probability and statistics may be misleading or not completely understood. In many cases, data are collected over a short period of time in hopes of estimating the results of processes or driving forces (hydrologic, hydraulic, biological, etc.) that are not well defined. Thus, samples are taken and inferences about the longer time period for driving forces are made. There exists terminology that relates to these estimates, some of the terminology is shown in Table 9.1.

9.2

PROBABILITY AND STATISTICS CONCEPTS

Because of the extreme variability and lack of deterministic relationships for rainfall, runoff, and other hydrologic processes, it is frequently necessary to use probability and statistics concepts to aid in defining and predicting these events. Some of the basic ideas and concepts of probability and statistics are defined in this section.

9.2.1   Definition of Probability

Probability is empirically defined as the number of times a specific event occurs from the total number of events measured, or

$$Pr(X) = x/n; \qquad \lim n \to \infty \tag{9.1}$$

where

$Pr(X)$ = probability of event X

x = number of occurrences of X event

n = total number of recorded outcomes

9.2.2   Independence

When the occurrence of one event does not affect the occurrence of another, the two events are independent. As an example, the percent impervious area of a watershed is independent of volume of rainfall per year. Rainfall is independent of watershed characteristics. However, runoff is dependent on watershed

TABLE 9.1 Terminology Related to Statistical Observations

TERM	DESCRIPTION
Accuracy	The closeness of a measurement to the true value of the quantity being measured or to an accepted reference value.
Bias	A systematic variation or lack of randomness in a set of observations that results from a systematic error in data collection or analysis.
Confidence level	A quantitative expression of the reliability of an estimated value. The expression is usually stated in probability terms.
Consistency	A property of numbers that is related to sample size. As sample size increases, a consistent sample does not deviate from the population mean more or less than a fixed amount.
Efficiency	A measure of the quality of an estimator or set of observations. Efficiency is inversely proportional to the variance. A sample is more efficient if it has a smaller variance than another sample.
Independent	One event (i.e., rainfall) is independent of another (pipe roughness) when the occurrence of the second event has no bearing whatsoever on the occurrence or nonoccurrence of the first event.
Mutually exclusive	The occurrence of one event (i.e., rainfall) precludes the occurrence of another (i.e., evaporation).
Precision	The variation in an observation or set of observations due to random error. It is the measure of the repeatability of a series of observations or measurements.
Random error	Chance fluctuations in the value of a variable that occur when a series of measurements are taken under the exact same conditions.
Reliability	The expression of how well a model or other predictor technique measures what it is supposed to measure, including both accuracy and precision properties. Refers also to the consistency and precision of an instrument or measurement technique.
Repeatability	The precision associated with an individual observer taking several measurements of the same variable under the same conditions but at different times using the same equipment or measurement techniques.
Sample	A small number of observations from a larger number of potential observations. A random sample is one of which each observation has the same probability of being choosen.
Sensitivity	The ability of an instrument (or instrument plus observer) to measure changes in a variable or the ability of a model or other mathematical predictor to produce realistic responses in output variables when levels of input variables are changed.

TABLE 9.1 *(Continued)*

TERM	DESCRIPTION
Significance	In data analysis, significance refers to the relationship of a number of some reference value. In statistical analyses the term should be qualified with a probability statement.
Sufficiency	The degree to which a parameter derived from a given sample represents or extracts information from the corresponding population.
Tolerance	The allowable deviation from a numerical standard or the range of variation permitted a given number.
Uncertainty	The variation of a variable or the tendency of outcomes to vary when repeated measurements are made under identical conditions. Uncertainty consists of both random and systematic error.

characteristics. The probability of the occurrence of two independent events is the product of both probabilities or their intersection (symbolized by $\cap$).

$$\Pr\{A \cap B\} = P\{A\} \cdot P\{B\} \tag{9.2}$$

Another probability statement is one for which either one event or both can occur. It is called a union (symbolized by $\cup$). An example would be the probability of either runoff or rainfall or both occurring.

9.2.3 Conditional Probability

A conditional probability is one which depends on the occurrence of some other event. Almost all probabilities are conditional in a space or time relationship. Example statements are (1) the probability of a 5-in. rainfall event given data for the midwestern United States, (2) the probability of at least 1-in. of runoff given a 10-in. snowfall in Alaska during December, or (3) the probability of a 3-in. rainfall given a dry period of 72 hr following a storm event. In these three statements, specific quantities of the hydrologic variable are specified and after the word "given" is the conditional statement.

9.2.4 Empirical Probabilities

It is most likely that exact probabilities will never be obtained because the sample size hardly ever approaches the total number of outcomes (trials) for hydrologic processes. However, samples of the recorded outcomes can be tabulated with associated empirical probabilities.

Most hydrologic processes occur in patterns and the engineer, hydrologist, and planner must determine and use this pattern. One way of describing a pattern is to develop a frequency distribution for the values of the hydrologic process. A frequency distribution is a plot of the values of a hydrologic process as the abscissa and the frequency of occurrence as the ordinate. If the frequency is divided by the total number of samples, the ordinate is expressed as empirical probability. To use a probability or frequency distribution effectively, one must understand fundamental probability properties and the development of a distribution.

◻ **EXAMPLE PROBLEM 9.1**

Consider calculation of a probability for average yearly stream flow greater than 40 m³/sec, given stream flow records for 50 years. As an additional qualification, the users of this probability wish to know if this flow rate is exceeded in a year and now how many times per year. On examining the stream flow data, it was determined that 40 m³/sec was exceeded in 10 yearly recordings. Therefore, the empirical probability based on a sample size of 50 is:

Solution

$$Pr(X > 40 \text{ m}^3/\text{sec}) = 10/50 = .20$$

This estimate for Example Problem 9.1 was made from a number of possible outcomes and is a sample of that population. As more data are collected, the empirical probability will become more accurate.   ◻

9.2.5 Probability Properties

Hydrologic events can be assumed to be discrete but often are continuous variables. Regardless of the assumption, the properties of probability distributions are analogous for discrete, $Pr(x)$, and continuous, $f(x)$, cases:

$$Pr(x) \quad \text{or} \quad f(x) \geq 0$$

and

$$\sum_{\substack{\downarrow \\ (\text{all } x)}} Pr(x) = 1 \quad \text{or} \quad \int_{-\infty}^{+\infty} f(x) = 1 \qquad (9.3)$$

The sum of probabilities is referred to as the cumulative distribution function and is written as:

1. Less than type:

$$F(x) = \Pr(X \le x) = \sum_{\substack{\downarrow \\ z \le x}} \Pr(z) \qquad (9.4)$$

$$F(x) = \Pr(X \le x) = \int_{-\infty}^{x} f(z)\, dz \qquad (9.5)$$

2. Greater than type (exceedence):

$$G(x) = \Pr(X \ge x) = 1 - \sum \Pr(z) = 1 - F(x) \qquad (9.6)$$

$$G(x) = \Pr(X \ge x) = \int_{x}^{\infty} f(z)\, dz \qquad (9.7)$$

9.2.6 Graphical Presentations of Probability

Since some people have strong aversions to equations and symbols or there exists a need to determine the shape (or type) of distributions, there is a need for graphic presentations of hydrological data. One such graphic is the

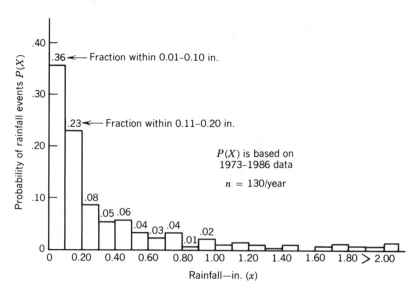

FIGURE 9.1a Rainfall probability histogram — Orlando Jetport. *Source:* U.S. Department of Commerce, 1973 – 1986.

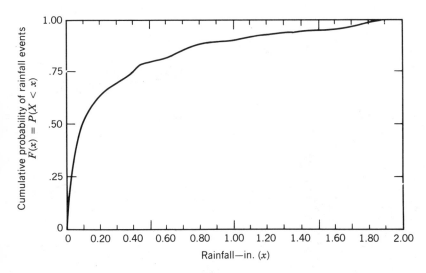

FIGURE 9.1*b* Rainfall cumulative probability distribution – Orlando Jetport.

histogram—a plot of empirical probabilities corresponding to process values. Details for development of a histogram are presented in Section 9.5.1. An example is shown here to illustrate its use.

A histogram of rainfall data using thirteen years of rainfall event data is shown in Figure 9.1*a*. The rainfall quantity is the total rain per storm event, where a storm event is defined by any uninterrupted rainfall proceeded by 4 hr or more of no rainfall. Cumulative frequency distributions of rainfall are shown for the less than type for Orlando, Florida (Figure 9.1*b*); Austin, Texas; and Baltimore, Maryland in Figure 9.2. Note that the histograms have a similar shape. These figures illustrate the estimated probability of rainfall per storm event being less than or equal to a stated volume. For example, the probability of rainfall being less than or equal to 0.50 in. is approximately 80%. Local climatological data can be used to construct rainfall, temperature, wind speed, or other types of histogram. Once the histogram has been determined, a theoretical probability distribution can be assigned to the random events.

9.2.7 Central Tendency and Variability

Another means to describe a distribution is by a central value, variability and skewness. Skewness is a measure for the degree of asymmetry. Right skewness indicates a distribution with greater variability to the right (typically, the distribution is "stretched" to the right). Similarly, there is a left skewness and

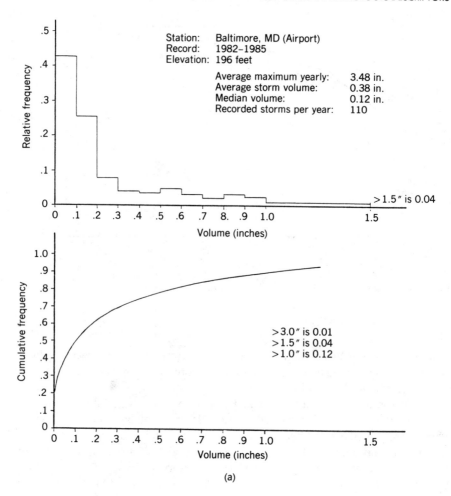

FIGURE 9.2 Rainfall cumulative probability distributions.

a perfectly symmetrical distribution about the central value. The untransformed data of Figure 9.1a indicate a right skewed distribution.

The most common measure of central tendency is the mean of the empirical (observed) data or first moment about the origin, and is defined by

$$\bar{x} = \frac{1}{n} \sum_{i=1}^{n} x_i \tag{9.8}$$

where

$\bar{x}$ = mean value sample estimate

x_i = data points for all measurements i

n = total number of data points

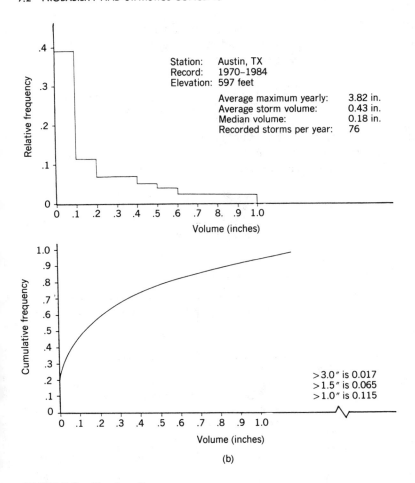

FIGURE 9.2 (Continued)

Other measures of central tendency are the median or middle value of the ordered empirical data and the mode or value that appears most frequently (peak of a distribution).

The most common measure of variability of a sample is the standard deviation (s) and the square of the standard deviation is known as the variance (s^2). The standard deviation has the units of the variable itself, while the variance is the square of the values and possibly more difficult to interpret. The variance of the sample is calculated from:

$$s^2 = \left[\frac{1}{(n-1)}\right] \sum_{i=1}^{n} (x_i - \bar{x})^2 \tag{9.9}$$

The estimate for the variance of the sample is based on $(n-1)$ samples, reportedly because $\bar{x}$ is used in the estimate and replaces one of the samples,

x_i. This is called a reduction in the degree of freedom or an unbiased estimate. The variance also is known as the second moment of the distribution. Relative variability among sample data sets can be compared using the coefficient of variability (C_v), as defined by

$$C_v = \frac{s}{\bar{x}} \tag{9.10}$$

The third moment of a distribution would estimate the skewness or weights on either side of the mean. An estimator for the true population skewness (G) using the sample observation is:

$$G = \frac{n \sum_{i=1}^{n} (x_i - \bar{x})^3}{(n-1)(n-2)s^3} \tag{9.11}$$

☐ EXAMPLE PROBLEM 9.2

For the following data recorded in mm-annual rainfall, calculate the mean, standard error, coefficient of variability, and skewness. Discuss the results.

	LOCATION			LOCATION	
YEAR	SCRANTON, PA	ORLANDO, FL	YEAR	SCRANTON, PA	ORLANDO, FL
1950	602	1150	1968	680	1252
1951	541	1035	1969	480	892
1952	732	1341	1970	922	1494
1953	446	860	1971	710	1200
1954	584	1196	1972	454	1026
1955	690	1244	1973	635	1162
1956	724	1299	1974	699	1227
1957	832	1363	1975	703	1150
1958	717	1248	1976	814	1143
1959	659	1190	1977	710	1190
1960	571	1040	1978	784	1340
1961	692	1274	1979	507	994
1962	840	1401	1980	512	1043
1963	730	1296	1981	852	1350
1964	630	1162	1982	671	1109
1965	618	1100	1983	784	1206
1966	687	1291	1984	842	1304
1967	777	1340	1985	649	1156

Solution

	SCRANTON		ORLANDO	
STATISTICAL MEASURE	mm	in.	mm	in.
Mean	679	26.72	1196	47.07
Standard deviation	118	4.64	140	5.50
Skewness	−0.19	−0.19	−0.37	−0.37
Coefficient of variability	0.17	0.17	0.12	0.12

These are calculated using the formulas of this section on a programmed calculator or by means of a computer program. The student is urged to at least do the calculations by calculator (longhand) once, then by a programmed calculator or computer program. The results indicate a higher average in Orlando than in Scranton, 1196 mm and 679 m, respectively. The variability in the yearly averages is relatively lower in Orlando as measured by the coefficient of variability although the standard deviation is higher in Orlando. The distributions both have a slight negative (left) skewness. □

9.3

PROBABILITY DISTRIBUTIONS

Seven probability distributions are discussed. The first two are discrete, the remaining ones are continuous. All are useful to describe hydrologic events. The last three are needed most frequently for flood flow events.

9.3.1 Binomial Distribution

A random variable (X), that can assume two values, where the probability of one value, p, has a binomial distribution if its probability distribution function can be written as

$$\Pr(x) = \binom{n}{x} p^x (1 - p)^{n-x} \qquad \text{for } x = 0, 1, \ldots, n \qquad (9.12)$$

where

$$\binom{n}{x} = \frac{n!}{x!(n - x)!}$$

p = probability of one value, usually defined as a success, $0 \le p \le 1$

n = number of trials

x = number of successes

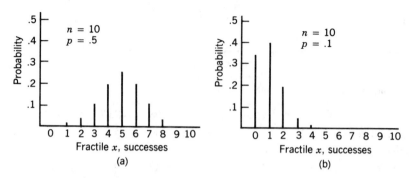

FIGURE 9.3   Binomial distribution.

A graph of the binomial distribution with fixed n and p would be similar to that shown in Figure 9.3.

☐   **EXAMPLE PROBLEM 9.3**

You are in charge of a field crew measuring stage downstream from a regulated reservoir. Every time the stage is greater than 5 m the regulatory agency has successfully determined a violation of state and federal standards. If the probability of violation over a long period of time is 0.20, what are some conclusions when four out of six stage measures are greater than 5 m during runoff conditions?

Solution

The probability of four out of six violations (successes) is very rare or $\Pr(x = 4) = \binom{6}{4} .2^4 (.8)^2 = .015$. Thus, the violations have increased or the sample is characteristic of direct runoff rather than general stream flow data. Possible mixed populations are involved, that is, runoff (non-point), reservoir releases (point), and groundwater conditions. The random or nonexplained nature of hydrologic events can be analyzed using the binomial distribution.   ☐

9.3.2   Poisson Distribution

Stream flow can be characterized by a Poisson distribution when it is input to a reservoir. Over a fixed period of time, stream flow is considered an "arrival" at the contemplated reservoir site. These arrivals characteristically follow a Poisson distribution. The random variable (X) in these situations has a

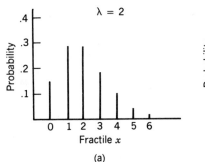
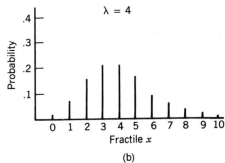

FIGURE 9.4 Poisson distribution.

Poisson distribution if its probability density function can be written as

$$\Pr(x) = \frac{\lambda^x e^{-\lambda}}{x!} \qquad \text{for } x = 0, 1, 2, \ldots \qquad (9.13)$$

where

λ = positive constant (mean value of arrivals)

x = any nonnegative integer

e = a constant = $2.7182\ldots$

A graph of the Poisson distribution is typically right skewed as in Figure 9.4.
  The Poisson distribution is useful for design of reservoirs when surface water inputs of seepage are not described by a deterministic (nonrandom) relationship. It is possible that the random portion of inputs or outputs can be described by the Poisson distribution.

□ **EXAMPLE PROBLEM 9.4**

Assume that the water level change in a reservoir per month not explained by deterministic equations will average 1 cm and from a graphical plot the changes can be described by a Poisson distribution. Unit changes in depth are the closest measurements possible and are considered discrete. What is the probability of a 2-cm change in elevation during one month?

Solution

$$\Pr(x = 2) = \frac{1^2 e^{-1}}{2!} = .184$$

What is the probability of *at most a* 2-cm change? This is the cumulative probability or:

$$Pr(x = 0) + Pr(x = 1) + Pr(x = 2)$$

or

$$F(x \leq 2) = .368 + .368 + .184 = .92 \quad \square$$

9.3.3 Normal Distribution

One of the most important continuous probability distributions is the normal. Its distribution function is

$$f(x) = \left(\frac{1}{\sigma\sqrt{2\pi}}\right)\exp\left[^{-1/2}\left(\frac{x-\mu}{\sigma}\right)^2\right] \qquad \text{for } -\infty < x < \infty \quad (9.14)$$

where

σ = standard deviation
x = any value
μ = population mean

A graph of the typical normal density function is shown in Figure 9.5.

☐ **EXAMPLE PROBLEM 9.5**

Suppose that the average yearly concentration of total phosphorus in a stream is 1.65 mg/L with a variance of 0.64 mg^2/L^2. These averages are based on weekly samples averaged for one year. Thus, the sample size for the average yearly values is 52. Twelve years of data are available. During a rainy year (25% more than average), the yearly average concentration for that year (1 of 12 years) was 2.20 mg/L. What is the probability that yearly average concentrations will be equal to or greater than 2.20 mg/L?

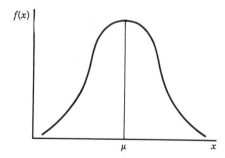

FIGURE 9.5　Normal distribution.

Solution

The response to this question relies on the assumption of the application of the central limit theorem, which states that the distribution of mean values is normal. Solving Equation 9.14 is usually done by tables or the use of standard deviates (number of standard deviations on either side of the mean value). Statistical tables are presented in Appendix D, and are used with the standard normal deviate, calculated as: $z = (x - \bar{x})/s$. For this problem:

$$z = \frac{(2.20 - 1.65)}{.8} = .6875$$

Using the Table D.1, Appendix D, the probability of being less than 2.20 mg/L is .7541, or 75% of the time the average yearly concentrations will be less than 2.20 mg/L and 25% of the time the average yearly concentrations will be greater than 2.20 mg/L. □

9.3.4 Log-Normal Distribution

A plot of average weekly flow rates is generally right skewed and does not appear to be a normal distribution. However, if the log of weekly values is plotted as a histogram, the resulting distribution may be normal. The characteristic shapes are shown in Figure 9.6. The distribution function is

$$f(x) = \frac{1}{\sigma x \sqrt{2\pi}} \exp\left[-\frac{1}{2}\left(\frac{\ln x - \mu}{\sigma}\right)^2\right] \quad \text{for } x > 0 \quad (9.15)$$

Note that μ and σ are the mean and standard deviation of $\ln(x)$. If the

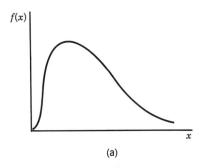

(a)

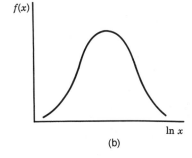

(b)

FIGURE 9.6 Log-normal distribution.

probability of being between two values is required, it can be calculated using:

$$\Pr(a \le X \le b) = \int_a^b \frac{1}{\sigma\sqrt{2\pi}\,x} \exp\left[-\frac{1}{2}\left(\frac{\ln X - \mu}{\sigma}\right)^2\right] dx \qquad (9.16)$$

or with the use of normal tables:

$$\Pr(a \le X \le b) = F\left(\frac{\ln b - \mu}{\sigma}\right) - F\left(\frac{\ln a - \mu}{\sigma}\right) \qquad (9.17)$$

9.3.5 Exponential Distribution

The exponential distribution is used in the study of reservoir holding volumes and rainfall intensities. It is a continuous random variable having the following form:

$$f(x; \lambda) = \lambda e^{-\lambda x} \qquad \text{for all } x \ge 0$$

and

$$F(x; \lambda) = 1 - e^{-\lambda x} \qquad (9.18)$$

where λ = constant > 0 and the inverse of the average.

The interarrival time distribution for two successive arrivals of flows to a detention pond will characteristically follow an exponential distribution as shown in Figure 9.7. If the average interevent time is 84 hr, $\lambda = \frac{1}{84}$ and the probability of an interevent time less than 5 days (120 hr) is .76.

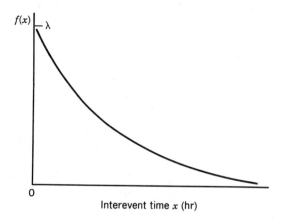

FIGURE 9.7 Exponential distribution.

$p_r(X = x)$

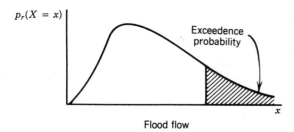

Flood flow

FIGURE 9.8 Flood peak distributions.

9.3.6 Gumbel Distribution

Gumbel or Type I distributions (Gumbel, 1945) have been used to describe annual flow events. A generalized flood flow diagram is shown as Figure 9.8. Most food flow probability distributions have similar shapes. Flood flows can be approximated by a Gumbel distribution to estimate flood probabilities. The Gumbel distribution has its skewness fixed at +1.14. The largest flood flow/year over 365 daily values is picked for each year. The distribution of yearly flood flows is then plotted and an exceedence probability calculated from

$$1 - F(x) = 1 - e^{-e^{-b}} \tag{9.19}$$

where
$b = (1/0.7797s)(x - \bar{x} + 0.45s)$
x = magnitude of the flood (m³/sec)
$\bar{x}$ = average flood magnitude (m³/sec)
s = standard deviation of flood magnitudes (m³/sec)

☐ **EXAMPLE PROBLEM 9.6**

If flood flows on a large watershed in Pennsylvania has an average value of 1200 m³/sec with a variance of 62,500 m³/sec, what is the probability that a flood will be equal to or exceed 2000 m³/sec using the Gumbel distribution?

Solution

Calculating the reduced variate, b, then the probability one obtains

$$b = \frac{1}{0.7797(250)} [(2,000 - 1,200 + .45(250)]$$

$$= 4.68$$

TABLE 9.2 Gumbel Probability and Return Period

REDUCED VARIATE b	PROBABILITY OF EXCEEDENCE	RETURN PERIOD (RECURRENCE INTERVAL)
.367	.50	2.0
1.367	.20	5.0
2.250	.10	10.0
2.970	.05	20.0
3.199	.04	25.0
3.902	.02	50.0
4.601	.01	100.0
5.296	.005	200.0

and

$$1 - F(x) = 1 - e^{-e^{-4.62}} = .0098$$

which means that this flood has a chance of occurring approximately one time each 100 years. □

Since the exceedence probability is a direct function of the value of b, Table 9.2 may be of some help in determining the probabilities.

9.3.7 Log-Pearson Type III

The log Pearson Type III distribution is used as the acceptable procedure for estimating flood flows (Work Group on Flood Flow Frequency; 1977). If a series of floods for each year are available, these are converted to logarithm values from which the skewness, mean and standard deviation are estimated. Exceedence probabilities are estimated using a normal distribution with adjustments for the skewness of the flood flows (Beard, 1962). Therefore, the skewness of the distribution is estimated from the transformed logarithm values using equation 9.11.

From the Water Resources Council Hydrology Committee (Work Group on Flood Flow Frequency, 1977), alternate computing formulas for skewness and standard deviation are

$$G = \frac{N^2(\Sigma X^3) - 3N(\Sigma X)(\Sigma X^2) + 2(\Sigma X)^3}{N(N-1)(N-2)s^3} \tag{9.20}$$

where

$$s = \left[\frac{(\Sigma X^2) - (\Sigma X)^2/N}{N - 1} \right]^{.5}$$
(9.21)

Knowing the skewness coefficient and the exceedence probability, it is possible to calculate the value of the corresponding flood using

$$X = \overline{X} + Ks$$
(9.22)

where

$$K = \frac{2}{G} \left[\left[\left(K_n - \frac{G}{6} \right) \left(\frac{G}{6} \right) + 1 \right]^3 - 1 \right] \quad \text{for } -1.0 < G < 1.0 \quad (9.23)$$

and

$$K = \text{Type III deviate}$$

$$K_n = \text{standard normal deviate for that probability}$$

Table D.3, Appendix D, can be used for estimating K.

The skew coefficient (G) is sensitive to extreme events and thus difficult to estimate using small samples (less than 100 yr). Adjustments for the skew coefficient are suggested as follows:

RECORD YEARS	SKEW VALUE	
≥ 100	G	(9.24)
$26 - 100$	$\left(\dfrac{N - 25}{75} \right) G + \left(1 - \dfrac{N - 25}{75} \right) G_g$	(9.25)
≤ 25	G_g	(9.26)

where
G_g = generalized skew coefficient for an area (Hardison, 1974)

9.4

RECURRENCE INTERVAL AND RISK

The recurrence interval (T_r) is the average interval of time within which an event will be equaled or exceeded. The recurrence interval should be based on a long-time history of the event. It is one of the more significant statistics and is easy to understand by a nontechnical person. Of course it must be emphasized that a long period of record is necessary because a rainfall that occurs once per 10-yr interval (10-yr recurrence interval) may occur with low probability 2 years in a row.

If an event is designated by $(X \geq x)$ and its probability of occurrences by $\Pr(X \geq x)$, the recurrence interval is the inverse of the probability, or

$$T_r = \frac{1}{\Pr(X \geq x)} = \frac{1}{G(x)}$$

$$T_r = \frac{1}{1 - \Pr(X \leq x)} = \frac{1}{1 - (1 - G(x))} \tag{9.27}$$

The probability that this event will not occur is:

$$1 - \Pr(X \geq x) = 1 - G(x) \tag{9.28}$$

The probability that this event will not occur in n time periods is calculated from the binomial distribution (see Section 9.3.1) as

$$\Pr(x = 0: n, \Pr) = \binom{n}{0}(1 - \Pr)^n (\Pr)^0$$

or

$$\Pr(0, n, p) = (1 - \Pr)^n \tag{9.29}$$

The probability (R) that this event, x, will occur at least once (one or more times) in n time periods is expressed by a term called risk, or

$$R = \sum_{z=1}^{n} \Pr(z; n, p) = 1 - \Pr(0; n, p) = 1 - (1 - \Pr)^n \tag{9.30}$$

If the time period is equal to one year, the recurring interval has been defined as the return period. This is the same definition of return period as used in the frequency–intensity–duration curves for rainfall.

☐   **EXAMPLE PROBLEM 9.7**

What is the probability of no rainfall volume during the next 3 yr greater than or equal to the one in 20-yr rainfall volume?

Solution

The probability of a 1 in 20-yr rainfall is the inverse of the return period or 1/20. Using Equation 9.29:

$$\Pr(0; 3, .05) = (1 - .05)^3 = .86 \quad \square$$

□ **EXAMPLE PROBLEM 9.8**

Given the annual peak gage heights of a canal, calculate the empirical probability and the return period of an annual peak greater than or equal to 17 m. The gage heights are

YEAR	ANNUAL HEIGHT (m)
1968	17
1969	21
1970	12
1971	10
1972	19
1973	14
1974	16
1975	12
1976	15

Solution

$$\Pr(X \geq 17) = \frac{x}{n} = \frac{3}{9} = 0.33 = G(x)$$

and

$$T_r = \frac{1}{G(x)} = 3 \text{ yr} \quad \square$$

9.4.1 Evaluation of Risk

Rewriting Equation 9.30 in terms of the return period (recurrence interval), the probability of a stated event (design discharge, rainfall) being exceeded at least once in a design life is a measure of the risk one takes. If n is the design life in years, and T_r is the recurrence interval, a tabulation of risk using Equation 9.30 is developed and shown in Table 9.3.

□ **EXAMPLE PROBLEM 9.9**

For a structure on a highway, it was decided a design life of 50 yr should be used. If the structure transports runoff, what is the risk of at least one exceedence if the runoff quantity is associated with the 100-yr discharge?

TABLE 9.3 Approximate Risk of At Least One Exceedence During a Design Life for a Recurrence Interval or Exceedence Probability

EXCEEDENCE PROBABILITY (G)	RECURRENCE INTERVAL (T_r)	DESIGN LIFE – YEARS (n)					
		2	5	10	25	50	100
.5	2	.75	.97	≅ 1.00	≅ 1.00	≅ 1.00	≅ 1.00
.2	5	.36	.67	.89	≅ 1.00	≅ 1.00	≅ 1.00
.1	10	.19	.41	.65	.93	.99	≅ 1.00
.04	25	.08	.18	.34	.64	.87	.98
.02	50	.04	.10	.18	.40	.64	.87[a]
.01	100	.02	.05	.10	.22	.39	.63
.002	500	.004	.01	.02	.05	.10	.18
.001	1000	.002	.005	.01	.03	.05	.10

[a]Example calculation: $R = 1 - (1 - 1/T_r)^n$
$$R = 1 - (1 - 1/50)^{100}$$
$$R = 1 - (.98)^{100} = 1 - .13 = .87$$

Solution

From Table 9.3, there is a 39% chance that the 100-yr discharge will occur during the 50-yr life of the project. ☐

☐ **EXAMPLE PROBLEM 9.10**

If the designer decides that a 10% risk of transport failure is acceptable, what is the recurrence interval for a design life of 50 yr?

Solution

Rearranging Equation 9.30 to solve for T_r.

$$T_r = \frac{1}{1 - (1 - R)^{1/n}}$$

$$= \frac{1}{1 - (1 - .10)^{1/50}} = 475 \text{ yr}$$

From Table 9.3, the approximate value is 500 yr. To reduce the risk using the data of Example Problem 9.9 from 39% to 10%, the transport structure must be designed with a peak flow associated with the 1/500-yr storm event. Thus, for very low levels of risk, accurate measures must be used to predict the values associated with the high-return period storm. ☐

9.4.2 Limited Samples and Uncertainty

When repeated measurements are made of the same hydrologic process there is variability in the estimate of the hydrologic process. Given a return period for rainfall, estimates for the volume of rainfall can and do vary for the same location. Uncertainty in the estimates can be reduced by eliminating sources of data collection and analyses errors. How accurate are these estimates? How accurate do they have to be for a given application? All these questions have to be answered with a limited database.

The accuracy of the data depends on the length of record available and on the assumed probability relationships (frequency distribution). The reliability of an estimate includes both the accuracy and the precision at which the event is measured. The reliability of the estimate can be measured by the confidence limit for that frequency. As the length of record increases, the reliability increases. Approximate values of reliability (percent chance) can be calculated for different exceedence probabilities (return periods). Approximate values are shown in Table 9.4. The results of being 10%, 25%, or 50% greater than or less than an estimate should be evaluated. In fact, from Table 9.4, there is approximately a 100% chance that the range of values of the estimate for the 2-yr return period with 25 yr of data will be within 50% of the estimated values. There is a 68% chance that the range of values will be within 10% of the estimate.

TABLE 9.4 Approximate Reliabilities (% chance) as a Function of Confidence Limit, Return Period, and Record Length

RETURN PERIOD (yr)	RECORD LENGTH (yr)	CONFIDENCE LIMIT (% ERROR)		
		± 10%	±25%	±50%
2	10	47	88	99
	25	68	99	100
	100	96	100	100
10	10	46	77	97
	25	50	93	99
	100	85	100	100
50	10	37	70	91
	25	46	91	97
	100	73	99	100
100	10	35	66	90
	25	45	89	98
	100	64	99	100

☐ **EXAMPLE PROBLEM 9.11**

If the frequency distribution estimate of the 100-yr storm event is 28 cm (11.0 in.) using 25 yr of data, and we wish to be 98% reliable in the estimate, what is the range of storm event values to satisfy this criteria?

Solution

From Table 9.4, there is a 98% chance that the estimated values will have a confidence interval of 50%, or the storm event can range from 14 cm (5.5 in.) to 42 cm (16.5 in.).   ☐

9.5

EMPIRICAL FREQUENCY DISTRIBUTION ANALYSIS

When hydrologic data are available for a location, then a statistical analysis of the data using frequency distributions is possible. Theoretical frequency distributions were defined in Section 9.3. More detail on the procedures for developing frequency distributions and for estimating the parameters of the distributions are presented in this section.

Before an analysis can be performed, a specific frequency distribution must be chosen with reasons for selection. Past experiences with rainfall and flood data generally indicate that these data will follow extreme event distributions, such as two parameter log-normal, log Pearson type III, Weibull, Gumbel, or the three parameter log-normal. A calculation of the skewness parameter (third moment) helps to identify the shape as an extreme event (positive skewness).

9.5.1 Histogram Development

A common way of arranging flow data is by order of magnitude (largest to smallest or smallest to largest). The arrangement is identified as a histogram or an empirical frequency distribution. One presentation is by classes or categories with associated frequencies for each class. If a large number of data points are available that permits grouping the data into 7 to 15 intervals (classes), then it is possible to represent the shape of a frequency distribution as a histogram. The histogram can be developed by noting the range of magnitudes and dividing the range into class intervals. There are no absolute rules concerning histogram construction. However, the following guidelines are helpful for tabulation (Table 9.5).

1.   Class intervals should not overlap (i.e., 1–25 mm, 26–50 mm, 51–75 mm, of rainfall, etc.).

TABLE 9.5   Maximum Annual Flow Rate Histogram Using Class Intervals

(1) FLOW RATE INTERVAL	(2) TALLY OF FREQUENCIES[a]	(3) NUMBER	(4) RELATIVE FREQUENCY (3) ÷ 29	(5) CUMULATIVE FREQUENCY Σ(4)
41–60	//	2	.069	.069
61–80	///	3	.103	.172
81–100	7HL //	7	.242	.414
101–120	7HL	5	.172	.586
121–140	7HL /	6	.207	.793
141–160	///	3	.103	.896
161–180	//	2	.069	.965
181–200	/	1	.035	1.000
	Totals	29	1.000	

[a]A tally of 10 events is noted as ⊠.

2. The intervals should include all the data points.
3. The intervals should be of uniform size except the beginning or ending ones that may be open (i.e., greater than or less than a given value).
4. The number of intervals should be changed and another graphic done for comparison to the previous one.

Using these simple guidelines, the flow rates of Table 9.6 can be used to develop a simple histogram. The data of Table 9.6 represents the day of the year on which the maximum annual flows occurred. A histogram for the data of Table 9.6 by class interval is shown in Table 9.5. From the histogram of Table 9.5, the shape of the distribution is noted as somewhat symmetrical but it is difficult to determine an exact theoretical distribution to fit the data. Also, there may be a possible positive skewness to the data.

9.5.2   Plotting Position Formulas

Another way to develop an empirical distribution is to use a method called "plotting position." One can arrange the data by order of magnitude (sort the data) and calculate an empirical cumulative probability of either a "less than" a certain value (smallest to largest) or "greater than" a certain value type (largest to smallest). The probability of a value being greater than is called the exceedence probability. There are various ways of determining the empirical distribution by plotting position formulas. Once all the data equal to a number n are ordered, an order number (identified as m) is assigned to the position

TABLE 9.6   A Listing by Month, Day, and
Year for the Banana River Watershed

YEAR	MONTH-DAY	RUNOFF (m^3/s)
1956	04–24	0.141E + 03
1957	05–16	0.900E + 02
1958	11–08	0.500E + 02
1959	03–25	0.109E + 03
1960	04–21	0.103E + 03
1961	12–25	0.142E + 03
1962	11–30	0.111E + 03
1963	06–01	0.750E + 02
1964	05–12	0.850E + 02
1965	03–16	0.630E + 02
1966	04–26	0.144E + 03
1967	05–11	0.135E + 03
1968	04–30	0.410E + 02
1969	07–24	0.123E + 03
1970	09–20	0.106E + 03
1971	06–08	0.121E + 03
1972	11–25	0.189E + 03
1973	07–22	0.640E + 02
1974	05–30	0.128E + 03
1975	04–04	0.176E + 03
1976	05–29	0.131E + 03
1977	09–11	0.164E + 03
1978	04–01	0.860E + 02
1979	05–09	0.137E + 03
1980	09–04	0.910E + 02
1981	08–23	0.990E + 02
1982	04–07	0.940E + 02
1983	05–28	0.920E + 02
1984	07–12	0.118E + 03

Average is .111E + 03 m^3/s.
Standard deviation is 0.357E + 02 m^3/s.

TABLE 9.7 Less Than or Equal to Probabilities Using Plotting Formulas

| SORTED FLOW RATES (cfs) | m PLOTTING POSITION | PLOTTING POSITION FORMULA PROBABILITIES | | | |
		WEIBULL $m/(n + 1)$	CALIFORNIA m/n	FOSTER $(2m - 1)/2n$	EXCEEDENCE $(m - 1)/n$
6	1	.125	.143	.071	0
14	2	.250	.286	.214	.143
36	3	.375	.429	.357	.286
42	4	.500	.571	.500	.429
58	5	.625	.714	.643	.571
90	6	.750	.857	.786	.714
99	7	.875	1.000	.929	.857

value. There are at least four plotting formulas in general use (Table 9.7). All have special advantages, however, the one used most frequently in stormwater management is Weibull (Benson, 1962), probably because it does not tend to over or underestimate the true probability at extreme points. Usually, greater than 25 data points are used. For a small number of data points (< 25) and for high-return periods, the Foster•formula gives a larger value than the Weibul formula and smaller than the California formula. The California and exceedence formulas generally can be used with a large number of data points but rarely with a small number of points. The exceedence formula is best for estimating the largest values (upper limit) while the California formula is best for estimating the lowest values (lower limit). The spread of the estimates among the four procedures is very small for shorter return periods but can be large toward the upper end (longer return periods). As the sample size increases, the probability estimates by the four plotting formulas tend to converge.

Using the Weibull formula, the data of Table 9.6 are ordered and shown in Table 9.8. The plot position is converted to a less than or equal to probability in column 3. The exceedence probability is one minus the less than probability and the return period is the inverse of the exceedence probability. Table 9.8 was obtained using a computer program; however, the calculations are relatively simple.

9.5.3 Annual and Partial Duration Series

The data of Table 9.8 was arranged as the maximum per time period (annual peak discharge values), thus it can be called an annual series. Another ordering is by size regardless of the time in which they occur. This is called a partial

TABLE 9.8   Weibull Order for Empirical Distribution Function

EVENTS: X(I) FLOW RATE (m^3/s)	m PLOT POSITION	$Pr = \dfrac{m}{(n+1)}$ PROBABILITY	$1 - Pr$ EXCEEDENCE PROBABILITY	T_r (yrs) RETURN PERIOD
41.00	1	.0333	.967	1.034
50.00	2	.0667	.933	1.071
63.00	3	.1000	.900	1.111
64.00	4	.1333	.867	1.154
75.00	5	.1667	.833	1.200
85.00	6	.2000	.800	1.250
86.00	7	.2333	.767	1.304
90.00	8	.2667	.733	1.364
91.00	9	.3000	.700	1.429
92.00	10	.3333	.667	1.500
94.00	11	.3667	.633	1.579
99.00	12	.4000	.600	1.667
103.00	13	.4333	.567	1.765
106.00	14	.4667	.533	1.875
109.00	15	.5000	.500	2.000
111.00	16	.5333	.467	2.143
118.00	17	.5667	.433	2.308
121.00	18	.6000	.400	2.500
123.00	19	.6333	.367	2.727
128.00	20	.6667	.333	3.000
131.00	21	.7000	.300	3.333
135.00	22	.7333	.267	3.750
137.00	23	.7667	.233	4.286
141.00	24	.8000	.200	5.000
142.00	25	.8333	.167	6.000
144.00	26	.8667	.133	7.500
164.00	27	.9000	.100	10.000
176.00	28	.9333	.067	15.000
189.00	29	.9667	.033	30.000

duration series or basic stage ordering. This ordering uses all data above a base flow. Over a 20-yr period, one may then elect to have 30 or more data points. This method may eliminate peak values for a given time because of their low values. Differences between the partial and annual series probability distributions tend to be greater at lower values which correspond to lower return periods. Beard (1962) indicated that the partial duration series is most useful for determining flood flows for those lower return periods (less than 10 yr). When using partial series of flood flows, one must be careful to insure independence. One peak flow may be influenced by another in a previous time period. One must also carefully choose a lower limit (cut off) because it affects the parameters of the resulting distribution. In many cases, it is best to use an annual series to compute a probability distribution and then convert the return periods to partial series return periods using Equation 9.31 (U.S. Department of Transportation, 1984).

$$T_p = 1/[\ln(T_A) - \ln(T_A - 1)] \qquad T_A > 1 \qquad (9.31)$$

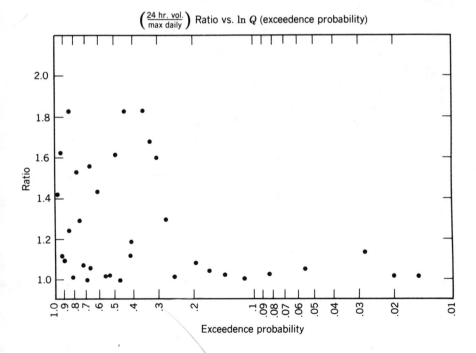

FIGURE 9.9   Ratio of partial to daily rainfalls as a function of exceedence probability.

TABLE 9.9 A Listing by Month, Day, and
Year for Maximum Daily Storms
for Each Year at Bushnell

YEAR	MONTH-DAY	RAINFALL (in.)
1918	09–27	0.200E + 01
1937	07–30	0.300E + 01
1938	06–22	0.380E + 01
1939	07–7	0.281E + 01
1940	07–4	0.290E + 01
1941	04–3	0.357E + 01
1942	02–24	0.155E + 01
1943	04–9	0.300E + 01
1944	10–19	0.760E + 01
1945	06–24	0.832E + 01
1946	06–27	0.253E + 01
1947	10–24	0.365E + 01
1948	07–2	0.350E + 01
1949	04–5	0.390E + 01
1950	09–6	0.908E + 01
1951	11–16	0.304E + 01
1952	05–20	0.309E + 01
1953	12–23	0.269E + 01
1954	07–26	0.394E + 01
1955	11–10	0.309E + 01
1956	10–16	0.413E + 01
1957	12–26	0.470E + 01
1958	03–2	0.308E + 01
1959	07–17	0.270E + 01
1960	07–29	0.527E + 01
1961	02–7	0.173E + 01
1962	05–28	0.280E + 01
1963	11–10	0.310E + 01
1964	09–11	0.382E + 01
1965	08–5	0.311E + 01
1966	05–8	0.302E + 01
1967	06–11	0.329E + 01
1968	10–19	0.379E + 01
1969	03–17	0.317E + 01
1970	02–3	0.397E + 01

TABLE 9.9 *(Continued)*

YEAR	MONTH-DAY	RAINFALL (in.)
1971	02–8	0.400E + 01
1972	03–31	0.665E + 01
1973	02–15	0.241E + 01
1974	06–25	0.690E + 01
1975	10–29	0.298E + 01
1976	6–5	0.298E + 01
1984	04–4	0.258E + 01
1985	8–18	0.515E + 01

Average is 0.378E + 01 in.
Standard deviation is 0.166E + 01 in.

where

T_P = return period partial series (years)

T_A = return period annual series (year)

9.5.4 Daily and True Interval Comparisons

Rainfall volumes are commonly reported on a daily basis (midnight to midnight). However, the maximum 24-hr rainfall volume may occur over another 24-hr period. It can be shown that for longer return periods (> 10 yr) the daily data can be used to estimate 24-hr rainfall events. A plot showing the ratio of 24 hr rainfall volumes (true interval) to maximum daily rainfall volume is shown in Figure 9.9 for Brooksville, Florida. The x axis is the exceedence probability and the return period is the inverse of the exceedence probability. Note the scatter of the data at low-return periods (high exceedence) and the convergence of the data to a 1.0 ratio at higher-return periods (low exceedence). Similar results are available for other locations.

☐ EXAMPLE PROBLEM 9.12

Using the data of Table 9.9 for Bushnell, Florida, order the data from smallest to largest and estimate the empirical frequency distribution using the Weibull plotting formula.

Solution

Using computer programs or simple calculations, Table 9.10 results. The reader should verify some of the calculations. ☐

TABLE 9.10 Empirical Cumulative Distribution Function

DATA FILE	:B:MYDBUSH.DAT
DATA TITLE	:MAXIMUM DAILY STORMS FOR EACH YEAR AT BUSHNELL
NUMBER OF DATA PTS	:43
UNITS USED	:INCHES

EVENTS: $X(I)$ (in.)	PLOT POSITION	$Pr = \dfrac{m}{(n+1)}$ PROBABILITY	$1 - Pr$ EXCEEDENCE PROBABILITY	T_r (yr) RETURN PERIOD
1.55	1	.0227	.977	1.023
1.73	2	.0455	.955	1.048
2.00	3	.0682	.932	1.073
2.41	4	.0909	.909	1.100
2.53	5	.1136	.886	1.128
2.58	6	.1364	.864	1.158
2.69	7	.1591	.841	1.189
2.70	8	.1818	.818	1.222
2.80	9	.2045	.795	1.257
2.81	10	.2273	.773	1.294
2.90	11	.2500	.720	1.333
2.98	12	.2727	.727	1.375
2.98	12	.2727	.727	1.375
3.00	14	.3182	.682	1.467
3.00	14	.3182	.682	1.467
3.02	16	.3636	.636	1.571
3.04	17	.3864	.614	1.630
3.08	18	.4091	.591	1.692
3.09	19	.4318	.568	1.760
3.09	19	.4318	.568	1.760
3.10	21	.4773	.523	1.913
3.11	22	.5000	.500	2.000
3.17	23	.5227	.477	2.095
3.29	24	.5455	.455	2.200
3.50	25	.5682	.432	2.316
3.57	26	.5909	.409	2.444
3.65	27	.6136	.386	2.588
3.79	28	.6364	.364	2.750
3.80	29	.6591	.341	2.933
3.82	30	.6818	.318	3.143
3.90	51	.7045	.295	3.385
3.94	32	.7273	.273	3.667
3.97	33	.7500	.250	4.000
4.00	34	.7727	.227	4.400
4.13	35	.7955	.205	4.889

TABLE 9.10   *(Continued)*

DATA FILE	:B:MYDBUSH.DAT
DATA TITLE	:MAXIMUM DAILY STORMS FOR EACH YEAR AT BUSHNELL
NUMBER OF DATA PTS	:43
UNITS USED	:INCHES

EVENTS: $X(I)$ (in.)	PLOT POSITION	$Pr = \dfrac{m}{(n + 1)}$ PROBABILITY	$1 - Pr$ EXCEEDENCE PROBABILITY	T_r (yr) RETURN PERIOD
4.70	36	.8182	.182	5.500
5.15	37	.8409	.159	6.286
5.27	38	.8636	.136	7.333
6.65	39	.8864	.114	8.800
6.90	40	.9091	.091	11.000
7.60	41	.9318	.068	14.667
8.32	42	.9545	.045	22.000
9.08	43	.9773	.023	44.000

9.6

REGRESSION AND CORRELATION ANALYSIS

Cause and effects relationships among hydrologic (discharge, volume runoff, mass of pollutants) and meterological parameters are frequently needed for engineering and planning investigations. Usually, a quantitative relationship within the investigative limits is desired. A variable for prediction depends on other independent variables. Many times it is assumed that the independent variables are measured with little or no error. The variability in the estimates for the independent variables is minimal. For example, the measurement of precipitation on a small watershed (< 5 ha) is generally representative of the watershed. Others, such as temperature, humidity and solar radiation, can be measured with a small error. However, the runoff from the watershed depends on the rainfall, soil moisture conditions and chance variation. Thus, the independent variable, x, may be fixed and with repeated values produce different values of the dependent variable, y. Some of the variability in the y variable may be explained by another independent variable, x_2, and the remaining variability is by chance. Thus, if this chance variability can be minimized, the estimate of the dependent variable can be improved.

9.6.1 Bivariate Case

For two variable situations, the x and y values are measured and a relation-ship between these two is determined. This relationship can be linear or

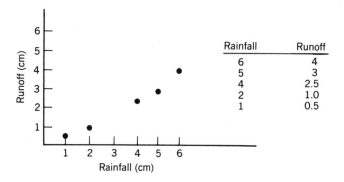

Rainfall	Runoff
6	4
5	3
4	2.5
2	1.0
1	0.5

FIGURE 9.10   Regression of runoff on rainfall.

nonlinear. Assume a linear relationship does exist and is given by:

$$y' = a + bx + \epsilon$$

where

y' = predicted dependent variable
x = independent variable
a, b = constants
ϵ = error with mean zero

Consider a situation in which runoff is estimated from rainfall. Data on runoff and rainfall are shown plotted in Figure 9.10. Runoff is dependent on rainfall.

We wish to minimize the variability in the estimate of runoff; therefore, a criterion for minimizing the variance of runoff (y variable) appears reasonable.

$$\text{Minimize} \sum_i (y_i - y')^2$$

and

$$\text{Minimize} \sum_i (y_i - a - bx_i)^2 \qquad (9.32)$$

Taking the partial derivatives of this equation with respect to the parameters a and b and setting these equal to zero, one obtains the "least square" estimators of a and b or those that minimize the variability in the estimate of the y variable. The partial derivatives result in normal equations, which are

$$\Sigma y_i = an + b\Sigma x_i$$

$$\Sigma x_i y_i = a\Sigma x_i + b\Sigma x_i^2 \qquad (9.33)$$

These normal equations are linear with two unknowns, a and b, and reduce to

$$a = \frac{(\Sigma x^2)(\Sigma y) - (\Sigma x)(\Sigma xy)}{n(\Sigma x^2) - (\Sigma x)^2}$$

$$b = \frac{n(\Sigma xy) - (\Sigma x)(\Sigma y)}{n(\Sigma x^2) - (\Sigma x)^2} \qquad (9.34)$$

☐   **EXAMPLE PROBLEM 9.13**

For the data of Figure 9.10, what is the best estimate of the linear regression equation for runoff by measuring rainfall?

Solution

Regression Coefficients Tabulation

x	x^2	y	y^2	$x \cdot y$
6	36	4	16	24
5	25	3	9	15
4	16	2.5	6.25	10
2	4	1	1	2
1	1	.5	.25	.5
Σ 18	82	11	32.5	51.5

$$a = \frac{(82)(11) - (18)(51.5)}{(5)(82) - 18^2}$$

$$a = -0.29$$

$$b = \frac{(5)(51.5) - (18)(11)}{(5)(82) - 18^2}$$

$$b = .69$$

The linear equation of best fit is

$$\text{Runoff} = -.29 + .69 \text{ rainfall} \ (1.0 < \text{rainfall} < 6.0 \text{ cm})$$

It is noted in the above equation that the limits of fit are rainfall quantities between 1 and 6 cm. These are the limits of the raw data and should be presented with an equation.   ☐

A linear equation of best fit has been assumed in the above example; however, if a curvilinear equation is assumed, the least squares estimators above can be used if the curvilinear equation can be transformed into a linear equation. Some example transformations are

$$y = \alpha \cdot \beta^x \tag{9.35}$$

and

$$\log y = \log \alpha + x \log \beta$$

$$y = ae^{-bx} \quad (\text{note } \alpha = a, \quad \beta = b) \tag{9.36}$$

and

$$\ln y = \ln a - bx$$

Multiple (more than two variables) regression is derived by a similar procedure as the bivariate case. For the three-variable case, the equation for minimum variance is

$$\sum (Y_i - a - bX_{1i} - bX_{2i})^2 \tag{9.37}$$

and the resulting equations are

$$\sum y = an + b_1 \sum x_1 + b_2 \sum x_2$$

$$\sum x_1 y = a \sum x_1 + b_1 \sum x_1^2 + b_2 \sum x_1 x_2$$

$$\sum x_2 y = a \sum x_2 + b_1 \sum x_1 x_2 + b_2 \sum x_2^2$$

As before, there are three equations and three unknowns, which are easily solved using the calculators and computers of today.

9.6.2   Correlation

Up to this point, it has been assumed that the regression equations were "best fit" estimators of the dependent variable. This best fit has to be quantified in terms of the degree of variability explained in the dependent variable by measuring the independent variability and using the "least squares" estimator. If the total variance in y is expressed by s^2 and the unexplained variance is given by s_u^2, the fraction of variance explained is

$$r^2 = 1 - \frac{s_u^2}{s^2} \tag{9.38}$$

and the sample correlation coefficient or measure of goodness of fit is given by

$$r = \pm \sqrt{1 - \frac{s_u^2}{s^2}} \qquad (9.39)$$

When the explained variance approaches the total variance, the correlation coefficient approaches either $+1$ or -1. Perfect correlation exists when $r = +1$ or -1. Inverse correlation is a negative value of r and results when the variables are inversely related to one another. The computation formula for r is derived as follows:

$$r^2 = \text{explained fraction} = 1 - \text{unexplained fraction}$$

$$r = \pm \sqrt{1 - \frac{\Sigma(y - y')^2}{\Sigma(y - \bar{y})^2}} \qquad (9.40)$$

which reduces to

$$r = \frac{n(\Sigma xy) - (\Sigma x)(\Sigma y)}{\sqrt{n(\Sigma x^2) - (\Sigma x)^2} \sqrt{n(\Sigma y^2) - (\Sigma y)^2}} \qquad (9.41)$$

☐ **EXAMPLE PROBLEM 9.14**

Calculate the correlation coefficient for the data of Example Problem 9.13. What percentage variation is explained?

Solution

$$r = \frac{5(51.5) - (18)(11)}{\sqrt{5(82) - 18^2} \sqrt{5(32.5) - 11^2}}$$

$$= .996$$

$$r^2 = .992 \quad \text{or} \quad 99.2\% \text{ variation explained} \quad \square$$

9.7
SUMMARY

Many meteorologic and hydrologic processes can be defined using probability and statistics concepts and formulas. Empirical data form the basis for determining the type of theoretical distribution that "best" fits the situation.

- In hydrologic studies empirical data form the basis for determining frequency distributions. Computer programs can aid in this determination.

- All distributions are defined by measures of (1) central tendency, (2) variability, and (3) skewness. These are also referenced as the first, second, and third moment of a distribution.

- Return period or recurrence interval is the inverse of exceedence probability. It is based on the assumption of a long period of time over which changes will not affect the average time interval.

- A histogram can describe graphically the shape of a frequency distribution. There are useful guidelines for developing histograms in the text.

- There are plotting position formulas for empirical data. The Weibull formula is widely used.

- The ordering or ranking of data by magnitude is called a partial series. If ordered by time, the series is called annual.

- The exceedence probability can be developed from a cumulative distribution function.

- The risk involved with a hydrologic event is defined as the probability of at least one exceedence during a design life. It can be quantified using equation 9.30.

- The Gumbel distribution and log-Pearson Type III are extreme event distributions used extensively for the description and analyses of hydrologic events.

- The exponential distribution is being used to aid in the description of rainfall and runoff events.

- Bivariate regression analysis can be used to determine the "best" fit line between two variables. A correlation coefficient is used to measure the "goodness of fit" of the dependent variable explained using the "best" equation.

9.8

PROBLEMS

1. a. What is the approximate reliability at which you can estimate a hydrlogic event with a return of 10 yr if you are using 25 yr of data and you wish to be within ±25% of the true estimate?
   b. What is your record length if you wish to be 100% reliable?

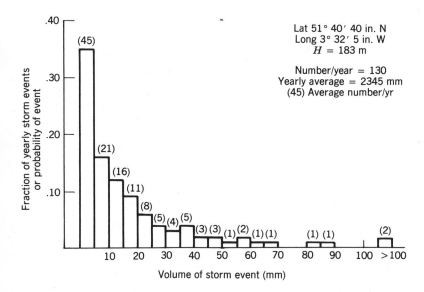

FIGURE 9.11 Volume frequency distributions — Treherbert Park, Mid-Glamorgan, U.K.

2. a. For the data of Example Problem 9.8, calculate a measure of central tendency and a measure of variability.
   b. If the years 1977 through 1980 were added as 16, 14, 22, and 18 m, respectively, how does skewness, mean, and the coefficient of variability change?

3. Explain what is meant by skewness and give an example and show a frequency distribution for a right-skewed distribution.

4. A flood flow analysis is completed on a tributary to the Delaware River. A Gumbel-type distribution is believed to be representative of annual flood peaks. If the average flood peak is 4000 m³/sec and the standard deviation is 600 m³/sec, what is the magnitude of a flood with a recurrence interval of 20 yr?

5. What is the probability that a drought that is more severe than a drought of a return period of once in 50 yr will occur only once in 100 yr?

6. For the histograms shown in Figures 9.11 and 9.12, develop a cumulative frequency distribution on the fraction of storms with volume less than or equal to a stated volume. Compare these results for rainfall in Wales to that of the Orlando Jetport. Comment on all statistical measures.

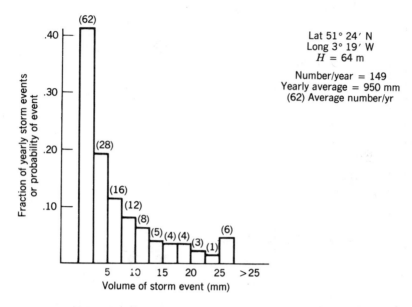

FIGURE 9.12   Volume frequency distribution — Barry, South Glamorgan, U.K.

7. Using the cumulative distribution function of Figure 9.1a, a cumulative rainfall volume distribution function was developed as presented in Figure 9.13. The lower curve, labeled "no diversion," was developed assuming that the rainfall volume was accumulated up to and including the stated event rainfall volume. The upper curve assumes that the stated rainfall event volume will be diverted for treatment and then the remaining amount is discharged. If 1 in. of every rainfall is diverted for treatment, 80% of the yearly rainfall volume will be treated. Using data for your area, develop a similar curve. (*Hints*: Volume of rainfall per year is the product of the frequency of that event interval times the average rainfall for that interval and the diversion volume is the sum of rainfall up to the diversion volume plus the sum of diversion volume and the frequency of exceedence.

$$F(\text{Vol}|\text{Diversion Vol.}) = \sum_{i=0}^{\text{Diversion Vol.}} P(i)_i \bar{x}_i n$$

$$+ \sum_{i=\text{Diversion Volume}}^{\infty} P(i)_i \text{Diversion Vol.} n$$

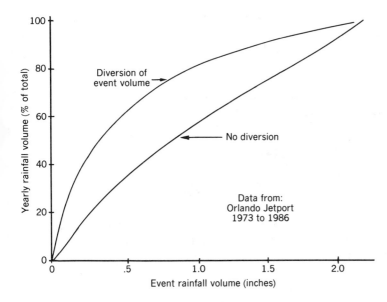

FIGURE 9.13 Percentage of yearly rainfall volume and diversion volume for each and every storm.

8. For the data for Figure 9.10, determine an equation of the form runoff = K precipitation, or determine K. This assumes that the intercept is equal to zero.

9. Using the 1950–1985 data of Example Problem 9.2 for one of the locations, develop a histogram and comment on the shape of the distribution (use six class intervals). Also, calculate the average, standard deviation, and skewness if the first 5 yr of data were missing. Comment on the results as compared to the calculations using all the data.

10. In the analyses of annual flood peaks on a stream with 60 yr of records, it was determined that the annual flood peaks follow a Gumbel-type distribution with an annual mean peak of 83,333 cfs.
   a. What is the probability that an annual flood magnitude greater than 110,000 cfs will not occur in 25 yr? The sample standard deviation is 10,000.
   b. What is the probability that this 110,000 cfs flood flow will occur at least once in 25 yr?
   c. What is the probability that exactly two floods equal to or greater than 110,000 cfs will occur in the next 25 yr?

11. For the following flow rate data, use the four plotting position formulas of Table 9.6 and plot the annual series empirical data on probability paper. Comment on the results.

YEAR	PEAK FLOW (m^3/s)	YEAR	PEAK FLOW (m^3/sec)
1970	602	1979	178
1971	214	1980	249
1972	106	1981	365
1973	312	1982	250
1974	280	1983	912
1975	143	1984	404
1976	190	1985	136
1977	236	1986	101
1978	737		

12. Using the maximum yearly rainfall data of Table 9.8 construct a histogram of rainfall. Comment on the shape of the histogram.

13. Cumulative probability distributions for rainfall intensity (i), duration (D), and interevent time (Δ) are used for the following estimates.

$$\Pr(i \leq 0.40 \text{ in./hr}) = 0.98$$

$$\Pr(D \geq 6 \text{ hr}) = 0.05$$

$$\Pr(\Delta \geq 92 \text{ hr}) = 0.10$$

a. If there were 100 events/year, calculate the return period and the number of events per year for each rainfall description (i, D, Δ).
b. Also, what is the return period and number of events per year for a storm of intensity greater than 0.40 in./hr and a duration greater than 6 hr?

14. From the following independent flow rate data, develop an empirical probability distribution using annual series. Then a distribution using partial series data for flows over 200 m^3/s. What is the flow rate estimate for the 1 in 10-yr storm using both the annual and partial series data? Use

the Weibull method for the empirical distributions. The highest two peak flows per year are as follows:

YEAR	PEAK FLOW (m^3/s)		YEAR	PEAK FLOW (m^3/s)	
1970	602	390	1979	178	120
1971	214	174	1980	249	145
1972	106	88	1981	365	204
1973	312	140	1982	250	170
1974	280	210	1983	912	350
1975	143	138	1984	404	100
1976	190	108	1985	136	135
1977	236	190	1986	101	99
1978	737	304			

15. A water resources project has a design life of 50 yr. The hydrologic variable of interest follows a log normal distribution with a mean equal to 10 in. and a standard deviation of 2.5 in. If hydrologic design criteria calls for 12.5-in value, what is exceedence probability and the risk involved over a 4-yr period with this design criteria? Does the risk change if the distribution is a Gumbel type?

16. A 1 in 100-yr rainfall volume for a 24-hr time period is 10 in.
    a. What is the probability that this rainfall volume will not occur in the next 5 yr?
    b. What is the risk you assume if there is at least one exceedence in the design life of 5 yr?
    c. Assuming that the distribution can be approximated by a Gumbel one, what is the average if the standard deviation is 1.5 in.?

9.9

COMPUTER-ASSISTED PROBLEMS

1. For the following rainfall intensity and time data, estimate a relationship between intensity and time to minimize the estimate of intensity. Use least squares linear regression for the equation $i = b/(a + t)$.

t-TIME (min)	*i*-INTENSITY (in./hr)
5	6.72
10	5.16
15	4.26
30	3.02
60	1.95

2. Using the data of Problem 1, what is your estimate using two other equation forms? Comment on the results.

3. Expand the computer program developed for Problem 4 (Section 3.12) to calculate standard deviation, coefficient of variability, and skewness.

4. Use the linear regression program to determine a "best-fit" mathematical relationship between the rainfall data of Example Problem 9.2. Comment on the "best fit." First, one location is the dependent variable. Then find another fit assuming the other location is the dependent variable.

9.10

REFERENCES

Beard, L.R. 1962. "Statistical methods in Hydrology," U.S. Army Corps of Engineers, Civil Works Project CW-151.

Benson, M.A. 1962. "Plotting Positions and Economics of Engineering Planning," *ASCE, Journal of the Hydraulics Division*, November, No. 88, pp. 57–71.

Gumbel, E.J. 1945. "Floods Estimated by the Probability Method," *Engineering News Record*, **134**, pp. 833–837.

Hardison, C.H. 1974. "Generalized Skew Coefficient of Annual Floods in the United States and Their Application," *Water Resources Research*, **10**(5), pp. 745–752.

U.S. Department of Commerce, 1973–1986. "Local Climatological Data," National Oceanic and Atmospheric Administration, Asheville, NC.

U.S. Department of Transportation. 1984. *Hydrology*. FHWA Report No. 1P-84-15, Federal Highway Administration, McLean, Virginia, pp. 45–52.

Work Group on Flood Flow Frequency—Hydrology Committee. 1977. "A Uniform Technique for Determining Flood Flow Frequency," Bulletin No. 15, Thomas S. Kleppe, Chairman, Water Resources Council.

....
....
....

10

GROUNDWATER
HYDROLOGY

Groundwater hydrology is a study area of hydrology concentrating on the storage and movement of water beneath the ground surface. It is an important study area for many reasons. One reason is that some streams and lakes are fed primarily by groundwaters. Another reason is the management of stormwater can be accomplished by on-site infiltration and regional ponds for infiltration. To encourage groundwater recharge in some areas, on-site and areawide infiltration is mandated by municipal regulations. Still another reason is that vast storage volumes of water are available under the ground and pipes (wells) can penetrate the storage areas to extract water for beneficial uses. Over 25% of nonsaline water used in the United States is extracted from groundwater. This does not include the hydroelectric power generation use of water. The study of the hydrologic cycle would not be complete without an understanding of the exchanges of water between ground and surface supplies. This chapter presents information to aid in quantifying groundwater storage and movement with definition of terms relating to groundwater.

10.1

THE OCCURRENCE OF GROUNDWATER

Groundwater is water resident beneath the ground surface. It results from waters that infiltrate from the ground surface and percolates to the underlying strata. Infiltrated groundwaters pass through an unsaturated zone in route to a saturated zone. The water table separates the two zones. The pressure at the water table is atmospheric.

There can be a capillary fringe to which water will rise above the water table. In fine silty sand, the capillary rise can be as high as 50 cm, while the rise in gravel is only about 2 or 3 cm. It is called the soil–moisture region. The water in this region fluctuates in quantity as the vegetation uses moisture and percolation from infiltrated waters occurs. Percolated water (gravity water), capillary water, and air exist among the soil particles. The percolated water moves downward in primarily the larger soil pores. The smaller the pore spaces, the less gravity movement of waters resulting from infiltration.

Soil moisture is measured as the loss in weight of soil after being oven dried at 103 to 105°F. Higher temperatures may burn off organics. After percolated water has passed through the soil, that soil moisture remaining is defined as the field capacity and is essentially the water retained in the soil at a tension pressure of about 0.33 atm (Colman, 1947). When plants can no longer use water from the soil, the remaining soil moisture is said to be at the wilting point. The soil moisture difference between field capacity and wilting point is called available water moisture. This is useful water storage. Commonly reported moisture values for different soils are shown in Table 10.1.

The water table level will fluctuate and may be directly related to precipitation. When reporting levels, the time and date of measurement should be reported. The quantity of water that can be stored under the surface depends on the porosity of the subsurface strata, the type of liquid and adjacent underground soil and water table conditions. The media in which

TABLE 10.1   Common Moisture Values as a Percent of Dry Soil Weight

SOIL TYPE	FIELD CAPACITY (AFTER PERCOLATION)	WILTING (AFTER PLANT USE)	AVAILABLE (FIELD WILTING)
Sand	5	2	3
Sandy loam	12	5	7
Loam	19	10	9
Silty loam	22	13	9
Clay loam	24	15	9

groundwater moves are characterized by many factors, two of which are void spaces (porosity) and resistance (permeability).

10.1.1   Porosity

Porosity (n_p) is defined as the ratio of void volume to total volume and may range from a small fraction to about 0.90.

$$n_p = \frac{V_v}{V} = \frac{(V - V_m)}{V} = 1 - \frac{V_m}{V} \qquad (10.1)$$

where

n_p = porosity (subscript p because n is used in Manning's equation)
V_v = volume of the voids
V = total volume of sample
V_m = volume of the soil (material)

The volume of the soil can be determined by dividing the weight of the "dry" soil by the specific weight (soil solid specific gravity times unit weight of water). In a granular mass composed of uniform spheres with the loosest possible packing, $n_p = 47.6\%$, and with the densest possible, $n_p = 26\%$.

Regional water-bearing strata, called aquifers, often consist of unconsolidated material like sandstones and limestones. These strata usually have porosity values ranging from 5 to 15%. Gravel and sand aquifers have higher porosities. Limestone itself is relatively impervious but is soluble in water and so frequently has wide joints and solution passages that make the rock similar to a very porous rock in its capacity to hold water over a wide area. For a material to be permeable, the pores must be connected.

10.1.2   Permeability

The water in the pores of an aquifer is subject to gravitational forces and so tends to flow downward through the connected pores of the material. The resistance to this underground flow varies widely. The rate at which water moves through the pores of the material (permeability or hydraulic conductivity) is a measure of this resistance. Aquifers with large pores such as coarse gravels are said to have a high permeability, and those with very small microscopic pores such as clay, have a low permeability.

If two piezometers are placed in the groundwater, the velocity of the groundwater can be calculated with the idealized conditions of Figure 10.1 using the relationship of change in head per length of flow or

$$v = K \left[\frac{(h_1 + z_1) - (h_2 + z_2)}{L} \right] \qquad (10.2)$$

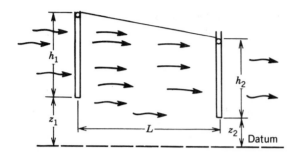

FIGURE 10.1   One-dimensional groundwater flow.

where

K = permeability (length/time)
L = distance between piezometers (length)
h = pressure heads (length)
z = elevation heads (length)
v = Darcy velocity (length/time)

Equation 10.2 and modifications are called the Darcy equations after the French hydrologist Henri Darcy, who discovered that velocity was proportional to hydraulic gradient. The factor of proportionality is the permeability.

Permeability can be determined in the laboratory using permeameters. Two types are used: constant head where constant pressure heads are maintained at the inlet and outlet, and falling head where constant head is maintained only at the outlet end. Schematics of the equipment are shown in Figure 10.2. The constant head is suitable for estimating the permeability of soils like sands and gravels, whereas the falling head is more suitable for soils of relatively low permeability, like fine silt.

For the constant head permeameter the volume flow rate through a given cross-section area perpendicular to flow is given by the continuity equation ($Q = Av$). Rearranging Equation 10.2 for $K = vL/\Delta H$ yields Equation 10.3 with sample area equal to πR^2 and H equal to ΔH.

$$K = \frac{LQ}{H\pi R^2} \qquad (10.3)$$

where

K = permeability (m/day, ft/day)
H = head loss (m or ft)
L = sample height (m or ft)
Q = outlet flow rate (m^3/day, ft^3/day)
R = radius of sample

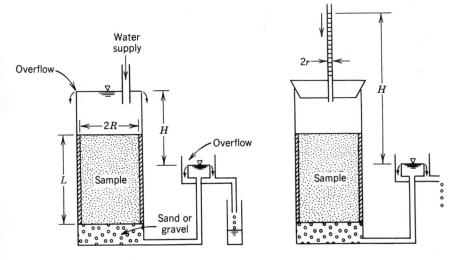

FIGURE 10.2 Permeameters — constant head on left, falling head on right.

The permeability from the falling-head permeameter also can be expressed by an equation. In the small, narrow standpipe, flow rate can be expressed as

$$Q = \pi r^2 \frac{dh}{dt} \qquad (10.4)$$

where

$$r = \text{radius of standpipe (m, ft)}$$

and on the basis of flow through the sample as

$$Q = K \pi R^2 \frac{H}{L} \qquad (10.5)$$

Equating the two expressions for flow rate and integrating, one obtains

$$K = \left(\frac{Lr^2}{tR^2} \right) \ln \left(\frac{H_1}{H_2} \right) \qquad (10.6)$$

where
H_1 = starting height of water column (m, ft)
H_2 = ending height of water column (m, ft)
t = time required for water to drop (day)

The rate of water movement through a soil matrix itself is called seepage or pore velocity and is greater than the Darcy velocity because the flow area is reduced. The unrestricted flow rate measured using Darcy velocity must be equal to the flow rate through the soil media, thus the two flow rates can be equated as

$$Q_{\text{Darcy}} = Q_{\text{Seepage}}$$

$$vA = v_s A_s$$

where

v_s = seepage velocity (m/day)
v = Darcy velocity (m/day)
A = total area (m^2)
A_s = seepage area (m^2)

and the seepage area is expressed as

$$A_s = n_p A$$

Thus the seepage velocity can be calculated from the Darcy velocity by substituting for A_s:

$$vA = v_s n_p A$$

or

$$v_s = v/n_p \tag{10.7}$$

The residence time in the soil is less than the residence time considering the total flow area because the seepage velocity of flow in the soil is greater.

10.1.3   Factors Affecting Permeability

Permeability estimates may vary locally due to variability in soil materials. If soil changes are expected, a suitable number of samples should be taken. Solution cavities and other groundwater channels may also affect estimates.

   If the soil materials do not change, then other factors also may affect permeability, such as temperature, ionic composition, and presence of entrapped air. Temperature has an effect on water viscosity, and thus on permeability. Higher temperatures mean lower viscosity. Thus, the water will have less resistance for movement through the soil, and the permeability will increase. The change in permeability is linear. Values of permeability are normally expressed at 20°C and values of permeabilities at other temperatures are calculated using

$$K_t = \left(\frac{\mu_{20}}{\mu_t}\right) K_{20} \tag{10.8}$$

where

K_t = permeability at temperature $t°C$
μ_{20} = absolute viscosity at $20°C$ [g/cm(sec)]
μ_t = absolute viscosity at $t°C$ [g/cm(sec)]
K_{20} = permeability at $20°C$

As water passes through clay materials, the pores may be very small causing larger ions in the water to be removed. Thus, the soil behaves like a selective membrane. At high water gradients, monovalent cations are retarded more so than the divalent ones. McNeal (1968) developed a sodium absorption ratio (SAR) with calcium and magnesium:

$$SAR = 2Na/(Ca + Mg) \tag{10.9}$$

where
SAR = sodium absorption ratio (SAR)
Na = sodium concentration (meq/L)
Ca = calcium concentration (meq/L)
Mg = magnesium concentration (meq/L)

At a given salt concentration, permeability decreases with increasing SAR, as shown in Figure 10.3.

Completely saturated soils are used to determine permeabilities in the laboratory. However, entrapped air in the soils physically reduces the permeability. In sandy soils, the permeability in the unsaturated zone may be only about one-half the permeability at saturation (Bouwer, 1966). Entrapped air may also occur after a rapid rise or fall of the groundwater table.

10.1.4 Some Common Permeability Values

The common units of permeability are meters/day or feet/day. However, units of centimeter/hour or inches/hour also are useful for faster moving waters and other units such as gallons per minute/square feet and feet/second are used where rate values are in similar units.

Investigators have tried to relate the permeability of a soil to its physical properties (grain size, density, porosity) and found some empirical formulas which were primarily useful for site specific results. One such formula often identified as specific or intrinsic permeability was developed for clean water

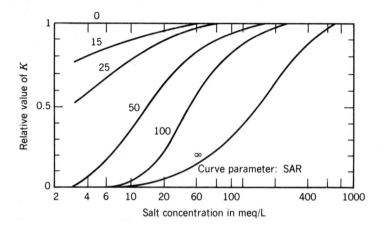

FIGURE 10.3 Permeability changes with SAR.

supply filter sands and is

$$K = C(d_{10})^2 \tag{10.10}$$

where

K = premeability coefficient (m/day)
d_{10} = grain size (mm) of sand for which 10% is finer
C = regression constant (average value = 1000)

Well-mixed (heterogeneous) soil often displays the simple relationship given by Equation 10.10 and is solely a function of the porous medium. Possible

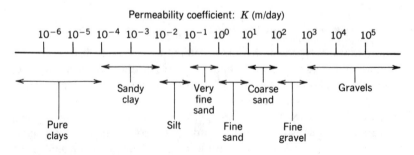

FIGURE 10.4 Range of permeability in soils.

TABLE 10.2 Approximate Average Porosity, Specific Yield, and Permeability
of Various Soil Materials (partly adopted from Bouwer, 1966 and Todd, 1980)

MATERIAL	POROSITY (%)	SPECIFIC YIELD (%)	AVERAGE PERMEABILITY K	
			(gpd/ft^2)	(m/day)
Clay	45	3.0	0.01	0.0004
Sand	35	25.0	1,000.00	41.0000
Gravel	25	22.0	100,000.00	4,100.0000
Gravel & sand	20	16.0	10,000.00	410.0000
Sandstone	15	8.0	100.00	4.1000
Limestone, shale	5	2.0	1.00	0.0410
Quartzite, granite	1	0.5	0.01	0.0004

range of K's for various natural soils are shown in Figure 10.4. These are to
be used only as representative values.

Table 10.2 illustrates some values for permeabilities, porosity, and specific
yield for various soil materials. Specific yield is the ratio of the volume of
water released to a unit volume of saturated, unconfined aquifer material.
Expressed as a percentage, it is calculated from the ratio of volume of water
removed to total volume of the soil multiplied by 100. If expressed as a
fraction, it is called storage coefficient. The permeability numbers should be
considered as only general estimates.

10.2

AQUIFERS AND SPRINGS

An aquifer is a water-bearing soil or rock that can release its water in sufficient
quantities to make it economically feasible to develop for water supply. The
aquifer can be either confined or unconfined, depending on whether or not a
water table or free water surface exists under atmospheric pressure. Springs
result when water either drains by gravity or is forced from the ground. Water
enters the ground and is forced by gravity to percolate into lower strata.

As groundwater percolates into the aquifer, it will reach a level at which
the aquifer is saturated. This saturation surface may approach the ground
resulting in apparent horizontal flow. Waters closest to the ground surface or
surficial waters can fluctuate greatly during the course of a year. The surficial
waters fall during dry time periods and rise in rainy weather. The upper water

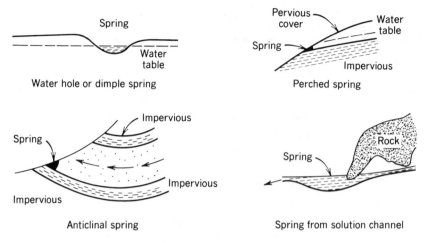

FIGURE 10.5 Typical spring classifications.

surface in the deep aquifers and the surficial waters are usually moving slowly toward the nearest free water surface such as a lake or river, or the sea. However, if there is an impermeable layer underlying an aquifer and this layer outcrops on the ground surface, then the groundwater will appear on the surface and is called a spring. There are at least four different classes of springs as shown in Figure 10.5.

It is equally possible for a groundwater aquifer to become overlain by impermeable material and thus be under pressure. These aquifers, receiving water from distant sources, are called confined aquifers and the surface to which the water would rise in a standpipe if it could, is called the piezometric surface. Wells drilled into such confined aquifers are called artesian wells, and the aquifers are called artesian aquifers. If the piezometric surface is above ground level and an artesian well penetrates the aquifer, a flowing well results. A fracture or flow in the impermeable overlay of an artesian aquifer will result in an artesian spring. Sometimes areas of impermeable material may exist in an aquifer. This may happen through geological faulting or through a lens of clay occurring in an otherwise sandy area. A small local water table, called a perched water table, may result, and this can often be a long way above the true piezometric surface.

10.2.1 Aquifers — An Example

The aquifers described above can be found in many regions of the world. They can provide in these regions much of the fresh water used for public, industrial, and agricultural use. As an example, the state of Florida contains

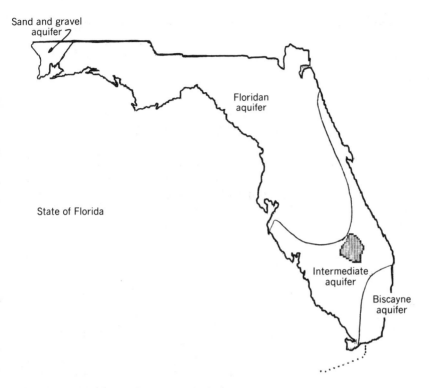

FIGURE 10.6 An example of principal aquifers. *Source:* National Water Summary — Florida, 1985.

abundant groundwater resources. The average freshwater withdrawals from the four major aquifers of the state amounted to 3800 million gallons per day (MGD) in 1980. Irrigation withdrawals alone accounted for 42% of this average daily quantity. The four principal aquifers are shown in Figure 10.6. The Biscayne aquifer of South Florida consists of limestone, sandstone, and sand. It is an unconfined aquifer. Total water withdrawn is in the order of 500 MGD. The intermediate aquifer is limestone and discontinuous with shell beds and clay layers. The largest of the four is the Floridan. This consists of limestone and dolomite. It is confined in deep areas and unconfined in outcrop areas and currently provides over 500 million gallons per day. The sand and gravel aquifer of Northwest Florida is unconfined near upper-surface areas and confined in deeper areas. Springs are abundant with 27 of the United States' 78 first-magnitude springs resident in Florida. The groundwater reservoirs are primarily recharged from infiltrated and percolated rain waters. In the Biscayne aquifers, a recharge potential is maintained by the storage of runoff waters (fresh water) in canals. Maintenance of a high water table in this area is important to minimize saltwater intrusion. Annual recharge rates for the four major Florida aquifers have been related to rainfall and found to vary yearly from less than one inch to a maximum of about 5 in.

10.3

MOVEMENT OF GROUNDWATERS

Except in large caverns and fissures, groundwater flow is almost exclusively laminar. It has been shown that the velocity of flow in capillary tubes is proportional to the slope S of the energy gradient. Darcy confirmed the applicability of this principle to flow in uniform sands, and Equation 10.2 can be rewritten as

$$V = KS \qquad\qquad (10.11)$$

Assuming the continuity equation is valid for a particular part of an aquifer, of area A, flow rate is estimated from

$$Q = VA = KAS \qquad\qquad (10.12)$$

where Q is the flow rate (volume per unit time) through a cross-sectional area A of aquifer. Note that the velocities are relatively slow compared to surface flows. Thus, velocity heads are negligible in groundwater flow. The slope, S, is either the slope of the water table or the piezometric surface.

The flow through an aquifer with width Y and depth D in gallons per day can be written if area is equal to YD:

$$Q = YDKS \qquad\qquad (10.13)$$

Equation 10.13 is similar to the equation for the flow of electricity (Ohm's law) where S is analogous to the gradient of the voltage drop, KYD to the conductance of the circuit, and Q to the amperage.

The transmissivity of an aquifer is the flow in gallons per day (cubic meters per day) through a section of aquifer 1 ft (1 m) wide under a hydraulic gradient of unity. The unit of measure commonly used in the United States is gallons per day per foot width. The product KD in Equation 10.13 is often combined into a parameter called transmissivity with Equation 10.13 rewritten as

$$Q = YTS \qquad\qquad (10.14)$$

where T is the aquifer transmissivity.

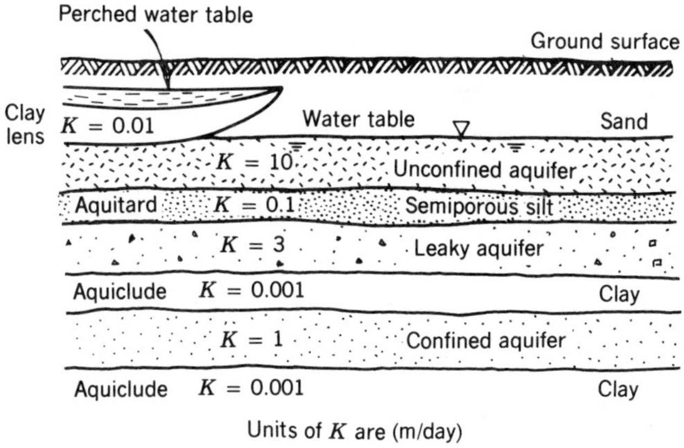

FIGURE 10.7 Aquifer definitions (with sample K values — metric units).

Once recharge water has infiltrated, its percolation downwards to the groundwater storage depends on the geological structure as well as on the rock composition. Figure 10.7 shows a section through a series of sedimentary rocks in which it is most usual to find productive aquifers—beds of rock with high porosity that are capable of holding large quantities of water. In general, the older the rock formation, the more consolidated is the rock material and the less likely it is to contain water. Igneous and metamorphic rocks are not good sources of groundwater unless weathered and/or fractured. The sedimentary rock strata have different compositions and porosities. In the much simplified diagram, layers of porous sands of limestones are subdivided by less porous material such as silt or clay that inhibits water movement. Semiporous beds that allow some seepage of water through them are known as aquitards; they slow up percolation to the porous layers below, which are called leaky aquifers since they can lose as well as gain water through an aquitard. The clay beds that are mainly impermeable are called aquicludes and the porous layers between them are confined aquifers in which the water is under pressure. Water pressure between aquifers will determine water movement. In the top sandy layer, the water table at atmospheric pressure marks the variable upper limit of the unconfined aquifer, although locally a lens of clay can hold up the groundwater to form a perched water table.

☐   **_EXAMPLE PROBLEM 10.1_**

An area of land is underlain by glacial soils, which include a thick sand horizon. Under the soils is a rock layer. Both the sand and rock layers contain groundwater. The water from the rock horizon is abstracted for a

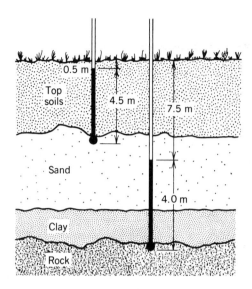

FIGURE 10.8 Piezometer installation for liquid waste disposal proposal.

public water supply. It is proposed that contaminated effluent be disposed of by pumping it into the sand horizon.

Would this lead to contamination of the public water supply source? Assume that the density of groundwater in the rock horizon is 1000 kg/m³, that of the fluid in the sand layer (after mixing with the contaminated fluid) is likely to be 1040 kg/m³ and that site exploration drilling has shown the pressure head in the two layers (see Figure 10.8).

Solution

Flow occurs from high pressure to lower pressure. If the pressure in the sand horizon is greater than that in the rock layer, then the polluted water may be carried into the public water supply.

Pressure intensity (sand horizon) $= (\rho)(g)(h)$

$$= 1040 \times 9.81 \times 4.5$$

$$= 45.91 \text{ kN/m}^2$$

Pressure intensity (rock layer) $= 1000 \times 9.81 \times 4.0$

$$= 39.24 \text{ kN/m}^2$$

Pressure $= \gamma h = pg_l h$

Thus, a slightly higher pressure intensity exists in the sand and if there are breaks in the clay, the potential for the flow of contaminated fluid to the rock aquifer exists.   □

10.4

FLOW IN A CONFINED AQUIFER

An aquifer can be confined if its ceiling and floor are impermeable over an area of study. The pressure in this artesian aquifer forces water to be recorded at piezometric levels. If piezometric levels are measured at the same time for different locations, the gradient of flow can be established. Using this gradient, an estimate of flow can be made assuming no other inputs or outputs across the boundary of the aquifer. Darcy's law for one-dimensional flow can be used to solve simple systems of lateral and vertical groundwater flow. Vertical-flow components are often neglected where groundwater moves primarily in the lateral direction (DeWiest, 1965). Consider the schematic of the confined aquifer as shown in Figure 10.9. Construction of an energy balance yields Equation 10.15.

$$\frac{V_1^2}{2g} + \frac{P_1}{\gamma} + h_1 = \frac{V_2^2}{2g} + \frac{P_2}{\gamma} + h_2 + \Delta h \text{ (head loss)} \qquad (10.15)$$

where

V_1, V_2 = velocity heads

g = gravitational constant

γ = unit weight of fluid

h = piezometric heads

L = length of artesian aquifer between piezometric measurements (Figure 10.9)

D = thickness of aquifer (Figure 10.9)

Δh = head loss

$P_1 P_2$ = pressure

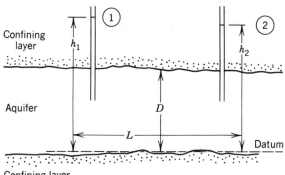

FIGURE 10.9 Schematic of confined aquifer.

Normally, V_1 and V_2 are similar and the difference in pressure and elevation is measured by the piezometer, or:

$$\Delta h = \frac{P_1}{\gamma} + z_1 - \frac{P_2}{\gamma} + z_2$$

or for length ΔL,

$$S = \Delta h / \Delta L \text{ (energy gradient slope)} \qquad (10.16)$$

and using the definition of permeability

$$V = KS \qquad (10.17)$$

substituting Equation 10.16 into Equation 10.17 for a differential length (ΔL) gives

$$V = K(\Delta h / \Delta L) \qquad (10.18)$$

which is an expression of Darcy's law with $\Delta h / \Delta L$ a positive value for decreasing head. A negative sign may be present on the right-hand side of the equation if Δh is negative.

Now, let $Q = AV$, thus Equation 10.18 becomes $Q = KA(\Delta h / \Delta L)$ and per unit width ($A = D$), thus $Q' = DV$ and

$$Q' = KD(\Delta h / \Delta L) \qquad (10.19)$$

and assuming head varies linearly:

$$\Delta h / \Delta L = \frac{(h_1 - h_2)}{L} \qquad (10.20)$$

10.5

FLOW IN AN UNCONFINED AQUIFER

For an unconfined aquifer, a similar equation can be developed. Figure 10.10 illustrates the schematic of an example unconfined aquifer.

$$Q = KA \, dh / dL \qquad (10.21)$$

Area varies along the path of flow and for unit width $A = y(1)$ thus $Q' = Ky \, dy / dL$ with y the variable on depth, thus integration of

$$Q' \int_0^L dL = K \int_{h_2}^{h_1} y \, dy$$

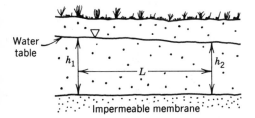

FIGURE 10.10 Unconfined aquifer schematic.

results in

$$Q' = \frac{K\left(h_1^2 - h_2^2\right)}{2L} \tag{10.22}$$

which is known as the Dupuit equation.

☐ ***EXAMPLE PROBLEM 10.2***
_____

Estimate the discharge from a large reservoir through a permeable sand/clay mixture with $K = 40$ gal/ft^2-day. The face of the permeable dam is 4 ft deep and the discharge pipe is 2 ft in diameter. A schematic of the physical situation is shown in Figure 10.11.

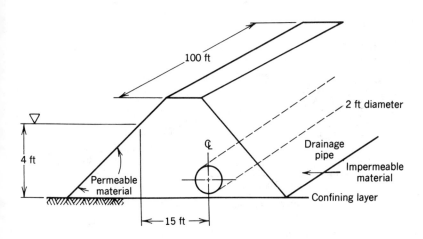

FIGURE 10.11 Reservoir seepage.

Solution

$$Q' = (K/2L)(h_2^2 - h_1^2) = \frac{40 \text{ gal/ft}^2\text{-day}}{2(15)\text{ft}}(4^2 - 2^2)$$

$$= (40/30)(16 - 4) = 16 \text{ gal/ft-day and for 100 feet } Q = 1600 \text{ gal/day}$$

$$Q = 1600 \text{ gal/day} \times 1 \, CF/7.48 \text{ gal} = 214 \text{ ft}^3\text{-day}$$

Decrease in pond elevation if pond has a surface area of 1 acre:

$$\left[214 \text{ ft}^3/43{,}560 \text{ ft}^2\right] \times 12 \text{ in./ft} = 0.06 \text{ in./day} \quad \square$$

10.6

UNIFORM INFILTRATION AND DRAINAGE

An unconfined aquifer with the saturated zone above and sloping toward a surface water body can contribute groundwater flow to the surface source. Consider an unconfined aquifer with a uniform rate of infiltration being applied over an area. Once the percolated waters reach the superficial water table, drainage moves towards a free standing surface water body, as shown in Figure 10.12. Again, using Darcy's law with lateral flow and velocity at distance x equal to v_x, one can write

$$v_x = K\left(\frac{\Delta h}{\Delta x}\right) \tag{10.23}$$

where $\Delta h/\Delta x$ = slope of the water table, taken as a positive value.

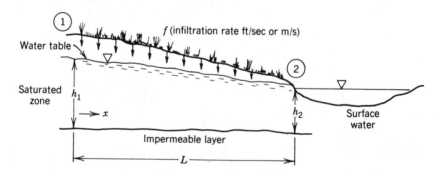

FIGURE 10.12   Uniform infiltration with drainage to surface waters.

The flow per unit width of aquifer is

$$Q = KA(\Delta h/\Delta x) \quad \text{and} \quad A = h \text{ for unit width}$$

thus

$$Q' = Kh(\Delta h/\Delta x)(\text{units are: ft}^3/\text{ft-sec, m}^3/\text{m-s}) \tag{10.24}$$

also, note $Q' = fx$, thus one can write from a mass balance:

$$fx = Kh\left(\frac{\Delta h}{\Delta x}\right)$$

and

$$Kh\,\Delta h = fx\,\Delta x \tag{10.25}$$

Integration between the limits of infiltration produces

$$K\left(h_1^2 - h_2^2\right) = fL^2$$

and

$$h_1 = \left(h_2^2 + fL^2/K\right)^{1/2} \tag{10.26}$$

where
h_1 = height of water table at boundary upgradient
h_2 = height of surface water table at pond
L = distance of point 1 from the surface water
f = infiltration rate
K = permeability

10.7

WELL SYSTEMS

A well is a system of pipes for removing or injecting fluids into a subsurface area. The subsurface hydraulics are altered or controlled. The construction of a well can use drilling equipment, casings, grouting, well screens, pipe fittings, and the pump facility. Some injection wells may operate by gravity and thus do not require a pump. Also, not all wells use all the other equipment during construction. Examples of two completed wells are shown in Figure 10.13. For the consolidated soils, casing is not needed; however in unconsolidated soils (typically sand and gravel) casing is necessary. The well screen is used when

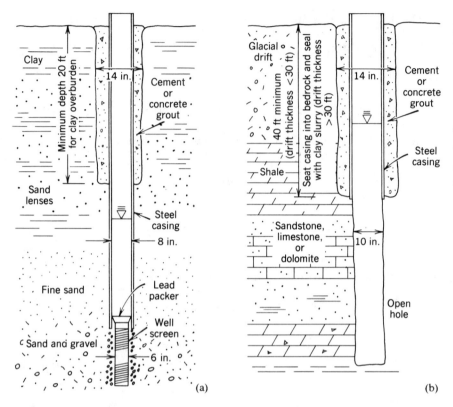

FIGURE 10.13 (*a*) Well in unconsolidated sediments (sand and gravel). (*b*) Well in consolidated sediments (Campbell & Lehr, 1977).

water is being removed from the aquifer. The drilling of the well is usually done by one of the following methods (Campbell and Lehr, 1977).

1. *Cable Tool.* A cable with bottom bit that crushes the formation material. The cuttings are usually removed by bailing or recirculating a slurry.
2. *Rotary Hydraulic.* A rotating bit usually using a water-based slurry with dry material. Cuttings are removed from the outside of the casing by continuously circulating slurry and removed fluid.
3. *Reverse Circulation.* Same as (2) but cuttings are removed from the inside of the casing. Slurry is injected on the outside of the casing.
4. *Air.* Same as (2) except forced air is used.
5. *Air Percussion.* A percussion mechanism is attached to the bit and rotary motion persists.
6. *Hollow Rod.* Same as (1) except cuttings travel up the casing and shorter more rapid strokes are noted.

7. *Jet.* Same as (6) except evacuated cuttings return up the outside of the casing.
8. *Driven.* The well is driven using repeated blows on a plugged pipe.

Well-point systems are composed of many wells placed close enough to each other to be able to intercept flow from the same area. Well points are used to remove contaminated ground waters or lower the water table in shallow aquifers.

Aquifer permeability and the storage coefficient are used to describe the hydraulic characteristics. The storage coefficient is the volume of water yielded per unit horizontal area and unit drop in water table (unconfined aquifer) or piezometric surface (confined aquifer). Thus, if a water table aquifer yields 2 m^3 of water during a drop of 4 m in a horizontal area of 10 m^2, the storage coefficient is 0.05 or 5%. The yield or performance of a well can be determined under equilibrium or nonequilibrium conditions. For equilibrium conditions to be met, the cone of depression caused by pumping must be stabilized.

10.7.1 Yield of a Confined Aquifer

When the well fully penetrates a horizontal confined aquifer (Figure 10.14), flow to the well comes from all directions (i.e., radial two-dimensional flow). By pumping the well at a steady rate and waiting until the well level is constant, observation of the drawdown levels h_1 and h_2 at observation wells at a known distance r_1 and r_2, from the pumped well allows estimation of the permeability of the aquifer. If the permeability of an aquifer is multiplied by the thickness (or height) of an aquifer, then the term known as transmissivity can be calculated. As presented earlier, the dimension of transmissivity is length^2/time, for example m^2/day or gal/day-ft (1 m^2/day = 80.5 gpd/ft). In practice, the groundwater levels from two or more observation wells at different radii are more useful than water levels in the well itself. To ensure a steady flow, there must be continuous recharge to the aquifer from sources distant to the well. Assuming also that the aquifer is homogeneous and isotropic and is not affected by compression in dewatering, the equilibrium flow to the well at any radius r can be expressed by

$$Q = (2\pi r)\frac{KD\,dh}{dr} \tag{10.27}$$

where
Q = pumping rate (ft^3/s)
$2\pi r$ = perimeter of a cylindrical shell (ft)
K = permeability (ft/s)
D = thickness of aquifer (ft)

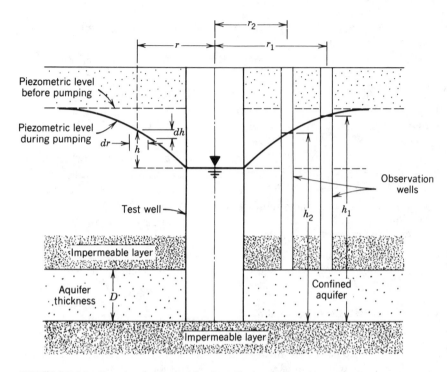

FIGURE 10.14 Pumping from a confined aquifer.

Integrating, one obtains

$$Q = 2\pi DK \frac{(h_1 - h_2)}{\ln (r_1/r_2)} \tag{10.28}$$

and $T = KD$

$$Q = 2\pi T \frac{(h_1 - h_2)}{\ln (r_1/r_2)} \tag{10.29}$$

Rearranging and changing units in Equation 10.28, the coefficient of permeability may be determined from

$$K = \frac{[528Q \log_{10} (r_1/r_2)]}{[D(h_1 - h_2)]} \tag{10.30}$$

where

K = permeability (gpd/ft^2)
Q = flow (gpm)
D, r, h = units of feet

☐ **EXAMPLE PROBLEM 10.3**

For an artesian aquifer 150 ft thick and composed of fine sand, a well is pumped to equilibrium at 1000 gpm. The drawdown at an observation well 400 ft away is 2 ft and at 40 ft it is 12 ft. What is the permeability?

Solution

Using Equation 10.30 with Q = 1000 gpm, D = 150 ft, and the differential drawdown is 10 ft.

$$K = \frac{[528(1000)\log(400/40)]}{150(10)} = 352 \text{ gpd/ft}^2 \quad ☐$$

10.7.2 Yield of an Unconfined Aquifer at Equilibrium

The yield and permeability of an unconfined aquifer can be determined by performing a pumping test from a well with observation wells similar to that done for the confined aquifers. The physical situation is shown in Figure 10.15. Here, flow is assumed to be radial with a horizontal water table. The rate of flow is written as

$$Q = (2\pi r)(K)(h)(dh/dr) \quad (10.31)$$

Integration yields

$$Q\int_{r_2}^{r_1} dr/r = (2\pi K)\int_{h_2}^{h_1} h(dh)$$

or

$$Q = \frac{K\pi(h_1^2 - h_2^2)}{\ln(r_1/r_2)} \quad (10.32)$$

If Q, r_1, r_2, h_1, and h_2 are determined from field measurements, then K can be calculated, or if K is known, the discharge can be calculated for specified drawdown conditions. For a change in flow rate units to gpm, Equation 10.32

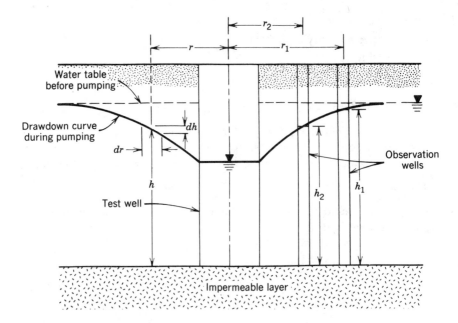

FIGURE 10.15 An unconfined aquifer.

is rewritten as

$$K = \frac{1055Q \log_{10}(r_1/r_2)}{[h_1^2 - h_2^2]} \tag{10.33}$$

where

$Q = $ gpm

$K = $ gpm/ft^2

$r, h = $ ft

In practice, Equations 10.32 and 10.33 are considered valid as long as the drawdown equilibrium condition does not exceed one-half the original aquifer thickness.

□ **EXAMPLE PROBLEM 10.4**

Calculate the steady-state discharge if the drawdown at observation wells remains constant at 20 ft and 15 ft corresponding to observation wells 100 ft and 200 ft from the proposed well location. The unconfined aquifer permeability is 70.0 gpm/ft^2 and the aquifer thickness is 80 ft.

Solution

Rearrange Equation 10.33 with

$$h_1 = 80 - 15 = 65 \text{ ft}$$

$$h_2 = 80 - 20 = 60 \text{ ft}$$

$$Q = \frac{[70.0(65^2 - 60^2)]}{[1055 \log (200/100)]} = 137.8 \text{ gpm} \quad \square$$

10.7.3   Unsteady Flow

Equilibrium equations usually overestimate permeability and thus the yield of a well when equilibrium is not obtained. This is the usual situation in practice because when a well is first pumped, a large quantity of water comes from the initial cone of depression and equilibrium usually takes a significant time to achieve. There are two methods for solution namely one by Theis (Todd, 1980) and the other by Cooper and Jacob (1946). The Theis method is usually solved by evaluating an infinite series equation form. This procedure involves the graphical superimposition of two curves. Often, this procedure can be short-ened, simplified, and more accurate when the observation distance from the well is small and the time for analysis is large. For these situations, Cooper and Jacob (1946) found an expression for T as follows:

$$T = (264Q/\Delta h) \log_{10} (t_2/t_1) \tag{10.34}$$

where

$T =$ transmissivity (gpd/ft)
$Q =$ well discharge (gpm)
$\Delta h =$ drawdown per time period (ft)
$t_2, t_1 =$ time periods for analysis

The field data for drawdown are plotted on semilog paper as shown in Figure 10.16. As time increases, a straight line relation results. If t_2 and t_1 correspond to one log cycle, then Equation 10.34 reduces to

$$T = \frac{264Q}{\Delta H} \tag{10.35}$$

and Δh equals the drawdown distance over one log cycle (feet).

The slope and the intercept (t_0) permits computation of the variables used in the storage equation (10.36).

$$S_c = 0.3T\frac{(t_0)}{r^2} \tag{10.36}$$

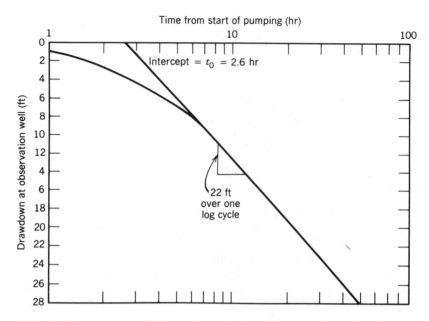

FIGURE 10.16   A Cooper-Jacob transmissibility graph.

where

S_c = storage coefficient (volume yield per unit horizontal area and per unit drop in entire area water table (unconfined) or piezometric surface (confined aquifer))

t_0 = time corresponding to zero drawdown (days)

r = distance from test to observation well (feet)

The storage coefficient for an unconfined aquifer is the specific yield.

☐   **EXAMPLE PROBLEM 10.5**

Using the data of Figure 10.16, calculate the transmissivity and storage coefficient if the well discharge were 900 gpm and the distance of the observation well from the well is 100 ft.

Solution

$$T = \frac{264Q}{\Delta h} = \frac{264(900)}{22.0} = 10,800 \text{ gpd/ft}$$

and

$$S_c = \frac{0.3(10{,}800)(2.6/24)}{100^2} = 0.035 \quad \square$$

10.8

CONJUNCTIVE USE

Conjunctive use occurs when both surface and groundwater sources are used to supply water. An engineer may have a choice of sources. It may be both technically and economically wise to develop both sources and use them jointly to minimize cost. The advantage of using two sources of supply is that the variations in the quantity and quality of surface water do not usually coincide with those of groundwater. Thus, a more economical and reliable supply can be maintained by switching from one source to the other when needed. Groundwater is usually a more reliable source when available surface water tends to be at a minimum, yet the surface water can be drawn on first during rainy seasons when rainfall excess is at a maximum. This allows the groundwater storage to be replenished naturally by infiltation and percolation.

There are several conjunctive use schemes being planned and practiced and their success has been documented. Engineers and planners should study all sources to determine the relative economic worth. Computer modeling is usually practiced to determine operating rules for both sources.

Conjunctive use schemes can also refer to the optimal use of two or more surface reservoirs and the reuse of wastewater. For example, multiple reservoirs with inflows from different watersheds and with different yields may be operated together to maximize the available water. A single reservoir may be used in connection with a diversion from another river, or a surface water source may be supplemented by the output from a desalination or wastewater plant.

When we apply the techniques of mathematical programming with the masses of data such as inflows, storage capacities, pumping rates, and the like, we can evaluate the minimum cost yields for any combination of sources.

10.9

SUMMARY

Groundwater hydrology is an important study because of its potential application areas. Streamflow, stormwater infiltration, potable water from groundwaters, saltwater intrusion, groundwater recharge, and waste injection are a few areas where hydrology concepts and equations are used.

- The storage and movement of groundwater can be quantified using the equations of this chapter.
- In the unsaturated zone of an unconfined aquifer, soil moisture exists as both percolated (gravity) water and capillary water. Water available to plants is determined by defining the difference between field and wilting moisture content.
- Permeability is a measure of the rate at which water moves in the soil whereas porosity is a measure of void space. Specific yield is the volume of water released per unit volume of soil. These properties vary with the type of soil.
- Flow rate computation equations are available for both the confined aquifer (Equation 10.19) and the unconfined aquifer (Equation 10.22).
- Seepage of groundwater from the surficial aquifer to a surface water body can be estimated using the unconfined aquifer equation. Also, if a constant infiltration to the water table can be defined, Equation 10.26 can be used to determine the rise in the groundwater table and then the unconfined aquifer equation can be used.
- Leaky aquifers exist where the confining strata are not completely impervious. The equations for this are beyond the scope of this work but are found in other publications (Hantush, 1960; Walton, 1970).
- Equations to estimate the yield from confined (Equation 10.29) and unconfined (Equation 10.32) aquifers have been developed assuming a steady-state condition has been achieved.
- When equilibrium is not obtained, methods to estimate yield were developed. A method by Cooper and Jacob (1946) was presented.

10.10

PROBLEMS

1. Calculate the coefficient of permeability for a soil with a 10% finer grain size of 0.14 mm. Then classify the soil by its texture. What is an approximate value for the soil porosity and specific yield?

2. A laboratory premeability test is used to estimate the coefficient of permeability for an aquifer. It is a standard test at a temperature of 60°F. If the aquifer temperature varies from 40°F to 50°F during the year, what is the lowest estimate of actual permeability in the aquifer? If the laboratory estimate is 200 gpd/ft^2?

3. A well is pumped at an equilibrium flow of 454 gpm to determine a confined aquifer permeability. The thickness of the aquifer is 100 ft and the drawdown in observation wells is noted as 3 ft and 9 ft at 100 ft and 10 ft, respectively, from the pumped well. What is the permeability?

4. Using the same data from Problem 3 except consider an unconfined aquifer that was totally saturated before pumping, what is the estimate of permeability?

5. An estimate of groundwater flow into a lake is required to complete a water volume balance on the lake. Runoff, outflow, precipitation, evaporation, and transpiration are known. An unconfined aquifer exists with an impermeable membrane at approximate elevation of 30 ft. The soil permeability has been estimated at 6 m/day. An observation well is established 20.2 ft from the lake and the groundwater in the surficial aquifer is measured at elevation 52.13 ft. The lake level at this time was 50 ft. What is the inflow estimate in units of m^3/s and cfs if the circumference of the lake is 400 m?

6. Calculate the transmissivity and the storage coefficient using the unsteady flow method given the following data. Water was pumped from a well at a rate of 950 gpm. The observation well was 80 ft from the pumped well.

ELAPSED TIME (hr)	DRAWDOWN (ft)
1	1.0
2	2.6
3	4.7
4	5.7
5	6.5
6	8.0
8	10.3
10	12.4
12	15.0
18	18.0
25	21.2
35	24.0

7. What is the Darcy velocity of groundwater flowing through a sand with a permeability of 10 m/day given that two piezometers, placed 10 m apart, give the following data.

	PIEZOMETER 1 (m)	PIEZOMETER 2 (m)
Elevation head	0	−3
Pressure head	0.2	.1

8. The water table 3000 ft away from a lake has an elevation of 64 ft. Use Darcy's law to find the velocity of the groundwater 3000 ft away from the

lake. The elevation of the lake is 60 ft, and the soil surrounding the lake is a fine sand.

9. A soil sample weighting 1.05 lb fills a 500-cm³ container. The sample is placed in a 103°F oven overnight and is weighed again the next day. If the weight after drying is 0.85 lb and the specific gravity of the soils granuals is 2.65, what is the porosity of the soil sample?

10. What is the porosity ratio of a soil if a 1-m³ sample contains 10% voids by volume?

11. If the permeability of a sand is found to be 10 m/day at 30°C, what is its permeability at 20°C?

12. Determine the travel distance for groundwater from a stormwater detention pond to a lake. Filtration material has been placed in the ground between the pond and the lake and has a permeability of 10^{-2} ft/sec with a porosity of 0.2. The difference in elevation between the water surface in the pond and the water surface of the lake is 10 ft. If the residence time is 5.8 days, what is the travel path length? Also, determine the concentration of a chemical discharged to the lower lake if the initial concentration is 5000 mg/L and the rate of removal through the filtration column is one-half for every day of residence time (half-life is one day).

10.11

REFERENCES

Bouwer, H. 1966, "Rapid Field Measurement of Air Entry Value and Hydraulic Conductivity of Soil," *Water Resources Research*, **2**, pp. 729–738.

Campbell, M.D. and Lehr, J.H. 1977. "Well Cost Analysis," *Water Well Technology*, 4th ed. McGraw-Hill, New York.

Colman, E.A. 1947. "A Laboratory Procedure for Determining Field Capacity of Soils," *Soil Science*, **63**, p. 277.

Cooper, H.H, Jr. and Jacob, C.E. 1946. "A Generalized Graphical Method for Evaluating Formation Constants and Summarizing Well-Field History," *Transactions of the American Geophysico Union*, **27**, pp. 526–534.

DeWiest, R.J.M. 1965. "History of the Dupuit–Forchheimer Assumptions in Groundwater Hydraulics," *Transactions American Society of Agricultural Engineers*, **8**, pp. 508–509.

Hantush, M.S. 1960. "Modification of the Theory of Leaky Aquifers," *Journal of Geophysical Research*, **65**, pp. 3713–3725.

McNeal, B.L. 1968. "Prediction of the Effects of Mixed-Salt Solutions on the Soil Hydraulic Conductivity," *Proceedings of the Soil Science Society of America*, **32**, pp. 190–193.

National Water Summary—Florida. 1985. "Florida Groundwater Resources," U.S. Geological Survey Water-Supply Paper 2275.

Todd, D.K. 1980. *Ground Water Hydrology*. Wiley, New York.

Walton, William C. 1970. *Groundwater Resource Evaluation*. McGraw-Hill, New York.

....
....
....

11

VOLUME
AND PEAK
DISCHARGE
MANAGEMENT

This chapter presents applications of hydrologic concepts for the management of flow rates and volume of runoff. Both surface and groundwater hydrology principles are used. Some of the contents of this chapter could be used after reading the first eight chapters to demonstrate applications.

The applications and additional concepts presented in this chapter are developed to help understand and develop:

1. Surface water availability from streamflow records.
2. Design storm concepts.
3. Stormwater detention pond designs.
4. Culverts as outflow control devices.
5. Stormwater off-line retention pond design.
6. Swale design.
7. French drains to lower water tables and as outflow control devices.
8. Case studies on the details related to hydrograph peak attenuation using detention ponds.

11.1

SURFACE WATER AVAILABILITY FROM STREAMFLOW

Streamflow records and measurement were presented in Chapter 5. One of the applications for streamflow data is the determination of volume and water discharged at the point of measurement over a period of time and the expected yield (rate of removal) from an impoundment reservoir at the site.

The networks of ground and surface water gages provide quantity data that help determine water volume availability. The future water needs of such users as municipalities, agricultures, and industries can be established. Then the investigator must estimate the availability of water. It is at this point that the gaging measurements are applied.

For a surface reservoir site to be developed, the sources of water are identified. The average annual rainfall is a first indicator of possible water availability. The existence of perennial (constantly flowing) rivers is a significant indication of the magnitude of surface sources. Also, a search for suitable groundwater aquifers can be made at the same time.

The yield (volume of water per time period) of the source needs to be investigated before a supply can be relied on for the design life of a project. Once a suitable source of water has been found, some form of storage is essential to guarantee continuous supplies. If the supplies are to come from surface waters, a storage reservoir must be constructed. Frequently, natural lakes can be used or modified for use. Water from groundwater sources is usually already in some type of reservoir storage. A feasibility study for evaluating a possible surface reservoir site would include:

1. A watershed survey to determine watershed and reservoir areas and storage volumes.

2. A geological survey of the sites for the storage structure (dam or well).

3. Hydrological assessments of the flows at the sites for yield (volume/time) and storage (volume).

4. Appraisal of any land use changes and the future amenity value of existing or future structures.

5. Preliminary design and cost estimation.

Feasibility studies are done for several possible sources in order to determine the source with sufficient yield and minimum cost. It is necessary to make estimates of the yields in relationship to the amount of storage that would be available at each proposed site.

11.1.1   Volume and Yield of a Surface Water Reservoir

How much water can be withdrawn per time period (yield or draft) from a given size of reservoir? How much volume must be stored in a reservoir to achieve a desired yield over a period of time? These are among the basic questions that a designer and operator of a reservoir must ask.

For a fixed storage capacity in a reservoir the yield during a drought period of great severity must be estimated. If a higher yield is required than that supplied by the reservoir, the capacity would need to be supplemented by other sources. To ensure adequate storage for a specified yield or to evaluate the yield of an assumed storage, a study of all net inputs at the reservoir site is needed. Expected losses by evaporation, transpiration and infiltration from the reservoir must be used to reduce available reservoir storage. The sum of inflow minus reservoir losses is net inflow.

Design and evaluation is done using deterministic (fixed) yields and net inputs or stochastic net inputs and yields. Discharges with time that are known with certainty and representative of all flows are used for deterministic models. For stochastic models, data are synthesized (generated from probability distributions) with the length of generated data usually exceeding the design life of the structure.

11.1.2   Mass Curve (Ripple's Method)

This is a deterministic model using a series of streamflow data to help calculate the volume and yield of a proposed reservoir site. For each time sequence, the cumulative input volumes are plotted against time. The volumes are cumulated from streamflow. The cumulative volume curve is expressed as a function of streamflow as

$$\text{Volume} = \int Q \, dt = \sum Q(\Delta t) \tag{11.1}$$

The technique is demonstrated using Figure 11.1. The difference between any two points on the cumulative volume curve (solid line) is a storage volume for that period of time, assuming no losses from the reservoir. The yield is the rate of demand for water (dotted line). It is represented in Figure 11.1 as a constant value but in practice it changes with time. An example are yields for agricultural uses which change with crop production. The yield changes are reflected by changes in the slope of the yield line.

The method assumes the reservoir is empty at the start of a drought period. A drought period is defined as one in which the inflow rate is less than the yield. The maximum difference between the yield and the cumulative volume curve is the reservoir size needed before the drought period. Several

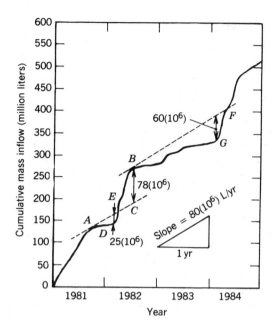

FIGURE 11.1 The use of a mass curve to determine the reservoir capacity required to produce a specific yield.

drought periods are evaluated and a decision on reservoir size and yield is made from the several periods. The results are only as accurate as the data input. This usually requires a long-term streamflow record.

☐   ***EXAMPLE PROBLEM 11.1***

To obtain a water yield of $80(10^6)$ L/yr for the inflows shown in Figure 11.1, what reservoir capacity is required?

Solution

The solution requires one to draw tangents to the mass curve. At points A and B the tangents have slopes equal to the yield of $80(10^6)$ L/yr. The maximum departure between yield and mass occurs at G and is $60(10^6)$ L, which is the required reservoir capacity. The reservoir would be empty at point G, and at F it would be full again. The reservoir is assumed to be full at A, depleted by $25(10^6)$ L of storage at D, and full again at E. When the reservoir is full, all inflow in excess of the demand would be discharged downstream. If the reservoir is full at point A, it will fill again at point E and between points C and B there will be an excess of $78(10^6)$ L.   ☐

The yield that can be expected given a reservoir capacity may also be determined using mass curves (Figure 11.1). To accomplish this, lines are drawn tangent to the high points of the mass curve (A and B) so that their maximum departure from the mass curve does not exceed the specified reservoir capacity. The resulting slopes estimate the yields that can be expected each year with the specified storage capacity. Also note that the demand line must intersect the mass curve at some point, otherwise the reservoir will not refill.

◻ **EXAMPLE PROBLEM 11.2**
_____

If a reservoir of $30(10^9)$ L capacity is built for which the mass curve of Figure 11.2 applies, what yield will be available?

Solution

In this problem, the storage level is specified first, then the yield (slope) is calculated. In Figure 11.2, the tangents to the mass curve are drawn to

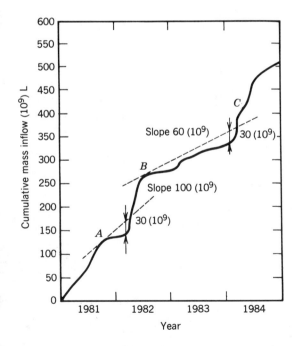

FIGURE 11.2 The use of a mass curve to determine the possible yield from a reservoir of specified capacity.

specify a maximum departure from the mass curve equal to $30(10^9)$ L. The tangent from B has the least slope, $60(10^9)$ L/yr, so this is the minimum yield. The tangent at A indicates a possible yield of $100(10^9)$ L/yr, but this demand could not be satisfied between points B and C without storage in excess of $30(10^9)$ L. □

11.1.3 Modification of Storage Volumes

Cumulative mass inflow can be modified to incorporate supplemental sources of input such as additions from groundwater. Also, losses over extended periods of time, such as those from evapotranspiration and seepage can be used to reduce cumulative mass. Evapotranspiration losses may be significant and thus affect the storage capacity. The lower portion of Figure 11.3 illustrates decreasing cumulative mass in a reservoir during low or zero surface water input times. This decrease is contrasted to a situation with no loss in a reservoir as shown in the upper portion of Figure 11.3. When losses and supplemental sources are incorporated into the analysis, storage capacity may and usually will change or yield will be adjusted.

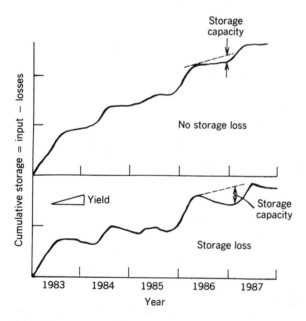

FIGURE 11.3 Cumulative storage with and without storage losses.

11.1.4 Stochastic Models

In mass curve analysis, it was assumed that flow rates would repeat themselves every time period (year) without deviation. However, the patterns are not exactly repeated every year. Thus, more years of data or other methods which preserve the history of the streamflow are useful, such as (1) random generation and (2) serial correlation matrices (Markov processes). To initiate an understanding of the methods, terms are defined in Table 11.1.

Since streamflow, evapotranspiration, and seepage are stochastic processes, it is possible to assign a probability to a reservoir being full or empty. All hydrologic data can be used and probability distributions estimated for net inflow. In addition, a probability distribution for demand rates (yields) can be developed.

When probability distributions are used to extend streamflow or rainfall records, the hydrologic records will be preserved. These distributions are useful to preserve the history of the hydrologic events and to extend the record length. This extension and others are sometimes known as techniques of operational hydrology.

A probability distribution is a realistic expression of the "chances" or probability of satisfying demands. Using probability distributions, decisions can be made that better reflect the actual historical nature of the hydrologic process. It is more acceptable to the decision-making community (voters, elected officials, appointed government people) to make a statement, such as "the reservoir as designed will satisfy the water needs of our projected populations 99% of the time." This statement can be made using stochastic models.

The operation of a reservoir can be considered on a discrete time basis. The contents of the reservoir at any time (t), is given by

$$V_t + Q_t(\Delta t) - Y_t = V_{t+1} \qquad (11.2)$$

where V_t is the reservoir volume at time t, $Q_t(\Delta t)$ is the volume of inflow during the time period, and Y_t is the volume demand or releases (yields over time) during the same time interval.

Equation 11.2 also is used to estimate the size of a reservoir as a function of inflows and yields. Constraints on the maximum size of the reservoir are used and realistic results can be determined.

As an example of stochastic methods, Hardison (1966) developed estimates for reservoir size and yield based on probability of annual streamflow data. He used probability frequency distributions to fit the empirical data. Thus, he was able to determine a quantitative index on the variability of flow and storage requirements. His work was applied to 22 major watersheds in the contiguous United States (Lof and Hardison, 1966). The variability of annual

TABLE 11.1   Stochastic Models

DEFINITIONS FOR STOCHASTIC MODELS

1. *Serial Correlation.*   A variable at time (t) is dependent on past data $(t - n)$: $n = 1 \ldots k$ (i.e., correlated in time). Example: Streamflow data in the Oklawaha River at time $(t - n)$. Usually, n is of the orders of hours or days.

2. *Cross Correlation.*   One variable correlated with another variable at the same time (t) but at different places. Example: Streamflow in Boggy Creek correlated with streamflow in the Little Econ River at time (t) (i.e., correlated in space).

3. *Conditional Probability.*   Pr(A|B), used to describe both serial and cross correlations, read as probability of event A given event B.

4. *Discrete Probability Distributions.*   Approximations (in most cases) for the continuous probability distributions of streamflow, reservoir release volumes, and other hydrologic events. Discrete distributions are usually made to simplify mathematical manipulations.
   Let

$$\text{Pr}_i = \text{probability of flows}$$

$$\text{Pr}_i = \frac{\text{flow within interval } i \, (\text{number of times})}{\text{Total number of data pionts}}$$

$$\sum_{i=1}^{n} \text{Pr}_i = 1.0$$

5. *Markov Processes.*   Stochastic model utilizing conditional probabilities. As an example, consider the serial correlation of daily streamflow.
   Let

$$\text{Pr}_{i\,j} = \text{conditional probability of the current (any time) daily streamflow being within interval } j \text{ given last time interval's streamflow } i$$

$$= \frac{\text{number of flows in } j \text{ following } i}{\text{total number of flows in } i}$$

then

$$\sum_{j=1}^{m} \text{Pr}_{i\,j} = 1 \qquad (\text{for all } i)$$

surface water yields were measured by the coefficient of variability or the index of variability. The coefficient of variability is the standard deviation of annual yield divided by the average annual yield, while the index is the standard deviation of the common logarithms. The coefficient of variability ranged from a low of .2 in the New England area to a high of 1.0 in the South Pacific. The maximum yield (net flow adjusted for losses) for the 22 watersheds for 98 of 100 years was about 3660 billion L/day (about 1000 billion gal/day). This requires a storage capacity of 3.6 billion ac-ft but only 2 billion ac-ft of storage can be made available. These studies indicate a yield and required reservoir storage with a probability of .98 (98 out of 100).

11.1.5 Random Generation (Independent Events)

The use of random generation procedures assumes that successive hydrologic events are independent and a known probability distribution can be found that represents the true forces generating the hydrologic events. Consider as an example, streamflow data. Certainly, on a large river system, the flows in a short time period, days or hours, appear to be serial correlated with previous time period flows or the probability of one flow rate given another is

$$\text{Probability } \{Q_{t+1}|Q_t\} \neq 0 \tag{11.3}$$

where

Q_{t+1} = average flow in time period $(t + 1)$, L^3/t
Q_t = average flow in time period (t), L^3/t

If the probability expressed by Equation 11.3 were zero or near zero, then one could state the flows to be independent. Independent events are defined as

$$\text{Probability } \{A|B\} = 0 \tag{11.4}$$

where A and B = hydrologic events.

□ **EXAMPLE PROBLEM 11.3**

Given the following streamflow data during low flow and the beginning of a rising limb of a hydrograph, determine the probability of a 30-m³/s flow following a 20-m³/s flow.

TIME (DAYS)	AVERAGE FLOW (m³/s)	TIME (DAYS)	AVERAGE FLOW (m³/s)
1	20	5	20
2	15	6	30
3	20	7	35
4	20	8	40

Solution

The event specified is the transition of flow from 20 to 30 m³/s. Thus, the beginning flow value must be 20 m³/s. This value occurs four times in the very limited data set. The number of times the flow of 30 m³/s follows 20 m³/s is once, therefore, the probability is calculated as

$$\text{Probability } \{Q_{t+1}|Q_t\} = \text{probability}\{30|20\} = 1/4$$

Also, the probability of 20 m³/s given 20 m³/s is .5 and the probability of 15 m³/s given 20 m³/s is .25. Thus, the probability of flow values of any magnitude given 20 m³/s must add up to 1.0, which is the case. Note that this is a very small amount of data and are used only to illustrate the calculation of probability that demonstrates dependence of flow in one period of time on another. □

The period of time necessary to use a random generation procedure for streamflows is usually seasonal average data or yearly averages. Rainfall data separated by 4 to 6 hours of nonrainfall usually constitute sufficient time to justify independence in rainfall.

Consider again the problem of specifying the size of a reservoir, but this time use a random generation of streamflow into the reservoir, call it $Q_{i,t}$ where i = average flow interval and t = time period. A discrete probability distribution is developed for streamflow and is graphically shown in Figure 11.4. The general inventory equation (mass balance) is rewritten to specify the random streamflow and releases (see Figure 11.5)

$$V_t + Q_{i,t}(\Delta t) - Y_t = V_{t+1} \tag{11.5}$$

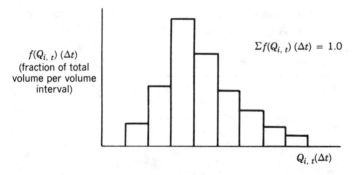

FIGURE 11.4   A discrete probability distribution on streamflow.

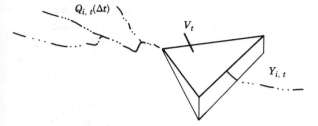

FIGURE 11.5   A reservoir schematic.

and

$$\text{Max}\{V_i\} = V_{\text{max}} \qquad \forall i \tag{11.6}$$

subject to

1. Starting reservoir volume, V_0 is assumed equal to the minimum.

$$V_0 = V_m$$

2. A minimum reservoir volume, V_m, must be maintained, so that Y_i may equal zero during some time period i.

$$V_i \geq V_m \qquad \forall i$$

3. No negative releases or reservoir sizes.

$$V_i \geq 0 \qquad Y_i \geq 0 \qquad \forall i$$

Also, the probability of a specified volume of reservoir at any time can be determined as

$$\text{Pr}\{V_{i,t}\} = \frac{x_{V_{i,t}}}{n_t} \tag{11.7}$$

where

$x_{V_{i,t}}$ = number of times reservoir volume is equal to the interval V_i
n_t = total number of time periods

In schematic form, Equation 11.5 can be shown as Figure 11.5.

The streamflow data must be estimated relative to the history of its probability distribution. The more streamflow data, the more accurate the empirical probability distribution, and a continuous theoretical distribution with unbounded limits can be estimated. This would allow the estimation of very large and very small streamflow values. These distributions were presented in Chapter 9. Our intent here is to develop the procedure for generating flow rates from discrete probability distributions of independent flow rates. Since the generation of flow rates do not depend on previous flow rates, and the distribution (Figure 11.4) of flows must be reproduced over a long period of time, a technique that is not biased toward the choice of flow or is strictly random in its choice must be used. Random numbers are numbers that have an equal probability of choice. Furthermore, to reproduce a probability distribution, a proportional number of random numbers can be assigned to the fraction of the total per interval. For example,

$$\text{If} \qquad Q_{it} = 20 \text{ m}^3/\text{s with 4\% frequency}$$

$$= 30 \text{ m}^3/\text{s with 8\% frequency}$$

$$= 40 \text{ m}^3/\text{s with 15\% frequency}$$

then given 100 random numbers, 4 numbers would be assigned to 20 m³/s, 8 numbers to 30 m³/s, and 15 numbers to 40 m³/s. This technique of streamflow generation is called Monte Carlo.

11.1.6 Serial Correlation

For shorter time periods, the serial correlation of going from one hydrologic state to another can be determined. When using streamflow data, it is advantageous to divide the streamflow into periods of time with similar hydrologic characteristics such as low flow, increasing streamflow values, decreasing streamflow values, wet season, and dry season. The quantity of data needed are usually in the order of 10 yr or more of daily values. The number of years depends on how accurately one can define the conditional discrete probability distributions or estimate from the discrete distribution the form of a theoretical one. One must define the probability of going from one streamflow to another. Since there are more than one streamflow, a matrix of probabilities is defined: it is called a conditional probability matrix.

Given two streamflow states ($i = 1, 2$) and four transition states ($j = 1, 2, 3, 4$), the two discrete distributions result as shown in Figure 11.6. The information given on these distributions can be expressed in a matrix of conditional probabilities, called a transition probability matrix (Figure 11.7).

Random generation can then be used to generate the flow data given the transition matrix. In practice, transition matrices are developed for a rising limb, a falling limb, and base flow. In addition, the timing for the beginning of the rising limb is determined from rainfall data or an interevent probability distribution on streamflow. Peak flows can be related to rainfall excess or rainfall. The usual way of generating the flow-rate data is by means of a heuristic computer program and most recently by expert systems.

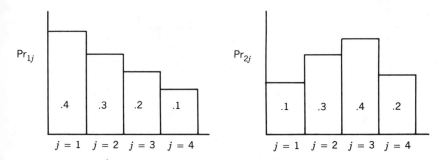

FIGURE 11.6 Serial discrete probability distributions.

Streamflow—state j (time $y + 1$)

		1	2	3	.	.	.	m
Streamflow state i (time y)	1	.4	.3	.2				
	2	.1	.3	.4	.	.	.	
	.		.					
	.		.					
	.		.					
	n							

FIGURE 11.7 A transition probability matrix.

11.2

DESIGN STORMS

For the calculation of peak discharge, questions of major significance revolve around the choice of the design storms. It is significant because of the time involved in calculating the peak discharge. Not all storm events can be tested to determine the worst discharge. An economic analysis with the calculation of cost/benefit ratios, indicates a best choice for the frequency (return period) for a design storm. The design storm is chosen, and the runoff volume (rainfall excess) and peak discharge are calculated usually based on frequency/intensity/duration curves given for the particular area. The peak of the rainfall excess is important for design of conduits (open or closed) and rainfall excess is used for design of storage systems. The input and output hydrographs provide the needed information to design and operate a water detention facility. If an outlet structure exists, then we can determine an outflow hydrograph. Then, the input hydrograph for a number of storm durations can

TABLE 11.2 Design Frequencies for Highway Structures

	USUAL DESIGN FREQUENCIES IN YEARS	
TYPE OF STRUCTURE	MOTORWAYS, INTERSTATE AND CONTROLLED ACCESS HIGHWAYS	OTHER HIGHWAYS AND FRONTAGE ROADS[a]
Inlets and sewers	10	2–5
Inlet for depressed roadways	50	2–10
Culverts	50	2–10
Small bridges	50	10–50
River crossings	50	10–50

Source: Florida Department of Transportation, Drainage Manual, 1986.
[a] Varies with state and local regulations.

be used to determine the size of a storage basin. One of the objectives in this chapter is to develop rainfall excess (volume) and runoff hydrographs (flow rates), which relate to both conduit and detention basin design.

11.2.1 Design Storm Frequency

The selection of a design storm rainfall frequency is best made only after economic analyses of benefits and costs are performed. However, these studies are expensive and not a routine undertaking. In addition, the results frequently depend on many variables such as land use, soil types, topography, economic activity, and meteorological factors. Therefore, most municipalities, state and federal agencies will specify the design frequency for most drainage design, such as the 10- or 25-yr frequency rainfall based on studies conducted elsewhere, preferably on similar watersheds. Table 11.2 shows some examples of usual design frequencies.

Rainfall frequency–intensity information for use in drainage design is readily available in such publications as the U.S. Weather Bureau Technical paper No. T.P. 40 (U.S. Weather Bureau, 1961), textbooks, and state (i.e. Florida DOT) drainage manuals (1986). The rainfall frequency–intensity data in these publications were intended for design by the Rational Method, in which the rainfall duration is assumed equal to or greater than the time of concentration in the watershed. Also, a uniform rainfall distribution occurs throughout the rainfall duration. Of course, these assumptions are rarely good for large watersheds, so other procedures must be examined.

11.2.1 Design Duration and Distribution

When a situation requires the development of a hydrograph, the duration of the particular frequency rainfall and the distribution of the rainfall must be known. Standard rainfall duration and/or distribution curves have been adopted by many government and consulting organizations for specific areas. For instances, Orange County, Florida, has an unofficial 25-yr frequency, 24-hr design rainfall developed after the floods of 1960. Golding (1973) plotted dimensionless mass curves of rainfall to compare major rainfalls in central Florida with Orange County's standard distribution and the SCS's Type II distribution. In addition, the U.S. Weather Bureau published suggested storm distributions for the southeastern United States (Figure 11.8). Golding concluded that Orange County's standard distribution was compatible with major storms in the central Florida area and with the SCS Type II distribution.

Using a rainfall of specific duration and volume, we can find the amount of rain falling during specified intervals using some standard or selected

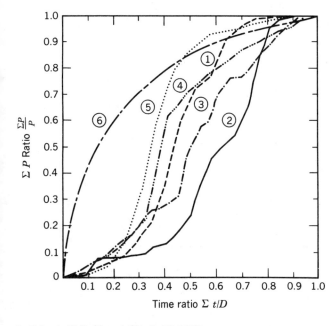

1. Orlando W.B. Airport, March 15, 1960   ---------
2. Orange City, September 10–11, 1960   _____
3. Orlando W.B. Airport, October 15–16, 1956 —··—··—··—
4. SCS Type II   —···—···—···
5. Orange County   ················
6. Weather Bureau   —— — ——

FIGURE 11.8 Dimensionless mass curves of rainfall. *Source:* Golding, 1973.

TABLE 11.3   Design Rainfall — 25-yr Frequency, 6-hr Duration, 15-min Increments

TIME (min)	TIME (hr)	ΣP (in.)	ΔP (in.)	ΣR^a (in.)	ΔR (in.)
0	0	0	0	0	0
15	0.25	0.10	0.10	0.00	0.00
30	0.50	0.21	0.11	0.02	0.02
45	0.75	0.33	0.12	0.07	0.05
60	1.00	0.48	0.15	0.15	0.08
75	1.25	0.64	0.16	0.27	0.12
90	1.50	0.81	0.17	etc.	
105	1.75	1.08	0.27		
120	2.00	1.38	0.30		
135	2.25	2.46	1.08		
150	2.50	3.60	1.14		
165	2.75	3.90	0.30		
180	3.00	4.20	0.30		
195	3.25	4.44	0.24		
210	3.50	4.68	0.24		
225	3.75	4.86	0.18		
240	4.00	5.01	0.15		
255	4.25	5.16	0.15		
270	2.50	5.28	0.12		
285	4.75	5.40	0.12		
300	5.00	5.52	0.12		
315	5.25	5.64	0.12		
330	5.50	5.76	0.12		
345	5.75	5.88	0.12		
360	6.00	6.00	0.12		

^{a}For $CN = 95$.

distribution. Applying the SCS's Type II standard distribution to a 25-year, 6-hr rainfall of 6 in. results in the rainfall at 15-min intervals shown in Table 11.3.

Applying Orange County's Standard Distribution to a 25-yr frequency, 24-hr rainfall of 8.17 in. results in the rainfall increments (30 min) shown in Table 11.4. Both the 6-in. and 8.17-in. storms were reduced because of the

TABLE 11.4 Design Rainfall — Orange County 25-yr Frequency, 24-hr Duration, 30-min Increments

TIME (hr)	ΔP (in.)	ΣP (in.)	TIME (hr)	ΔP (in.)	ΣP (in.)
0	0	0	12.5	0.18	7.16
0.5	0.01	0.01	13.0	0.18	7.34
1.0	0.01	0.02	13.5	0.12	7.46
1.5	0.02	0.04	14.0	0.11	7.57
2.0	0.02	0.06	14.5	0.05	7.62
2.5	0.05	0.11	15.0	0.05	7.67
3.0	0.06	0.17	15.5	0.04	7.71
3.5	0.11	0.28	16.0	0.04	7.75
4.0	0.12	0.40	16.5	0.04	7.79
4.5	0.17	0.57	17.0	0.04	7.83
5.0	0.17	0.74	17.5	0.04	7.87
5.5	0.18	0.92	18.0	0.04	7.91
6.0	0.19	1.11	18.5	0.03	7.94
6.5	0.50	1.61	19.0	0.03	7.97
7.0	0.50	2.11	19.5	0.03	8.00
7.5	0.52	2.63	20.0	0.03	8.03
8.0	0.52	3.15	20.5	0.02	8.05
8.5	0.85	4.00	21.0	0.02	8.07
9.0	0.86	4.36	21.5	0.02	8.09
9.5	0.58	5.44	22.0	0.02	8.11
10.0	0.57	6.01	22.5	0.02	8.13
10.5	0.30	6.31	23.0	0.02	8.15
11.0	0.30	6.61	23.5	0.01	8.16
11.5	0.19	6.80	24.0	0.01	8.17
12.0	0.18	6.98			

large size of the watershed. For larger watersheds, the point measured maximum rainfall is rarely found over the entire watershed. The average volumes for the entire watershed is less. Thus, an aerial reduction factor can be developed. A graph for allowable reduction in point measure rainfall is given in T.P. No. 40 (U.S. Weather Bureau, 1961). For example, consider a 3-hr storm, the point measured rainfall is reduced by 10% for a 13,000-ha (50 mi^2) watershed and by 20% for a 52,000-ha (200 mi^2) watershed.

☐ **_EXAMPLE PROBLEM 11.4_**

To illustrate the calculation of rainfall excess using the curve number procedure, consider the precipitation record of the 25-yr, 6-hr design rainfall shown in Table 11.3. Rainfall excess is determined on a cumulative basis using cumulative rainfall, then time incremental values of rainfall are determined by subtracting the cumulative values of rainfall excess before and after the time increment. First calculate or determine the curve number, say $CN = 95$, a highly impervious area. Therefore, the maximum storage is

$$S' = \frac{1000}{95} - 10 = 0.53 \text{ in.}$$

and the maximum excess is $6 - 0.53 = 5.47$ in.

The following example calculations assume that rainfall excess is zero if cumulative rainfall is less than 20% of the maximum soil saturation. However, this is not common with a high curve number, like $CN = 95$ but is used to illustrate calculations.
At 15 min

$$P = .10 \qquad R = \frac{[0.10 - 0.2(0.53)]^2}{[0.10 + 0.8(0.53)]} = 0.00 \text{ in.}$$

At 30 min

$$P = .21 \qquad R = \frac{[0.21 - 0.2(0.53)]^2}{[0.21 + 0.8(0.53)]} = 0.02 \text{ in.}$$

At 45 min

$$P = .33 \qquad R = \frac{[0.33 - 0.2(0.53)]^2}{[0.33 + 0.8(0.53)]} = 0.07 \text{ in.}$$

$$\text{and} \qquad 0.07 - 0.02 = 0.05 \text{ in. rainfall excess}$$

At 60 min

$$P = .48 \qquad R = \frac{[0.48 - 0.2(0.53)]^2}{[0.48 + 0.8(0.53)]} = 0.15 \text{ in.}$$

$$\text{and} \qquad .15 - .07 = 0.08 \text{ in. rainfall excess}$$

At 75 min

$$P = .64 \qquad R = \frac{[0.64 - 0.2(0.53)]^2}{[0.64 + 0.8(0.53)]} = 0.27 \text{ in.}$$

$$\text{and} \qquad 0.27 - 0.15 = 0.12 \text{ in. rainfall excess}$$

and so on.   ☐

To calculate rainfall excess from precipitation records, curve numbers may be used, as mentioned previously. For various *CN* values, a variety of rainfall excess histories are tabulated or graphed as shown in Figures 11.9 through 11.12. The problem can be completed by additional (somewhat extensive) hand calculations, or by use of a computer program. The reader is encouraged to do some additional calculations by hand and to execute a few computer runs using SMADA.

Recall that the type of ground cover and soil types will affect rainfall excess. Figure 11.13 illustrates the reduction in rainfall excess with decreasing curve numbers. These curve numbers must be estimated for each runoff area. Therefore, adequate information on soil type and land use must be available.

Rainfall excess is important for the design of urban water transmission and storage systems. The designer should compare various duration storms to determine which storm is most critical and therefore should be used. In the computation of design hydrographs, generally the shorter duration design rainfalls will result in a higher peak flow because of the short time period and higher-intensity rainfall. However, the longer duration storms must be studied to validate this general statement.

For the design of a detention basin, generally a longer-duration rainfall event should be used. The total volume of rainfall is usually greater and will require a larger-sized basin than from a short duration event of the same frequency.

Some water management regulations for developing lands specify that the peak discharge before development must equal the peak discharge after development. The choice of rainfall duration will affect the volume of storage needed to meet this requirement. To illustrate this variable sizing of detention systems, consider a simplified explanation using the rational formula to estimate hydrographs using the FID (Frequency–Intensity–Duration) curves of Figure 11.14. Note from Figure 11.15 that the peak discharge decreases as the duration increases. By fixing the outflow hydrograph rate, the detention storage area can be estimated as the difference between the input and output hydrograph.

Peak flow as computed by the Rational Method is closely related to a hydrograph with a base length equal to two times the time of concentration. This situation holds true only if the duration of the rainfall is assumed equal to the time of concentration. If the rainfall duration is longer than the time of concentration, a trapezoidal shaped hydrograph results with a peak flow again equal to CiA as was previously derived. However, the peak flow of the trapezoidal hydrograph is smaller than that of the triangular hydrograph as the intensity of rainfall i decreases with the duration of the rainfall. A rainfall–frequency–intensity curve is shown on Figure 11.14. Thus, for any rainfall frequency–intensity–duration curve, one can draw a family of hydrographs as shown in Figure 11.15; each one with a larger rainfall duration. The triangular hydrograph shown in Figure 11.15 (in which it is assumed that the

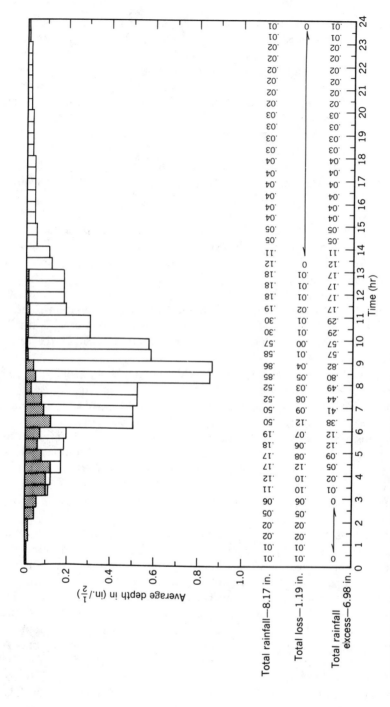

FIGURE 11.9 A hyetograph of 25-yr design rainfall, curve 90, 24-hr duration. *Source:* Golding, 1974.

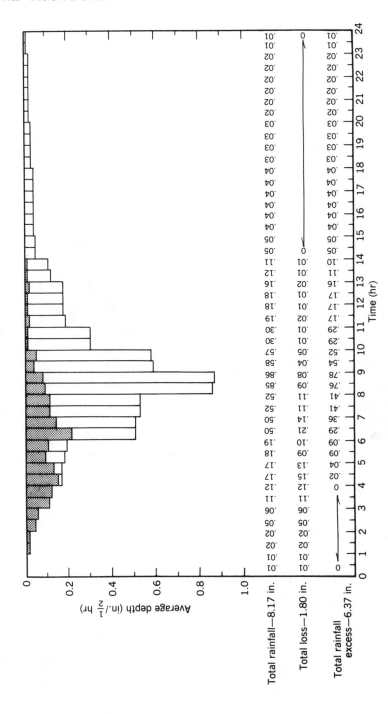

FIGURE 11.10 A hyetograph of 25-yr design rainfall, curve 85, 24-hr duration. *Source:* Golding, 1974.

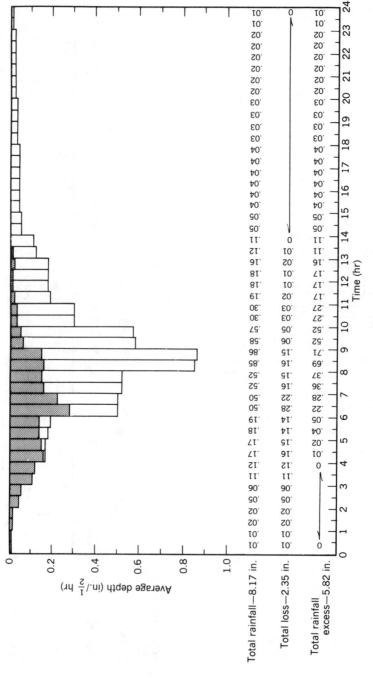

FIGURE 11.11   A hyetograph of 25-yr design rainfall, curve 80, 24-hr duration. *Source:* Golding, 1974.

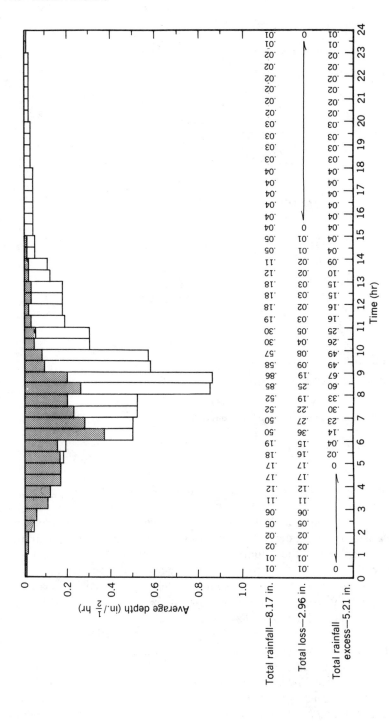

FIGURE 11.12 A hyetograph of 25-yr design rainfall, curve 75, 24-hr duration. *Source:* Golding, 1974.

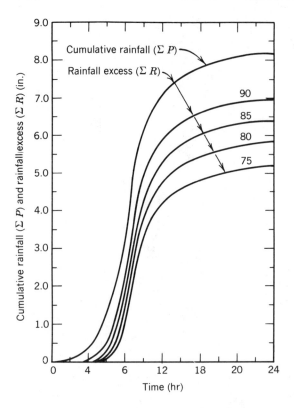

FIGURE 11.13   Mass curves of rainfall and direct runoff, 25-yr frequency, 24-hr rainfall.

duration of the rainfall is equal to the time of concentration) gives, as previously stated, the maximum value of Q $(= Q_p)$ and is normally used by the engineer to size pipes and other systems. However, the other hydrograph (trapezoidal) result in greater volumes of runoff, the areas under each trapezoidal hydrograph being the volumes of runoff in each case.

Once such a family of hydrographs is developed, a detention basin size can easily be computed if the allowable outflow rate from the basin is established. In some regulations, the outflow rate is set as the natural flow in the receiving stream prior to any development.

If the allowable outflow rate is plotted on the family of hydrographs, the required storage volume can be computed. The maximum area (storage volume) below one of the trapezoidal hydrographs and above the plotted allowable outflow rate (cross-hatched area in Figure 11.15) can be estimated.

The obvious advantages of computing the storage area using a hydrograph by the Rational Method procedure are ease and simplicity. The obvious

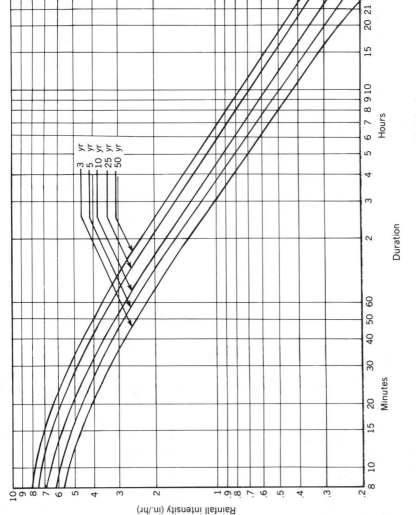

FIGURE 11.14 Rainfall intensity-duration zone 3, Jacksonville, FL. *Source:* Florida State Department of Transportation.

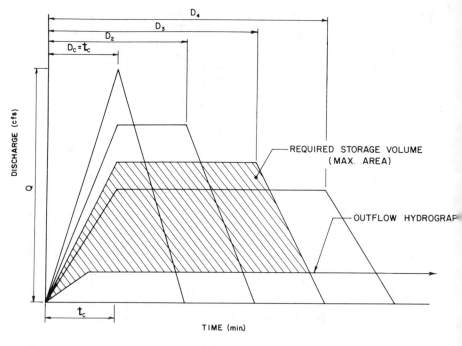

FIGURE 11.15   A family of hydrographs, rational method procedure.

disadvantage is possible inaccuracy. However, where small homogeneous watersheds are involved (i.e., ≤ 10 ac or less), this method will generally produce satisfactory results.

Considering the rainfall–intensity–duration curves, the short-duration (approximately 2 hr or less) storms should be used for design of transport and possibly detention facilities in smaller areas. The long-duration storms are more useful in design of detention facilities for larger watersheds. However, many short- and long-duration storms must be used to calculate detention basin size to determine the worst case (maximum storage volume).

11.3

HYDROGRAPH ATTENUATION IN A STORMWATER DETENTION BASIN

One of the major problems associated with new urban development is the increased volumes and rates of stormwater runoff generated within previously natural watersheds. Runoff volume is increased when natural pervious land

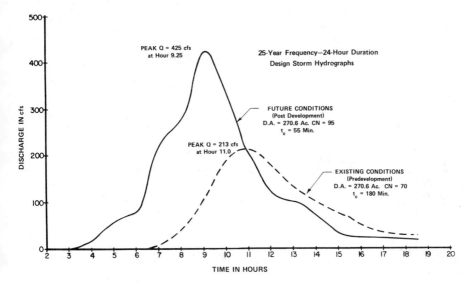

FIGURE 11.16 Typical subbasin hydrographs.

surfaces are covered by such impervious structures as buildings, roadways, and parking lots and when natural depressions are removed, which serve as storage areas for ponded surface runoff in their natural state. The rate of runoff, including peak flow rates, is significantly increased when structural drainage systems such as storm sewers, swales, and ditches are constructed, which greatly reduced the time of concentration of runoff. Figure 11.16 illustrates existing and future condition runoff hydrographs for a drainage basin resulting using a 24-hr duration storm. The existing condition hydrograph represents the runoff generated within the basin in its natural developed state, whereas the future condition hydrograph represents the runoff generated after development has taken place. As indicated by these hydrographs, both the peak rate and the volumes of runoff are significantly increased as a result of development within the watershed.

Increased volumes and rates of runoff generated by urban developments most often intensify downstream flooding problems, and, in some cases, especially in areas of flat terrain where backwater effects are significant, upstream flooding problems are also intensified, due to the limited conveyance and storage capacities of natural drainageways to handle the increased problem and rate of runoff from contributory watersheds.

Many urban governments and other public agencies responsible for stormwater drainage and local flood control have been giving increasing attention to practical and economical means of reducing the losses and

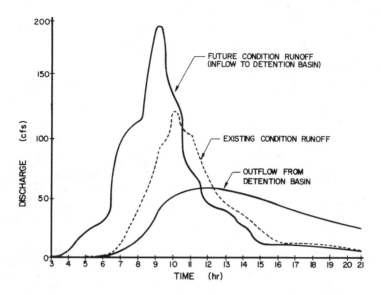

FIGURE 11.17 Typical detention system hydrographs.

inconveniences caused by flooding created by increased surface runoff. In many areas, local governments are realizing the importance of responsible stormwater management and some have adopted policies, especially in areas with identified flooding problems, that require that land developers take appropriate steps to ensure that peak runoff flow rates after development are not in excess of those that prevailed prior to development.

To meet such requirements, various on-site detention facilities are being incorporated into many planned developments, the most common of which include roof top storage, parking-lot storage, and multipurpose detention and retention basins and ponds (Poertner, 1974). On-site detention of any type generally refers to storage of excess runoff on the site prior to its discharge into downstream drainage systems and gradual release of the temporarily stored runoff after the peak of the runoff inflow has passed.

The effect of a detention facility on runoff flow rates can be shown most descriptively by observing the inflow and outflow hydrographs for a detention pond, as shown in Figure 11.17. Note that although the total volume of runoff (area under the curves) is not reduced, the flow rate leaving the detention facility is significantly lower than the inflow rate. The objective, then, of any on-site detention facility is simply to regulate the runoff from a given rainfall event and to control discharge rates to reduce the impact on downstream drainage systems either natural or man made. Generally, detention facilities will not reduce the total volume of runoff but will simply redistribute the rate of runoff over a certain period of time by providing temporary "live" storage of a certain amount of the runoff. The volume of temporary live storage provided is the volume indicated by the area between the inflow and outflow hydrographs as shown in Figure 11.17.

The major benefit derived from properly designed and operated detention facilities is the reduction in downstream flooding problems. Other benefits include reduced costs of downstream drainage facilities, reduction in pollution of receiving streams, and even enhancement of aesthetics within a development area by providing the core of blue–green areas for parks and recreation.

Although the beneficial effects of stormwater detention are generally recognized, standard engineering design methods have not been developed that are universally accepted by designers of facilities or by the agencies that review and approve the designs. However, there do exist practical conventional techniques and procedures that provide useful guidelines to engineers who have not had extensive experience in the design of detention facilities. General guidelines are presented to demonstrate technically accepted methods and techniques that can be used in the design of such facilities.

The basic purpose of a stormwater detention basin is to reduce the rate of runoff from a contributory subbasin by providing temporary storage of excess runoff. Therefore, the major design considerations are, of course, the volume of storage required and the maximum permitted release rate. Although the storage volume required can be determined in a number of ways, the most commonly used criterion is to provide sufficient storage to limit the maximum rate of outflow from the detention basin to a maximum permitted release rate (Poertner, 1974). The volume of storage required and the maximum permitted release rate are, therefore, ultimately related. A more detailed discussion of this interrelationship of storage and outflow will be presented later in Section 11.3.1. Before discussing the more technical aspects and design procedures involved in the engineering design of detention basin facilities, some of the more general design considerations that should be considered throughout the design phases are mentioned briefly.

Throughout the design process, the designer should be committed to considering the potential impacts of the completed facility. Such impacts can be positive or negative and can be as broadly classified as social, economic, political, and environmental. Designers can often influence the positive or negative aspects of these impacts by their careful evaluation and decisions made in the design process. Generally speaking, the completed facility should provide for safety to people and wildlife and protection of real property and wildlife habitats. From an economical standpoint, the facility should provide for the lowest capital and annual costs attainable within project constraints. Multipurpose use of the facility and esthetic enhancement of the general area should also be major considerations. Above all, the facility should function in such a manner as to be compatible with overall drainage systems both upstream and downstream and to promote a watershed approach to providing stormwater drainage and flood control.

This section does not emphasize general design considerations such as these just mentioned since they can often be quite intangible as well as site specific; rather, we present some of the generally accepted hydrologic design procedures and concepts as a basis for the application of general hydrologic and hydraulic principles involved in the engineering design of detention basin facilities. However, the general design considerations should be considered seriously through the design process of any detention basin facility.

Many management practices exist to attenuate (reduce peak flow) the hydrograph. Source controls, such as reducing impervious areas, catch basin design modifications, and on-site ponding all serve to reduce the hydrograph peak flow. The quantity of pollutants removed are, however, different and must also be examined before decisions are made on the procedures to reduce hydrograph peak flow.

11.3.1 Storage and Outflow Hydrographs

The common way to reduce the peak runoff from a particular watershed is to construct a holding pond (detention) to store the runoff (i.e., provide a volume (reservoir or pipe storage) to store a portion of the volume of runoff from the watershed and then to slowly remove the detained water from the pond). An outlet control structure is provided to allow the temporarily stored water to flow out within a specified period of time so that part of the detention storage is again available when the next storm rainfall occurs. Thus, both the storage volume and outlet device control the rate of discharge. Unfortunately, in flat terrain there are few, if any, natural reservoir sites. However, there are usually lakes and borrow pits available that can be used as holding ponds and can "control" the contributary drainage areas thereto.

In sewer systems, larger underground pipes with outlet control devices (inlet control to sewer) can be used for peak flow reduction. A self-regulating device with no moving parts and no energy consumption would be ideal. Such devices are marketed under the name "Hydro-Brake" (shown in Figure 11.18). The principle of operation is to essentially use the static head in storage to create back pressures that reduce flow rates. As the pressure at discharge increases, the flow patterns within the device start a violent swirling motion, forming a vortex that creates the back pressure. Relative to a straight orifice, discharge rates have been reduced by 60 to 90% (H.I.L. Technology Inc., Scarlborough, Maine).

Consider as an example the basin that produced the runoff hydrograph shown in Figure 7.4 (Golding, 1974). Located in this particular drainage basin is an existing large borrow pit lake, which is ideally situated for reducing peak flow. Using the available storage therein and using a 36-in. reinforced concrete pipe culvert as the outflow spillway, the runoff hydrograph was attenuated to a

Main Types of Hydro-Brakes

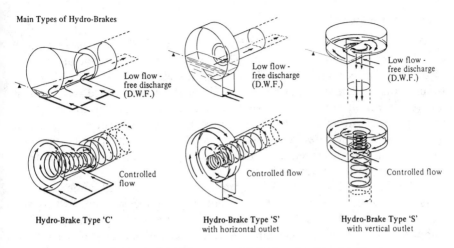

Low flow - free discharge (D.W.F.)

Low flow - free discharge (D.W.F.)

Low flow - free discharge (D.W.F.)

Controlled flow

Controlled flow

Controlled flow

Hydro-Brake Type 'C'

Hydro-Brake Type 'S' with horizontal outlet

Hydro-Brake Type 'S' with vertical outlet

FIGURE 11.18   Hydro-brake liquid flow control (D.W.F. = Dry Weather Flow).

peak of only 49 cfs. The routing procedures of Chapter 8 were used to route through the reservoir storage available in the borrow pit lake.

In this particular case, the peak of the hydrograph was reduced from 991 to 49 ft^3/sec, admittedly an unusual situation. However, peak flows can be drastically reduced (up to 90%) by the use of available reservoir storage in existing lakes, borrow pits, etc. Generally, approximately 10 to 20% of small drainage basins up to 1.0 mi^2 area with corresponding water depths from 5 to 20 ft are required to significantly reduce peak discharge. For the situation reported by Golding (1974) the area of the borrow pit detention reservoir, 25 ac, amounted to approximately 10% of the contributory 238-ac watershed. The depth at maximum storage was approximately 5 ft.

Of interest in this particular situation was the fact that tailwater caused by a downstream culvert actually delayed flow out of this lake until hour 5 and reduced the outflow to approximately 22 ft^3/sec until hour 7, at which time critical depth at the culvert outlet took over and increased flow to 49 ft^3/sec. Normally, substantial outflow would probably start at hour 2.

For the hydrograph attenuation reported by Golding (1974), much time has elapsed for the runoff to flow out of the reservoir storage basin. Assuming that outflow through the pipe culvert spillway remained constant at 49 ft^3/sec (actually it decreased with time because the head on the culvert decreased as water flowed out of the holding pond), it would take a little over two days for the culvert to empty the pond. A convenient conversion factor to remember is that 1 ft^3/sec for one day is equal to about 2 ac-ft (ft^3/sec days × 1.98 = ac-ft). Therefore, 49 ft^3/sec for one day is equal to approximately 98 ac-ft, which compares with 107 ac-ft in the basin.

11.3.2   Case Studies

To demonstrate the preliminary design procedures of the previous sections, a simplified example design problem will be solved to illustrate the application of technically acceptable hydraulic and hydrologic methods and techniques. Assume that a detention pond is to be designed for a proposed development for which runoff hydrographs were computed. Assume that the proposed development is in an area in which the local governing agency requires that future peak runoff rates resulting from a 25-yr frequency, 24-hr duration design storm do not exceed those that exist under predevelopment conditions for the same design storm.

The 25-yr, 24-hr runoff hydrograph for the watershed under natural, predevelopment conditions has been computed using the SCS unit hydrograph method (shown in Figure 11.19 along with the future conditions hydrograph as computed by the same procedure). As indicated by the existing-conditions hydrograph, the peak runoff flow rate is 213 ft³/sec, which will then be the maximum permissible release rate from the detention basin as required by the governing agency. The inflow hydrograph to the proposed detention basin is, then, the future conditions hydrograph shown in Figure 11.19. Using the inventory equation, the cumulative volume of inflow minus the cumulative volume of outflow at any time is equal to the volume stored at the time. Therefore, an estimate of the total volume required can be determined by

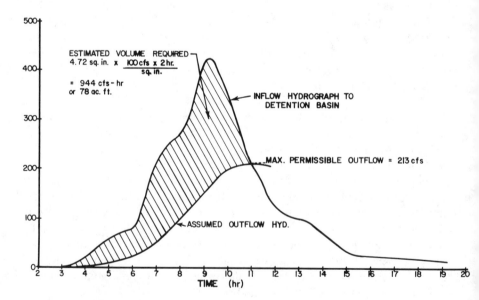

FIGURE 11.19   Require storage volume.

measuring the area between the inflow hydrograph and the assumed outflow hydrograph. As indicated in Figure 11.19, an estimated volume of 944 $ft^3/$ sec-hr or 78 ac-ft is determined.

Based on an evaluation of the downstream drainage facilities, the normal control water surface elevation should not be lower than elevation 92 mean sea level (MSL); based on the existing topography around the site of the proposed pond, the maximum design stage should not exceed elevation 96, not including an allowance for a 1-ft freeboard. Therefore, the maximum depth of live storage for the detention basin is the difference in these two elevations, or 4 ft.

The average area required for the detention basin can then be approximated by dividing the estimated storage required by the depth of live storage. The estimated average area required is, therefore, 78 ac-ft divided by 4 ft or 19.5 ac. Note that this area only approximates the area required at approximately the average depth of live storage, which, in this case, is approximately 2 ft above the control elevation or about elevation 94 MSL. Since the area is only an approximation, it should be used only as a starting point for development of the storage–elevation relationship.

To simplify the computation of the storage–elevation relationship in the preliminary design of relatively large irregularly shaped detention basins with relatively constant and flat side slopes of about 10 horizontal to 1 vertical flatter, it is usually sufficient to approximate the change in area for every foot of change in depth by the following relationship:

$$\Delta A_d = \frac{(SS \times SL_d)}{43{,}560}$$

where

ΔA_d = the change in area in acres for every foot of change in water depth from the average depth, d

SS = the ratio of horizontal to vertical length of the side slopes

SL_d = the shore length in feet at the average depth, d

$43{,}560$ = square feet per acre

A preliminary layout of the detention basin can then be made such that the area at elevation 94 MSL is about 19.5 ac as shown in Figure 11.20. Then, by scaling the shoreline length and applying the above relationship, a storage–elevation curve can be computed and plotted as shown in Figure 11.20. Note that the areas at various elevations in column 4 of the computation table are computed by adding to the average area the product of ΔA_d (the change in area per unit change in depth) and d (the depth from the average elevation either positive or negative). Average areas between each elevation are then computed in column 5; incremental volumes of storage between the changes in volume in column 7; and the storage–elevation curve is then plotted from the points in columns 1 and 8.

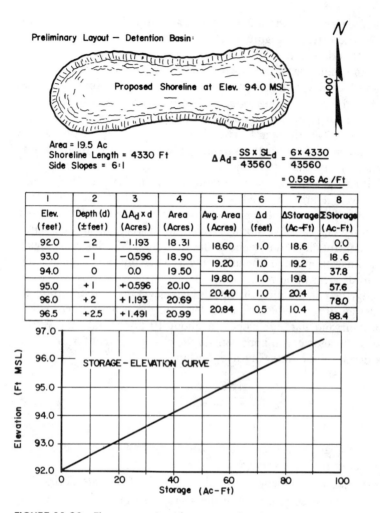

Preliminary Layout — Detention Basin:

Proposed Shoreline at Elev. 94.0 MSL

400' N

Area = 19.5 Ac
Shoreline Length = 4330 Ft
Side Slopes = 6:1

$$\Delta A_d = \frac{SS \times SL_d}{43560} = \frac{6 \times 4330}{43560}$$

$$= 0.596 \ Ac\ /Ft$$

1	2	3	4	5	6	7	8
Elev. (feet)	Depth (d) (±feet)	$\Delta A_d \times d$ (Acres)	Area (Acres)	Avg. Area (Acres)	Δd (feet)	ΔStorage (Ac-Ft)	ΣStorage (Ac-Ft)
92.0	−2	−1.193	18.31	18.60	1.0	18.6	0.0
93.0	−1	−0.596	18.90	19.20	1.0	19.2	18.6
94.0	0	0.0	19.50	19.80	1.0	19.8	37.8
95.0	+1	+0.596	20.10	20.40	1.0	20.4	57.6
96.0	+2	+1.193	20.69	20.84	0.5	10.4	78.0
96.5	+2.5	+1.491	20.99				88.4

STORAGE – ELEVATION CURVE

Elevation (Ft MSL)

Storage (Ac-Ft)

FIGURE 11.20   The computation of a storage-elevation curve.

The assumptions and approximations used in developing the storage–elevation relationship in this manner will, of course, limit the accuracy of the results to some extent. However, in the preliminary design of large detention systems of this type, sufficient accuracy is usually obtained by making such approximations. At any rate, on completion of the final design of the detention system, an actual storage–elevation curve should be computed using a final grading plan for the basin that can be compared to the curve used in the preliminary design computations.

The next step is to determine a trial size for the outfall structure. In this problem, a weir spillway with a crest elevation at 92 MSL will be used as the control structure, and it will be assumed that a free outfall condition will exist at all times. Knowing the maximum permissible discharge rate and the maximum allowable stage or headwater elevation, the structure can be sized by applying the rectangular weir formula to determine the required weir length. Assuming a weir discharge coefficient of 3.2, the required length is computed as follows:

$$B = Q/CH^{3/2} = 213/\left[3.2(96 - 92)^{3/2}\right] = 8.32 \text{ ft}$$

and rounding off: use $B = 8.5$ ft. Other types of flow control devices can be used. The theoretical flow characteristics are represented as follows.

For a circular orifice (Equation 5.18)

$$Q = CA_o\sqrt{2gh}$$

where
Q = orifice discharge (ft^3/sec)
C = coefficient of discharge
A_o = orifice cross-sectional area (ft^2)
g = gravitational acceleration constant = 32.2 ft/sec^2

Note: When water surface behind orifice falls below the top of the orifice opening, the equation for a simple weir opening should be used (Equation 5.13).

$$Q = CBH^{3/2}$$

where
C = equivalent weir coefficient of discharge
B = equivalent weir length (ft)
H = hydraulic head above bottom of weir opening (ft)

A rating curve of discharge vs. stage for the proposed structure can then be computed by again applying the rectangular weir formula solving for Q at various stages in the detention basin. The required computations and the plotted rating curve for this structure are shown in Figure 11.21.

As we stated previously, the inventory equation as applied in reservoir routing states that the volume of inflow minus the volume of outflow over a given time interval is equal to the change in volume stored over the time

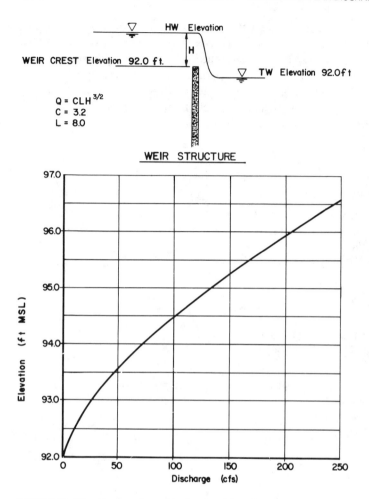

FIGURE 11.21   Computation of hydraulic rating curve.

interval. In most applications of the inventory equation, the flow and storage variables are expanded and were developed in Chapter 8 (Equation 8.29).

$$\bar{I} = \frac{(I_1 + I_2)}{2} \qquad \bar{O} = \frac{(O_1 + O_2)}{2} \qquad \text{and} \qquad \Delta S = S_2 - S_1$$

where

I_1 and I_2 = inflow rates at time 1 and subsequent time 2

O_1 and O_2 = outflow rates at time 1 and subsequent time 2

S_1 and S_2 = volumes stored at time 1 and time 2, respectively

Dividing both sides of the inventory equation by Δt and substituting terms:

$$\bar{I} - \bar{O} = \frac{\Delta S}{\Delta t}$$

$$\bar{I} - \frac{(O_1 + O_2)}{2} = \frac{(S_2 - S_1)}{\Delta t}$$

$$\bar{I} - \frac{O_1}{2} - \frac{O_2}{2} = \frac{S_2}{\Delta t} - \frac{S_1}{\Delta t}$$

Rearranging terms, the following equation results:

$$\frac{S_2}{\Delta t} + \frac{O_2}{2} = \bar{I} + \frac{S_1}{\Delta t} - \frac{O_1}{2}$$

Since both storage (S) and outflow (O) are functions of the water surface elevation in the detention basin and if Δt is held constant, then there exists a relation for outflow, O, as a function of the compound variable $(S/\Delta t + O/2)$. Furthermore, if the average inflow, $\bar{I}$, outflow, O, and storage, S, are known for a given time, then the equation can be rewritten with only one unknown variable, that is, $(S_2/\Delta t + O_2/2)$ or rewriting Equation 8.30:

$$N_2 = \left(\frac{S_2}{\Delta t} + \frac{O_2}{2} \right) = \bar{I} + \left(\frac{S_1}{\Delta t} + \frac{O_1}{2} \right) - O_1$$

This then is the working form of the inventory equation. Other hydrologic methods typically rearrange the terms of the inventory equation in much the same manner as done here to obtain the equation in a working form for the actual routing procedure.

Having the inventory equation in the form of Equation 8.30 allows for the development of a relationship between O_2 and $(S_2/\Delta t + O_2/2)$, which if plotted in graphic form is generally referred to as the storage-indicating working curve for solution of the inventory equation in the actual routing process.

Using the storage–elevation curve for the detention basin and the hydraulic rating curve for the outlet structure, the points of the storage-indicating working curve for the example problem can be computed and plotted as shown in Figure 11.22 for a routing interval, Δt, of 30 min. Due to mathematical instability, usually caused by high inflow rates, large changes result in stage over one routing time step. Thus, portions of the outflow hydrograph can be distorted, and negative rates may occur during recession periods if O_2 is greater than $(S_2/\Delta t + O_2/2)$. It is, important, therefore, when using this method to be certain that a small enough time interval is selected so that

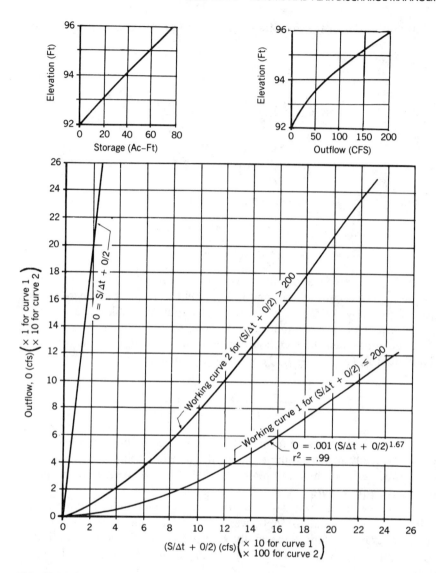

FIGURE 11.22   The computation of the storage-indicating curve.

numerical instability problems do not interfere with the accuracy of the routing computations.

An easy way to determine whether a small enough time step has been selected is to plot a line of equal values on the working curve that represents $O_2 = (S_2/\Delta t + O_2/2)$. If the working curve falls below this line, then a small enough time interval is being used, since O_2 will always be less than $(S_2/\Delta t + O_2/2)$, as shown in Figure 11.22.

TABLE 11.5 Reservoir Routing Operations Table (Storage-Indicating Method)
$$(S_2/\Delta t + O_2/2) = \bar{i} + (S_1/\Delta t + O_1/2) - O_1$$

1 TIME (hr)	2 INFLOW, I (ft^3/sec)	3 AVG. INFLOW, $\bar{i}$ (ft^3/sec)	4 $s/\Delta t + O/2$ $= \bar{i} + S_1/\Delta t$ $+ O_1/2 - O_1$ (ft^3/sec)	OUTFLOW, O^a (ft^3/sec)
2.5	0	0	0	0
3.0	0.7	0.4	0.4	0.0
3.5	6.6	3.6	4.0^b	0.1
4.0	18.6	12.6	16.5^c	0.2
4.5	35.8	27.2	43.5	0.5
5.0	56.0	45.9	88.8	2.2
5.5	69.9	63.0	149.6	5.6
6.0	79.5	74.7	218.7	10
6.5	130.4	105.0	313.7	15
7.0	206.8	169.8	468.3	25
7.5	247.6	228.2	671.5	43
8.0	268.7	258.2	886.7	66
8.5	328.6	298.6	1119.3	92
9.0	413.1	370.8	1398.1	125
9.5	403.7	408.4	1681.5	163
10.0	348.0	375.8	1894.3	191
10.5	283.9	316.0	2019.3	206
11.0	209.8	246.8	2060.1	210
11.5	162.0	185.8	2036.0	208
12.0	122.3	142.2	1970.2	202
12.5	107.5	114.9	1883.1	190
13.0	102.3	104.9	1798.0	179
13.5	90.0	96.2	1715.2	168
14.0	72.6	81.3	1628.5	156
14.5	54.5	63.6	1536.1	143
15.0	34.2	44.4	1437.5	130
15.5	26.4	30.3	1337.8	118
16.0	23.5	25.0	1244.8	106
16.5	22.6	23.1	1161.9	96
17.0	22.3	22.4	1088.3	88
17.5	22.2	22.2	1022.5	81
18.0	22.2	22.2	963.7	74
18.5	20.4	21.3	911.9	68
19.0	17.4	18.9	865.2	64

[a] Estimate from plot.
[b] $3.6 + 0.4 - 0 = 4.0$.
[c] $12.6 + 4.0 - 0.1 = 16.5$.

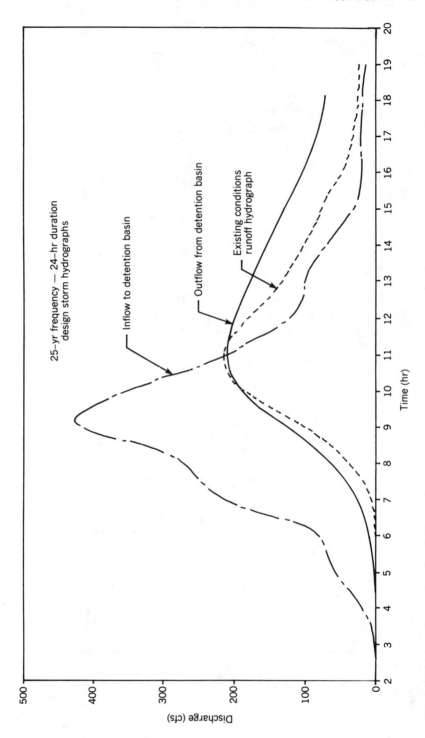

FIGURE 11.23   Inflow and outflow hydrographs.

Once the working curve for the detention system has been developed and the ordinates of the inflow hydrograph are available at time intervals of Δt, a routing operations table can be developed as shown in Table 11.5. As shown in this table, the ordinates of the inflow hydrograph are placed in column 2 and the average inflow rates, $\bar{I}$, are computed and placed in column 3 by arithmetically averaging the inflow rates between each time step. Also, the values of $(S/\Delta t + O/2)$ and outflow O at the initial time are taken as zero.

With the operations table in this form, the mathematical routing procedure can begin. The value of $(S/\Delta t + O/2)$ can be computed for the second time step. Therefore, $(S_2/\Delta t + O_2/2) = \bar{I} + (S_1/\Delta t + O_1/2) - O_1 = 0.4 + 0.0 - 0.0 = 0.4$. Then, from the storage-indicating working curve, the value of O_2 can be determined from the value of $(S_2/\Delta t + O_2/2) = 0.4$. From the working curve, a value of O_2 at time = 0.5 h is determined to be zero. The equation gives a more exact value of 0.0002.

The outflow rate for the next time step is then determined in the same manner. Again, applying the continuity equation, we get $(S_2/\Delta t + O_2/2) = 3.6 + 0.4 - 0.0$ or 4.0. From the working curve with $(S/\Delta t + O/2) = 4.0$ one gets an outflow rate O_2 at time = 1 hr of 0.1 ft^3/sec.

This procedure is then repeated for each successive time step until all the ordinates of the outflow hydrograph have been computed. Table 11.5 shows the completed operations table for this routing procedure.

From the ordinates of the outflow hydrograph from the detention pond for the design storm being used, we can plot the hydrograph and evaluate the performance of the first trial design of the detention system. As shown in Figure 11.23, the inflow and outflow hydrographs are plotted with the existing conditions runoff hydrograph for the drainage pond. Note here that the peak outflow rate from the detention pond is 210 ft^3/sec as compared to a peak existing conditions runoff rate of 213 ft^3/sec. Based on the criteria of the governing agency, our system is slightly overdesigned; however, the effects of timing of the flood flow rates should also be considered.

This example problem has been simplified. Complications resulting from neglect of infiltration hydrographs, quality transformations, quality removal efficiencies, costs, and variable tailwater conditions can require additional work.

11.4

CULVERTS

Stormwater detention ponds are frequently connected together with culverts. A typical culvert is a hydraulically short (generally, less than a few hundred feet) conduit that conveys stormwaters from one detention pond to another, or through an embankment, or past some other type of flow obstruction. When

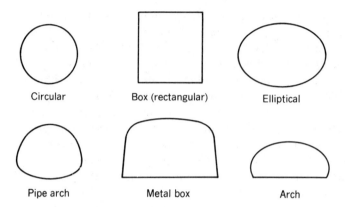

Circular   Box (rectangular)   Elliptical

Pipe arch   Metal box   Arch

FIGURE 11.24 Commonly used culvert shapes.

water passes through the culvert, friction forces, inlet losses, and exit losses force water on the upstream side to pond at a deeper elevation. Thus, various inlet configurations and a variety of materials are used in culvert design to decrease head losses. In addition, there are a variety of culvert shapes as shown in Figure 11.24. The selected shape is based on construction cost, limitation on upstream water surface elevation, embankment heights, and flow-rate limitations.

Flow rates through a culvert may be improved by reducing friction losses at the inlet side. Since upstream ponded areas and natural channel characteristics are usually wider than the culvert width (barrel width), there is a flow contraction at the culvert. A more gradual flow transition will lessen the energy loss; leveled edges are more efficient than square ones, and side or slope tapered inlets further reduce the flow contraction. The different types of inlet contractions are shown in Figures 11.25, 11.26, 11.27 (Federal Highway Administration, 1985). Other factors affect flow rates and headwater conditions, many of which must be examined when determining culvert sizes, inlet construction details, and headwater elevations. These factors are listed in Table 11.6. Inlet control occurs when the culvert barrel is capable of passing more flow than the inlet will accept. Outlet control occurs when the culvert barrel is not capable of passing as much flow as the inlet will accept.

When free surface flow (otherwise known as open channel flow) exists, the flow control is determined by knowing critical depth and a dimensionless ratio using average velocity and depth of flow, known as Froude number, F_r.

$$F_r = \frac{\bar{V}}{\sqrt{gy}}$$

(11.8)

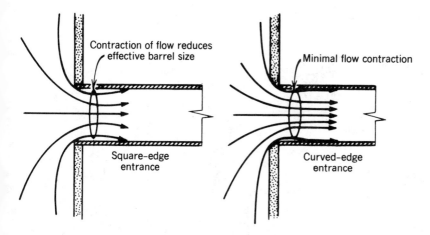

FIGURE 11.25 Entrance contractions (schematic).

where
$\overline{V}$ = average velocity = Q/A (ft/s) (m/s)
Q = flow rate (ft^3/s) (m^3/s)
A = cross-sectional area of flow (ft^2) (m^2)
y = depth of flow (ft) (m)
g = gravitational acceleration, 32.2 ft/sec^2 (9.8 m/sec^2)

and

$$y = \frac{A}{w} \qquad (11.9)$$

where

$$w = \text{width of the free surface (ft) (m)}$$

When $F_r > 1.0$, flow is supercritical; if $F_v < 1.0$, flow is subcritical; and if $F_r = 1.0$, flow is critical. The characterization of subcritical and supercritical determine the location of a control section and the type of control. The control section of a culvert control by the inlet is located just inside the entrance, because critical depth (minimum specific energy) is located at or near this location and the flow downstream is supercritical. A typical inlet control is shown in Figure 11.28. Important variables are defined in Figure 11.28 such as headwater, tailwater, and critical depth. If subcritical flow exists in the culvert and a control section exists downstream, or critical depth is found at the end

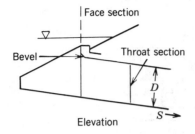

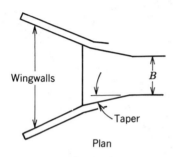

FIGURE 11.26   A side-tapered inlet. *Source:* The Federal Highway Administration, 1985.

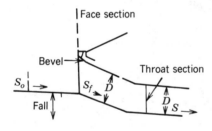

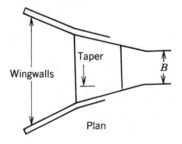

FIGURE 11.27   A slope-tapered inlet. *Source:* The Federal Highway Administration, 1985.

TABLE 11.6 Factors Influencing Culvert Performance

FACTOR	INLET CONTROL	OUTLET CONTROL
Headwater elevation	X	X
Inlet area	X	X
Inlet edge configuration	X	X
Inlet shape	X	X
Barrel roughness		X
Barrel area		X
Barrel shape		X
Barrel length		X
Barrel slope[a]		X
Tailwater elevation		X

Source: Federal Highway Administration (1985).
[a]Barrel slope affects inlet control performance to a small degree but may be neglected.

of the culvert, outlet control conditions exist. Typical outlet controls are shown in Figure 11.29.

The total head loss through the culvert can be estimated using the following equation which is the sum of head losses at the entrance, barrel friction, and exit losses assuming near zero velocity downstream. If bends or other minor losses were involved, they would also be included.

$$H = \left(k_e + \left(29n^2L/R^{1.33} \right) + 1 \right)\left(V^2/2g \right) \qquad (11.10)$$

where

k_e = entrance loss coefficient (see Table 11.7)

n = Manning's roughness coefficient (see Table 5.3)

L = conduit length (ft)

R = hydraulic radius (ft)

If tailwater conditions downstream result in a significant downstream velocity

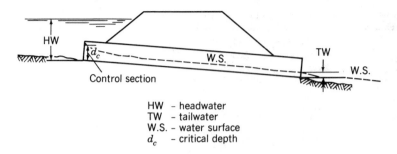

HW – headwater
TW – tailwater
W.S. – water surface
d_c – critical depth

FIGURE 11.28 A typical inlet control, flow conditions.

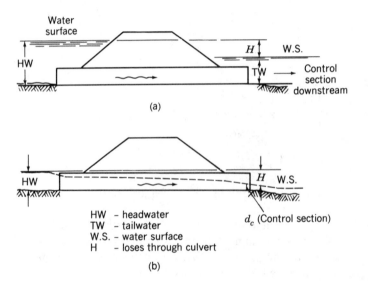

HW – headwater
TW – tailwater
W.S. – water surface
H   – loses through culvert

(b)

FIGURE 11.29 A typical outlet control, flow conditions. (*a*) Submerged. (*b*) Unsubmerged.

V_d, then the exit loss is modified as

$$H_{\text{exit}} = 1.0\left(\frac{V^2}{2g} - \frac{V_d^2}{2g}\right) \tag{11.11}$$

Thus, headwater elevation can be calculated given the tailwater condition, conduit shape, conduit material, and flow rate.

$$HW = TW + H \tag{11.12}$$

TABLE 11.7 Entrance Loss Coefficients: Outlet Control, Full or Partly Full Entrance Head Loss

$$H_e = k_e\left(\frac{V^2}{2g}\right)$$

TYPE OF STRUCTURE AND DESIGN OF ENTRANCE	COEFFICIENT k_e
Pipe, Concrete	
Projecting from fill, socket end (groove end)	.2
Projecting from fill, sq. cut end	.5
Headwall or headwall and wingwalls	
Socket end of pipe (groove end)	.2
Square edge	.5
Rounded (radius = $1/12\,D$)	.2
Mitered to conform to fill slope	.7
End section conforming to fill slope[a]	.5
Beveled edges, 33.7° or 45° bevels	.2
Side- or slope-tapered inlet	.2
Pipe, or Pipe Arched, Corrugated Metal	
Projecting from fill (no headwall)	.9
Headwall or headwall and wingwalls square edge	.5
Mitered to conform to fill slope, paved or	
unpaved slope	.7
End section conforming to fill slope[a]	.5
Beveled edges, 33.7° or 45° bevels	.2
Side- or slope-tapered inlet	.2
Box, Reinforced Concrete	
Headwall parallel to embankment (no wingwalls)	
Square edged on 3 edges	.5
Rounded on 3 edges to radius of 1/12 barrel	
dimension, or beveled edges on three sides	.2
Wingwalls at 30° to 75° to barrel	
Square edged at crown	.4
Crown edge rounded to radius of 1/12 barrel	
dimension, or beveled top edge	.2
Wingwall at 10° to 25° to barrel	
Square edged at crown	.5
Wingwalls parallel (extension of sides)	
Square edged at crown	.7
Side- or slope-tapered inlet	.2

Source: Federal Highway Administration (1985).
[a]"End section conforming to fill slope," made of either metal or concrete, are the sections commonly available from manufacturers. From limited hydraulic tests they are equivalent in operation to a headwall in both *inlet* and *outlet* control. Some end sections, incorporating a *closed* taper in their design have a superior hydraulic performance.

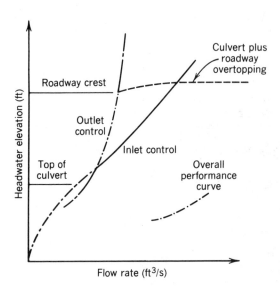

FIGURE 11.30   A culvert performance curve with roadway overtopping.

where
HW = headwater depth (ft)
TW = tailwater depth (ft)
H = headloss through culvert (ft)

A storage discharge relationship must be developed, but a culvert can function under inlet or outlet control depending on flow conditions, tailwater, and headwater (stage) conditions. Thus, both inlet and outlet control relations must be developed as shown in Figure 11.30. Culvert discharge curves are similar to the orifice curves that act both as a wier and orifice. However, a culvert can have one more control section (inlet, outlet, and throat of a contraction) plus embankment overtopping. An overall discharge curve would be made up of the controlling curves producing the least discharge. Using this combined discharge, it is now possible to determine headwaters for any flow rate since headwaters determine flow rates.

11.5

OFF-LINE RETENTION (INFILTRATION PONDS)

Stormwater volume and pollutants in the stormwater can be controlled by diverting the stormwater to infiltration ponds adjacent to the sewer line. The quantity diverted can be expressed in terms of the depth of runoff over the entire watershed or the diversion of the runoff from the first quantity (depth) of precipitation. Examples of both criteria are to (1) divert the first half-inch of runoff (over the total watershed) and (2) divert the runoff from the first inch of rainfall. If the runoff coefficient for a watershed is .5, then the runoff from the first inch of rainfall is the same as the first half-inch of runoff. Thus, the criteria may be consistent with one another.

The percent volume control can be determined from a cumulative distribution on storm event rainfall volume (Figures 9.1b and 9.13). From Figure 9.1b, the frequency of storms diverted as a function of storm volume can be determined (i.e., 90% of all events have less than 1 in.). From Figure 9.13, which is derived from Figure 9.1b, the percent of yearly volume diverted as a function of storm volume can be determined. As an example, 80% of yearly volume is diverted if the diversion is set to capture the first inch of runoff (runoff = rainfall) for each and every storm.

An easy to use design criteria formula (State of Florida, 1988) to control 80% of the yearly volume of runoff is

$$DV = \frac{CPA}{12} \tag{11.13}$$

where
DV = diversion volume (ac-ft)
C = runoff coefficient (≥ 0.5)
P = 1 inch rainfall volume (if Figure 9.13 is applicable)
A = watershed area (ac)
12 = conversion factor (in./ft)

The calculations using Equation 11.13 require that the runoff coefficient always be greater than .5 or the largest runoff coefficient be used consistent with published values (Table 7.3).

A cumulative frequency curve on rainfall volume and a diversion frequency curve for yearly volume should not be developed for specific areas and percentage control should be noted to determine precipitation volume (inches). The runoff coefficient used is usually the greatest for a particular land-use designation because of the fact that the complete infiltration volume may not be recovered before the next rainfall runoff event. This stochastic event of rainfall may be compensated for by building a larger pond. By simulating the rainfall runoff events over a long period of time, the largest pond volume to accumulate the diversion of the runoff from each and every event can be calculated.

Wanielista (1977) simulated the rainfall–runoff events and diversion into percolation ponds for a 20-yr historical record. The rainfall record was for the central Florida area. The percolation pond had a minimum infiltration rate of

TABLE 11.8   Pond Volume for Diverted Runoff as a Function of Diversion Volume

DIVERSION VOLUME (in.) OF EACH AND EVERY STORM[a]	RUNOFF DIVERTED[b]	V, VOLUME OF 5-ft-DEEP POND FOR 100% IMPERVIOUS AREA (ac-ft)
0.25	48	$0.016A^{1.28}$
0.38	55	$0.032A^{1.21}$
0.50	62	$0.046A^{1.18}$
0.75	72	$0.09A^{1.11}$
1.00	80	$0.14A^{1.07}$

where A = total watershed area in acres

[a] Usually equal to the fraction of runoff from 1 in. of rainfall.
[b] Based on Figure 9.13.

1 in./hr. For a completely impervious area and a percolation pond at a maximum depth of 5 ft, the efficiency of diversion and design volume of the percolation pond is calculated using the simulation (stochastic) equations in Table 11.8.

If the watershed area is not completely impervious and a composite curve number can be estimated for the watershed, the following equation is used to calculate the volume of a percolation pond that has a maximum depth of 5 ft.

$$V_S = V_I[0.59 + 0.37(CN_c/100)] \qquad (11.14)$$

where

     V_S = volume of 5-ft-deep percolation pond (ac-ft)
     CN_c = composite curve number
     V_I = volume for 100% impervious area, Table 11.8 (ac-ft)

The percolation pond can be built at less depth but occupy greater surface area for a given volume of runoff. However, the less deep pond will infiltrate a depth (amount) of stormwater in less time than a deeper pond because of the lesser depth. An infiltration rate of 1 in./hr can drain a 2-ft-deep pond in 24 hr, whereas a 4-ft-deep pond will take more than 24 hr. Therefore, less deep ponds are more likely to recover storage capacity before the next runoff event and the size of the pond to store the first specified amount of runoff from each and every storm event will be less. A formula developed for the meteorological conditions of Florida that relates depth of percolation pond to storage volume is

$$V_D = V_M + \left[\frac{V_S - V_M}{4} \right](D - 1) \qquad \text{for } D < 5 \qquad (11.15)$$

where

V_D = pond volume for depth D (ac-ft)
D = water depth (ft)
$V_M = (A \times DI)/12$ and DI = diversion depth (in.)
                                   A = watershed area (ac)
                               12 = conversion factor (in./ft)

☐   **EXAMPLE PROBLEM 11.5**

A 24-ac multiunit family residential area with an average lot size of 1/4 ac is required by state law to treat the runoff from the first inch of rainfall using off-line retention (diversion to percolating ponds). What size of pond do you specify if the pervious area is classified as Hydrologic Soil Group B and the maximum pond depth is 4 ft? Use both the state of Florida design criteria and the equations derived from simulating rainfall-runoff.

Solution

Using state of Florida criteria and a runoff coefficient for single family residential of .6 (Table 7.3), Equation 11.13 is used. Figure 9.13 is applicable for the design.

$$DV = \frac{CPA}{12}$$

$$= (.6)(1)(24)/12$$

$$= 1.2 \text{ ac-ft}$$

Using the simulation equations, the percent directly connected area is 38% (Table 4.4) and $CN_c = 75$. The diversion volume must be equal to or greater than 0.38 in. (use equation from Table 11.8) with $A = 24$ ac.

$$V_I = .032 A^{1.21}$$

$$= .032(24)^{1.21}$$

$$= 1.50 \text{ ac-ft}$$

and

$$V_M = (A \times DI)/12$$

$$= [(24)(.38)]/12 = 0.76 \text{ ac-ft}$$

$$V_5 = V_I(.59 + .37CN_c/100)$$

$$= 1.50[(0.59 + 0.37(75)/100] = 1.30 \text{ ac-ft}$$

for 4-ft-deep pond:

$$V_4 = V_M + \left[\frac{V_5 - V_M}{4}\right](D - 1)$$

$$= 0.76 + \left[\frac{1.30 - 0.76}{4}\right](4 - 1) = 1.17 \text{ ac-ft}$$

Thus, by using a simplified design formula or the simulation formulas,. the results are comparable for this specific watershed. □

11.6

SWALE DESIGN

Swales are vegetated open channels that infiltrate and transport runoff waters. By incorporating the hydrologic processes of runoff and infiltration, a swale design based on quantity is possible. Low velocities are important to prevent particle transport and loss of soil. The vegetation within the swales are very effective for the removal of solids and retention of soil (Lord, 1986). Erosion can be lessened by a vegetative area immediately after construction.

Wanielista et al. (1988) reported on the design of swales that had a seasonal high water table at least 1 ft below the bottom of a swale. They conducted 20 field tests doing a mass balance on runoff input to a swale and its output. The difference in input and output was the infiltration volume, from which an infiltration rate was calculated. Limiting infiltration rates during actual swale operation were estimated at 5 to 7.5 cm/hr (2–3 in./hr). The soils at the sites were classified according to the American Association of State Highway and Transportation Officials (AASHTO) soil classification systems as A-3 and A-2-4, which are fine sand and silty sand soils, respectively. For the same swales, the double ring infiltrometer and used to estimate the limiting infiltration rates. They were recorded at 12.5 to 50 cm/hr (5–20 in./hr).

Using a mass balance of input and output waters in a swale system, Equation 11.16 was developed to estimate the length of a swale necessary to infiltrate all the input rainfall excess from a specific storm event using a triangular shaped cross-sectional area. Another equation was developed for a trapezoidal cross-sectional shape (see Appendix E for a complete derivation).

$$L = \frac{KQ^{5/8}S^{3/16}}{N^{3/8}f} \tag{11.16}$$

where

$L =$ length of swale (m or ft)
$Q =$ average runoff flow rate (m^3/s or cfs)
$S =$ longitudinal slope (m/m or ft/ft)
$N =$ Manning's roughness coefficient (for overland flow) (Table 7.1)
$f =$ infiltration rate (cm/hr or in./hr)
$K =$ constant that is a function of side slope parameter Z(1 vertical/ Z horizontal) and is defined as

Z (SIDE SLOPE) (1 VERTICAL/Z HORIZONTAL)	K (SI UNITS) ($f =$ cm/hr, $Q = m^3/s$)	K (ENGLISH UNITS) ($f =$ in./hr, $Q =$ cfs)
1	98,100	13,650
2	85,400	11,900
3	71,200	9,900
4	61,200	8,500
5	54,000	7,500
6	48,500	6,750
7	44,300	6,150
8	40,850	5,680
9	38,000	5,285
10	35,670	4,955

For most watersheds, the length of a swale necessary to infiltrate 3 in. of runoff waters was found to be excessive or at least twice the distance available. Thus, some type of swale block (berm) or on-line detention/retention may be more helpful. Pitt (1986) indicated the most cost effective solution for the reduction of runoff volume, residual solids, and bacteria was infiltration. This result is similar to that of Yousef et al. (1985) who recommended that swale blocks should be considered to reduce further the chemical constituents and runoff volumes.

Using as a design criteria, the runoff volume for 7.5 cm (3 in.) of rainfall and storage of noninfiltrated runoff, Wanielista et al. (1988) have developed swale block designs for highway applications. Basically, the swale block volume can be calculated for a fixed length of swale and a triangular cross section using

Volume of runoff − volume of infiltration = swale block volume

$$Q(\Delta t) - Q_f(\Delta t) = \text{volume of swale}$$

$$Q(\Delta t) - \left[\frac{LN^{3/8}f}{KS^{3/16}}\right]^{8/5}(\Delta t) = \text{swale volume} \qquad (11.17)$$

where

Q_f = average infiltration rate (m³/sec)
Δt = runoff hydrograph time (sec)

Swale volume must be available to contain the runoff waters. In highway designs for high speed situations, safety must be considered, thus a maximum depth of water equal to 0.5 m (about 1.5 ft) and flow line slopes on the berms of 1 vertical/20 horizontal are recommended. Along lower-speed highways or in some residential/commercial urban settings, steeper flow line berm slopes (1 on 6) are acceptable.

☐ **EXAMPLE PROBLEM 11.6**

Consider as an example, a swale section along Interstate 4 near Orlando, Florida. The parameters of Equation 11.17 are

$N = 0.05$

$S = 0.0279$

$Q = 0.0023$ m³/sec (0.08 cfs)   for $\Delta t = 100$ min

$f = 7.5$ cm/hr (3.0 in./hr)

$Z = 7$

a. What swale length would be necessary to infiltrate all the waters (using Equation 11.16)?

$$L = \left[44{,}300(0.0023)^{5/8}(0.0279)^{3/16}\right]/\left[(0.05)^{3/8}(7.5)\right] = 208 \text{ m}$$

b. Only 76 m (250 ft) were available, thus how much storage volume is necessary (using Equation 11.17)?

$$(0.0023)(60)(100) - \left[\frac{(76)(0.05)^{3/8}(7.5)}{44{,}300(0.0279)^{3/16}}\right]^{8/5} 60(100) = \text{volume}$$

and volume of storage = 11.1 m³.   ☐

11.7

FRENCH DRAINS

A french drain is a perforated or slotted pipe placed in select backfill aggregate material with a fabric filter surrounding the aggregate as shown in Figure 11.31. Also, a french drain may consist solely of aggregate materials. The purpose of a french drain is to lower the water table or remove stormwater through the bank of a stormwater pond (peak rate and volume control).

Sometimes, open channels can be used to lower a water table, but open ditches are not always acceptable in developed areas. The banks of an open ditch also may be eroded from a high groundwater table. Thus, an underground piping system (french drain) that removes the water without removing the soil particles may be necessary. Excessive soil loss reduces the carrying capacity of the soil and can cause subsidence. Some types of protective filter material and select aggregate placed adjacent to the erodable soils can provide a solution to soil loss. A fabric filter must be specified to prevent piping, reduce fabric filter clogging, and pass the water. These criteria must all be present.

The retention ability of a filter material to retain soil is a function of its openings and the size of the soil particles. Cedergren et al. (1972) reports on a criteria that states that the equivalent opening size of the fabric (standard test method for fabrics) divided by the nominal diameter of soil particles for which 85% of the soil degradation is finer must be less than 2 to retain the soil and prevent excess piping. Particles larger than the fabric pore size will be retained, and some of the smaller ones will interact with the fabric filter and will be impacted. Other smaller ones will be "bridged" between the fabric and the soil particles and further retention is possible. Clogging of the filter can be minimized by specifying the expected hydraulic gradient of the groundwater during the selection process. The permeability of the fabric filter should be at least 10 times greater than the protected soil, which should allow the soil water to drain.

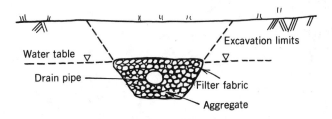

FIGURE 11.31 A French drain.

Proper specification of the size of pipe and trench depth below the expected water table is necessary if the water table is to be lowered. Darcy's law (see Chapter 10) can be used to approximate the seepage from saturated soil into the french drain. Rewriting Equation 11.13 as

$$\frac{Q}{L} = KAS \tag{11.18}$$

where

Q/L = seepage rate, CFD/foot of trench
  A = area normal to seepage flow for a 1-ft-long trench (ft^2/ft)
  K = permeability (ft/day)
  S = slope of flow line (ft/ft)

Note that the flow rate units are cubic feet per day (CDF) rather than the customary cubic feet per second, which implies relatively low flow rates.

Since the water table will fluctuate, the area normal to flow will fluctuate. The maximum water table elevation is chosen, and the flow rate (size of trench) determined from this condition. Permeability of the soil can be

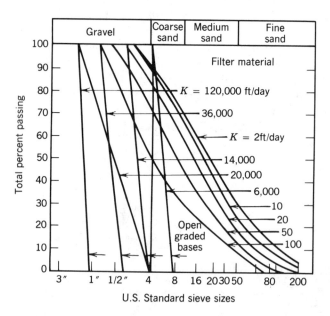

FIGURE 11.32   Aggregate permeabilities. *Source:* Cedergren et al., 1972.

estimated using laboratory or field permeability tests. Generally, lower values are chosen for determining drawdown time and higher values for determining pipe sizes.

For the aggregate that is used around the pipe, its permeability must be specified to ensure that it is greater than the predicted soil. Typical aggregate permeabilities as they relate to grain-size distribution (sieve) analysis are shown in Figure 11.32. Furthermore, the aggregate must not deteriorate over time. Some limestones do break down and form an impermeable material. Cross-sectional area and hydraulic gradients are usually determined by site conditions, thus permeabilities of rock should be specified for desired flow conditions. During seepage, some fine soil particles do enter the aggregate, thus reducing the permeability.

☐ **EXAMPLE PROBLEM 11.7**

Consider a french drain that has a 4-ft wide × 3-ft-deep cross section. It must discharge seepage water at a rate of 2500 ft³/day for the 100 ft of drain. The drain slope is 1 ft/100 ft, and the length of drain is 100 ft. What must the permeability of the backfill aggregate be to ensure proper drainage?

Solution

Use Darcy's equation $Q/L = KAS$ where $Q/L = 2500(100) = 250$ ft³/day-foot of drain. Thus, $250 = K(3 \times 4)(.01)$ and $K = 2083$ ft/day. Since permeability will probably decrease over time, an aggregate with greater than 2083 ft/day should be selected. An aggregate with a permeability of about 3000 ft/day or greater should be specified. ☐

11.8

SUMMARY

This chapter presented material useful for both (1) reservoir design and operation and (2) stormwater pond volume and peak flow management. Stormwater management systems can be used to attenuate hydrographs. The degree of attenuation can be accomplished by both volume and discharge control.

• Yield is the rate of water released from a reservoir.
• Mass diagrams for streamflow or runoff events are useful to estimate retention volumes (sizing of reservoirs) and yields.

- Stochastic yields, evapotranspiration, seepage, and streamflow can be used to evaluate reservoir sizes and yield.

- Detention pond outflow rates can be adjusted using weirs, orifices, and culverts.

- Design storm frequency is usually specified based on an economic analysis. The largest size of detention pond is determined using this frequency and a number of storms of different duration.

- French drains remove water from the ground and are used in high water table areas and beneath stormwater ponds to draw down the ponded water.

- Off-line retention ponds can be used to divert a fraction of yearly runoff water for treatment.

- Swales can be designed to infiltrate a volume of runoff water.

11.9

PROBLEMS

1. Explain how a mass diagram is developed from streamflow data assuming that only one year of streamflow data are available. Discuss and illustrate your answer on a graph indicating how the size of a reservoir and yield can be determined.

2. Explain why you would use a stochastic model for determining yield for a specific size reservoir.

3. What are the precipitation increments in 30-min intervals and the cumulative precipitation resulting from a 4.2-in. storm using the SCS Rainfall Distribution Type II? Assume a 6-hr-duration storm.

4. What shape does the rainfall excess hydrograph have (draw cumulative rainfall excess graphs) for the rainfall distribution of Problem 2 if the CN were 60 and 80.

5. The following data were gathered for a 100-min storm on a 2-ac watershed. Assume that infiltration capacity is reached at 100 min and that unused infiltration capacity is available for future rainfall storage at a specific time. Estimate the rainfall excess (in inches and in ac-ft) at the end of 100 min.

TIME (min)	HYETOGRAPH PRECIPITATION INTENSITY (in./hr)	INFILTRATION CAPACITY (in./hr)
0	0.0	0.0
5	0.1	1.2
10	0.3	1.0
15	0.5	1.0
20	0.6	0.9
25	0.9	0.8
30	1.2	0.8
35	1.4	0.6
40	1.6	0.5
45	1.3	0.5
50	1.2	0.4
60	0.8	0.4
70	0.7	0.3
80	0.5	0.3
90	0.2	0.3
100	0.1	0.3

6. Solve Problem 5, assuming that unused infiltration capacity at one time is not available for rainfall excess storage in the future.

7. For the flow rate data of Table 11.9, select a station and plot the monthly flow rates. Estimate the total flow volume in cubic meters and cubic feet. Also draw a mass curve for the year. Compare your answer to the annual volume using the annual mean of Table 11.9.

8. For the following empirical probability distribution on streamflow, generate two years of data assuming that the flow rates are independent.

FLOW RATES/MONTH (AVERAGE cfs)	FREQUENCY (FRACTION)
20	.05
30	.15
40	.25
50	.20
60	.15
70	.10
80	.05
90	.03
100	.02

9. Use the generated streamflow data of Problem 8 to calculate the maximum size of a reservoir if the release rate is at 40 cfs or the previous period storage volume, whichever is the least amount. The net loss from evaporation and gain from infiltration and direct precipitation is zero. The starting volume is 50 cfs. Also, what is the maximum release rate if the maximum size of the reservoir is 150 cfs?

10. A vertical wall reservoir tank outside of Miami, Florida, has a very dense clay lining, no vegetation, and three intermittent flowing canals that lead into it. During one winter, there is no rainfall recorded in the month of January. The depth of the reservoir at the beginning of January is 22 ft. If the surface area of the reservoir is 5 ac and the daily demand is 500,000 gal/day, what is the depth of the reservoir (using data from this text) on February 1? Be sure to consider all inputs and outputs. Also, comment on how the management of this reservoir might be improved.

11. Using the annual mean volume discharge from any station in Table 5.5, estimate the rainfall excess per year for the catchment. Present your answer in units of centimeters and inches.

12. Estimate the surface water storage at the end of one year for a watershed area, using the U.S. Geological Survey Water-Data Report and U.S. Department of Commerce Climatological Data. Use monthly increments. What assumptions must be made to estimate the end-of-year storage? Example water quantity and precipitation data are attached at the end of these questions (Tables 11.9 and 11.10 can be used).

13. Develop a mass curve for the following stream flow volume data. Next, determine the size of reservoir necessary to ensure a water yield of 4000 m³/ month over the 2-yr period. Discuss your assumptions used to solve the problem.

MONTH/YEAR	1000 m³	MONTH/YEAR	1000 m³
Jan. 1985	5.0	Jan. 1986	3.8
Feb. 1985	7.4	Feb. 1986	9.4
March 1985	8.3	March 1986	6.8
April 1985	3.6	April 1986	0.2
May 1985	2.1	May 1986	3.1
June 1985	1.6	June 1986	0.4
July 1985	0.4	July 1986	1.1
Aug. 1985	2.8	Aug. 1986	8.4
Sept. 1985	6.9	Sept. 1986	8.9
Oct. 1985	12.4	Oct. 1986	6.4
Nov. 1985	3.4	Nov. 1986	1.7
Dec. 1985	0.3	Dec. 1986	3.6

TABLE 11.9 Watershed Data for Shingle Creek at Campbell, FL (U.S. Geological Survey, 1973)

DISCHARGE (ft^3/sec), WATER YEAR OCTOBER 1972 TO SEPTEMBER 1973

DAY	OCT	NOV	DEC	JAN	FEB	MAR	APR	MAY	JUNE	JULY	AUG	SEP
1	53	39	71	76	298	115	88	41	36	97	293	319
2	63	35	65	72	281	105	101	41	36	128	366	384
3	78	32	65	73	359	94	101	30	36	75	332	389
4	84	42	62	69	297	94	121	41	33	134	301	369
5	71	73	62	69	256	89	124	41	30	237	279	386
6	70	66	62	65	233	78	108	40	30	217	278	401
7	60	49	65	65	214	84	85	37	36	281	305	403
8	60	49	59	54	196	73	136	33	33	220	332	396
9	60	42	59	75	189	79	120	49	30	168	330	406
10	66	39	55	67	445	80	111	53	33	151	303	417
11	73	39	52	80	352	80	90	41	30	127	281	414
12	73	39	55	189	291	73	81	37	30	119	274	428
13	63	39	52	161	270	72	75	33	27	139	260	440
14	56	43	41	130	274	60	83	36	27	128	251	404
15	56	49	41	112	286	60	82	32	30	125	241	391
16	53	42	63	108	274	54	81	38	36	103	208	387
17	53	45	49	112	252	58	72	31	30	91	184	354
18	53	42	50	121	239	62	62	27	24	82	164	306
19	53	39	44	121	246	68	65	33	33	115	149	284
20	65	42	44	118	214	62	64	32	36	118	150	264
21	63	49	37	115	193	50	55	32	47	88	157	240
22	53	45	106	154	178	53	51	31	97	82	183	240
23	49	45	97	397	163	54	50	28	131	100	381	231
24	49	42	86	476	157	59	38	28	144	91	375	219

(Continued)

TABLE 11.9   (Continued)

DISCHARGE (ft³/sec), WATER YEAR OCTOBER 1972 TO SEPTEMBER 1973

DAY	OCT	NOV	DEC	JAN	FEB	MAR	APR	MAY	JUNE	JULY	AUG	SEP
25	46	43	86	412	147	49	34	37	97	88	313	220
26	46	64	82	337	142	90	38	31	81	85	285	415
27	35	61	82	360	136	79	27	25	70	97	280	890
28	25	57	83	436	126	73	41	22	59	112	276	291
29	28	68	79	501	—	78	41	24	51	112	271	681
30	32	69	83	426	—	73	37	33	70	117	263	624
31	35	—	80	347	—	78	—	36	—	149	277	—
Total	1,724	1,428	2,017	5,898	6,713	2,266	2,262	1,073	1,483	3,977	8,342	12,093
Mean	55.6	47.6	65.1	190	240	73.1	75.4	34.6	49.4	128	269	403
Max	84	73	106	501	445	115	136	53	144	281	381	890
Min	25	32	37	54	126	49	27	22	24	75	149	219
ac-ft	3,420	2,830	4,000	11,700	13,320	4,490	4,490	2,130	2,940	7,890	16,550	23,990
Cal yr	1972	Total 35,641	Mean 97.4	Max 472	Min 18	ac-ft 70,690						
Wtr yr	1973	Total 49,276	Mean 135	Max 490	Min 22	ac-ft 97,740						

Location—Lat 28°16'01″, long 81° 26'53″, in SE quarter sec. 31, T.25 S., R.29 E., Osceola County, near left bank at downstream side of bridge on country road, 100 ft (30 m) downstream from Atlantic Coast Line Railroad Bridge, 0.8 mi (1.3 km) northeast of Campbell, and 2.5 (4.0 km) upstream from Lake Tohopekaliga.

Drainage area—180 mi² (466 km²) approximately; includes part of watershed in Reedy Creek Swamp.

Period of record—October 1968 to 1973.

Gage—Water-stage recorder. Datum of gage is at mean sea level. Water-stage recorder for Lake Tohopekaliga used as auxiliary gauge for this station.

Average discharge—5 yr, 109 cfs (3.087 m³/s), 78,970 ac-ft/yr (97.4 hm³/yr).

Extremes—Current year: Maximum discharge, 906 cfs (25.7 m³/s), September 27 (gage height, 58.10 ft or 17.709 m); minimum daily discharge. 22 cfs (0.62 m³/s) May 28; minimum gage height, 51.85 ft (15.804 m) June 15.

Period of record: Maximum discharge, 1,510 cfs (42.8 m³/s) October 5, 1969 (gage height, 59.72 ft or 18.203 m); minimum daily discharge, 31 cfs (0.088 m³/s) May 9, 10, 1971; minimum gage height, 49.78 ft (15.173 m) May 10, 1971.

Remarks—Records fair. Considerable flow diverted from Reedy Creek Swamp into Shingle Creek above station.

TABLE 11.10 Monthly Precipitation Records (U.S. Department of Commerce) Total precipitation (in.)

YEAR	JAN	FEB	MAR	APR	MAY	JUNE	JULY	AUG	SEPT	OCT	NOV	DEC	ANNUAL
1934[a]	1.04	3.37	4.33	4.58	8.08	13.35	9.00	1.27	3.14	1.50	0.09	0.55	50.30
1935	1.37	2.79	0.70	2.26	2.42	2.47	10.13	7.61	9.79	4.07	0.85	4.81	49.27
1936[a]	4.11	6.29	2.90	1.58	3.58	11.28	2.63	4.95	5.81	3.07	2.21	1.77	52.18
1937	0.97	5.00	2.97	3.78	4.47	5.22	5.14	13.14	9.37	4.55	3.67	0.82	59.10
1938	0.73	0.81	1.74	0.34	6.30	4.49	4.81	4.36	5.30	3.88	1.49	0.30	34.55
1939	1.21	0.35	1.75	4.97	4.87	15.64	6.34	8.90	5.24	1.67	0.39	1.07	52.42
1940	2.14	2.89	4.23	4.44	1.72	6.67	10.14	8.04	7.35	0.37	0.22	5.81	54.02
1941	4.69	4.16	2.47	5.53	2.73	8.18	9.44	6.45	4.76	5.33	3.61	2.29	52.65
1942	2.32	3.03	5.83	2.32	1.17	10.57	2.01	6.71	4.17	0.24	0.12	2.80	41.29
1943	1.19	0.50	3.92	1.53	5.42	3.66	5.17	5.85	7.18	3.04	0.87	1.28	39.61
1944	2.14	0.10	3.69	4.07	2.83	6.43	11.04	5.39	4.52	8.53	0.11	T	48.84
1945	3.86	0.11	0.54	1.47	2.93	13.70	7.06	5.28	15.87	1.61	1.00	2.52	55.95
1946	2.24	2.96	1.15	0.81	4.24	7.78	8.56	10.06	7.75	3.32	0.97	0.28	50.13
1947	0.87	4.78	5.55	4.98	2.81	11.61	13.90	6.71	8.87	4.83	1.90	0.66	67.47
1948	6.44	1.84	4.05	1.08	0.97	1.97	8.76	12.30	10.81	2.55	0.45	1.31	52.53
1949	0.31	0.47	0.29	3.02	2.54	7.97	6.05	8.83	8.25	1.51	1.22	3.82	44.28
1950	0.15	0.48	3.44	4.82	2.93	5.55	8.27	3.48	7.93	14.51	0.09	4.30	55.95
1951	0.52	2.28	0.96	5.99	1.40	5.08	14.51	7.84	9.34	3.08	4.86	2.06	57.92
1952	0.70	5.47	6.67	2.88	2.45	2.32	4.43	6.51	4.94	3.69	0.74	0.65	41.45
1953	2.86	2.89	3.03	6.18	1.87	6.28	6.85	15.19	8.84	3.50	4.78	3.58	65.86
1954	0.45	1.16	0.99	4.44	3.55	5.81	13.64	4.39	3.99	5.07	2.68	1.80	47.97
1955	2.00	1.12	1.59	1.36	3.13	4.73	6.88	6.65	6.97	4.10	2.17	1.56	42.26

(Continued)

TABLE 11.10 (Continued)

YEAR	JAN	FEB	MAR	APR	MAY	JUNE	JULY	AUG	SEPT	OCT	NOV	DEC	ANNUAL
1956	1.66	0.90	0.16	4.03	3.70	5.41	3.88	6.10	6.27	8.24	1.26	0.30	43.91
1957	0.91	1.93	3.76	4.74	8.58	4.39	4.35	9.45	7.47	1.68	0.82	2.85	50.93
1958	4.49	2.83	6.16	3.79	2.68	3.83	9.93	3.40	1.65	7.27	2.48	2.69	51.20
1959	2.78	4.55	7.69	4.91	4.44	7.95	8.02	6.77	8.33	5.97	0.99	1.37	63.77
1960^a	1.49	5.64	10.54	2.55	0.50	9.50	19.57	3.20	11.21	3.17	0.30	1.07	68.74
1961	1.75	2.82	2.21	0.28	0.43	8.08	9.93	6.99	4.84	2.87	0.92	0.66	41.78
1962	1.11	2.08	3.55	1.58	2.74	3.11	12.77	5.11	12.24	1.90	2.46	1.70	50.35
1963	3.17	4.76	2.69	1.23	3.56	6.67	3.83	3.54	6.72	0.46	6.39	2.26	45.28
1964	6.18	3.4	4.65	2.14	2.74	6.11	6.68	9.00	9.47	1.64	0.45	1.91	54.39
1965	1.79	3.67	3.02	0.66	0.52	7.36	11.55	5.49	5.99	4.06	1.06	2.23	47.40
1966	4.45	6.31	2.57	1.92	6.57	9.77	6.73	7.76	6.25	1.98	0.09	0.99	55.39
1967	0.84	5.49	1.31	0.28	1.69	11.16	4.63	6.83	5.84	0.35	0.03	2.42	40.91
1968	0.65	2.76	2.27	0.30	3.72	18.26	5.60	3.44	5.91	5.47	2.82	0.88	52.10
1969	2.22	3.30	5.52	2.38	1.40	5.04	6.73	7.17	6.44	9.45	0.87	4.66	55.18
1970	4.05	6.77	3.66	0.45	4.08	4.92	5.97	5.91	3.25	2.60	0.24	2.05	43.96
1971	0.45	2.98	1.46	1.52	4.31	4.39	8.29	7.51	2.98	3.06	1.21	1.93	40.09
1972	0.99	4.96	5.06	1.39	3.76	6.33	3.98	16.11	0.43	2.34	4.11	1.89	51.35
1973	4.82	2.73	4.13	2.82	4.74	6.63	6.24	7.33	11.53	1.10	0.74	2.56	55.37
Record Mean^b	2.18	2.97	3.43	2.57	3.14	6.83	8.25	7.08	7.17	3.97	1.58	1.88	51.05

^{a}Indicates a break in the data sequence during the year or season due to a station move or relocation of instruments. See station location table.
^{b}Record mean values above (not adjusted for instrument location changes listed in the station location table) are means for the period beginning in 1943.

14. For the months of May through September of Problem 13, assume evaporation losses from the reservoir of 400 m³ per month. How does this affect your yield?

15. Plot the flow rates for two months from any streamflow records or using Table 11.9, plot the time period from January 11 through March 10, 1973. Estimate the volume flow rate under this streamflow and then report the answer in units of cubic feet, cubic meters, and inches over the entire watershed area of 180 mi².

16. What are the rainfall excess increments in 30-min intervals and the inflow rates (cfs) for a 100-ac impervious area for 6 hr from a 4-in. storm over 6-hr using the SCS/CN procedure if the maximum soil storage (S') is 0.5 in.? Now route this rainfall excess through the new channel of Example Problem 8.5.

TIME	P (in.)	INFLOW (in.)	INFLOW (cfs)	OUTFLOW (cfs)
0	0.00			
30	0.17			
60	0.20			
90	0.26			
120	1.89			
150	1.34			
180	0.34			
210	0.29			
240	0.30			
270	0.22			
300	0.15			
330	0.18			
360	0.10			

What is the "routed" flow (output hydrograph) at 120 min if $t_c = \Delta t = 30$ min? No other information is available.

17. Using the Weather Bureau hyetograph dimensionless mass curve and the SCS type II, which curve would produce maximum peak discharge for a highly impervious urban area with zero initial abstraction? Describe and show some calculations.

18. Determine the depth of a french drain (saturated depth) if the width is 3 ft, the effective permeability of the aggregate is 2000 ft/day, and the rate of discharge for 100 ft of trench is 1000 ft³/day. The trench slope along the flow line is 0.001. Discuss your answer.

19. A detention pond design for your local area is needed to store the runoff from a 1-hr design storm with a 3-yr return period. The watershed area is 100 ac with a composite $CN = 80$. If you do not have FID curves for your area, use zone 7 curve in Appendix C.
   a. Size the pond (acres and acre-feet) if the pond is 3 ft deep and assume a rectangular pond.
   b. How long (to the nearest hour) will it take to drain 90% of the pond water if an infiltration test yielded the following?

$$\text{Initial infiltration} = 5 \text{ in./hr} = f_0$$

$$\text{Final infiltration} = 1 \text{ in./hr} = f_c$$

$$\text{Recession constant} = 2/\text{hr} = K$$

20. a. A 20-ac residential area has a runoff coefficient of .50. Size an off-line retention pond with length = width with water depth of 4 ft and side slopes of 1 on 1 to accommodate the runoff from 1 in. of rainfall. Specify the surface area of the pond and the bottom area, along with the total volume.
   b. Add another 1-ft depth of pond as freeboard. Also, if a 10-ft-wide buffer and maintenance area is needed around the pond, what is the total acreage of the off-line retention area?

21. A pre- versus postdevelopment hydrograph analysis for a 100-ac watershed must be completed. The precondition watershed has a runoff coefficient of .2 and a hydrograph shape with a peak attenuation factor of .31 with $t_c = 120$ min. The postcondition is most likely to have a hydrograph shape similar to the standard SCS–peak attenuation factor, a runoff coefficient of .4, a time of concentration of 1 hr, and a rainfall intensity of 5 in./hr. Draw both hydrographs and estimate the peak discharge. Next, estimate the storage volume that approximates the condition of pre- versus postpeak discharge. Express storage in terms of cubic feet.

22. a. Determine a length of swale with Bermuda grass and an infiltration rate of 4 in./hr. It is scheduled to be a triangular section with one on six side slopes and a longitudinal slope of .005. The swale must effectively percolate all the runoff that comes from a half-acre impervious area and a constant rainfall intensity of 0.5 in./hr.
   b. If only 400 ft of swale are available and the runoff hydrograph lasts for 200 min, how much additional storage is necessary?

23. A 20-ac subdivision has as a design rainfall intensity specification of 3.7 in./hr. The area is 38% impervious with all the impervious areas being directly connected. The soil type defined by the SCS is A. The pervious area does not contribute runoff. The time of concentration for the

watershed is 60 min. One may wish to substitute an intensity from an FID curve (25-yr return frequency) from your own area.
 a. What is the peak discharge using the rational formula?
 b. What is the rainfall excess in liters?
 c. What is the approximate lot size?

24. A corrugated metal pipe under a roadway passes 30 cfs at design conditions. The downstream pond at design invert elevation is 250.5 ft. What is the elevation of the upstream pond if the connecting 3-ft-diameter pipe is 100 ft long with a Manning's coefficient of .015 and a tail water depth of 6 ft? There is no headwall on the corrugated metal pipe.

25. Obtain a year of flow rate data or use the data of Table 11.9 to generate a serial transition matrix for daily data. Be careful to identify at least three different flow periods and at least five flow states for each flow period. It is frequently helpful to plot the data first. Next, generate a hydrograph with one peak discharge.

11.10

COMPUTER-ASSISTED PROBLEMS

1. An area of the county requires use of the 1- in 1-yr storm frequency for detention basin design (use appropriate FID curves). What duration (1 or 6 hr) produces the largest detention basin if the watershed area is 50 ac, the rational coefficient is .8, the output hydrograph starts at 1 hr at a constant 10 ft^3/sec, and the time of concentration is 1 hr? Compare only the two duration storms and use the rational formula.

2. For a 25-yr, 2-hr storm from any FID curve, develop the incremental storm volumes (10-min increments) according to a dimensionless cumulative mass rainfall curve. For a 270.6-ac watershed that is 75% impervious, 100% directly connected impervious area, has a curve number of 80 for pervious area and time of concentration of 55 min, develop two hydrographs using the SCS hydrograph procedure with $K = 484$ and $K = 300$. Comment on the differences.

3. Change the soil type in Problem 2 to a curve number of 53.5 and comment on the hydrograph relative to Problem 2.

4. Assume another completely different dimensionless cumulative rainfall distribution and compare all the hydrographs for the assumptions of Problems 2 and 3.

5. Using the SMADA program and the SCS unit–time unit–hydrograph procedure, develop the resulting hydrograph using the watershed data of Problem 2, a hydrograph attenuation factor of 250, and a constant rainfall of 2 in. over 4 hr. Discuss input assumptions, use $t = 10$ min.

6. Increase the attenuation factor of Problem 5 to 350 with the same input assumptions. Now change the hyetograph to 0.25 in. for the first hour, 0.50 in. for the second hour, 1 in. for the third hour, and 0.25 in. for the fourth hour. How does the resulting hydrograph plot compare to the others? Discuss peak and shape.

7. Develop two instantaneous hydrographs for the watershed of Problem 2. Use the hyetograph of your choice. The percentage of the impervious area that is directly connected is 60 and should be used in the analysis. One hydrograph is estimated without any stormwater management. The second hydrograph is estimated considering 1 in. of initial abstraction over the total area (stormwater management). Compare resulting hydrograph shapes and comment on your results.

8. Increase the total rainfall volume of Problem 2 by 1.5 in. and compare answers.

9. Using a 24-hr storm, 100-yr return period and the watershed description of Problem 2 except a directly connected area of 80% and a time of concentration of 5 hr, develop a hydrograph at 1-hr intervals using the SCS Type II rainfall distribution. State all assumptions.

10. Using the working curve 2 of Figure 11.22, develop a best fit equation using 10 data points from the graph. Also develop two linear equations to "best" fit the line.

11.11

REFERENCES

Carroll, Robert G., Jr. 1983. "Geotextile Filter Criteria," prepared for the *1983 Symposium on Geotextiles*, Transportation Research Board, U.S. Federal Highway Administration, Washington, DC, January.

Cedergren, H.R., O'Brien, K.H., and Arman, J.A. 1972. "Guidelines for the Design of Subsurface Drainage Systems for Highway Structural Sections," Report No. FHWA-RD-72-30, prepared for the Federal Highway Administration, June, p. 25.

Federal Highway Administration (FHWA). 1985. *Hydraulic Design of Highway Culverts*, Hydraulic Design Series No. 5, McLean, VA.

Golding, B.L. 1974. "Master Drainage Plan Florida Center," Reynolds, Smith and Hills, Inc., Jacksonville, FL, Vol. 1.

Hardison, C.H. 1966. "Storage to Augment Low Flow," *Proceedings of Reservoir Yield Symposium*, Water Research Association, Wallingford, England.

Lof, G.O. and Hardison, C.H. 1966. *Storage Requirements for Water in the United States*, Resources for the Future. Washington, DC.

Lord, B.N. 1986. "Effectiveness of Erosion Control," *Urban Runoff Technology*, Engineering Foundation Conference, New England College, Henniker, NH, June, p. 210.

Pitt, R. 1986. "The Incorporation of Urban Source Area Controls in Wisconsin's Priority Watershed Projects," *Urban Runoff Technology*, Engineering Foundation Conference, New England College, Henniker, NH, June, p. 140.

Poertner, H. H. 1974. "Practices in Detention of Urban Stormwater Runoff," *Special Report No. 43*, American Public Works Association, Chicago.

State of Florida. 1988. *Administrative Code, Chapter 17.25* Tallahassee, FL.

U.S. Geological Survey. 1973. *Water Resources Data for Florida*, Water Resources Division. Tallahassee, FL, p. 63.

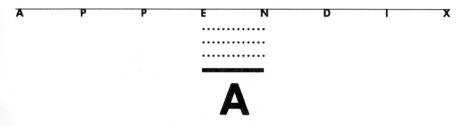

NOTATION

A	Watershed area	a	Regression constant
A	Area	a	Stage-discharge coefficient
A	Soil hydrologic group	BI	Boundary input
Ac	Acres	BO	Boundary output
A_i	Area between isochromes	B	Soil hydrologic group
A_x	Cross-section area	B	Width of Parshall Flume Throat
AC	Average cost		
ADP	Antecedent dry period	B	Width of weir
ADT	Average daily traffic	B	Water surface width
ALOSS	Potential rain loss rate	B	Subsurface flow
AMC	Antecedent moisture condition	BOD	Biochemical oxygen demand
A_o	Area of orifice	b	limiting value
A_s	Water surface area	b	Constant
$\overline{A_s}$	Average surface area	b	Regression coefficient
A_u	drainage area of u stream order	b	Stage-storage coefficient
		b	Bottom width of channel
a	Estimate of skewness	C	Empirical coefficient

445

C	Constant shape factor	D	Duration of rainfall
C	Soil hydrologic group	D	Soil hydrologic group
C'	Constituent concentration	D	Dustfall
C_z	Chezy's roughness coefficient	D	Depth of pond or water
C	Concentration	D'	Incremental rainfall excess duration
C	Runoff coefficient	DA	Drainage area
C	Cropping management factor in universal soil loss equation	DCIA	Directly connected impervious area
		DD	Dust and dirt accumulation
C_1	Constituent input to a system	DI	Diversion volume (inches)
		DO	Dissolved oxygen
C_2	Constituent output from a system	DV	Diversion volume (Ac-Ft)
		D_W	Dustfall on watershed
C_d	Discharge coefficient	d	Depth of flow
C_i	Runoff coefficient— impervious surface	d	Depth of gutter flow
		d'	Fraction directly connected impervious area
CA	Contributing area		
C_N	Rectangular weir coefficient	d_s	Depth of snowpack
CN	Rainfall excess curve number	E	Evaporation
		E_S	Depth of evaporation from snow
C_o	Initial organic concentration		
		E	Washoff decay coefficient
C_e	Equilibrium concentration	E_P	Pan evaporation
C_P	Runoff coefficient —pervious surface	E_L	Lake evaporation
		E	Saturated vapor pressure
C_v	Coefficient of variation	EFF	Effectiveness
C_e	Storage coefficient	ET	Evapotranspiration
C_{60}	60° triangular weir coefficient	EMV	Expected monetary value
		ERAIN	Watershed coefficient
C_{90}	90° triangular weir coefficient	EVAP	Long-term evaporation
		E_0	Relative flow fraction
$\overline{C}$	Composite concentration	e	Vapor pressure
CRF	Capital recovery factor	e_a	Vapor pressure of air
CUML	Cumulative rain loss	e_s	Vapor pressure of snowpack
c	Wave celerity	e_0	Saturation vapor pressure
c_s	Snowpack specific heat	e	Symbol for exponential of
c_1	Storage coefficient	F	Accumulated mass infiltration
c_2	Storage coefficient		

F	Available watershed storage (STORM model)	I_A	Initial rainfall abstraction
F	Force	I_0	Initial infiltration rate
F	Frequency factor	I_c	Ultimate or constant infiltration rate
F	Flood event	IR	Instantaneous runoff hydrograph
F_r	Froude number		
FW	Future worth	IUH	Instantaneous unit hydrograph
$F(t)$	Infiltration volume as a function of time		
		i	Rainfall intensity
$F(x)$	Cumulation distribution function	i	Interest rate
		$i(t - \tau)$	Rainfall intensity at time $(t - \tau)$
$F(x, y)$	Cumulative joint distribution function		
		K	A recession constant
f	Infiltration rate	K	Frequency factors
f	Relative humidity	K	Hydraulic conductivity
f	Function symbol	K_T	Thermal conductivity
f	Pipe friction factor	K	Muskingum storage coefficient
f_c	Ultimate infiltration rate		
f_0	Initial infiltration rate	K	Swale constant
$f(x)$	Probability density function	K	Storage coefficient
f'	First derivative of function	K	Baseflow recession constant
G	Population skew coefficient	K	Permeability
$G(x)$	Exceedance probability	K_r	routing constant for Santa Barbara
G_S	Specific gravity		
g	Acceleration constant of gravity	K_s	Hydraulic conductivity at saturation
g	Skew coefficient	K_i	Recession limb coefficient
g	Grams	K'	Composite storage coefficient
ΔH	Energy change		
H	Reservoir depth above spillway	k'	Constant
		k	Saturated permability
H	Head	k	Snowmelt watershed constant
H_{exit}	Exit loss coefficient		
h	Head	k	Consumptive use coefficient
h	Curb inlet height	k	Proportionality constant
h	Depth of unconfined aquifer	k	Convolution recession constant
		k	Pearson Type II deviate
I	Inflow	k_e	Culvert entrance loss and snow evaporation constant
I	Inflow rate		

k_s	Seasonal consumptive use coefficient	n	Number of events
L	Length of curb opening	n	Regression parameter
L	Stream length	n	Stage-discharge coefficient
L	Length	n	Manning's roughness coefficient
L	Lag time	n	Shape parameter
L	Length of overland flow	n	An empirical constant
L	Channel length	n_p	Porosity
L	Length of gutter	O	Outflow volume
L_f	Latent heat of fusion	O	Out rate
L_p	Depth of percolating water	O_i	ith outflow rate
L_T	Length of slotted pipe	O_p	Peak outflow rate
L_u	Depth of unsaturated soil column	OR	Overflow rate
M	Mass	P	Precipitation volume
M	Carbon weight	P	Erosion control practice factor in USLE
MC	Marginal cost	P	Precipitation depth
MAX	Maximum	P	Accumulated rainfall depth
MIN	Minimum	P	Loading
m	Kinematic parameter	P_a	The antecedent precipitation index
m	Mass	P_G	Perimeter of grate opening
m	Aquifer thickness	P_0	Initial amount of pollutant
m	Stage-storage coefficient	P_{OW}	Annual wet weather loading
m	Regression coefficient	P_p	Piezometric potential
m	Plot position	Pr	Probability
N	Outflow–storage relationship	P_t	Amount of pollutant remaining on ground at time t
N	Number of future trials		
N	Annual precipitation	P_i	Isohyetal cell average precipitation
N_D	Number of days without runoff	PD	Population density
N_R	Reynolds	PW	Present worth
N_u	Number of stream segments of order u	$\bar{P}$	Mean of 24-hr annual maximum rain depths
n	Number of storm hydrograph ordinates	p	Pressure
n	Number of years or observations	p	Permeability
		p	Monthly daytime hours
n	Retardance (Kerby formula)	p_c	Pan coefficient
		Q	Streamflow

Q	Discharge	R_M	Efficiency of sediment removal
$\overline{Q}$	Average discharge		
Q_I	Interflow	RAIN	Long-term average rainfall
Q_i	ith flow in sequence	r	Rainfall excess rate
Q_j	jth annual flow	r	Radius
Q_p	Peak discharge	r	Correlation coefficient
Q	Hydrograph ordinate value	r	Reaction rate
Q_t	Discharge at time t	r_{avg}	Average street runoff rate
$Q(t)$	Surface runoff rate at time t	S	Storage
		S'	Storage potential of soil
Q_w	Overland flow discharge rate, also gutter depression flow (Appendix F)	S	Weighted physical slope of the main sewer
		S	Potential maximum retention in ground
Q_{10}	10-yr peak flow rate		
$Q_{2.33}$	Mean annual flood rate	S	Energy gradient
Q_{50}	50-yr flow rate	S	Overland slope
Q_{100}	100-yr flow rate	S_c	Groundwater aquifer storage coefficient
Q_i^0	Observed hydrograph flow rate		
		SS	Ratio of horizontal to vertical length of side slope
Q'	Discharge per unit width		
q	Specific discharge	S_t	Lake storage at time t
q	Discharge per unit area	S_s	Soil storage percentage
q	Runoff rate	SL_d	Shoreline length at depth d
q	Flow rate	SFF	Sinking fund factor
q	Overland flow discharge rate	SNM	Daily snowmelt
		S_n	Standard deviation of annual maximum rain depths
q	Specific adsorption capacity		
q_0	Initial discharge		
R	Risk	S_p	Total storage potential
R	Rainfall excess	S_x	Roadway cross-slope
R	Return flow	S_y	Specific yield
R	Hydraulic radius	S_{yx}	Standard error of estimated runoff
R	Runoff depth		
$\overline{R}$	Weighted hydraulic radius of the main sewer flowing full	s	Linear slope parameter
		s^2	Variance
		s	Standard deviation
RA	Ratio of impervious area to total area	T	Transpiration
		T_D	Dewpoint temperature
R_I	Runoff rate from impervious surface	T	Temperature
		T_r	Recurrence interval

T	Transmissivity	V	Velocity
T	Width of gutter flow	Vn	Product of velocity and
T	Travel time overland		Manning's roughness
T'	Temperature		coefficient
	differental—snowmelt	V_5	Volume of pond at 5-ft
TC	Total cost		depth
T_A	Return period, annual series	$V(A)$	Monetary value of (A)
T_a	Air temperature	V_M	Minimum volume of pond
t_b	Time base of the	V_R	Runoff volume from mean
	hydrograph		storm
t_c	Time of concentration	V_P	Volume of pond
T_e	Temperature of evaporated	V_D	Volume of pond at depth D
	water	V_I	Volume of pond from
T_{max}	Daily maximum		impervious area
	temperature	v_s	Settling velocity
T_0	Water surface temperature	v_0	Design settling velocity
T_p	Partial series return period	W	Power
t_p	Time to peak	W	Withdrawal
t_r	Recession limit time	W	Width of depressed area
τ	Temperature	W	Width of watershed
t	Time	W	Width of overland flow
t	Frequency of occurrence	W_i	Weighted area
t_e	Time of equilibrium of	W_0	Width of curb inlet opening
	runoff rate	WT	Weighted flow
t_l	Lag time	w	Rectangular channel width
t_d	Pond detention time	w_s	Average watershed slope
t_w	Hydraulic residence time	X	Random variable
	(lakes)	X	Weight of organics
U	Unit hydrograph ordinates		adsorbed
U	Consumptive use of water	x	Weighting factor
U	Wind velocity	$\bar{x}$	First moment about the
U	Stream order		origin (mean)
u	Average wind velocity	Y	Release flow
u	Velocity in x direction	y	Depth of flow
V	Volume	Z	Side slope of a channel
V	Volume of water	Z_o	Optimal solution
V	Aquifer volume	z	Elevation
$\bar{V}$	Average velocity	z	Standard deviation
		z_0	Roughness parameter

α	Angle	μ_r'	rth moment about the origin
α	Regression constant	$\rho = \rho_w$	Density of water
α	Kinematic parameter	σ	Standard deviation
α_p	Portion of advective energy	σ^2	Variance
β	Regression coefficient	υ	Kinematic viscosity
β	Fluid compressibility	τ	Time parameter
Γ	Gamma function	ν	Darcy's velocity
γ	Specific weight	ν_s	Seepage velocity
θ_s	Soil water content at saturation	α	Loading coefficient
θ_i	Initial soil water content	β	Loading coefficient
Φ	Infiltration index	Δ	Interevent time
ρ_s	Snowpack density	Ω	Pond empty rate
μ	Mean value	λ	Multiplier
μ	Dynamic viscosity	λ	Exponential distribution constant
		Ψ	Capillary suction pressure head

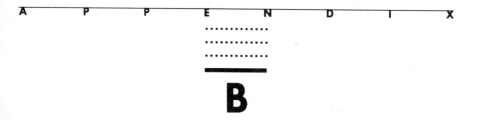

B

METRIC
UNITS WITH
ENGLISH
EQUIVALENTS

Length

Metric Units

millimeter	(mm)	10 mm = cm
centimeter	(cm)	100 cm = m
meter	(m)	1000 m = km
kilometer	(km)	

English equivalents

meters	× 39.37	= inches ×	0.0254 =	meters
meters	× 3.28	= feet ×	0.3049 =	meters
kilometers	× 0.62	= miles ×	1.6129 =	kilometers
millimeters	× 0.039	= inches ×	25.4 =	millimeters
centimeters	× 0.394	= inches ×	2.54 =	centimeters

Example: Convert 3 m to feet. 3 m × 3.28 ft/m = 9.84 ft

Area

Metric Units

square millimeter	(mm^2)	$10^2\ mm^2 = cm^2$
square centimeter	(cm^2)	$10^4\ cm^2\ = m^2$
square meter	(m^2)	$10^6\ m^2\ = km^2$
hectare	(ha)	$10^2\ ha\ = km^2$

English Equivalents

$mm^2 \times\ \ 0.00155 = in^2\ \times 645.16\ = mm^2$

$cm^2 \times\ \ 0.155\ \ \ = in.^2 \times\ \ 6.45\ = cm^2$

$m^2\ \ \times 10.764\ \ = ft^2\ \times\ \ 0.093 = m^2$

$km^2 \times\ \ 0.384\ \ \ = mi^2 \times\ \ 2.605 = km^2$

$km^2 \times 247.10\ \ \ \ = ac\ \times\ \ 0.004 = km^2$

$ha\ \ \times\ \ 2.471\ \ \ = ac\ \times\ \ 0.405 = ha$

$ha\ \ \times\ \ 0.00386 = mi^2 \times 259\ \ \ \ = ha$

Mass

Metric Units

milligram	(mg)	1000 mg = g
gram	(g)	1000 g = kg
kilogram	(kg)	1000 kg = 1 tonne (t)

English Equivalents

milligram $\times\ \ 0.01543 =$ grains $\times\ \ 64.809 =$ mg

gram $\ \ \ \ \ \times\ \ 0.0022\ \ =$ pounds $\times 453.6\ \ \ \ =$ gram

gram $\ \ \ \ \ \times 15.43\ \ \ \ \ =$ grains $\times\ \ \ 0.065 =$ gram

kilogram $\times\ \ 2.205\ \ \ \ =$ pounds $\times\ \ \ 0.454 =$ kg

kilogram $\times\ \ 0.0011\ \ =$ ton $\ \ \ \ \times 907.20\ \ =$ kg

tonne (t) $\times\ \ 1.1023\ \ =$ ton $\ \ \ \ \ \ \times\ \ 0.907 =$ tonne

(using 2000 pounds ton (short ton))

Volume

Metric Units

cubic centimeter	(cm^3)	$10^6\ cm^3 = m^3$
cubic meter	(m^3)	$10^3 L\ \ \ \ = m^3$
liter	(L)	$10^3\ cm^3 = L$

English Equivalents

$cm^3 \times\ \ 0.061\ \ \ \ \ \ = in.^3\ \times 16.393\ \ \ \ \ \ = cm^3$

$m^3\ \ \times 35.314\ \ \ \ = ft^3\ \ \times\ \ 0.028\ \ \ \ \ = m^3$

$L\ \ \ \times\ \ 1.057\ \ \ \ \ \ = qt.\ \ \times\ \ 0.946\ \ \ \ \ = L$

English Equivalents (Continued)

L	$\times$ 0.264	= gal $\times$ 3.788	= L
L	$\times$ 0.81(10^{-6})	= ac-ft $\times$ 1.235(10^6)	= L
m^3	$\times$ 0.41(10^{-3})	= SFD $\times$ 2.45(10^3)	= m^3
	(second foot day)		

Time

Metric Units = English Units

second	(sec)	86,400 sec = 1 day
day	(day)	365 day = yr or a
year	(yr or a)	(366 days every 4 years)

Force

Metric Unit with English Equivalent

newton   (N) $\times$ 0.22481 = lb (weight)

$\times$ 7.24   = lb (force)

Commonly Used Conversion Factors

Linear Velocity

$$m/sec \times 3.280 = fps \times 0.305 = m/sec$$
$$km/sec \times 2.230 = mph \times 0.448 = km/sec$$
$$km/hr \times 0.621 = mph$$
$$km/hr \times 0.540 = knots$$

Flow or Discharge

$m^3/sec \times 15.850(10^3)$	= gpm $\times$ 0.063(10^{-3})	= m^3/sec
$m^3/sec \times 2.12(10^3)$	= cfm $\times$ 0.472(10^{-3})	= m^3/sec
$m^3/sec \times 35.314$	= cfs $\times$ 0.283	= m^3/sec
$L/sec \times 15.850$	= gpm $\times$ 0.063	= L/sec
$m^3/sec \times 22.82$	= MGD $\times$ 0.0438	= m^3/sec
$L/day \times 0.264$	= GPD $\times$ 3.788	= L/day

Loading

$kg/km \times 3.576$	= lb/mi $\times$ 0.280	= kg/km
$kg/ha \times 0.892$	= lb/ac $\times$ 1.21	= kg/ha
$kg/ha \times 0.286$	= $ton/mi^2 \times$ 3.50	= kg/ha
$kg/ha \times 0.446(10^{-3})$	= ton/ac $\times$ 2.24(10^3)	= kg/ha
$kg/m^3 \times 0.065$	= $lb/ft^3 \times$ 15.38	= kg/m^3
$m^3/m^2 \times 3.28$	= $ft^3/ft^2 \times$ 0.305	= m^3/m^2

Density

$kg/cm^3 \times 0.0624 \quad = lb/ft^3 \times 16.026 \quad = kg/cm^3$

$lb/gal \quad \times 1.2 \times 10^5 = mg/L \times 8.33 \times 10^{-6} = lb/gal$

$kg/m^3 \quad \times 0.065 \quad = lb/ft^3 \times 15.38 \quad = kg/m^3$

Commonly Used Conversions

Area

$43,560 \ ft^2 \ = 1 \ ac$

$4,840 \ \ yd^2 = 1 \ ac$

$144 \quad in.^2 = 1 \ ft^2$

$640 \quad ac \ = 1 \ mi^2$

Volume

$7.48 \ gal \ = 1 \ ft^3$

$1728 \ in.^3 = 1 \ ft^3$

$1 \ MGD \ = 694.4 \ gpm$

$8.34 \ lb \ = 1 \ gal \ (of \ water)$

$62.43 \ lb \ = 1 \ ft^3 \ (of \ water)$

Mass

$2000 \ lb = 1 \ ton$

$454 \ g \ = 1 \ lb$

$7000 \ gr = 1 \ lb$

$2240 \ lb = 1 \ long \ ton$

Other Conversions

Pressure

$2.307 \ ft \ H_2O = 1 \ lb/in.^2$

$2.036 \ in. \ Hg \ = 1 \ lb/in.^2$

$14.70 \ psia \quad = 1 \ atm$

$29.92 \ in \ Hg \quad = 1 \ atm$

$33.93 \ ft \ H_2O \ = 1 \ atm$

$76.0 \ cm \ Hg \quad = 1 \ atm$

$0.205 \ kg/m^2 = 1 \ lb/ft^2$

Miscellaneous

$in. \cdot mi^2 \ \times \ 26.9 \quad = SFD \qquad \times \ 2.45(10^3) \ = m^3$

$in. \cdot mi^2 \ \times \ 53.3 \quad = ac\text{-}ft \qquad \times \ 1.235(10^3) = m^3$

$SFD/mi^2 \times \ 0.0372 = in. \qquad \times \ 25.4 \qquad = mm$

$CFS \quad \times \ 0.992 \ = ac\text{-}in./hour \times 101.6 \qquad = m^3/hr$

$lb/gal \quad \times 120(10^3) = mg/L$

Miscellaneous (Continued)

$g = 9.806 \text{ m/s}^2 = 32.174 \text{ ft/s}^2$

standard conditions 4°C, 706 mm Hg

ρ water $= 1.94 \text{ slugs/ft}^3 = 1000 \text{ kg/m}^3$ (4°C)

γ water $= 62.43 \text{ lb/ft}^3 = 9806 \text{ N/m}^3$ (4°C)

for permeability:

1 ft/day $= 0.305 \text{ m/day} = 7.48 \text{ gal/day-ft}^2$

for transmissivity:

$1 \text{ ft}^2/\text{day} = 0.0929 \text{ m}^2/\text{day} = 7.48 \text{ gal/day-ft}$

Also

$\log_e 10 = 2.30259$

$e = 2.7'828$

Physical Properties of Water

Source: Hydraulic Models ASCE Manual 25, New York, 1942.

TEMPERATURE (°F)	SPECIFIC WEIGHT γ (lb/ft³)	DENSITY ρ (slugs/ft³)	VISCOSITY $\mu \times 10^5$ lb(s/ft²)	KINEMATIC VISCOSITY $\nu \times 10^5$ (ft²/s)
32	62.42	1.940	3.746	1.931
40	62.42	1.940	3.229	1.664
50	62.41	1.940	2.735	1.410
60	62.36	1.938	2.359	1.217
70	62.29	1.936	2.050	1.059
80	62.22	1.934	1.799	0.930
90	62.13	1.931	1.595	0.826
100	62.00	1.927	1.424	0.739
110	61.87	1.923	1.284	0.667

SI Unit Prefixes

PREFIX	SYMBOL	MULTIPLES	PREFIX	SYMBOL	MULTIPLES
tera	T	10^{12}	deci	d	10^{-1}
giga	G	10^{9}	centi	c	10^{-2}
mega	M	10^{6}	milli	m	10^{-3}
kilo	k	10^{3}	micro	μ	10^{-6}
hecto	h	10^{2}	nano	n	10^{-9}
deka	da	10	pico	p	10^{-12}

....
....
....

C

NONDIMENSIONAL RAINFALL AND FREQUENCY-INTENSITY-DURATION CURVES

TABLE C.1   SCS Type II: Rainfall Distribution (24 hr)

NONDIMENSIONAL		NONDIMENSIONAL			NONDIMENSIONAL		NONDIMENSIONAL	
TIME	RAINFALL	TIME	RAINFALL		TIME	RAINFALL	TIME	RAINFALL
.000	.000	.521	.735		.094	.026	.615	.849
.010	.002	.531	.758		.104	.029	.625	.856
.021	.005	.542	.776		.115	.032	.635	.863
.031	.008	.552	.791		.125	.035	.646	.869
.042	.011	.563	.804		.135	.038	.656	.875
.052	.014	.573	.815		.146	.041	.667	.881
.063	.017	.583	.825		.156	.044	.677	.887
.073	.020	.594	.834		.167	.048	.688	.893
.083	.023	.604	.842		.177	.052	.698	.898

continued

TABLE C.1   *(Continued)*

NONDIMENSIONAL		NONDIMENSIONAL		NONDIMENSIONAL		NONDIMENSIONAL	
TIME	RAINFALL	TIME	RAINFALL	TIME	RAINFALL	TIME	RAINFALL
.188	.056	.708	.903	.354	.133	.875	.965
.198	.060	.719	.908	.365	.140	.885	.968
.208	.064	.729	.913	.375	.147	.896	.971
.219	.068	.740	.918	.385	.155	.906	.974
.229	.072	.750	.922	.396	.163	.917	.977
.240	.076	.760	.926	.406	.172	.927	.980
.250	.080	.771	.930	.417	.181	.938	.983
.260	.085	.781	.934	.427	.191	.948	.986
.271	.090	.792	.938	.438	.203	.958	.989
.281	.095	.802	.942	.448	.218	.969	.992
.292	.100	.813	.946	.458	.236	.979	.995
.302	.105	.823	.950	.469	.257	.990	.998
.313	.110	.833	.953	.479	.283	1.000	1.000
.323	.115	.844	.956	.490	.387		
.333	.120	.854	.959	.500	.663		
.344	.126	.865	.962	.510	.707		

TABLE C.2   SCS Type III: Rainfall Distribution (24 hr)

NONDIMENSIONAL		NONDIMENSIONAL		NONDIMENSIONAL		NONDIMENSIONAL	
TIME	RAINFALL	TIME	RAINFALL	TIME	RAINFALL	TIME	RAINFALL
.000	.000	.521	.702	.135	.034	.656	.878
.010	.002	.531	.729	.146	.037	.667	.886
.021	.005	.542	.751	.156	.040	.677	.893
.031	.007	.552	.769	.167	.043	.688	.900
.042	.010	.563	.785	.177	.047	.698	.907
.052	.012	.573	.799	.188	.050	.708	.911
.063	.015	.583	.811	.198	.053	.719	.916
.073	.017	.594	.823	.208	.057	.729	.920
.083	.020	.604	.834	.219	.060	.740	.925
.094	.023	.615	.844	.229	.064	.750	.929
.104	.026	.625	.853	.240	.068	.760	.933
.115	.028	.635	.862	.250	.072	.771	.936
.125	.031	.646	.870	.260	.076	.781	.940

continued

TABLE C.2   *(Continued)*

NONDIMENSIONAL TIME	NONDIMENSIONAL RAINFALL	NONDIMENSIONAL TIME	NONDIMENSIONAL RAINFALL	NONDIMENSIONAL TIME	NONDIMENSIONAL RAINFALL	NONDIMENSIONAL TIME	NONDIMENSIONAL RAINFALL
.271	.080	.792	.944	.396	.167	.917	.981
.281	.085	.802	.947	.406	.178	.927	.983
.292	.089	.813	.951	.417	.189	.938	.986
.302	.094	.823	.954	.427	.202	.948	.988
.313	.100	.833	.957	.438	.216	.958	.991
.323	.107	.844	.960	.448	.232	.969	.993
.333	.115	.854	.963	.458	.250	.979	.996
.344	.122	.865	.966	.469	.271	.990	.998
.354	.130	.875	.969	.479	.298	1.000	1.000
.365	.139	.885	.972	.490	.339		
.375	.148	.896	.975	.500	.500		
.385	.157	.906	.978	.510	.662		

TABLE C.3   Corps of Engineers Design Storms

Hr	(vol. $\approx$ 7.90 in.) P_{inc}	ΣP	(vol. $\approx$ 9.00 in.) P_{inc}	ΣP	(vol. $\approx$ 11.00 in.) P_{inc}	ΣP
0.0	—	—	—	—	—	—
0.5	0.06	0.06	0.06	0.06	0.08	0.08
1.0	0.06	0.12	0.06	0.12	0.08	0.16
1.5	0.06	0.18	0.06	0.18	0.08	0.24
2.0	0.06	0.24	0.06	0.24	0.08	0.32
2.5	0.06	0.30	0.06	0.30	0.08	0.40
3.0	0.06	0.36	0.07	0.37	0.09	0.49
3.5	0.06	0.42	0.07	0.44	0.09	0.58
4.0	0.06	0.48	0.07	0.51	0.09	0.67
4.5	0.08	0.56	0.09	0.60	0.11	0.78
5.0	0.08	0.64	0.09	0.69	0.11	0.89
5.5	0.09	0.73	0.11	0.80	0.13	1.02
6.0	0.09	0.82	0.11	0.91	0.13	1.15
6.5	0.09	0.91	0.11	1.02	0.13	1.28
7.0	0.09	1.00	0.11	1.13	0.13	1.41
7.5	0.13	1.13	0.15	1.28	0.19	1.60
8.0	0.13	1.26	0.15	1.43	0.19	1.79
8.5	0.13	1.39	0.15	1.58	0.19	1.98

continued

TABLE C.3   *(Continued)*

Hr	(vol. ≈ 7.90 in.)		(vol. ≈ 9.00 in.)		(vol. ≈ 11.00 in.)	
	P_{inc}	ΣP	P_{inc}	ΣP	P_{inc}	ΣP
9.0	0.13	1.52	0.15	1.73	0.19	2.17
9.5	0.14	1.66	0.16	1.89	0.20	2.37
10.0	0.14	1.80	0.16	2.05	0.20	2.57
10.5	0.14	1.94	0.16	2.21	0.20	2.77
11.0	0.14	2.08	0.16	2.37	0.20	2.97
11.5	0.16	2.24	0.18	2.55	0.22	3.19
12.0	0.16	2.40	0.18	2.73	0.22	3.41
12.5	0.19	2.59	0.22	2.95	0.26	3.67
13.0	0.21	2.80	0.23	3.18	0.29	3.96
13.5	0.29	3.09	0.33	3.51	0.41	4.37
14.0	0.30	3.39	0.34	3.85	0.42	4.79
14.5	0.46	3.85	0.52	4.37	0.64	5.43
15.0	0.46	4.31	0.52	4.89	0.64	6.07
15.5	0.73	5.04	0.83	5.72	1.01	7.08
16.0	0.81	5.85	0.92	6.64	1.12	8.20
16.5	0.34	6.19	0.39	7.03	0.47	8.67
17.0	0.33	6.52	0.38	7.41	0.46	9.13
17.5	0.18	6.70	0.21	7.62	0.25	9.38
18.0	0.17	6.87	0.20	7.82	0.24	9.62
18.5	0.11	6.98	0.13	7.95	0.15	9.77
19.0	0.11	7.09	0.13	8.08	0.15	9.92
19.5	0.09	7.18	0.11	8.19	0.13	10.05
20.0	0.09	7.27	0.11	8.30	0.13	10.18
20.5	0.09	7.36	0.10	8.40	0.12	10.30
21.0	0.09	7.45	0.10	8.50	0.12	10.42
21.5	0.08	7.53	0.09	8.59	0.11	10.53
22.0	0.08	7.61	0.09	8.68	0.11	10.64
22.5	0.09	7.70	0.08	8.76	0.10	10.74
23.0	0.07	7.77	0.08	8.84	0.10	10.84
23.5	0.07	7.84	0.08	8.92	0.10	10.94
24.0	0.06	7.90	0.08	9.00	0.06	11.00

FIGURE C.1   Zones for precipitation frequency-intensity-duration (FID) curves.

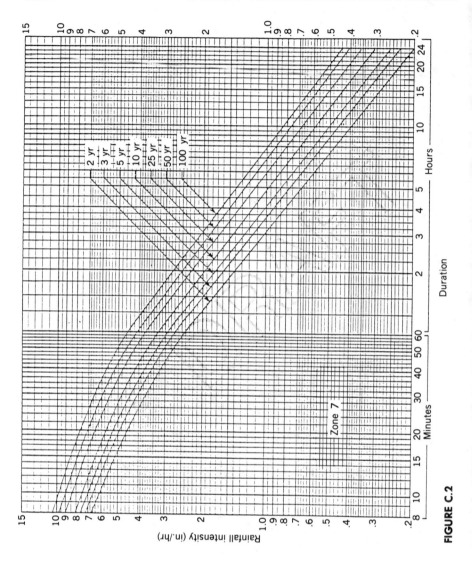

FIGURE C.2

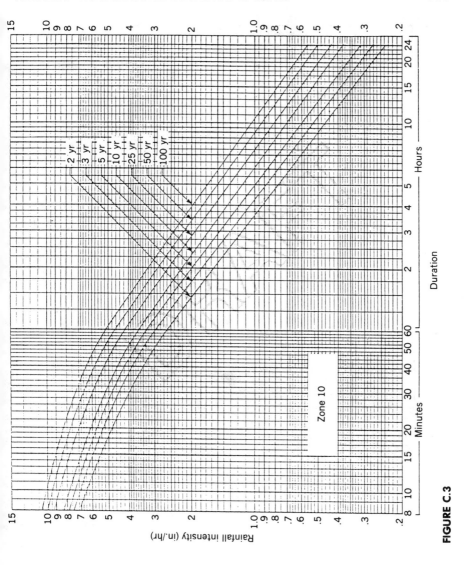

FIGURE C.3

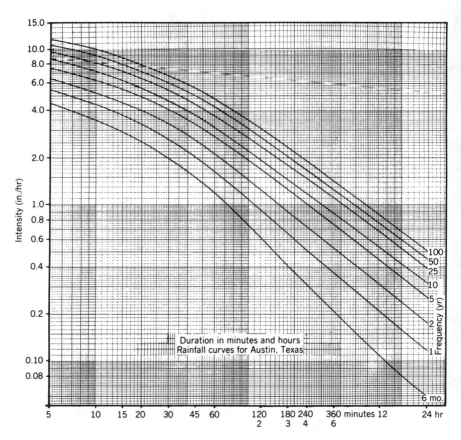

FIGURE C.4

D

STATISTICAL
TABLES

TABLE D.1   Normal Distribution Function Table

$$F(z) = \frac{1}{\sqrt{2\pi}} \int_{-\infty}^{z} e^{-1/2 t^2}\, dt$$

z	.0	.0100	.0200	.0300	.0400	.0500	.0600	.0700	.0800	.0900
.0	.5000	.5040	.5080	.5120	.5160	.5199	.5239	.5279	.5319	.5359
.10	.5398	.5438	.5478	.5517	.5557	.5596	.5636	.5675	.5714	.5733
.20	.5793	.5832	.5871	.5910	.5948	.5987	.6026	.6064	.6103	.6141
.30	.6179	.6217	.6255	.6293	.6331	.6368	.6406	.6443	.6480	.6517
.40	.6554	.6591	.6628	.6664	.6700	.6736	.6772	.6808	.6844	.6879
.50	.6915	.6950	.6985	.7019	.7054	.7088	.7123	.7157	.7190	.7224
.60	.7257	.7291	.7324	.7356	.7389	.7422	.7454	.7486	.7517	.7549
.70	.7580	.7611	.7642	.7673	.7703	.7734	.7764	.7793	.7823	.7852
.80	.7881	.7910	.7939	.7967	.7995	.8023	.8051	.8078	.8106	.8133
.90	.8159	.8186	.8212	.8238	.8264	.8289	.8315	.8340	.8365	.8389
1.00	.8413	.8437	.8461	.8485	.8508	.8531	.8554	.8577	.8599	.8621
1.10	.8643	.8665	.8686	.8708	.8729	.8749	.8770	.8790	.8810	.8830
1.20	.8849	.8869	.8888	.8906	.8925	.8943	.8962	.8980	.8997	.9015
1.30	.9032	.9049	.9066	.9082	.9099	.9115	.9131	.9147	.9162	.9177
1.40	.9192	.9207	.9222	.9236	.9251	.9265	.9278	.9292	.9306	.9319

z	.00	.01	.02	.03	.04	.05	.06	.07	.08	.09
1.50	.9332	.9345	.9357	.9370	.9382	.9394	.9406	.9418	.9429	.9441
1.60	.9452	.9463	.9474	.9484	.9495	.9505	.9515	.9525	.9535	.9545
1.70	.9554	.9564	.9573	.9582	.9591	.9599	.9608	.9616	.9625	.9633
1.80	.9641	.9648	.9656	.9664	.9671	.9678	.9686	.9693	.9699	.9706
1.90	.9713	.9719	.9726	.9732	.9738	.9744	.9750	.9756	.9761	.9767
2.00	.9772	.9778	.9783	.9788	.9793	.9798	.9803	.9808	.9812	.9817
2.10	.9821	.9826	.9830	.9834	.9838	.9842	.9846	.9850	.9854	.9857
2.20	.9861	.9864	.9868	.9871	.9874	.9878	.9881	.9884	.9887	.9890
2.30	.9893	.9895	.9898	.9901	.9904	.9906	.9909	.9911	.9913	.9916
2.40	.9918	.9920	.9922	.9924	.9926	.9928	.9930	.9932	.9934	.9936
2.50	.9938	.9940	.9941	.9943	.9944	.9946	.9948	.9949	.9951	.9952
2.60	.9953	.9955	.9956	.9957	.9958	.9960	.9961	.9962	.9963	.9964
2.70	.9965	.9966	.9967	.9968	.9969	.9970	.9971	.9972	.9973	.9974
2.80	.9974	.9975	.9976	.9977	.9977	.9978	.9979	.9979	.9980	.9981
2.90	.9981	.9982	.9982	.9983	.9983	.9984	.9985	.9985	.9985	.9986
3.00	.9986	.9987	.9987	.9988	.9988	.9988	.9989	.9989	.9990	.9990
3.10	.9990	.9991	.9991	.9991	.9991	.9992	.9992	.9992	.9993	.9993
3.20	.9993	.9993	.9993	.9994	.9994	.9994	.9994	.9995	.9995	.9995
3.30	.9995	.9995	.9995	.9996	.9996	.9996	.9996	.9996	.9996	.9996
3.40	.9997	.9997	.9997	.9997	.9997	.9997	.9997	.9997	.9997	.9997

TABLE D.2 Binomial Distribution Function

$$B(x;N,p) = \sum_{k=0}^{x} \binom{N}{x} p^k (1-p)^{N-k}$$

N	x	.05	.10	.15	.20	.25	.30	.35	.40	.45	.50
2-	0	.9025	.8100	.7225	.6400	.5625	.4900	.4225	.3600	.3025	.2500
	1	.9975	.9900	.9775	.9600	.9375	.9100	.8775	.8400	.7975	.7500
3-	0	.8574	.7290	.6141	.5120	.4219	.3430	.2746	.2160	.1664	.1250
	1	.9928	.9720	.9393	.8960	.8437	.7840	.7183	.6480	.5748	.5000
	2	.9999	.9990	.9966	.9920	.9844	.9730	.9571	.9360	.9089	.8750
4-	0	.8145	.6561	.5220	.4096	.3164	.2401	.1785	.1296	.0915	.0625
	1	.9860	.9477	.8905	.8192	.7383	.6517	.5630	.4752	.3910	.3125
	2	.9995	.9963	.9880	.9728	.9492	.9163	.8735	.8208	.7585	.6875
	3	1.0000	.9999	.9995	.9984	.9961	.9919	.9850	.9744	.9590	.9375
5-	0	.7738	.5905	.4437	.3277	.2373	.1681	.1160	.0778	.0503	.0313
	1	.9774	.9185	.8352	.7373	.6328	.5282	.4284	.3370	.2562	.1875
	2	.9988	.9914	.9734	.9421	.8965	.8369	.7648	.6826	.5931	.5000
	3	1.0000	.9995	.9978	.9933	.9844	.9692	.9460	.9130	.8688	.8125
	4	1.0000	1.0000	.9999	.9997	.9990	.9976	.9947	.9898	.9815	.9688

6-

0	.0156	.0277	.0467	.0754	.1176	.1780	.2621	.3771	.5314	.7351
1	.1094	.1636	.2333	.3191	.4202	.5339	.6554	.7765	.8857	.9672
2	.3438	.4415	.5443	.6471	.7443	.8306	.9011	.9527	.9842	.9978
3	.6563	.7447	.8208	.8826	.9295	.9624	.9830	.9941	.9987	.9999
4	.8906	.9308	.9590	.9777	.9891	.9954	.9984	.9996	.9999	1.0000
5	.9844	.9917	.9959	.9982	.9993	.9998	.9999	1.0000	1.0000	1.0000

7-

0	.0078	.0152	.0280	.0490	.0824	.1335	.2097	.3206	.4783	.6983
1	.0625	.1024	.1586	.2338	.3294	.4449	.5767	.7166	.8503	.9556
2	.2266	.3164	.4199	.5323	.6471	.7564	.8520	.9262	.9743	.9962
3	.5000	.6083	.7102	.8002	.8740	.9294	.9667	.9879	.9973	.9998
4	.7734	.8471	.9037	.9444	.9712	.9871	.9953	.9988	.9998	1.0000
5	.9375	.9643	.9812	.9910	.9962	.9987	.9996	.9999	1.0000	1.0000
6	.9922	.9963	.9984	.9994	.9998	.9999	1.0000	1.0000	1.0000	1.0000

8-

0	.0039	.0084	.0168	.0319	.0576	.1001	.1678	.2725	.4305	.6634
1	.0352	.0632	.1064	.1691	.2553	.3671	.5033	.6572	.8131	.9428
2	.1445	.2201	.3154	.4278	.5518	.6785	.7969	.8948	.9619	.9942
3	.3633	.4770	.5941	.7064	.8059	.8862	.9437	.9786	.9950	.9996
4	.6367	.7396	.8263	.8939	.9420	.9727	.9896	.9971	.9996	1.0000
5	.8555	.9115	.9502	.9747	.9887	.9958	.9988	.9998	1.0000	1.0000
6	.9648	.9819	.9915	.9964	.9987	.9996	.9999	1.0000	1.0000	1.0000
7	.9961	.9983	.9993	.9998	.9999	1.0000	1.0000	1.0000	1.0000	1.0000

continued

TABLE D.2 *(Continued)*

N	x	.05	.10	.15	.20	.25	.30	.35	.40	.45	.50
9-	0	.6302	.3874	.2316	.1342	.0751	.0404	.0207	.0101	.0046	.0020
	1	.9288	.7748	.5995	.4362	.3003	.1960	.1211	.0705	.0385	.0195
	2	.9916	.9470	.8591	.7382	.6007	.4628	.3373	.2318	.1495	.0898
	3	.9994	.9917	.9661	.9144	.8343	.7297	.6089	.4826	.3614	.2539
	4	1.0000	.9991	.9944	.9804	.9511	.9012	.8283	.7334	.6214	.5000
	5	1.0000	.9999	.9994	.9969	.9900	.9747	.9464	.9006	.8342	.7461
	6	1.0000	1.0000	1.0000	.9997	.9987	.9957	.9888	.9750	.9502	.9102
	7	1.0000	1.0000	1.0000	1.0000	.9999	.9996	.9986	.9962	.9909	.9805
	8	1.0000	1.0000	1.0000	1.0000	1.0000	1.0000	.9999	.9997	.9992	.9980
10-	0	.5987	.3487	.1969	.1074	.0563	.0282	.0135	.0060	.0025	.0010
	1	.9139	.7361	.5443	.3758	.2440	.1493	.0860	.0464	.0233	.0107
	2	.9885	.9298	.8202	.6778	.5256	.3828	.2616	.1673	.0995	.0547
	3	.9990	.9872	.9500	.8791	.7759	.6496	.5138	.3823	.2660	.1719
	4	.9999	.9984	.9901	.9672	.9219	.8497	.7515	.6331	.5044	.3770
	5	1.0000	.9999	.9986	.9936	.9803	.9527	.9051	.8338	.7384	.6230
	6	1.0000	1.0000	.9999	.9991	.9965	.9894	.9740	.9452	.8980	.8281
	7	1.0000	1.0000	1.0000	.9999	.9996	.9984	.9952	.9877	.9726	.9453
	8	1.0000	1.0000	1.0000	1.0000	1.0000	.9999	.9995	.9983	.9955	.9893
	9	1.0000	1.0000	1.0000	1.0000	1.0000	1.0000	1.0000	.9999	.9997	.9990

n = 11

k										
0	.0005	.0014	.0036	.0088	.0198	.0422	.0859	.1673	.3138	.5688
1	.0059	.0139	.0302	.0606	.1130	.1971	.3221	.4922	.6974	.8981
2	.0327	.0652	.1189	.2001	.3127	.4552	.6174	.7788	.9104	.9848
3	.1133	.1911	.2963	.4256	.5696	.7133	.8389	.9306	.9815	.9984
4	.2744	.3971	.5328	.6683	.7897	.8854	.9496	.9841	.9972	.9999
5	.5000	.6331	.7535	.8513	.9218	.9657	.9883	.9973	.9997	1.0000
6	.7256	.8262	.9006	.9499	.9784	.9924	.9980	.9997	1.0000	1.0000
7	.8867	.9390	.9707	.9878	.9957	.9988	.9998	1.0000	1.0000	1.0000
8	.9673	.9852	.9941	.9980	.9994	.9999	1.0000	1.0000	1.0000	1.0000
9	.9941	.9978	.9993	.9998	1.0000	1.0000	1.0000	1.0000	1.0000	1.0000
10	.9995	.9998	1.0000	1.0000	1.0000	1.0000	1.0000	1.0000	1.0000	1.0000

n = 12

k										
0	.0002	.0008	.0022	.0057	.0138	.0317	.0687	.1422	.2824	.5404
1	.0032	.0083	.0196	.0424	.0850	.1584	.2749	.4435	.6590	.8816
2	.0193	.0421	.0834	.1513	.2528	.3907	.5583	.7358	.8891	.9804
3	.0730	.1345	.2253	.3467	.4925	.6488	.7946	.9078	.9744	.9978
4	.1938	.3044	.4382	.5833	.7237	.8424	.9274	.9761	.9957	.9998
5	.3872	.5269	.6652	.7873	.8822	.9456	.9806	.9954	.9995	1.0000
6	.6128	.7393	.8418	.9154	.9614	.9857	.9961	.9993	.9999	1.0000
7	.8062	.8883	.9427	.9745	.9905	.9972	.9994	.9999	1.0000	1.0000
8	.9270	.9644	.9847	.9944	.9983	.9996	.9999	1.0000	1.0000	1.0000
9	.9807	.9921	.9972	.9992	.9998	1.0000	1.0000	1.0000	1.0000	1.0000
10	.9968	.9989	.9997	.9999	1.0000	1.0000	1.0000	1.0000	1.0000	1.0000
11	.9998	.9999	1.0000	1.0000	1.0000	1.0000	1.0000	1.0000	1.0000	1.0000

continued

TABLE D.2 *(Continued)*

N	x	.05	.10	.15	.20	.25	.30	.35	.40	.45	.50
13-	0	.5133	.2542	.1209	.0550	.0238	.0097	.0037	.0013	.0004	.0001
	1	.8646	.6213	.3983	.2336	.1267	.0637	.0296	.0126	.0049	.0017
	2	.9755	.8661	.6920	.5017	.3326	.2025	.1132	.0579	.0269	.0112
	3	.9969	.9658	.8820	.7473	.5843	.4206	.2783	.1686	.0929	.0461
	4	.9997	.9935	.9658	.9009	.7940	.6543	.5005	.3530	.2279	.1334
	5	1.0000	.9991	.9925	.9700	.9198	.8346	.7159	.5744	.4268	.2905
	6	1.0000	.9999	.9987	.9930	.9757	.9376	.8705	.7712	.6437	.5000
	7	1.0000	1.0000	.9998	.9988	.9944	.9818	.9538	.9023	.8212	.7095
	8	1.0000	1.0000	1.0000	.9998	.9990	.9960	.9874	.9679	.9302	.8666
	9	1.0000	1.0000	1.0000	1.0000	.9999	.9993	.9975	.9922	.9797	.9539
	10	1.0000	1.0000	1.0000	1.0000	1.0000	.9999	.9997	.9987	.9959	.9888
	11	1.0000	1.0000	1.0000	1.0000	1.0000	1.0000	1.0000	.9999	.9995	.9983
	12	1.0000	1.0000	1.0000	1.0000	1.0000	1.0000	1.0000	1.0000	1.0000	.9999
14-	0	.4877	.2288	.1028	.0440	.0178	.0068	.0024	.0008	.0002	.0001
	1	.8470	.5846	.3567	.1979	.1010	.0475	.0205	.0081	.0029	.0009
	2	.9699	.8416	.6479	.4481	.2811	.1608	.0839	.0398	.0170	.0065
	3	.9958	.9559	.8535	.6982	.5213	.3552	.2205	.1243	.0632	.0287
	4	.9996	.9908	.9533	.8702	.7415	.5842	.4227	.2793	.1672	.0898
	5	1.0000	.9985	.9885	.9561	.8883	.7805	.6405	.4859	.3373	.2120
	6	1.0000	.9998	.9978	.9884	.9617	.9067	.8164	.6925	.5461	.3953
	7	1.0000	1.0000	.9997	.9976	.9897	.9685	.9247	.8499	.7414	.6047

n	x										
	8	.7880	.8811	.9417	.9757	.9917	.9978	.9996	1.0000	1.0000	1.0000
	9	.9102	.9574	.9825	.9940	.9983	.9997	1.0000	1.0000	1.0000	1.0000
	10	.9713	.9886	.9961	.9989	.9998	1.0000	1.0000	1.0000	1.0000	1.0000
	11	.9935	.9978	.9994	.9999	1.0000	1.0000	1.0000	1.0000	1.0000	1.0000
	12	.9991	.9997	.9999	1.0000	1.0000	1.0000	1.0000	1.0000	1.0000	1.0000
	13	.9999	1.0000	1.0000	1.0000	1.0000	1.0000	1.0000	1.0000	1.0000	1.0000
15-	0	.0000	.0001	.0005	.0016	.0047	.0134	.0352	.0874	.2059	.4633
	1	.0005	.0017	.0052	.0142	.0353	.0802	.1671	.3186	.5490	.8290
	2	.0037	.0107	.0271	.0617	.1268	.2361	.3980	.6042	.8159	.9638
	3	.0176	.0424	.0905	.1727	.2969	.4613	.6482	.8227	.9444	.9945
	4	.0592	.1204	.2173	.3519	.5155	.6865	.8358	.9383	.9873	.9994
	5	.1509	.2608	.4032	.5643	.7216	.8516	.9389	.9832	.9978	.9999
	6	.3036	.4522	.6098	.7548	.8689	.9434	.9819	.9964	.9997	1.0000
	7	.5000	.6535	.7869	.8868	.9500	.9827	.9958	.9994	1.0000	1.0000
	8	.6964	.8182	.9050	.9578	.9848	.9958	.9992	.9999	1.0000	1.0000
	9	.8491	.9231	.9662	.9876	.9963	.9992	.9999	1.0000	1.0000	1.0000
	10	.9408	.9745	.9907	.9972	.9993	.9999	1.0000	1.0000	1.0000	1.0000
	11	.9824	.9937	.9981	.9995	.9999	1.0000	1.0000	1.0000	1.0000	1.0000
	12	.9963	.9989	.9997	.9999	1.0000	1.0000	1.0000	1.0000	1.0000	1.0000
	13	.9995	.9999	1.0000	1.0000	1.0000	1.0000	1.0000	1.0000	1.0000	1.0000
	14	1.0000	1.0000	1.0000	1.0000	1.0000	1.0000	1.0000	1.0000	1.0000	1.0000
16-	0	.0000	.0001	.0003	.0010	.0033	.0100	.0281	.0743	.1853	.4401

continued

TABLE D.2 *(Continued)*

N	x	.05	.10	.15	.20	.25	.30	.35	.40	.45	.50
	1	.8108	.5147	.2839	.1407	.0635	.0261	.0098	.0033	.0010	.0003
	2	.9571	.7893	.5614	.3518	.1971	.0994	.0451	.0183	.0066	.0021
	3	.9930	.9316	.7899	.5981	.4050	.2459	.1339	.0651	.0281	.0106
	4	.9991	.9830	.9209	.7982	.6302	.4499	.2892	.1666	.0853	.0384
	5	.9999	.9967	.9765	.9183	.8103	.6598	.4900	.3288	.1976	.1051
	6	1.0000	.9995	.9944	.9733	.9204	.8247	.6881	.5272	.3660	.2272
	7	1.0000	.9999	.9989	.9930	.9729	.9256	.8406	.7161	.5629	.4018
	8	1.0000	1.0000	.9998	.9985	.9925	.9743	.9329	.8577	.7441	.5982
	9	1.0000	1.0000	1.0000	.9998	.9984	.9929	.9771	.9417	.8759	.7728
	10	1.0000	1.0000	1.0000	1.0000	.9997	.9984	.9938	.9809	.9514	.8949
	11	1.0000	1.0000	1.0000	1.0000	1.0000	.9997	.9987	.9951	.9851	.9616
	12	1.0000	1.0000	1.0000	1.0000	1.0000	1.0000	.9998	.9991	.9965	.9894
	13	1.0000	1.0000	1.0000	1.0000	1.0000	1.0000	1.0000	.9999	.9994	.9979
	14	1.0000	1.0000	1.0000	1.0000	1.0000	1.0000	1.0000	1.0000	.9999	.9997
	15	1.0000	1.0000	1.0000	1.0000	1.0000	1.0000	1.0000	1.0000	1.0000	1.0000
17-	0	.4181	.1668	.0631	.0225	.0075	.0023	.0007	.0002	.0000	.0000
	1	.7922	.4818	.2525	.1182	.0501	.0193	.0067	.0021	.0005	.0001
	2	.9497	.7618	.5198	.3096	.1637	.0774	.0327	.0123	.0041	.0012
	3	.9912	.9174	.7556	.5489	.3530	.2019	.1028	.0464	.0184	.0064
	4	.9988	.9779	.9013	.7582	.5739	.3887	.2348	.1260	.0596	.0245
	5	.9999	.9953	.9681	.8943	.7653	.5968	.4197	.2639	.1471	.0717

x										
6	1.0000	.9992	.9917	.9623	.8929	.7752	.6188	.4478	.2902	.1662
7	1.0000	.9999	.9983	.9891	.9598	.8954	.7872	.6405	.4743	.3145
8	1.0000	1.0000	.9997	.9974	.9876	.9597	.9006	.8011	.6626	.5000
9	1.0000	1.0000	1.0000	.9995	.9969	.9873	.9617	.9081	.8166	.6855
10	1.0000	1.0000	1.0000	.9999	.9994	.9968	.9880	.9652	.9174	.8338
11	1.0000	1.0000	1.0000	1.0000	.9999	.9993	.9970	.9894	.9699	.9283
12	1.0000	1.0000	1.0000	1.0000	1.0000	.9999	.9994	.9975	.9914	.9755
13	1.0000	1.0000	1.0000	1.0000	1.0000	1.0000	.9999	.9995	.9981	.9936
14	1.0000	1.0000	1.0000	1.0000	1.0000	1.0000	1.0000	.9999	.9997	.9988
15	1.0000	1.0000	1.0000	1.0000	1.0000	1.0000	1.0000	1.0000	1.0000	.9999
16	1.0000	1.0000	1.0000	1.0000	1.0000	1.0000	1.0000	1.0000	1.0000	1.0000

18-

x										
0	.3972	.1501	.0536	.0180	.0056	.0016	.0004	.0001	.0000	.0000
1	.7735	.4503	.2241	.0991	.0395	.0142	.0046	.0013	.0003	.0001
2	.9419	.7338	.4797	.2713	.1353	.0600	.0236	.0082	.0025	.0007
3	.9891	.9018	.7202	.5010	.3057	.1646	.0783	.0328	.0120	.0038
4	.9985	.9718	.8794	.7164	.5187	.3327	.1886	.0942	.0411	.0154
5	.9998	.9936	.9581	.8671	.7174	.5344	.3550	.2088	.1077	.0481
6	1.0000	.9988	.9882	.9487	.8610	.7217	.5491	.3743	.2258	.1189
7	1.0000	.9998	.9973	.9837	.9431	.8593	.7283	.5634	.3915	.2403
8	1.0000	1.0000	.9995	.9957	.9807	.9404	.8609	.7368	.5778	.4073
9	1.0000	1.0000	.9999	.9991	.9946	.9790	.9403	.8653	.7473	.5927
10	1.0000	1.0000	1.0000	.9998	.9988	.9939	.9788	.9424	.8720	.7597
11	1.0000	1.0000	1.0000	1.0000	.9998	.9986	.9938	.9797	.9463	.8811
12	1.0000	1.0000	1.0000	1.0000	1.0000	.9997	.9986	.9942	.9817	.9519

continued

TABLE D.2 *(Continued)*

N	x	.05	.10	.15	.20	.25	.30	.35	.40	.45	.50
	13	1.0000	1.0000	1.0000	1.0000	1.0000	1.0000	.9997	.9987	.9951	.9846
	14	1.0000	1.0000	1.0000	1.0000	1.0000	1.0000	1.0000	.9998	.9990	.9962
	15	1.0000	1.0000	1.0000	1.0000	1.0000	1.0000	1.0000	1.0000	.9999	.9993
	16	1.0000	1.0000	1.0000	1.0000	1.0000	1.0000	1.0000	1.0000	1.0000	.9999
	17	1.0000	1.0000	1.0000	1.0000	1.0000	1.0000	1.0000	1.0000	1.0000	1.0000
19-	0	.3774	.1351	.0456	.0144	.0042	.0011	.0003	.0001	.0000	.0000
	1	.7547	.4203	.1985	.0829	.0310	.0104	.0031	.0008	.0002	.0000
	2	.9335	.7054	.4413	.2369	.1113	.0462	.0170	.0055	.0015	.0004
	3	.9868	.8850	.6841	.4551	.2631	.1332	.0591	.0230	.0077	.0022
	4	.9980	.9648	.8556	.6733	.4654	.2822	.1500	.0696	.0280	.0096
	5	.9998	.9914	.9463	.8369	.6678	.4739	.2968	.1629	.0777	.0318
	6	1.0000	.9983	.9837	.9324	.8251	.6655	.4812	.3081	.1727	.0835
	7	1.0000	.9997	.9959	.9767	.9225	.8180	.6656	.4878	.3169	.1796
	8	1.0000	1.0000	.9992	.9933	.9713	.9161	.8145	.6675	.4940	.3238
	9	1.0000	1.0000	.9999	.9984	.9911	.9674	.9125	.8139	.6710	.5000
	10	1.0000	1.0000	1.0000	.9997	.9977	.9895	.9653	.9115	.8159	.6762
	11	1.0000	1.0000	1.0000	1.0000	.9995	.9972	.9886	.9648	.9129	.8204
	12	1.0000	1.0000	1.0000	1.0000	.9999	.9994	.9969	.9884	.9658	.9165
	13	1.0000	1.0000	1.0000	1.0000	1.0000	.9999	.9993	.9969	.9891	.9682
	14	1.0000	1.0000	1.0000	1.0000	1.0000	1.0000	.9999	.9994	.9972	.9904

15	.9978	.9995	.9999	1.0000	1.0000	1.0000	1.0000	1.0000	1.0000	1.0000
16	.9996	.9999	1.0000	1.0000	1.0000	1.0000	1.0000	1.0000	1.0000	1.0000
17	1.0000	1.0000	1.0000	1.0000	1.0000	1.0000	1.0000	1.0000	1.0000	1.0000
18	1.0000	1.0000	1.0000	1.0000	1.0000	1.0000	1.0000	1.0000	1.0000	1.0000
0	.0000	.0000	.0000	.0002	.0008	.0032	.0115	.0388	.1216	.3585
1	.0000	.0001	.0005	.0021	.0076	.0243	.0692	.1756	.3917	.7358
2	.0002	.0009	.0036	.0121	.0355	.0913	.2061	.4049	.6769	.9245
3	.0013	.0049	.0160	.0444	.1071	.2252	.4114	.6477	.8670	.9841
4	.0059	.0189	.0510	.1182	.2375	.4148	.6296	.8298	.9568	.9974
5	.0207	.0553	.1256	.2454	.4164	.6172	.8042	.9327	.9887	.9997
6	.0577	.1299	.2500	.4166	.6080	.7858	.9133	.9781	.9976	1.0000
7	.1316	.2520	.4159	.6010	.7723	.8982	.9679	.9941	.9996	1.0000
8	.2517	.4143	.5956	.7624	.8867	.9591	.9900	.9987	.9999	1.0000
9	.4119	.5914	.7553	.8782	.9520	.9861	.9974	.9998	1.0000	1.0000
10	.5881	.7507	.8725	.9468	.9829	.9961	.9994	1.0000	1.0000	1.0000
11	.7483	.8692	.9435	.9804	.9949	.9991	.9999	1.0000	1.0000	1.0000
12	.8684	.9420	.9790	.9940	.9987	.9998	1.0000	1.0000	1.0000	1.0000
13	.9423	.9786	.9935	.9985	.9997	1.0000	1.0000	1.0000	1.0000	1.0000
14	.9793	.9936	.9984	.9997	1.0000	1.0000	1.0000	1.0000	1.0000	1.0000
15	.9941	.9985	.9997	1.0000	1.0000	1.0000	1.0000	1.0000	1.0000	1.0000
16	.9987	.9997	1.0000	1.0000	1.0000	1.0000	1.0000	1.0000	1.0000	1.0000
17	.9998	1.0000	1.0000	1.0000	1.0000	1.0000	1.0000	1.0000	1.0000	1.0000
18	1.0000	1.0000	1.0000	1.0000	1.0000	1.0000	1.0000	1.0000	1.0000	1.0000
19	1.0000	1.0000	1.0000	1.0000	1.0000	1.0000	1.0000	1.0000	1.0000	1.0000

20-

TABLE D.3 *K* Standard Deviates: Log Pearson Type III Positive Skew Values (+ *G*)

EXCEEDENCE PROBABILITY *P* / *G*	.999	.990	.975	.950	.900	.500	.100	.050	.025	.010	.001
.0	−3.090	−2.326	−1.960	−1.645	−1.282	.000	1.281	1.645	1.960	2.326	3.090
.1	−2.948	−2.253	−1.912	−1.616	−1.270	−0.166	1.292	1.673	2.007	2.400	3.233
.2	−2.808	−2.178	−1.864	−1.586	−1.258	−0.330	1.301	1.700	2.053	2.472	3.377
.3	−2.670	−2.104	−1.814	−1.555	−1.245	−0.500	1.309	1.726	2.098	2.544	3.521
.4	−2.533	−2.030	−1.764	−1.523	−1.231	−0.665	1.317	1.750	2.142	2.615	3.666
.5	−2.400	−1.954	−1.714	−1.491	−1.216	−0.830	1.323	1.774	2.185	2.686	3.810
.6	−2.688	−1.880	−1.662	−1.458	−1.200	−0.099	1.330	1.797	2.227	2.755	3.955
.7	−2.140	−1.806	−1.611	−1.423	−1.835	−0.116	1.333	1.818	2.268	2.823	4.100
.8	−2.017	−1.733	−1.560	−1.388	−1.656	−0.132	1.336	1.840	2.308	2.891	4.244
.9	−1.899	−1.660	−1.507	−1.353	−1.147	−0.148	1.339	1.858	2.346	2.957	4.388
1.0	−1.786	−1.588	−1.455	−1.317	−1.280	−0.164	1.340	1.877	2.383	3.022	4.531
1.5	−1.313	−1.256	−1.200	−1.130	−1.018	−0.240	1.333	1.951	2.552	3.330	5.233
2.0	−0.999	.989	−0.975	.949	−0.895	−0.307	1.303	1.995	2.688	3.605	5.907
2.5	−0.800	−0.799	−0.797	−0.790	−0.770	−0.360	1.250	2.012	2.793	3.845	6.548
3.0	−0.667	−0.666	−0.666	−0.665	−0.660	−0.396	1.180	2.003	2.867	4.051	7.152
4.0	−0.500	−0.500	−0.500	−0.499	−0.499	−0.413	1.000	1.920	2.933	4.367	8.253
5.0	−0.400	−0.400	−0.400	−0.400	−0.400	−0.379	.795	1.773	2.909	4.457	9.219

6.0	−0.333	−0.333	−0.333	−0.333	−0.333	−0.330	.589	1.585	2.817	4.687	10.068
7.0	−0.285	−0.285	−0.285	−0.285	−0.285	−0.285	.400	1.377	2.676	4.726	10.813
8.0	−0.250	−0.250	−0.250	−0.250	−0.250	−0.249	.239	1.163	2.500	4.705	11.468
.0	−3.090	−2.326	−1.960	−1.645	−1.281	.000	1.281	1.645	1.960	2.326	3.090
−0.1	−3.233	−2.400	−2.007	−1.673	−1.291	.166	1.270	1.616	1.912	2.252	2.948
−0.2	−3.377	−2.472	−2.053	−1.700	−1.301	.033	1.258	1.586	1.863	2.178	2.808
−0.3	−3.352	−2.544	−2.098	−1.726	−1.309	.050	1.245	1.555	1.814	2.104	2.670
−0.4	−3.666	−2.615	−2.142	−1.750	−1.317	.066	1.231	1.523	1.764	2.029	2.532
−0.5	−3.810	−2.685	−2.185	−1.774	−1.323	.083	1.216	1.491	1.713	1.954	2.400
−0.6	−3.956	−2.755	−2.220	−1.800	−1.330	.099	1.200	1.457	1.662	1.880	2.268
−0.7	−4.100	−2.823	−2.268	−1.818	−1.332	.116	1.183	1.423	1.611	1.806	2.350
−0.8	−4.244	−2.891	−2.307	−1.839	−1.336	.132	1.166	1.388	1.560	1.732	2.184
−0.9	−4.388	−2.957	−2.346	−1.858	−1.338	.148	1.147	1.353	1.507	1.660	2.030
−1.0	−4.531	−3.022	−2.383	−1.876	−1.340	.164	1.127	1.317	1.455	1.588	1.884
−1.5	−5.233	−3.330	−2.552	−1.950	−1.333	.240	1.018	1.130	1.200	1.256	1.312
−2.0	−5.907	−3.605	−2.689	−1.995	−1.303	.306	.894	.949	.975	.990	.999
−2.5	−6.548	−3.845	−2.793	−2.012	−1.250	.360	.770	.790	.797	.799	.800
−3.0	−7.152	−4.051	−2.867	−2.003	−1.180	.395	.660	.665	.666	.666	.666
−4.0	−8.252	−4.367	−2.933	−1.920	−1.000	.413	.499	.500	.500	.500	.500
−5.0	−9.219	−4.573	−2.909	−1.773	−0.795	.380	.400	.400	.400	.400	.400
−6.0	−10.068	−4.686	−2.817	−1.585	−0.590	.329	.333	.333	.333	.333	.333
−7.0	−10.813	−4.726	−2.676	−1.377	−0.400	.285	.285	.285	.285	.285	.285

TABLE D.4 Parameters δ for Standard Error of Normal Distribution

EXCEEDENCE PROBABILITY IN PERCENT						
50.0	20.0	10.0	4.0	2.0	1.0	.2
CORRESPONDING RETURN PERIOD IN YEARS						
2	5	10	25	50	100	500
1.0000	1.1637	1.3496	1.5916	1.7634	1.9253	2.2624

TABLE D.5 Parameter δ for Standard Error of Log-Normal Distribution

	EXCEEDENCE PROBABILITY IN PERCENT						
	50.0	20.0	10.0	4.0	2.0	1.0	0.2
COEFFICIENT OF VARIATION	CORRESPONDING RETURN PERIOD IN YEARS						
	2	5	10	25	50	100	500
.05	.9983	1.2162	1.4323	1.7105	1.9087	2.0968	2.4939
.10	.9932	1.2698	1.5222	1.8453	2.0766	2.2979	2.7714
.15	.9848	1.3241	1.6187	1.9956	2.2676	2.5298	3.0993
.20	.9733	1.3784	1.7211	2.1613	2.4819	2.7940	3.4820
.25	.9589	1.4323	1.8289	2.3423	2.7202	3.0917	3.9241
.30	.9420	1.4855	1.9417	2.5383	2.9829	3.4246	4.4305
.35	.9229	1.5378	2.0591	2.7496	3.2708	3.7942	5.0065
.40	.9021	1.5890	2.1811	2.9762	3.5845	4.2023	5.6574
.45	.8801	1.6389	2.3074	3.2184	3.9251	4.6508	6.3890
.50	.8575	1.6876	2.4382	3.4766	4.2935	5.1418	7.2076
.55	.8351	1.7351	2.5735	3.7514	4.6910	5.6774	8.1196
.60	.8138	1.7814	2.7134	4.0435	5.1190	6.2604	9.1322
.65	.7945	1.8266	2.8583	4.3535	5.5790	6.8934	10.2529
.70	.7784	1.8709	3.0085	4.6826	6.0729	7.5794	11.4897
.75	.7669	1.9143	3.1644	5.0316	6.6024	8.3217	12.8513
.80	.7615	1.9570	3.3264	5.4018	7.1698	9.1238	14.3468
.85	.7635	1.9991	3.4949	5.7945	7.7773	9.9894	15.9861
.90	.7746	2.0408	3.6705	6.2109	8.4272	10.9225	17.7796
.95	.7959	2.0821	3.8536	6.6524	9.1221	11.9272	19.7381
1.00	.8284	2.1232	4.0449	7.1206	9.8646	13.0081	21.8734

TABLE D.6   Parameter δ for Standard Error of Gumbel Extreme
Value Distribution

SAMPLE SIZE n	EXCEEDENCE PROBABILITY IN PERCENT						
	50.0	20.0	10.0	4.0	2.0	1.0	0.2
	CORRESPONDING RETURN PERIOD IN YEARS						
	2	5	10	25	50	100	500
10	.9305	1.8540	2.6200	3.6275	4.3870	5.1460	6.9103
15	.9270	1.7695	2.4756	3.4083	4.1127	4.8173	6.4565
20	.9250	1.7249	2.3990	3.2919	3.9670	4.6427	6.2154
25	.9237	1.6968	2.3507	3.2183	3.8748	4.5322	6.0626
30	.9229	1.6772	2.3169	3.1667	3.8103	4.4547	5.9556
35	.9223	1.6627	2.2919	3.1286	3.7624	4.3973	5.8763
40	.9218	1.6514	2.2725	3.0990	3.7253	4.3528	5.8147
45	.9214	1.6424	2.2569	3.0752	3.6955	4.3171	5.7653
50	.9211	1.6350	2.2441	3.0555	3.6707	4.2874	5.7242
55	.9208	1.6288	2.2333	3.0390	3.6502	4.2626	5.6900
60	.9206	1.6235	2.2241	3.0249	3.6325	4.2414	5.6607
65	.9204	1.6190	2.2163	3.0130	3.6175	4.2234	5.6357
70	.9202	1.6149	2.2092	3.0022	3.6039	4.2071	5.6132
75	.9200	1.6114	2.2032	2.9929	3.5923	4.1932	5.5939
80	.9199	1.6083	2.1977	2.9846	3.5818	4.1806	5.5765
85	.9198	1.6055	2.1929	2.9771	3.5725	4.1694	5.5610
90	.9197	1.6030	2.1885	2.9704	3.5640	4.1592	5.5468
95	.9196	1.6007	2.1845	2.9643	3.5563	4.1500	5.5341
100	.9195	1.5986	2.1808	2.9586	3.5492	4.1414	5.5222

TABLE D.7   Parameter δ for Standard Error of Log-Pearson Type III Distribution

	EXCEEDENCE PROBABILITY IN PERCENT						
	50.0	20.0	10.0	4.0	2.0	1.0	0.2
	CORRESPONDING RETURN PERIOD IN YEARS						
COEFFICIENT OF SKEW	2	5	10	25	50	100	500
.0	1.0801	1.1698	1.3748	1.8013	2.1992	2.6369	3.7212
.1	1.0808	1.2006	1.4368	1.9092	2.3429	2.8174	3.9902
.2	1.0830	1.2310	1.4990	2.0229	2.4990	3.0181	4.3001
.3	1.0866	1.2610	1.5611	2.1414	2.6661	3.2373	4.6486
.4	1.0918	1.2906	1.6228	2.2639	2.8428	3.4732	5.0336
.5	1.0987	1.3200	1.6840	2.3898	3.0283	3.7247	5.4534
.6	1.1073	1.3493	1.7442	2.5182	3.2215	3.9905	5.9066
.7	1.1179	1.3786	1.8033	2.6486	3.4215	4.2695	6.3920
.8	1.1304	1.4083	1.8611	2.7802	3.6274	4.5607	6.9085
.9	1.1449	1.4386	1.9172	2.9123	3.8383	4.8631	7.4550
1.0	1.1614	1.4701	1.9717	3.0442	4.0532	5.1756	8.0303
1.1	1.1799	1.5032	2.0243	3.1751	4.2711	5.4969	8.6335
1.2	1.2003	1.5385	2.0751	3.3043	4.4909	5.8259	9.2631
1.3	1.2223	1.5767	2.1242	3.4311	4.7115	6.1613	9.9177
1.4	1.2457	1.6186	2.1718	3.5546	4.9319	6.5017	10.5959
1.5	1.2701	1.6649	2.2182	3.6741	5.1507	6.8456	11.2957
1.6	1.2951	1.7164	2.2640	3.7891	5.3669	7.1915	12.0155
1.7	1.3202	1.7741	2.3097	3.8989	5.5792	7.5378	12.7231
1.8	1.3450	1.8385	2.3562	4.0029	5.7865	7.8829	13.5064
1.9	1.3687	1.9104	2.4046	4.1008	5.9875	8.2252	14.2731
2.0	1.3907	1.9904	2.4560	4.1922	6.1812	8.5629	15.0508

TABLE D.8 Confidence Limit Deviate Values for Normal and Log-Normal Distributions

CONFIDENCE LEVEL	SYSTEMATIC RECORD LENGTH n	EXCEEDENCE PROBABILITY								
		.002	.010	.020	.040	.100	.200	.500	.800	.990
.05	10	4.862	3.981	3.549	3.075	2.355	1.702	.580	−.317	−1.563
	15	4.304	3.520	3.136	2.713	2.068	1.482	.455	−.406	−1.677
	20	4.033	3.295	2.934	2.534	1.926	1.370	.387	−.460	−1.749
	25	3.868	3.158	2.809	2.425	1.838	1.301	.342	−.497	−1.801
	30	3.755	3.064	2.724	2.350	1.777	1.252	.310	−.525	−1.840
	40	3.608	2.941	2.613	2.251	1.697	1.188	.266	−.656	−1.896
	50	3.515	2.862	2.542	2.188	1.646	1.146	.237	−.592	−1.936
	60	3.448	2.807	2.492	2.143	1.609	1.116	.216	−.612	−1.966
	70	3.399	2.765	2.454	2.110	1.581	1.093	.199	−.629	−1.990
	80	3.360	2.733	2.425	2.083	1.559	1.076	.186	−.642	−2.010
	90	3.328	2.706	2.400	2.062	1.542	1.061	.175	−.652	−2.026
	100	3.301	2.684	2.380	2.044	1.527	1.049	.166	−.662	−2.040

continued

TABLE D.8 *(Continued)*

CONFIDENCE LEVEL	SYSTEMATIC RECORD LENGTH n	EXCEEDENCE PROBABILITY .002	.010	.020	.040	.100	.200	.500	.800	.990
.95	10	1.989	1.563	1.348	1.104	.712	.317	−.580	−1.702	−3.981
	15	2.121	1.677	1.454	1.203	.802	.406	−.455	−1.482	−3.520
	20	2.204	1.749	1.522	1.266	.858	.460	−.387	−1.370	−3.295
	25	2.264	1.801	1.569	1.309	.898	.497	−.342	−1.301	−3.158
	30	2.310	1.840	1.605	1.342	.928	.525	−.310	−1.252	−3.064
	40	2.375	1.896	1.657	1.391	.970	.565	−.266	−1.188	−2.941
	50	2.421	1.936	1.694	1.424	1.000	.592	−.237	−1.146	−2.862
	60	2.456	1.966	1.722	1.450	1.022	.612	−.216	−1.116	−2.807
	70	2.484	1.990	1.745	1.470	1.040	.629	−.199	−1.093	−2.765
	80	2.507	2.010	1.762	1.487	1.054	.642	−.186	−1.076	−2.733
	90	2.526	2.026	1.778	1.500	1.066	.652	−.175	−1.061	−2.706
	100	2.542	2.040	1.791	1.512	1.077	.662	−.166	−1.049	−2.684

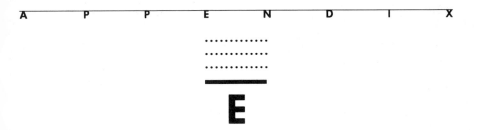

E

DERIVATION OF EQUATIONS FOR SWALE DESIGN

E.1

TRIANGULAR SHAPED SWALE

Recall that the total infiltration volume (F) per unit time equals the rate of infiltration (f) times the contact area (A) between the water and the swale bottom. This infiltration volume is expressed as

$$F = fA(\Delta t) \tag{E.1}$$

Whereas the contact area can be defined as the product of the wetted perimeter (P) and the length of the swale (L).

$$A = L \times P \tag{E.2}$$

487

For design, the volume of infiltration equals the volume of runoff water that enters the system, or

$$F = Q(\Delta t) \tag{E.3}$$

where Q = flow rate of water in ft^3/sec.

Substituting Equations (E.2) and (E.3) into Equation (E.1), we get

$$Q = L \times P \times f$$

and for solving L, we obtain

$$L = \frac{3600Q}{P \times f} \tag{E.4}$$

where 3600 is a conversion factor from cfs to ft^3/hr.

The perimeter of the swale depends on the rate of discharge through the swale. Thus, a relationship between the two is necessary to be able to use Equation E.4.

For a triangular section, the depth of flow (D) can be defined as

$$D = \frac{P}{2\sqrt{1 + Z^2}} \tag{E.5}$$

where

P = wetted perimeter of the swale
Z = horizontal component of side slope Z, which means Z horizontal per one vertical

so that

$$P = 2D\sqrt{1 + Z^2} \tag{E.6}$$

and the cross-sectional area of the flow can be expressed as

$$A = ZD^2 \tag{E.7}$$

One of the most common equations to compute flow of water in open channels is the Manning's equation. When the U.S. customary system of units is used, Manning's equation can be expressed as

$$Q = \frac{1.486}{n} AR^{2/3}S^{1/2} \tag{E.8}$$

where

Q = average flow rate (cfs)
n = coefficient of roughness
R = hydraulic radius (ft)
S = longitudinal slope of swale
A = cross-sectional area of flow (ft^2)

For trapezoidal sections, the hydraulic radius can be defined as

$$R = \frac{D}{2} \frac{Z}{\sqrt{1 + Z^2}} \tag{E.9}$$

Therefore, substituting Equations E.9 and E.7 into Equation E.8, we obtain

$$Q = \frac{1.486}{n} ZD^2 \left(\frac{DZ}{2\sqrt{1 + Z^2}} \right)^{2/3} (S)^{1/2} \tag{E.10}$$

or

$$Q = \frac{1.486}{1.59n} \frac{Z^{5/3}S^{1/2}D^{8/3}}{(1 + Z^2)^{1/3}} \tag{E.11}$$

and

$$Q = \frac{Z^{5/3}S^{1/2}D^{8/3}}{1.073n(1 + Z^2)^{1/3}} \tag{E.12}$$

Solving for D, it is found that

$$D = \left[\frac{1.073Qn(1 + Z^2)^{1/3}}{Z^{5/3}S^{1/2}} \right]^{3/8} \tag{E.13}$$

Substituting the value of D expressed in Equation E.13 into Equation E.6, the wetted perimeter can be expressed as

$$P = 2(1 + Z^2)^{1/2} \left[\frac{1.073Qn(1 + Z^2)^{1/3}}{Z^{5/3}S^{1/2}} \right]^{3/8} \tag{E.14}$$

Finally, if one substitutes the value of P into Equation E.4 we get

$$L = \frac{3600Q}{2\left[\dfrac{1.073Qn(1 + Z^2)^{1/3}}{Z^{5/3}S^{1/2}}\right]^{3/8}(1 + Z^2)^{1/2} \times \dfrac{f}{12}} \tag{E.15}$$

Note that f is divided by 12 in order to be able to use the common units of in./hr. Then,

$$L = \frac{3600Q}{\dfrac{2.054Q^{3/8}n^{3/8}(1 + Z^2)^{1/8}(1 + Z^2)^{1/2}f}{12Z^{5/8}S^{3/16}}} \tag{E.16}$$

and

$$L = \frac{21,032QZ^{5/8}S^{3/16}}{Q^{3/8}(1 + Z^2)^{5/8}fn^{3/8}} \tag{E.17}$$

Finally, we obtain

$$L = \frac{21,032Q^{5/8}Z^{5/8}S^{3/16}}{n^{3/8}(1 + Z^2)^{5/8}f} \tag{E.18}$$

where
L = length of swale (ft)
Q = average flow rate to be percolated (cfs)
Z = horizontal distance per one foot of elevation change inside slope
S = longitudinal or flow slope
n = Manning's roughness coefficient
f = infiltration rate (in./hr)

Equation E.18 can be used to predict the necessary length of swale to percolate certain amounts of runoff waters when U.S. Customary system of units is used.

When the International System of units is used, Manning's equation is written in the form

$$Q = \frac{1}{n}AR^{2/3}S^{1/2} \tag{E.19}$$

and Equation E.14 would be expressed as

$$P = 2 \left[\frac{1.5874 Q n (1 + Z^2)^{1/3}}{Z^{5/3} S^{1/2}} \right]^{3/8} (1 + Z^2)^{1/2} \qquad \text{(E.20)}$$

Substituting this value into Equation E.4, we get

$$L = \frac{3600Q}{2 \left[\dfrac{1.5874 Q n (1 + Z^2)^{1/3}}{Z^{5/3} S^{1/2}} \right]^{3/8} (1 + Z^2)^{1/2} \dfrac{f}{100}} \qquad \text{(E.21)}$$

Note that f is divided by 100 in order to use the infiltration rate in units of cm/hr. Then,

$$L = \frac{3600Q}{\dfrac{2.378 Q^{3/8} (1 + Z^2)^{5/8} f n^{3/8}}{100 Z^{5/8} S^{3/16}}} \qquad \text{(E.22)}$$

which can be expressed as

$$L = \frac{151,361 Q^{5/8} Z^{3/8} S^{3/16}}{n^{3/8} (1 + Z^2)^{5/8} f} \qquad \text{(E.23)}$$

where
L = length of swale (m)
Q = average flow rate (m³/s)
S = longitudinal slope
n = Manning's roughness coefficient
Z = side slope
f = infiltration rate (cm/hr)

Equation E.23 can be used to calculate the necessary length of swale (L) to percolate the runoff (Q) when the International System of units is used.

E.2

TRAPEZOIDAL SHAPED SWALE

Applying Manning's equation for U.S. Customary System of units, we obtain

$$Q = \frac{1.486}{n} A R^{2/3} S^{1/2} \tag{E.24}$$

For a trapezoidal section, the cross-sectional area of flow is defined

$$A = BD + ZD^2 \tag{E.25}$$

where

B = bottom width of the swale (ft)
D = depth of flow (ft)
Z = side slope

and, the wetted perimeter (P) can be defined as

$$P = B + 2D\sqrt{1 + Z^2} \tag{E.26}$$

Substituting $R = A/P$ and Equations E.25 and E.26 into Equation E.24, it is found that

$$Q = \frac{1.486}{n}(BD + ZD^2)\left[\frac{(B + ZD)D}{B + 2D(1 + Z^2)^{1/2}}\right]^{2/3} S^{1/2} \tag{E.27}$$

which equals

$$Q = \frac{1.486}{n}\frac{D^{5/3}(B + ZD)^{5/3}}{(B + 2D\sqrt{1 + Z^2})^{2/3}} S^{1/2} \tag{E.28}$$

For design, the most efficient section should be used. For a trapezoidal section, the most efficient section is defined as

$$\frac{B}{D} = 2(\sqrt{1 + Z^2} - Z) \tag{E.29}$$

Solving for D we get

$$D = \frac{B}{2(\sqrt{1 + Z^2} - Z)} \qquad (E.30)$$

Substituting

$$Q = \frac{1.486}{n} \frac{D^{5/3}\left[B + \dfrac{BZ}{2(\sqrt{1 + Z^2} - Z)}\right]^{5/3}}{\left[B + \dfrac{2B\sqrt{1 + Z^2}}{2(\sqrt{1 + Z^2} - Z)}\right]^{2/3}} S^{1/2} \qquad (E.31)$$

Solving for D we get

$$D = \left\{ \frac{nQ\left[B + \dfrac{B\sqrt{1 + Z^2}}{(\sqrt{1 + Z^2} - Z)}\right]^{2/3}}{1.486\left[B + \dfrac{BZ}{2(\sqrt{1 + Z^2} - Z)}\right]^{5/3}} \right\}^{3/5} \qquad (E.32)$$

and

$$D = \frac{Q^{3/5}\left(B + \dfrac{B\sqrt{1 + Z^2}}{\sqrt{1 + Z^2} - Z}\right)^{2/5} n^{3/5}}{1.268\left[B + \dfrac{BZ}{2(\sqrt{1 + Z^2} - Z)}\right]} \qquad (E.33)$$

Substituting in Equation E.26 we get

$$P = B + \frac{2Q^{3/5}n^{3/5}\left[\dfrac{B\sqrt{1 + Z^2}}{B + \sqrt{1 + Z^2} - Z}\right]^{2/5}}{1.268\left[B + \dfrac{BZ}{2(\sqrt{1 + Z^2} - Z)}\right]}(1 + Z^2)^{1/2} \qquad (E.34)$$

$$D = \left\{\frac{1.068nQ(1 + Z^2)^{1/3}}{S^{1/2}Z^{2/3}\left[2(1 + Z^2)^{1/2} - Z\right]}\right\}^{3/8} \qquad (E.35)$$

Substituting the value of D in Equation E.35 into Equation E.26 we get

$$P = B + 2\left\{\frac{1.068nQ(1 + Z^2)^{1/3}}{S^{1/2}Z^{2/3}\left[2(1 + Z^2)^{1/2} - Z\right]}\right\}^{3/8}(1 + Z^2)^{1/2} \quad \text{(E.36)}$$

Recall from the triangular section derivation that

$$L = \frac{Q(3600)}{P \times f} \quad \text{(E.37)}$$

which, for units of in./hr for the infiltration rate, can be expressed as

$$L = \frac{3600Q}{P \times \dfrac{f}{12}} \quad \text{(E.38)}$$

or

$$L = \frac{43,200Q}{P \times f} \quad \text{(E.39)}$$

Substituting the value of wetted perimeter defined in Equation E.36 into Equation E.39 we obtain

$$L = \frac{43,200Q}{\left(B + 2\left\{\dfrac{1.068nQ(1 + Z^2)^{1/3}}{S^{1/2}Z^{2/3}2\left[(1 + Z^2)^{1/2} - Z\right]}\right\}^{3/8}(1 + Z^2)^{1/2}\right)f} \quad \text{(E.40)}$$

where
L = length of swale (ft)
B = bottom width of swale (ft)
Q = average flow rate (cfs)
n = Manning's roughness coefficient
Z = side slope, horizontal component
S = longitudinal slope
f = infiltration rate of swale (in./hr)

If the International System of units is used, the length of swale necessary to percolate the runoff (Q) can be expressed as

$$L = \frac{360{,}000Q}{\left(B + 2 \left| \dfrac{nQ(1 + Z^2)^{1/3}}{S^{1/2}Z^{2/3}2\left[(1 + Z^2)^{1/2} - Z\right]} \right| \right)^{3/8} (1 + Z^2)^{1/2} f} \qquad (E.41)$$

where

L = length of swale (m)
Q = average flow rate (cfs)
f = infiltration rate (cm/hr)
n = Manning's roughness coefficient
Z = side slope, horizontal component
S = longitudinal slope
B = bottom width of swale (m)

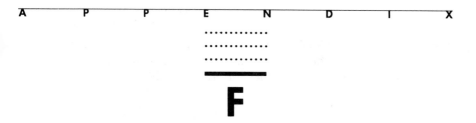

F

GUTTER,
INLETS,
AND ROADWAYS

F.1

INTRODUCTION

This appendix aids in the calculation of peak discharges and time of concentration for all small watersheds composed primarily of impervious surfaces (ie. roadways). The variables of major concern are the size of watershed, rainfall intensities, impervious materials, and the geometry of the roadway. The geometry variables include details on drainage slope, cross-slope, gutter cross sections, and inlet designs. These variables determine the depth of flow, velocity, and flow discharge, which then determines time of concentration.

Rainfall intensity to be used for estimating maximum discharge is specified by an estimate of the time of concentration. If the time of concentration were about 10 min, the FID curve will specify the intensity corresponding to a duration of 10 min and a specific return frequency (say 1 in 10 yr). Since the watershed area is relatively easy to define and the roadway watershed area is impervious, the peak discharge can be estimated using the rational formula. However, it may be necessary to check the assumption of the time of concentration because it affects the choice of rainfall intensity. Since there are many details of a hydraulic nature, not hydrologic, that affect roadway and gutter design, the details are outlined in this appendix.

F.2

GUTTER DESIGNS

Rainfall excess from a roadway watershed either is by overland flow or intercepted by some form of a gutter. Typical gutter shapes are of three types: Curb, V shaped, and curb with depressed gutter. All three cross-sections are shown in Figure F.1. Typical commercial area design is done using the curb type, whereas residential areas use both the curb and no-curb V shapes. The no-curb type is primarily used where swales (ditches that both infiltrate and transport) are used in a drainage plan, and usually average flow velocity is less than 2 fps.

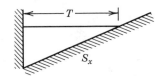

1. Curb with straight cross-slope

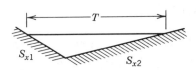

2. No curb, V-shaped gutter

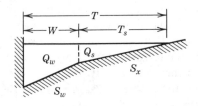

3. Curb with depressed gutter

FIGURE F.1 Typical gutter sections. *Source:* The Federal Highway Administration, 1984.

The variables used to determine flow rate (Q) for a gutter section are:

Longitudinal slope (ft/ft)	S
Cross-slope (ft/ft)	S_x
Width of flow (ft)	T
Depth of gutter flow (ft)	d
Width of depressed area (ft)	W

For a curb design with a depressed gutter area, two flow rates are calculated and designated as Q_s for standard area flow rate and Q_w for the depressed area. The total flow is the sum of Q_s and Q_w.

Since gutter flow is a form of open channel flow, a modified form of Manning's equation can be used. For such conditions, the hydraulic radius is adjusted for the very shallow flow. The modified formula for the curb type gutter is

$$Q = (0.56/n)S_x^{5/3}S^{1/2}T^{8/3} \tag{F.1}$$

TABLE F.1   Manning's n Values for Street and Pavement Gutters

TYPE OF GUTTER OR PAVEMENT	MANNING'S n
Concrete gutter, troweled finish	.012
Asphalt pavement	
Smooth texture	.013
Rough texture	.016
Concrete gutter with asphalt pavement	
Smooth	.013
Rough	.015
Concrete pavement	
Float finish	.014
Broom finish	.016
For gutters with small slope, where sediment may accumulate, increase above values of n by	.002

Note: Estimates are by the Federal Highway Administration.
Source: Department of Transportation, Federal Highway Administration (1984).

where

Q = gutter flow rate (cfs)
S_x = roadway cross-slope (ft/ft)
S = longitudinal slope (ft/ft)
T = width of flow (ft)
n = Manning's coefficient, see Table F.1

Manning's coefficients were determined by the U.S. Department of Transportation (1984). Various charts have been developed to aid in solving Manning's equation, one is shown in Figure F.2. Given longitudinal slope and cross-slope with an estimate of the water profile depth and width, and for a

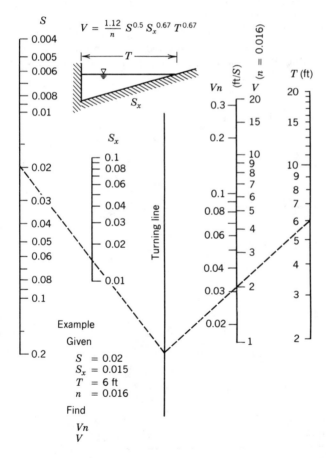

FIGURE F.2 Velocity in triangular gutter sections. *Source:* The Federal Highway Administration, 1984.

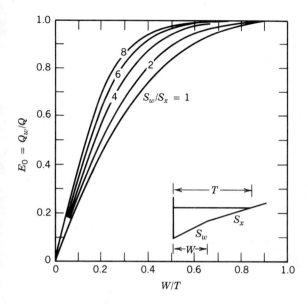

FIGURE F.3 The ratio of frontal flow to total gutter flow. *Source:* The Federal Highway Administration, 1984.

type of material, velocity (V) can be estimated. The quantity (Vn) refers to the product of velocity and Manning's coefficient. The solution to the example given in Figure F.2 is $V = 2$ ft/sec and $Vn = 0.032$ ft/sec.

For a depressed gutter or a section with composite cross slopes, use Figures F.1 and F.2 to calculate the flow Q_s, then use Figure F.3 to estimate the relative fraction of flow in the depressed section or

$$E_0 = \frac{Q_w}{Q} \tag{F.2}$$

where

E_0 = relative flow fraction
Q_w = flow rate in depressed area (cfs)
Q = total flow rate (cfs)

The total discharge is calculated from

$$Q = Q_s + Q_w \tag{F.3}$$

but $Q_w = E_0 Q$; thus

$$Q = Q_s + E_0 Q$$

and

$$Q = \frac{Q_s}{(1 - E_0)} \tag{F.4}$$

The depth of gutter flow and width of gutter flow are related by

$$d = TS_x \tag{F.5}$$

From the top of a continuous longitudinal slope to the end or bottom, the watershed area grows, and if the roadway width to the center line or cross-sectional slope peak remains constant, the area increases linearly. As the area increases, the depth and width of flow increases. Velocity of flow in the gutter is not constant but will vary with the depth and width of flow. If the watershed area varies linearly with gutter distance, an average velocity may be at first estimated as the velocity of flow at the midpoint in the watershed. This velocity is used to estimate time of concentration, and thus intensity of rainfall. Gutter design may be iterative. However, the gutter area must be capable of transporting the flow rate for any condition, otherwise overtopping or flooding will occur. Inlets to capture the water are designed to eliminate flooding.

F.3

INLET DESIGNS

There are essentially two types of inlets for the collection of stormwater: a curb opening and a gutter opening. These openings can also be used in combination. The typical curb and gutter inlets with grate are shown in Figure F.4. The curb inlet is formed by an opening in the curb face and generally has a depressed gutter section in front. The gutter inlet is formed by an opening in the gutter which is covered by a metal grate. These are usually square or rectangular in shape. However, in some applications, a slotted pipe that allows drainage to enter continuously along its longitudinal axis is used (see Figure F.5). The combination inlet is also shown in Figure F.5.

Curb-opening inlets allow a capture of a specific maximum quantity and flow rate. They operate as weirs up to a depth equal to the opening height (h), then the inlet operates as an orifice at about 1.4 times the opening height. There is a transition section of flow from the weir to orifice flow rate. The weir flow equation is

$$Q_i = 2.3(L + 1.8W_o)d^{1.5} \tag{F.6}$$

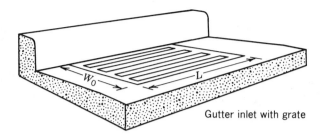

Gutter inlet with grate

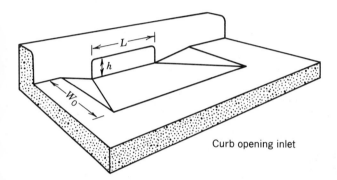

Curb opening inlet

FIGURE F.4   Perspective views of gutter and curb-opening inlets. *Source:* The Federal Highway Administration, 1984.

where
Q_i = capture flow rate of a curb opening (cfs)
L = length of curb opening (ft)
W_o = width of curb opening (ft)
d = depth at curb (ft) and $d \le h + d \le h + a$ where h = opening height (ft) and a = depressing depth (ft).

Without a depressed gutter, the weir flow equation for the curb opening is

$$Q_i = 2.3Ld^{1.5} \qquad d \le h \tag{F.7}$$

The orifice equation for the curb opening is

$$Q_i = 0.67A\left[2g\left(d - \frac{h}{2}\right)\right]^{1/2} \tag{F.8}$$

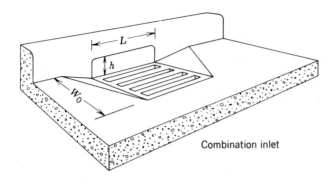

Combination inlet

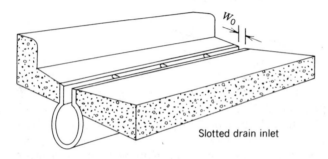

Slotted drain inlet

FIGURE F.5   Perspective views of combination and slotted drain inlets. *Source:* The Federal Highway Administration, 1984.

where

$A = hL$ = area of opening (ft^2)

g = acceleration due to gravity (32.2 ft/sec^2)

Capture efficiency is

$$E = \left(\frac{Q_i}{Q}\right)(100) \tag{F.9}$$

where

E = efficiency (%)

Q = total gutter flow (cfs)

Carryover is defined as

$$Q_c = Q - Q_i \qquad\qquad (F.10)$$

where Q_c = bypass or carry over flow (cfs). For a slotted pipe inlet with slot widths greater than 1.75 in., the length of inlet required for complete interception is

$$L_T = 0.6Q^{0.42}S^{0.3}\left(\frac{1}{nS_x}\right)^{0.6} \qquad\qquad (F.11)$$

where L_T = length of slotted pipe inlet (ft). The interception capacity of a gutter inlet can in very general terms be defined as

$$Q_i = 3.0P_G d^{1.5} \qquad\qquad (F.12)$$

where P_G = perimeter of a grate (ft).

There are many different grate configurations that affect the "catch" efficiency. Empirical design procedures for interception capacity and efficiencies for seven grate types, slotted inlets, curb inlets, and combination ones are given in greater detail by the U.S. Federal Highway Administration, FHWA (1984). Also presented are additional details on roadway geometry, embankment, inlets, bridge deck inlets, un-steady-state flow, and IDF curve development. Roadway designers are encouraged to review the FHWA publication and similar ones.

F.4

REFERENCE

Federal Highway Administration. 1984. HEC No. 12, U.S. Department of Transportation, McLean, VA.

....
....
....

G

DERIVATION OF THE FUNCTIONAL FORMS OF THE CONTINUOUS TIME CONVOLUTION FORMULAS

For this model, rainfall excess is convoluted with a routing function that can be changed with time to produce an output hydrograph. The model is derived from a mass balance, and it provides for nonlinearity of the routing function (impulse response) in the watershed. Another advantage of the routing response function is that it includes only one parameter to be estimated. This simplicity has enabled the convolution integral to be solved, thus allowing for time continuous solution of the model. Also, the model has been improved by representing the rainfall excess with straight line increasing or decreasing functions over any time interval to reflect more accurately the constantly changing amount of rainfall excess during a storm.

G.1

ROUTING FUNCTION

There have been several response functions developed by different hydrologists for the convolution integral, but most of these functions are based on empirical equations involving many parameters. The theory begins with the assumption that a linear relationship exists between the amount of storage and the outflow rate as given by

$$Q = kS \tag{G.1}$$

or in differential form

$$\frac{dQ}{dt} = k\left(\frac{dS}{dt}\right) \tag{G.2}$$

where
Q = outflow rate (L^3/t)
S = storage volume (L^3)
k = storage coefficient (t^{-1})
t = time (t)

where k is a type of friction factor reflecting the watershed's resistance to flow.

By using this relationship and a mass balance (continuity equation) for a watershed, the convolutional integral with the routing function can be derived in the following manner. The continuity equation for a watershed is

input − output ± generation = accumulation

Assuming there is no generation in the watershed then

$$r(t) - Q(t) = \frac{dS}{dt} \tag{G.3}$$

where $r(t)$ = input (rainfall excess rate).

Substitute the storage–outflow relationship (Equation G.2) into the continuity equation (Equation G.3), and there results

$$r(t) - Q(t) = \left(\frac{1}{k}\right)\left(\frac{dQ}{dt}\right) \tag{G.4}$$

Multiply both sides of Equation G.4 by the exponential function, e^{kt}, and we get

$$e^{kt}\frac{dQ}{dt} + ke^{kt}Q(t) = ke^{kt}r(t) \tag{G.5}$$

By definition:

$$\frac{d}{dt}(Qe^{kt}) = e^{kt}\frac{dQ}{dt} + ke^{kt}Q(t) \tag{G.6}$$

By substituting Equation G.5 into Equation G.6 we get:

$$\frac{d}{dt}(Qe^{kt}) = ke^{kt}r(t) \tag{G.7}$$

Separate the variables:

$$d(Qe^{kt}) = ke^{kt}r(t)\,dt \tag{G.8}$$

Integrate both sides:

$$\int d(Qe^{kt}) = \int ke^{kt}r(t)\,dt \tag{G.9}$$

Substitute τ (a dummy variable of time) for t in both sides of the equation where

$$t = \tau \qquad dt = d\tau$$

so when $t = 0$, $\tau = 0$, and when $t = t$, $\tau = t$:

$$d(Qe^{k\tau}) = ke^{k\tau}r(\tau)\,d\tau \tag{G.10}$$

Make the integrals definite by using the initial conditions at $t = 0$, $Q = Q_0$ and at $t = t$, $Q = Q(t)$:

$$\int_{Q_0,0}^{Q(t),t} d(Qe^{k\tau}) = \int_0^t ke^{k\tau}r(\tau)\,d\tau \tag{G.11}$$

By solving the left-hand side integral:

$$Q(t)e^{kt} - Q_0 = \int_0^t ke^{k\tau}r(\tau)\,d\tau \tag{G.12}$$

Q_0 is the runoff at $t = 0$ (also called base flow). If this flow is separated from the runoff caused by rainfall, then Q_0 is taken out of the equation and

$$Q(t)e^{kt} = \int_0^t ke^{k\tau}r(\tau)\,d\tau \tag{G.13}$$

where $Q(t)$ is the outflow rate excluding base flow. Dividing both sides of the equation by e^{kt} yields

$$Q(t) = e^{-kt} \int_0^t ke^{k\tau} r(\tau)\, d\tau \tag{G.14}$$

which equals

$$Q(t) = \int_0^t ke^{-(t-\tau)k} r(\tau)\, d\tau \tag{G.15}$$

Equation G.15 is the convolution equation using the assumption of an exponential routing response. The rainfall excess function is $r(\tau)$ and $ke^{-(t-\tau)k}$ is the exponential routing function.

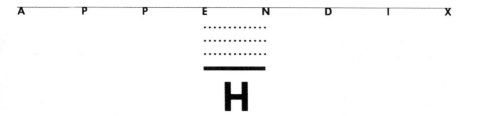

H

SELECTED
HYDROLOGIC
SOIL
CLASSIFICATIONS

TABLE H.1   Soil Names and Hydrologic Classifications

Aaberg	C	Aberdeen	D	Abscota	B
Aastad	B	Abes	D	Absher	D
Abac	D	Abilene	C	Absted	D
Abajo	C	Abington	B	Acacio	C
Abbott	D	Abiqua	C	Academy	C
Abbottstown	C	Abo	B/C	Acadia	D
Abcal	D	Abok	D	Acana	D
Abegg	B	Abra	C	Acasco	D
Abela	B	Abraham	B	Aceitunas	B
Abell	B	Absarkee	C	Acel	D

continued

TABLE H.1   *(Continued)*

Acker	B	Aeneas	B	Akela	C
Ackmen	B	Aetna	B	Aladdin	B
Acme	C	Afton	D	Alae	A
Aco	B	Agar	B	Alaeloa	B
Acolita	B	Agassiz	D	Alaga	A
Acoma	C	Agate	D	Alakai	D
Acove	C	Agawam	B	Alama	B
Acree	C	Agency	C	Alamance	B
Acrelane	C	Ager	D	Alamo	D
Acton	B	Agner	B	Alamosa	C
Acuff	B	Agnew	B/C	Alapaha	D
Acworth	B	Agnus	B	Alapai	A
Acy	C	Agua	B	Alban	B
Ada	B	Agua Dulce	C	Albano	D
Adair	D	Agua Fria	C	Albany	C
Adams	A	Aguadilla	B	Albaton	D
Adamson	B	Agualt	B	Albee	C
Adamstown		Agueda	B	Albemarle	B
Adamsville	C	Aguilita	B	Albertville	C
Adaton	D	Aguirre	D	Albia	C
Adaven	D	Agustin	B	Albion	B
Addielou	C	Ahatone	D	Albrights	C
Addison	D	Ahl	C	Alcalde	C
Addy	C	Ahlstrom	C	Alcester	B
Ade	A	Ahmeek	B	Alcoa	B
Adel	A	Aholt	D	Alcona	B
Adelaide	D	Ahtanum	C	Alcova	B
Adelanto	B	Ahwahnee	C	Alda	C
Adelino	B	Aibonito	C	Aldax	D
Adelphia	C	Aiken	B/C	Alden	D
Adena	C	Aikman	D	Alder	B
Adger	D	Ailey	B	Alderdale	C
Adilis	A	Ainakea	B	Alderwood	C
Adirondack		Airmont	C	Aldino	C
Adiv	B	Airotsa	B	Aldwell	C
Adjuntas	C	Airport	D	Aleknagik	B
Adkins	B	Aits	B	Alemeda	C
Adler	C	Ajo	C	Alex	B
Adolph	D	Akaka	A	Alexandria	C
Adrian	A/D	Akaska	B	Alexis	B

continued

TABLE H.1   *(Continued)*

Alford	B	Alpon	B	Ammon	B
Algansee	B	Alpowa	B	Amole	C
Algerita	B	Alps	C	Amor	B
Algiers	C/D	Alsea	B	Amos	C
Algoma	B/D	Alspaugh	C	Amsden	B
Alhambra	B	Alstad	B	Amsterdam	B
Alice	A	Alstown	B	Amtoft	D
Alicel	B	Altamont	D	Amy	D
Alicia	B	Altavista	C	Anacapa	B
Alida	B	Altdorf	D	Anahuac	D
Alikchi	B	Altmar	B	Anamite	D
Aline	A	Alto	C	Anapra	B
Alko	D	Altoga	C	Anasazi	B
Allagash	B	Alton	B	Anatone	D
Allard	B	Altus	B	Anaverde	D
Allegheny	B	Altvan	B	Anawalt	D
Allemands	D	Alum	B	Ancho	B
Allen	B	Alusa	D	Anchor Bay	D
Allendale	C	Alvin	B	Anchor Point	D
Allens Park	B	Alvira	C	Anchorage	A
Allensville	C	Alviso	D	Anclote	D
Allentine	D	Alvor	C	Anco	C
Allenwood	B	Amador	D	Anderly	C
Allessio	B	Amagon	D	Anders	C
Alley	C	Amalu	D	Anderson	B
Alliance	B	Amana	B	Andes	C
Alligator	D	Amargosa	D	Andorinia	C
Allis	D	Amarillo	B	Andover	D
Allison	C	Amasa	B	Andreen	B
Allouez	C	Amberson		Andreeson	C
Alloway		Amboy	C	Andres	B
Almac	B	Ambraw	C	Andrews	C
Almena	C	Amedee	A	Aned	D
Almont	D	Amelia	B	Aneth	A
Almy	B	Amenia	B	Angelica	D
Aloha	C	Americus	A	Angelina	B/D
Alonso	B	Ames	C	Angelo	C
Alovar	C	Amesha	B	Angie	C
Alpena	B	Amherst	C	Angle	A
Alpha	C	Amity	C	Anglen	B

continued

TABLE H.1 *(Continued)*

Angola	C	Appling	B	Arlando	B
Angostura	B	Apron	B	Arle	B
Anhalt	D	Apt	C	Arling	D
Aniak	D	Aptakisic	B	Arlington	C
Anita	D	Araby		Arloval	C
Ankeny	A	Arada	C	Armagh	D
Anlauf	C	Aransas	D	Armijo	D
Annabella	B	Arapien	C	Armington	D
Annandale	C	Arave	D	Armjohee	D
Anniston	B	Araveton	B	Armour	B
Anoka	A	Arbela	C	Armster	C
Anones	C	Arbone	B	Armstrong	D
Ansari	D	Arbor	B	Arnegard	B
Ansel	B	Arbuckle	B	Arnhart	C
Anselmo	A	Arcata	B	Arnheim	C
Anson	B	Arch	B	Arno	D
Ant Flat	C	Archabal	B	Arnold	B
Antelope Springs	C	Archer	C	Arnot	C/D
Antero	C	Archin	C	Arny	A
Antho	B	Arco	B	Arosa	C
Anthony	B	Arcola	C	Arp	C
Antigo	B	Ard	C	Arrington	B
Antilon	B	Arden	B	Arritola	D
Antioch	D	Ardenvoir	B	Arrolime	C
Antler	C	Ardilla	C	Arron	D
Antoine	C	Ardostook		Arrow	B
Antrobus	B	Aredale	B	Arrowsmith	B
Anty	B	Arena	C	Arroyo Seco	B
Anvik	B	Arenales		Arta	C
Anway	B	Arendsa	A	Artois	C
Anza	B	Arendtsville	B	Arvada	D
Anziano	C	Arenzville	B	Arvana	C
Apache	D	Argonaut	D	Arveson	D
Apakuie	A	Arguello	B	Arvilla	B
Apishapa	C	Argyle	B	Arzell	C
Apison	B	Arho	B	Asa	B
Apopka	A	Ariel	C	Asbury	B
Appian	C	Arizo	A	Aschoff	B
Applegate	C	Arkabutla	C	Ash Springs	C
Appleton	C	Arkport	B	Ashby	C

continued

TABLE H.1   *(Continued)*

Ashcroft	B	Atsion	C	Azarman	C
Ashdale	B	Atterberry	B	Azeltine	B
Ashe	B	Attewan	A	Azfield	B
Ashkum	C	Attica	B	Aztalan	B
Ashlar	B	Attleboro		Aztec	B
Ashley	A	Atwater	B	Azule	C
Ashton	B	Atwell	C/D	Azwell	B
Ashue	B	Atwood	B	Babb	A
Ashuelot	C	Au Gres	B	Babbington	B
Ashwood	C	Aubbeenaubbe	B	Babcock	C
Askew	C	Auberry	C/D	Babylon	A
Aso	C	Auburn	D	Baca	C
Asotin	C	Auburndale	B	Bach	D
Aspen	B	Audian	C	Bachus	C
Aspermont	B	Augsburg	B	Backbone	A
Assalon	B	Augusta	C	Baculan	A
Assinniboine	B	Auld	D	Badenaugh	B
Assumption	B	Aura	B	Badger	C
Astatula	A	Aurora	C	Badgerton	B
Astor	A/D	Austin	C	Bado	D
Astoria	B	Austwell	D	Badus	C
Atascadero	C	Auxvasse	D	Bagard	C
Atascosa	D	Auzqui	B	Bagdad	B
Atco	B	Ava	C	Baggott	D
Atencio	B	Avalanche	B	Bagley	B
Atepic	D	Avalon	B	Bahem	B
Athelwold	B	Avery	B	Baile	D
Athena	B	Avon	C	Bainville	C
Athens	B	Avonburg	D	Baird Hollow	C
Atherly	B	Avondale	E	Bajura	D
Atherton	B/D	Awbrey	D	Bakeoven	D
Athmar	C	Axtell	D	Baker	C
Athol	B	Ayar	D	Baker Pass	B
Atkinson	B	Aycock	B	Balaam	A
Atlas	D	Ayr	B	Balch	D
Atlee	C	Ayres	D	Balcom	B
Atmore	B/D	Ayrshire	C	Bald	C
Atoka	C	Aysees	B	Balder	C
Aton	B	Ayun	B	Baldock	B/C
Atrypa	C	Azaar	C	Baldwin	D

continued

TABLE H.1   *(Continued)*

Baldy	B	Barishman	C	Bassfield	B
Bale	C	Barker	C	Bassler	D
Ballard	B	Barkerville	C	Bastian	D
Baller	D	Barkley	B	Bastrop	B
Ballinger	C	Barlane	D	Bata	A
Balm	B/C	Barling	C	Batavia	B
Balman	B/C	Barlow	B	Bates	B
Balon	B	Barnard	D	Bath	C
Baltic	D	Barnes	B	Batterson	D
Baltimore	B	Barneston	B	Battle Creek	C
Balto	D	Barney	A	Batza	D
Bamber	B	Barnhardt	B	Baudette	B
Bamforth	B	Barnstead		Bauer	C
Bancas	B	Barnum	B	Baugh	B/C
Bancroft	B	Baron	C	Baxter	B
Bandera	B	Barrada	D	Baxtervillle	B
Bango	C	Barrett	D	Bayamon	B
Bangston	A	Barrington	B	Bayard	A
Bangur	B	Barron	B	Baybord	D
Bankard	A	Barronett	C	Bayerton	C
Banks	A	Barrows	D	Baylor	D
Banner	C	Barry	D	Bayshore	B/C
Bannerville	C/D	Barstow	B	Bayside	C
Bannock	B	Barth	C	Bayucos	D
Banquete	D	Bartine	C	Baywood	A
Barabou	B	Bartle	D	Bazette	C
Baraga	C	Bartley	C	Bazile	B
Barbary	D	Barton	B	Bead	C
Barboor	B	Bartonflat	B	Beadle	C
Barbourville	B	Bascom	B	Beales	A
Barclay	C	Basehor	D	Bear Basin	B
Barco	B	Bashaw	D	Bear Creek	C
Barcus	B	Basher	B	Bear Lake	C
Bard	D	Basile	D	Bear Prairie	C
Barden	C	Basin	C	Beardall	C
Bardley	C	Basinger	C	Bearden	D
Barela	C	Basket	C	Beardstown	A
Barfield	D	Bass	A	Bearmough	B
Barfuss	B	Bassel	B	Bearpaw	B
Barge	C	Bassett	B	Bearskin	D

continued

TABLE H.1   *(Continued)*

Beasley	C	Belfast	B	Benz	D
Beasun	C	Belfield	B	Beotia	B
Beaton	C	Belfore	B	Beowawe	D
Beatty	C	Belgrade	B	Bercail	C
Beaucoup	B	Belinda	D	Berda	B
Beauford	D	Belknap	C	Berea	C
Beaumont	D	Bellamy	C	Bereniceton	B
Beauregard	C	Bellavista	D	Berent	A
Beausite	B	Belle	B	Bergland	D
Beauvais	B	Bellefontaine		Bergstrom	B
Beaverton	A	Bellicum	B	Berino	B
Beck	C	Bellingham	C	Berkeley	
Becker	B	Bellpine	C	Berks	C
Becket	C	Belmont	B	Berkshire	B
Beckley	B	Belmore	B	Berlin	C
Beckton	D	Belt	D	Bermaldo	B
Beckwith	C	Belted	D	Bermesa	C
Beckwourth	B	Belton	C	Bermudian	B
Becreek	B	Beltrami	B	Bernal	D
Bedford	C	Beltsville	C	Bernard	D
Bedington	B	Beluga	D	Bernardino	C
Bedner	C	Belvoir	C	Bernardston	C
Beebe	A	Ben Hur	B	Bernhill	B
Beecher	C	Ben Lumond	B	Bernice	A
Beechy		Benclare	C	Berning	C
Beehive	B	Benevola	C	Berrendos	D
Beek	C	Benewah	C	Berryland	D
Beenom	D	Benfirld	C	Bertelson	B
Beezar	B	Benge	B	Berthoud	B
Begay	B	Benin	D	Bertie	C
Begoshian	C	Benito	D	Bertolotti	B
Behanin	B	Benjamin	D	Bertrand	B
Behemotosh	B	Benman	A	Berville	D
Behring	D	Benndale	B	Beryl	B
Beirman	D	Bennett	C	Bessemer	B
Bejucos	B	Bennington	D	Bethany	C
Belcher	D	Benoit	D	Bethel	D
Belden	D	Benson	C/D	Betteravia	C
Belding	B	Benteen	B	Betts	B
Belen	C	Bentonville	C	Beulah	B

continued

TABLE H.1   *(Continued)*

Bevent	B	Birchwood	C	Blackwater	D
Beverly	B	Birdow	B	Blackwell	B/D
Bew	D	Birds	C	Bladen	D
Bewleyville	B	Birdsall	D	Blago	D
Bewlin	D	Birdsboro	B	Blaine	B
Bexar	C	Birdsley	D	Blair	C
Bezzant	B	Birkbeck	B	Blairton	C
Bibb	B/D	Bisbee	A	Blake	C
Bibon	A	Biscay	C	Blakeland	A
Bickelton	B	Bishop	B/C	Blakeney	C
Bickleton	C	Bisping	B	Blakeport	B
Bickmore	C	Bissell	B	Blalock	D
Bicondoa	C	Bisti	C	Blamer	C
Biddeford	D	Bit	D	Blanca	B
Biddleman	C	Bitter Spring	C	Blanchard	A
Bidman	C	Bitteron	A	Blanchester	B/D
Bidwell	B	Bitterroot	C	Bland	C
Bieber	D	Bitton	B	Blandford	C
Bienville	A	Bixby	B	Blanding	B
Big Blue	D	Bjork	C	Blaney	B
Big Horn	C	Blachly	C	Blanket	C
Big Timber	D	Black Butte	C	Blanton	A
Bigel	A	Black Canyon	D	Blanyon	C
Bigelow	C	Black Mountain	D	Blasdell	A
Bigetty	C	Black Ridge	D	Blasingame	C
Biggs	A	Blackburn	B	Blazon	D
Biggsville	B	Blackcap	A	Blencoe	C
Bignell	B	Blackett	B	Blend	D
Bigwin	D	Blackfoot	B/C	Blendon	B
Bijou	A	Blackhall	D	Blethen	B
Billett	A	Blackhawk	D	Blevins	B
Billings	C	Blackleaf	B	Blevinton	B/D
Bindle	B	Blackleed	A	Blichton	D
Binford	B	Blacklock	D	Bliss	D
Bingham	B	Blackman	C	Blockton	C
Binnsville	D	Blackoak	C	Blodgett	A
Bins	B	Blackpipe	C	Blomford	B
Binton	C	Blackrock	B	Bloom	C
Bippus	B	Blackston	B	Bloomfield	A
Birch	A	Blacktail	B	Blooming	B

continued

TABLE H.1 *(Continued)*

Bloor	D	Bombay	B	Bosco	B
Blossom	C	Bon	B	Bosket	B
Blount	C	Bonaccord	D	Bosler	B
Blountville	C	Bonaparte	A	Bosque	B
Blucher	C	Bond	D	Boss	D
Blue Earth	D	Bondranch	D	Boston	C
Blue Lake	A	Bondurant	B	Bostwick	B
Blue Star	B	Bone	D	Boswell	D
Bluebell	C	Bong	B	Bosworth	D
Bluejoint	B	Bonham	C	Botella	B
Bluepoint	B	Bonifay	A	Bothwell	C
Bluewing	B	Bonilla	B	Bottineau	C
Bluffdale	C	Bonita	D	Bottle	A
Bluffton	D	Bonn	D	Boulder	B
Bluford	D	Bonner	B	Boulder Lake	D
Bly	B	Bonnet	B	Boulder Point	B
Blythe	D	Bonneville	B	Boulflat	D
Boardtree	C	Bonnick	A	Bourne	C
Bobs	D	Bonnie	D	Bow	C
Bobtail	B	Bonsall	D	Bowbac	C
Bock	B	Bonta	C	Bowbells	B
Bodell	D	Bonti	C	Bowdoin	D
Bodenburg	B	Booker	D	Bowdre	C
Bodine	B	Boomer	B	Bowers	C
Boel	A	Boone	A	Bowie	B
Boelus	A	Boonesboro	B	Bowman	B/D
Boesel	B	Boonton	C	Bowmansville	C
Boettcher	C	Booth	C	Boxelder	C
Bogan	C	Boracho	C	Boxwell	C
Bogart	B	Borah	A/D	Boy	A
Bogue	D	Borda	D	Boyce	B/D
Bohannon	C	Bordeaux	B	Boyd	D
Bohemian	B	Borden	B	Boyer	B
Boistfort	C	Border	B	Boynton	
Bolar	C	Bornstedt	C	Boysag	D
Bold	B	Borrego	C	Boysen	D
Boles	C	Borup	B	Bozarth	C
Bolivar	B	Borvant	D	Boze	B
Bolivia	B	Borza	C	Bozeman	A
Bolton	B	Bosanko	D	Braceville	C

continued

TABLE H.1   *(Continued)*

Bracken	D	Bremen	B	Brinkerton	D
Brackett	C	Bremer	B	Briscot	B
Brad	D	Bremo	C	Brite	C
Braddock	C	Brems	A	Britton	C
Bradenton	B/D	Brenda	C	Brizam	A
Brader	D	Brennan	B	Broad	C
Bradford	B	Brenner	C/D	Broad Canyon	B
Bradshaw	B	Brent	C	Broadalbin	C
Bradway	D	Brenton	B	Broadax	B
Brady	B	Brentwood	B	Broadbrook	C
Bradyville	C	Bresser	B	Broadhead	C
Braham	B	Brevard	B	Broadhurst	D
Brainerd	B	Brevort	B	Brock	D
Brallier	D	Brewer	C	Brockliss	C
Bram	B	Brewster	D	Brockman	C
Bramard	B	Brewton	C	Brocko	B
Bramble	C	Brickel	C	Brockport	D
Bramwell	C	Brickton	C	Brockton	D
Brand	D	Bridge	C	Brockway	B
Brandenburg	A	Bridgehampton	B	Brody	C
Brandon	B	Bridgeport	B	Broe	B
Brandywine	C	Bridger	A	Brogan	B
Branford	B	Bridgeson	B/C	Brogdon	B
Brantford	B	Bridget	B	Brolliar	D
Branyon	D	Bridgeville	B	Bromo	B
Brashear	C	Bridgport	B	Bronaugh	B
Brassfield	B	Briedwell	B	Broncho	B
Bratton	B	Brief	B	Bronson	B
Bravane	D	Briensburg		Bronte	C
Braxton	C	Briggs	A	Brooke	C
Braymill	A/D	Briggsdale	C	Brookfield	B
Brays	D	Briggsville	C	Brookings	B
Brayton	C	Brighton	A/D	Brooklyn	D
Brazito	A	Brightwood	C	Brookside	C
Brazos	A	Brill	B	Brookston	B/C
Brea	B	Brim	C	Brooksville	D
Breckenridge	D	Brimfield	C/D	Broomfield	D
Brecknock	B	Brimley	B	Broseley	B
Breece	B	Brinegar	B	Bross	B
Bregar	D	Brinkert	C	Broughton	D

continued

TABLE H.1   *(Continued)*

Broward	C	Bukreek	B	Buse	B
Brownell	B	Bull Run	B	Bush	B
Brownfield	A	Bull Trail	B	Bushnell	C
Brownlee	B	Bullion	D	Bushvalley	D
Broyles	B	Bullrey	B	Buster	C
Bruce	D	Bully	B	Butano	C
Bruffy	C	Bumgard	B	Butler	D
Bruin	C	Buncombe	A	Butlertown	C
Bruneel	B/C	Bundo	B	Butte	C
Bruno	A	Bundyman	C	Butterfield	C
Brunt	C	Bunejug	C	Button	C
Brush		Bunker	D	Buxin	D
Brussett	B	Bunselmeier	C	Buxton	C
Bryan	A	Buntingville	B/C	Byars	D
Brycan	B	Bunyan	B	Bynum	C
Bryce	D	Burbank	A	Byron	A
Bucan	D	Burch	B	Caballo	B
Buchanan	C	Burchard	B	Cabarton	D
Buchenau	C	Burchell	B/C	Cabba	C
Bucher	C	Burdett	C	Cabbart	D
Buckhouse	A	Buren	C	Cabezon	D
Buckingham		Burgess	C	Cabin	C
Buckland	C	Burgi	B	Cabinet	C
Bucklebar	B	Burgin	D	Cable	D
Buckley	B/C	Burke	C	Cabo Rojo	C
Bucklon	D	Burkhardt	B	Cabot	D
Buckner	A	Burleigh	D	Cacapon	B
Buckney	A	Burleson	D	Cache	D
Bucks	B	Burlington	A	Cacique	C
Buckskin	C	Burma		Caddo	D
Bucoda	C	Burmester	D	Cadeville	D
Budd	B	Burnac	C	Cadmus	B
Bude	C	Burnette	B	Cadoma	D
Buell	B	Burnham	D	Cador	C
Buena Vista	B	Burnside	B	Cagey	C
Buff Peak	C	Burnsville	B	Caguabo	D
Buffington	B	Burnt Lake	B	Cagwin	B
Buffmeyer	B	Burris	D	Cahaba	B
Buick	C	Burt	D	Cahill	B
Buist	B	Burton	B	Cahone	C

continued

TABLE H.1   *(Continued)*

Cahto	C	Camargo	B	Canoncito	B
Caid	B	Camarillo	B/D	Canova	B/D
Cairo	D	Camas	A	Cantala	B
Cajalco	C	Camascreek	B/D	Canton	B
Cajon	A	Cambridge	C	Cantril	B
Calabar	D	Camden	B	Cantua	B
Calabasas	B	Cameron	D	Canutio	B
Calais	C	Cameyville	C	Canyon	D
Calamine	D	Camgeny	C	Capac	B
Calapooya	C	Camillus	B	Capay	D
Calawah	B	Camp	B	Cape	D
Calco	C	Campbell	B/C	Cape Fear	D
Calder	D	Camphora	B	Capers	D
Caldwell	B	Campia	B	Capillo	C
Caleast	C	Campo	C	Caples	C
Caleb	B	Campone	B/C	Capps	B
Calera	C	Campspass	C	Capshaw	C
Calhi	A	Campus	B	Capulin	B
Calhoun	D	Camroden	C	Caputa	C
Calico	D	Cana	C	Caraco	C
Califon	D	Canaan	C/D	Caralampi	B
Calimus	B	Canadian	B	Carbo	C
Calita	B	Canadice	D	Carbol	D
Caliza	B	Canandaigua	D	Carbondale	D
Calkins	C	Canaseraga	C	Carbury	B
Callabo	C	Canaveral	C	Carcity	D
Callahan	C	Canburn	D	Cardiff	B
Calleguas	D	Cande	B	Cardington	C
Callings	C	Candelero	C	Cardon	D
Calloway	C	Cane	C	Carey	B
Calmar	B	Caneadea	D	Carey Lake	B
Calneva	C	Caneek	B	Careytown	D
Calouse	B	Canel	B	Cargill	C
Calpine	B	Canelo	D	Caribe	B
Calvert	D	Caney	C	Caribel	B
Calverton	C	Canez	B	Caribou	B
Calvin	C	Canfield	C	Carlin	D
Calvista	D	Canisted	C	Carlinton	B
Cam	B	Canninger	D	Carlisle	A/D
Camaguey	D	Cannon	B	Carlotta	B

continued

TABLE H.1   *(Continued)*

Carlow	D	Tusel	C	Ulricher	B
Carlsbad	C	Tuskeego	C	Ulupalakua	B
Carlsborg	A	Tusler	B	Uly	B
Carlson	C	Tusquitee	B	Ulysses	B
Carlton	B	Tustin	B	Uma	A
Carmi	B	Tustumena	B	Umapine	B/C
Carnasaw	C	Tuthill	B	Umiat	D
Carnegie	C	Tutni	B	Umikoa	B
Carnero	C	Tutwiler	B	Umil	D
Carney	D	Tuxedo		Umnak	B
Caroline	C	Tuxekan	B	Umpa	B
Carr	B	Twin Creek	B	Umpqua	B
Carrisalitos	D	Twining	C	Una	D
Carrizo	A	Twisp	B	Unadilla	B
Carsitas	A	Two Dot	C	Unaweep	B
Carsley	C	Tybo	D	Uncom	B
Carso	D	Tyee	D	Uncompangre	D
Carson	D	Tygart	D	Uneeda	B
Carstairs	B	Tyler	D	Ungers	B
Carstump	C	Tyndall	B/C	Union	C
Cart	B	Tyner	A	Uniontown	B
Cartagena	D	Tyrone	C	Unionville	C
Cartecay	C	Tyson	C	Unisun	C
Caruso	C	Uana	D	Updike	D
Caruthersville	B	Ubar	C	Upsal	C
Carver	A	Ubly	B	Upsata	A
Carwile	D	Ucola	D	Upshur	C
Turnbow	C	Ucolo	C	Upton	C
Turner	B	Ucopia	B	Uracca	B
Turnerville	B	Uddlpho	C	Urbana	C
Turney	B	Udel	D	Urbo	D
Turrah	D	Uffens	D	Urich	D
Turret	B	Ugak	D	Urne	B
Turria	C	Uhland	B	Ursine	D
Turson	B/C	Uhlig	B	Urtah	C
Tuscan	D	Uinta	B	Urwil	D
Tuscarawas	C	Ukiah	C	Usal	B
Tuscarora	C	Ulen	B	Ushar	B
Tuscola	B	Ullda	B	Usine	B
Tuscumbia	D	Ulm	B	Uska	D

continued

TABLE H.1   *(Continued)*

Utaline	B	Vandergrift	C	Venice	D
Ute	C	Vanderhoff	D	Venlo	D
Utica	A	Vanderlip	A	Venus	B
Utley	B	Vanet	D	Verboort	D
Utuado	B	Vang	B	Verde	C
Uvada	D	Vanhorn	B	Verdel	D
Uvalde	C	Vannoy	B	Verdella	D
Uwala	B	Vanoss	B	Verdico	D
Vacherie	C	Vantage	C	Verdigris	B
Vader	B	Varco	C	Verdun	D
Vado	B	Varelum	C	Vergennes	D
Vaiden	D	Varick	D	Verhalen	D
Vailton	B	Varina	C	Vermejo	D
Valby	C	Varna	C	Vernal	B
Valco	C	Varro	B	Vernalis	B
Valdez	B/C	Varysburg	B	Vernia	A
Vale	B	Vashti	C	Vernon	D
Valencia	B	Vasquez	B	Verona	C
Valent	A	Vassalboro	D	Vesser	C
Valentine	A	Vassar	B	Veston	D
Valera	C	Vastine	C	Vetal	A
Valkaria	B/D	Vaucluse	C	Veteran	B
Vallan	D	Vaughnsville	C	Veyo	D
Vallecitos	C/D	Vayas	D	Via	B
Valleono	B	Veal	B	Vian	B
Vallers	C	Veazie	B	Viboras	D
Valmont	C	Vebar	B	Viborg	B
Valmy	B	Vecont	D	Vickery	C
Valois	B	Vega	C	Vicksburg	B
Vamer	D	Vega Alta	C	Victor	A
Van Buren		Vega Baja	C	Victoria	D
Van Dusen	B	Vekol	D	Victory	B
Van Nostern	B	Velda	B	Vicu	D
Van Wagoner	D	Velma	B	Vida	B
Vanajo	D	Velva	B	Vidrine	C
Vananda	D	Vena	C	Vieja	D
Vance	C	Venango	C	Vienna	B
Vanda	D	Venator	D	Vieques	B
Vandalia	C	Veneta	C	View	C
Vanderdasson	D	Venezia	D	Vigar	C

continued

TABLE H.1   *(Continued)*

Vigo	D	Volkmar	B	Wahtigup	B
Vigus	C	Volney	B	Wahtum	D
Viking	D	Volperie	C	Waiaha	D
Vil	D	Voltaire	D	Waiakoa	C
Vilas	A	Volumer	D	Waialeale	D
Villa Grove	B	Volusia	C	Waialua	B
Villars	B	Vona	B	Waiawa	D
Villy	D	Vore	B	Waihuna	D
Vina	B	Vrodman	B	Waikaloa	B
Vincennes	C	Vulcan	C	Waikane	B
Vincent	C	Vylach	D	Waikapu	B
Vineyard	C	Wabanica	D	Waikomo	D
Vingo	B	Wabash	D	Wailuku	B
Vining	C	Wabasha	D	Waimea	B
Vinita	C	Wabassa	B/D	Wainee	B
Vinland	C	Wabek	B	Wainola	A
Vinsad	C	Waca	C	Waipahu	C
Vint	B	Wacota	B	Waiska	B
Vinton	B	Wacousta	C	Waits	B
Vira	C	Wadams	B	Wake	D
Viraton	C	Waddell	B	Wakeen	B
Virden	C	Waddups	B	Wakefield	B
Virgil	B	Wadell	B	Wakeland	B/D
Virgin Peak	D	Wadena	B	Wakonda	C
Virgin River	D	Wadesboro	B	Wakulla	A
Virtue	C	Wadleigh	D	Walcott	B
Visalia	B	Wadmalaw	D	Waldeck	C
Vista	C	Wadsworth	C	Waldo	D
Vives	B	Wages	B	Waldron	D
Vivi	B	Wagner	D	Waldroup	D
Vlasaty	C	Wagram	A	Wales	B
Voca	C	Waha	C	Walford	C
Vodermaier	B	Wahee	D	Walke	C
Voladora	B	Wahiawa	B	Wall	B
Volco	D	Wahikuli	B	Walla Walla	B
Volente	C	Wahkeena	B	Wallace	B
Volga	D	Wahkiacus	B	Waller	B/D
Volin	B	Wahluke	B	Wallington	C
Volinia	B	Wahmonie	D	Wallis	B
Volke	C	Wahpeton	C	Wallkill	C/D

continued

TABLE H.1   *(Continued)*

Wallman	C	Warrenton	B/D	Waukee	B
Wallowa	C	Warrior		Waukegan	B
Wallpack	C	Warsaw	B	Waukena	D
Wallrock	B/C	Warsing	B	Waukon	B
Wallsburg	D	Warwick	A	Waumbek	B
Wallson	B	Wasatch	A	Waurika	D
Walpole	C	Wasepi	B	Wauseon	B/D
Walsh	B	Washburn		Waverly	B/D
Walshville	D	Washde	C	Wawaka	C
Walters	A	Washington	B	Waycup	B
Walton	C	Washougal	B	Wayden	D
Walum	B	Washtenaw	C/D	Wayland	C/D
Walvan	B	Wasidja	B	Wayne	B
Wamba	B/C	Wasilla	D	Waynesboro	B
Wamic	B	Wassaic	B	Wayside	
Wampsville	B	Watab	C	Wea	B
Wanatah	B	Watauga	B	Weaver	C
Wanblee	D	Watchaug	B	Webb	C
Wando	A	Watchung	D	Weber	B
Wanetta	A	Waterboro		Webster	C
Wanilla	C	Waterbury	D	Wedekind	D
Wann	A	Waterino	C	Wedertz	C
Wapal	B	Waters	C	Wedge	A
Wapato	C/D	Watkins	B	Wedowee	D
Wapello	B	Watkins Ridge	B	Weed	B
Wapinitia	B	Wato	B	Weeding	A/C
Wapping	B	Watopa	B	Weedmark	B
Wapsie	B	Watrous	B	Weeksville	B/D
Warba	B	Watseka	C	Weepon	D
Ward	D	Watson	C	Wehadkee	D
Wardboro	A	Watsonia	D	Weikert	C/D
Wardell	D	Watsonville	D	Weimer	D
Warden	B	Watt	D	Weinbach	C
Wardwell	C	Watton	C	Weir	D
Ware	B	Waubay	B	Weirman	B
Wareham	C	Waubeek	B	Weiser	C
Warm Springs	C	Waubonsie	B	Weishaupt	D
Warman	D	Wauchula	B/D	Weiss	A
Warners	A/D	Waucoma	B	Weitchpec	B
Warren		Wauconda	B	Welaka	A

continued

TABLE H.1   *(Continued)*

Welby	B	Westville	B	Whitewood	C
Welch	C	Wethersfield	C	Whitley	B
Weld	C	Wethey	B/C	Whitlock	B
Welda	C	Wetterhorn	C	Whitman	D
Weldon	D	Wetzel	D	Whitney	B
Welduna	B	Weymouth	B	Whitore	A
Weller	C	Whakana	B	Whitsol	B
Wellington	D	Whalan	B	Whitson	D
Wellman	B	Wharton	C	Whitwell	C
Wellner	B	Whatcom	C	Wholan	C
Wellsboro	C	Whately	D	Wibaux	C
Wellston	B	Wheatley	D	Wichita	C
Wellsville	B	Wheatridge	C	Wichup	D
Welring	D	Wheatville	B	Wickersham	B
Wemple	B	Wheeler	B	Wickett	C
Wenas	B/C	Wheeling	B	Wickiup	C
Wenatcher	C	Whelchel	B	Wickliffe	D
Wendel	B/C	Whellon	D	Wickman	B
Wenham		Whetstone	B	Wicksburg	B
Wenona	C	Whidbey	C	Widta	B
Wentworth	B	Whippany	C	Widtsoe	C
Werlow	C	Whipstock	C	Wiehl	C
Werner	B	Whirlo	B	Wien	D
Weso	C	Whit	B	Wiggleton	B
Wessel	B	Whitaker	C	Wigton	A
Westbrook	D	Whitcomb	C	Wilbraham	C
Westbury	C	White Bird	C	Wilbur	C
Westcreek	B	White House	C	Wilco	C
Westerville	C	White Store	D	Wilcox	D
Westfall	C	White Swan	C	Wilcoxson	C
Westfield		Whitecap	D	Wildcat	D
Westford		Whitefish	B	Wilder	B
Westland	B/D	Whiteford	B	Wilderness	C
Westminster	C/D	Whitehorse	B	Wildrose	D
Westmore	B	Whitelake	B	Wildwood	D
Westmoreland	B	Whitelaw	B	Wiley	C
Weston	D	Whiteman	D	Wilkes	C
Westphalia	B	Whiterock	D	Wilkeson	C
Westplain	C	Whitesburg	C	Wilkins	D
Westport	A	Whitewater	B	Will	D

continued

TABLE H.1   *(Continued)*

Willacy	B	Winger	C	Wolfesen	C
Willakenzie	C	Wingville	B/D	Wolfeson	C
Willamar	D	Winifred	C	Wolford	B
Willamette	B	Wink	B	Wolftever	C
Willapa	C	Winkel	D	Wolverine	A
Willard	B	Winkleman	C	Wood River	D
Willette	A/D	Winkler	A	Woodbine	B
Willhand	B	Winlo	D	Woodbridge	C
Williams	B	Winlock	C	Woodburn	C
Williamsburg	B	Winn	C	Woodbury	D
Williamson	C	Winnebago	B	Woodcock	B
Willis	C	Winnemucca	B	Woodenville	C
Willits	B	Winneshiek	B	Woodglen	D
Willoughby	B	Winnett	D	Woodhall	B
Willow Creek	B	Winona	D	Woodhurst	A
Willowdale	B	Winooski	B	Woodinville	C/D
Willows	D	Winston	A	Woodly	B
Willwood	A	Winters	C	Woodlyn	C/D
Wilmer	C	Wintersburg	C	Woodmansie	B
Wilpar	D	Winterset	C	Woodmere	B
Wilson	D	Winthrop	A	Woodrock	C
Wiltshire	C	Wintoner	C	Woodrow	C
Winans	B/C	Winu	C	Woods Cross	D
Winberry	D	Winz	C	Woodsfield	C
Winchester	A	Wishard	A	Woodside	A
Winchuck	C	Wisheylu	C	Woodson	D
Wind River	B	Wishkam	C	Woodstock	C/D
Winder	B/D	Wiskam	C	Woodstown	C
Windham	B	Wisner	D	Woodward	B
Windmill	B	Witbeck	D	Woolman	B
Windom	B	Witch	D	Woolper	C
Windsor	A	Witham	D	Woolsey	C
Windthorst	C	Withee	C	Wooskow	B/C
Windy	C	Witt	B	Woosley	C
Wineg	C	Witzel	D	Wooster	C
Winema	C	Woden	B	Woostern	B
Winetti	B	Wolcottsburg		Wooten	A
Winfield	C	Woldale	C/D	Worcester	B
Wing	D	Wolf	B	Worf	D
Wingate	B	Wolf Point	D	Work	C

continued

TABLE H.1   *(Continued)*

Worland	B	Yamhill	C	Yuba	D
Worley	C	Yampa	C	Yuko	C
Wormser	C	Yamsay	D	Yukon	D
Worock	B	Yana	B	Yunes	D
Worsham	D	Yancy	C	Yunque	C
Worth	C	Yardley	C	Zaar	D
Worthen	B	Yates	D	Zaca	D
Worthing	D	Yauco	C	Zacharias	B
Worthington	C	Yawdim	D	Zachary	D
Wortman	C	Yawkey	C	Zafra	B
Wrentham	C	Yaxon	B	Zahill	B
Wright	C	Yeary	C	Zahl	B
Wrightman	C	Yeates Hollow	C	Zaleski	C
Wrightsville	D	Yegen	B	Zalla	A
Wunjey	B	Yelm	B	Zamora	B
Wurtsboro	C	Yenrab	A	Zane	C
Wyalusing	D	Yeoman	B	Zaneis	B
Wyard	B	Yesum	B	Zanesville	C
Wyarno	B	Yetull	A	Zanone	C
Wyatt	C	Yoder	B	Zapata	C
Wyeast	C	Yokohl	D	Zavala	B
Wyeville	C	Yollabolly	D	Zavco	C
Wygant	C	Yolo	B	Zeb	B
Wykoff	B	Yologo	D	Zeesix	C
Wyman	B	Yomba	C	Zell	B
Wymoose	D	Yomont	B	Zen	C
Wymore	C	Yoncalla	C	Zenda	C
Wynn	B	Yonges	D	Zenia	B
Wyo	B	Yonna	B/D	Zeniff	B
Wyocena	B	Yordy	B	Zeona	A
Xavier	B	York	C	Ziegler	C
Yacolt	B	Yorkville	D	Zigweid	B
Yahara	B	Yost	C	Zillah	B/C
Yahola	B	Youga	B	Zim	D
Yaki	D	Youman	C	Zimmerman	A
Yakima	B	Youngston	B	Zing	C
Yakus	D	Yourame	A	Zinzer	B
Yallani	B	Yovimpa	D	Zion	C
Yalmer	B	Ysidora	D	Zipp	C/D
Yamac	B	Yturbide	A	Zita	B

continued

TABLE H.1   *(Continued)*

Zoar	C	Zufelt	B/D	Zunhall	B/C
Zoate	D	Zukan	D	Zuni	D
Zohner	B/D	Zumbro	B	Zurich	B
Zook	C	Zumwalt	C	Zwingle	D
Zorravista	A	Zundell	B/C		

Source   U.S. Department of Agriculture, Soil Conservation Service 1986. *Urban Hydrology For Small Watersheds*. TA55. Washington, D.C. (June).
A blank hydrological soil group indicates the soil group has not been determined. Two soil groups such as B/C indicates the drained/undrained situation.

....
....
....

I

COMPUTER
PROGRAM
DESCRIPTIONS AND
EXAMPLE
OUTPUTS

I.1

CONTENT AND ORGANIZATION

In this appendix, preliminary details are presented on the content, organization, computer hardware, and use of computer programs. The programs have been designed to be used by individuals with a limited understanding of personal computers. However, individuals must have some knowledge of hydrology and stormwater management. Students of hydrology and stormwater management, along with people who practice in the planning, science, and engineering areas will find this appendix and the programs very beneficial because the appendix not only aids in understanding theory and practice but also reduces the time for learning and solving practical problems.

531

Each section of the appendix begins with a short introduction and a description of the computer information related to the section heading. There is one diskette available with this text. It is designated "HP" for hydrology programs. These programs are similar to other programs used to solve hydrology and stormwater management problems, and are written to be user friendly and for learning experiences. "User friendly" implies the existence of "prompts" or questions that are logically used to enter data or make decisions regarding the use of the data. The learning experience can be gained by solving problems repetitively. Repetitive runs are made relatively fast by the computer programs because most of the input and output data can be saved and comparisons made without extensive reentry of data.

As with all computation aids, the programs are specific to certain types of practical problems and theory. Thus, each program is described and example input data and solutions developed.

At the end of most chapters in this book are computer-assisted problem sections. These problems can be solved with a minimum of other reference material, but it is recommended that the reader consult this and other texts and reference material on hydrology, hydraulics, and stormwater management. These references will aid in understanding the data input and interpretation of results.

I.2

COMPUTER CONFIGURATION

The computer disks with programs are designed to operate on IBM Personal Computers or 100% equivalent compatibles with $5\frac{1}{4}$-in. size diskettes. All the programs are in the executable mode. The minimum characteristics for the hardware are:

1. IBM PC's or 100% compatibles, including XT or AT models.
2. Two double-sided floppy diskette drives (or one floppy drive with a hard disk).
3. Color monitor with IBM graphics adaptor (GA) or enhanced graphics adapter (a black- and white- monitor can be used but to obtain graphics an IBM-GA must be used). Note: A Hercules graphics card can not be used for graphics.
4. 512K bytes of RAM (memory).
5. Disk Operating System (DOS), version 3.2 or higher.

If you plan on using a diskette for data storage, format the diskette now for future use.

I.3

CARING FOR AND COPYING THE DISKETTES

All diskettes must be stored in an area not subjected to extreme heat, magnetic forces, fluid spills, or rough treatment. Keeping a diskette in a hot automobile has been known to erase or alter the program codes. A hard-covered case for carrying and storing the diskettes is valuable protection.

A copy of a program diskette should be made immediately after obtaining the diskette. You may have been properly caring for your diskettes, but accidents and pillage do occur.

Floppy System. To make a copy of the diskette, first, format a diskette with the DOS disk and place the GRAPHICS.COM file on it (call this your program diskette). Then, use the install command to copy the original program diskette to your program diskette. To make another copy, use a different program diskette. The original diskette may be copied four times. A commonly used procedure is to:

1. Place the DOS diskette in drive A.
2. Place the unformatted diskette in drive B.
3. A > FORMAT B:
4. A > COPY GRAPHICS.COM B:
5. Remove the DOS diskette from drive A.
6. Place the original program disk in drive A.
7. A > INSTALL B:

You are finished, remove both diskettes.

Hard Disk System. Copy to the hard disk (if available) by first making a subdirectory, then copying the programs directly onto the hard disk subdirectory. Usually, the hard disk is preferable for storage because the programs will run faster from the hard disk than from the floppy. A commonly used procedure is to:

1. Place HP program disk in drive A.
2. C > MD HP
3. C > CD\HP
4. C:\HP > A:
5. A:> INSTALL C:\HP

You are finished, remove the original diskette. After copying the diskette, store it in a safe place for future use. (*Note.* Additional copies of the program may be obtained by sending $30.00 U.S. to Dr. M. Wanielista, University of Central Florida, College of Engineering, Orlando FL 32816.)

I.4

INITIATING THE PROGRAMS

Your computer must be operational and "booted up" in a DOS format. After the system is up and running, an A > (known as A prompt) will appear. The prompt will appear for either the A, B, or C drive.

Place your program diskette in drive A, or from your hard disk, type "H" after the prompt and press the enter key.

$$A: > H$$

The main menu, shown in Table I.1, appears on the monitor. Each program will be described in detail in the following sections.

Once the menu is shown, the user decides which program to call and that number is "keyed." Immediately, the computer will move the program into memory and display another menu or questions. Some of the problems are large, thus it may take more than a few seconds to load the program. *Note.* You may exit the main menu by pressing the ESC (escape) key. Also, the ESC (escape) key can be used with the kinematic program (see Table I.2) to return to the main menu.

TABLE I.1 Main Menu—HP Programs

PROGRAM MENU: "ESC" KEY TO EXIT SYSTEM

1. *SMADA*: hydrographs using SCS and SBUH with detention/retention designs.
2. *Kinematic*: equation for overland flow using FID curves defined by user.
3. *Unit hydrographs* using matrix methods in discrete time form.
4. *Convolution* using functional form.
5. *Linear regression* by least squares.
   Make selection (1–5).

TABLE I.2 Kinematic Menu

```
                    KINEMATIC WAVE
      YOU WILL BE USING EXISTING FID FILES OR YOU
          MAY CREATE NEW FID FILES
      WILL A NEW FILE BE CREATED? Y)ES OR N)O?
      PRESS `ESC' KEY TO END ELSE ANY KEY TO CONTINUE
```

After completing the program, a prompt will ask if the user wishes to exit the program. This will return the user to the main menu. One may terminate a program by removing a disk or keying a control break. This will not return the user to the main menu.

I.5

HYDROGRAPHS AND THE MATRIX METHOD
(HYDROLOGY PROGRAMS MENU 3)

Computer programs for the estimation of hydrographs are presented in the next four sections. Each program is briefly described and an example problem is solved. The programs are classified as matrix methods, curve fit, continuous convolution, and SMADA (SCS, Santa Barbara, and Rational). Since time of concentration is important for the estimation of a hydrograph, the kinematic equation for overland flow as a function of rainfall intensity is also presented. The problems at the end of each chapter extend the concepts and reinforce an understanding of the particular computer program. In addition, many of the problems use data from practical situations.

This computer program is accessed from the HP main menu by pressing 3. Following is the response.

```
This program can generate a hydrograph by matrix methods
   or use a continuous convolution given any routing and rain-
     fall
   or find the best fit equation using least squares

   Enter (U) for matrix methods using unit hydrographs or
   (C) for convolution using continuous functions or
   (L) for least squares fit
?
```

The user keys U and presses ENTER to load the matrix method program. Given rainfall excess (R) and a unit hydrograph (U), the program multiplies by matrix methods according to:

$$Q = R \times U$$

where

$$
R = \begin{bmatrix}
R_1 & 0 & 0 & \cdots & 0 \\
R_2 & R_1 & 0 & \cdots & 0 \\
R_3 & R_2 & R_1 & \cdots & 0 \\
R_i & R_{i-1} & & & R_1
\end{bmatrix}
\quad
U = \begin{bmatrix}
U_1 \\
U_2 \\
U_3 \\
U_j
\end{bmatrix}
\quad
Q = \begin{bmatrix}
Q_1 \\
Q_2 \\
Q_3 \\
Q_k
\end{bmatrix}
$$

TABLE I.3   Output Data and Composite Hydrograph

PROJECT'S NAME:

Input Data   *Input Data*

UNIT HYDROGRAPH DATA		RAINFALL EXCESS DATA	
TIME (hr)	FLOW RATE (cfs)	TIME (hr)	RAINFALL EXCESS (in.)
0.0000	0.0000	0.0000	0.0000
0.2500	4.0000	0.2500	0.2000
0.5000	12.0000	0.5000	0.9000
0.7500	15.0000	0.7500	1.4000
1.0000	9.0000	1.0000	0.7000
1.2500	6.0000		
1.5000	3.0000		
1.7500	2.0000		
2.0000	1.0000		

Composite Hydrograph Data

TIME (hr)	FLOW RATE (cfs)
0.0000	0.0000
0.2500	0.8000
0.5000	6.0000
0.7500	19.4000
1.0000	34.9000
1.2500	38.7000
1.5000	29.1000
1.7500	17.8000
2.0000	10.4000
2.2500	5.8000
2.5000	2.8000
2.7500	0.7000
3.0000	0.0000

and the computations are expanded as

$$Q_1 = R_1U_1$$

$$Q_2 = R_2U_1 + R_1U_2$$

$$Q_3 = R_3U_1 + R_2U_2 + R_1U_3$$

and so on.

where
the hydrograph has k values, $k = i + j - 1$
and i = number of rainfall excess values
j = number of unit hydrograph values

TABLE I.4 Continuous Convolution Output

TIME (min)	ROUTED HYDROGRAPH (cfs)	TIME (min)	ROUTED HYDROGRAPH (cfs)
0	0.00	110	6.34
5	3.78	115	4.47
10	13.59	120	3.15
15	35.20	125	2.22
20	71.87	130	1.56
25	143.94	135	1.10
30	263.03	140	0.78
35	362.27	145	0.55
40	400.36	150	0.38
45	378.45	155	0.27
50	335.57	160	0.19
55	277.91	165	0.13
60	209.83	170	0.09
65	147.87	175	0.07
70	104.20	180	0.05
75	73.43	185	0.03
80	51.74	190	0.02
85	36.46	195	0.02
90	25.69	200	0.01
95	18.11	205	0.01
100	12.76	210	0.00
105	8.99	215	0.00

Example – Matrix Method

This example illustrates the use of the program input and output data. Rainfall excess for 1 hour in 15 minute increments is input. Also input is a 2 hour unit hydrograph resulting from the 15 minute rainfall excess. The user follows the prompted questions. The input data and composite hydrograph are shown in Table I.3.

I.6

BIVARIATE REGRESSION CURVE FIT
(HYDROLOGY PROGRAMS MENU 5)

A hydrograph shape and equation form can be estimated using a least-squares bivariate regression compute program. The criteria of best fit is to minimize the sum of the square of the differences between the measured and predicted values of the flow rates. In general, a polynomial of second or third degree is a good fit to the data. Other mathematical forms also may be tried.

Example – Polynomial Curve Fit

This option is accessed by keying the letter L for least-squares fit and following the questions. The unit hydrograph of Table I.4 is used as input. First, enter the data and then always check the data input by repeating the number input sequence. The input data should be repeated and return to the menu by only a carriage return. The F9 key is not required when checking. The output is shown in Figure I.1.

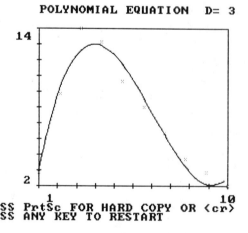

```
          POLYNOMIAL EQUATION   D= 3

  14 |
     |
     |
     |
     |
     |
     |
     |
   2 |
     |_____
        1                          10
 PRESS PrtSc FOR HARD COPY OR <cr>
 PRESS ANY KEY TO RESTART
```

FIGURE I.1   Computer output using the bi-variate regression curve fit (Menu 5) program.

I.7

CONTINUOUS CONVOLUTION (HYDROLOGY PROGRAMS MENU 4)

This program is accessed from the matrix program package by pressing C. The program can input any rainfall volume and converts rainfall to rainfall excess and then routes the excess. Rainfall excess is calculated for both impervious and pervious areas, and then both are summed. Any time interval can be used for the rainfall and any time scale can be used to calculate the hydrograph. The shape of the watershed or a percent of the watershed which contributes with time can be specified by the user. The general equation form is

$$Q(t) = \int_0^t Ke^{-(t-\tau)K} r(t) \, d\tau$$

where

$Q(t)$ = hydrograph
$Ke^{-(t-\tau)K}$ = routing function
$r(t)$ = rainfall excess

Example — Continuous Convolution

A rectangular-shaped 100-ac watershed that has 60 ac of directly connected impervious area and a time of concentration of 30 min has a pervious area curve number of 80, which reflects soil moisture and infiltration conditions. From a similar watershed, the hydraulic routing factor K is 0.07. Develop a hydrograph at 5-min intervals for a 1-hr rainfall with the following rainfall distributions (expressed in inches for 10-min intervals): 0.20, 0.50, 1.40, 1.00, 0.60, and 0.20.

The instantaneous rainfall assumes the total area contributes runoff and is:

TIME (min)	RAINFALL (in.)	INSTANTANEOUS RAINFALL EXCESS (cfs)	K VALUE (1/hr)
10	0.20	24.192	0.0700000
20	0.50	120.960	0.0700000
30	1.40	532.650	0.0700000
40	1.00	440.481	0.0700000
50	0.60	282.420	0.0700000
60	0.20	96.551	0.0700000

The resulting computer output is shown in Table I.4.

1.8

SMADA / SCS, SANTA BARBARA, RATIONAL
(HYDROLOGY PROGRAMS MENU 1)

This computer program is used for both hydrograph generation and storm-water management. It is accessed from the HP main menu by keying 1. SMADA is the acronym for stormwater management and design aid. The SMADA program menu is shown in Table I.5. Since rain and watershed data files can be stored in drives A, B, and C, and they may be used again and again, a directory of these files may be necessary before the program is initiated, thus the user can key D for directory and press enter. The user then specifies the drive [do not use a colon (:) after the drive letter]. Once the user continues with the program (key C), the program will prompt the user with questions. Frequently the user may wish to store the program results for printing at the end of a run, thus the user will be asked to specify a drive other than the one presently being used. If the program disk is in drive A, one may wish to specify B:, or C: (note the colon (:) is necessary for drive specification).

The hydrograph and stormwater management program (SMADA) is one that can be used in a multitude of ways. It is an interactive stormwater management package originally written in the BASIC language. It has an internal directory for file storage. Rainfall and watershed files can be created and used over and over again. Another diskette or a hard drive should be used for file storage. The output is in color and written to the screen, however one may exercise an option to generate a "hard" copy.

The program is a useful aid for:

1. Hydrograph generation via the rational, SCS, or Santa Barbara methods.
2. Calculating detention and off-line retention volumes.
3. Sizing pipes and open channels.
4. Evaluating design outlet structures.
5. Generating yearly pollutant loads.

TABLE I.5 SMADA Menu

```
                    SMADA
    STORMWATER MANAGEMENT AND DESIGN AID
    MENU:
    (D)IRECTORY LISTING
    (C)ONTINUE WITH PROGRAM
    (E)ND PROGRAM
    (P)RINT LAST RUN
      ?
```

SMADA can evaluate single or multi-land-use watersheds. For the same rainfall event, each specified subwatershed is evaluated for pollutant and hydrograph effects. The options of pre- versus post-development, pollutant/ retention, and peak flow/detention-type analyses are available for use on each subwatershed.

The three main data groups are (1) rainfall, (2) watershed, and (3) nodal network.

I.8.1 Rainfall Data

Rainfall data requires the input of storm duration in hours and the desired time increment in minutes to define the storm. This time increment will naturally be used to also define the hydrograph(s). The program allows for up to 96 time increments for both rainfall entries and hydrograph generation. As prompted by SMADA, enter the rainfall volume in inches for each time increment.

For user convenience, the inputed rain data is stored in a data file under a given name. In subsequent executions, the same rain data may be used by simply entering the file name. An assortment of storm data files is allowable, each with a unique name. If a desired file name entry does not exist or a new entry name is already being used, the user is informed of the problem and execution returns to the beginning of the rain data input section.

I.8.2 Watershed Data

Each land area to be evaluated requires the following data:

1. Drainage area (acres)
2. Time of concentration (minutes)
3. Percent impervious
4. Percentage of impervious that is directly drained
5. Initial abstraction for impervious area (inches)
6. Initial abstraction for pervious area (inches)
7. Curve number for pervious area

or

8. Horton's limiting infiltration rate (inches per hour)
9. Horton's initial infiltration rate (inches per hour)
10. Horton's depletion coefficient (per hour)

I.8.3 Nodal Network Data

The nodal network is defined by entering the following data concerning the transmission system between the nodes. When you are arranging the nodal network, remember that upstream nodes are numbered progressively less than a given node.

1. Distance between nodes (feet)
2. Cross-section—circle or trapezoid
3. Slope of proposed drainage
4. Manning's friction coefficient

SMADA will accommodate a maximum of nine nodes.

The following tables illustrate the use of the program for securing output copies (hard copies) and the type of output. There are many options. Once you continue, you have the option of printing the run or continuing with option for print after the run. If you wish to use the screen to view results, then continue with the program. If after running the program you wish to print it, answer "yes" to printing the file.

Table I.6 is an example printout using the rational method for hydrograph generation but with a variable hyetograph. The program converts the variable hyetograph to a constant hourly value. For this case:

$$Q_p = CiA = (0.4)(2.3)(50) = 46 \text{ cfs}$$

Note that the program calculated 46.38 cfs because of the conversion factor 1.008.

When using the program, a "file spec" format for watershed data is required, thus, always specify the resident file, such as A:FWSPRE.DAT. Also, the data of a file can be changed and the file name changed or kept the same. The change is illustrated in Table I.6. Table I.6 also illustrates the typical rational formula triangular-shaped hydrograph and off-line retention calculations for pollution control. The off-line causes the final hydrograph shape to change.

A listing of the tables with a brief description is as follows:

TABLE	DESCRIPTION
I.6	Rational formula hydrograph, changing watershed file, off-line retention and pollution option
I.7	SCS–unit–graph hydrograph, same rainfall hyetograph and watershed used to generate Table I.6, hydrograph attenuation factor of 484
I.8	Santa Barbara routing with same hyetograph and watershed
I.9	Two-watershed example with routing

TABLE I.6 Rational Formula Hydrograph

```
***********************************************************
*                                                         *
*     SMADA  -   STORMWATER MANAGEMENT AND DESIGN AID     *
*                                                         *
*                                                         *
***********************************************************


==============
PROJECT TITLE :  TEST RATIONAL
==============


============
DATE & TIME :  06-10-1986   09:03:35
============


***********************************************************
**************** R A I N F A L L    D A T A ***************
***********************************************************


TIME STEP      RAINFALL
---------      --------
    1             .2
    2             .4
    3             .7
    4             .6
    5             .3
    6             .1


***********************************************************
*********** W A T E R S H E D   A N A L Y S I S **********
***********************************************************

WATERSHED DATA FILE NAME = A:FWSPRE.DAT
SCS CURVE METHOD USED
DRAINAGE AREA (ACRES)=  50
TIME OF CONCENTRATION (MINUTES)=  67
PERCENT IMPERVIOUS =  25 %
PERCENTAGE OF IMPERV. AREA THAT IS DIRECTLY DRAINED  50
INITIAL ABSTRACTION FOR IMPERV. AREA (INCHES OVER IMPERVIOUS) 0
INITIAL ABSTRACTION FOR PERVIOUS AREA  (INCHES OVER PERVIOUS) 0
SCS CURVE NUMBER FOR THE PERVIOUS PORTION    61
WATERSHED DATA FILE NAME = A:FWSPRE.DAT
SCS CURVE METHOD USED
DRAINAGE AREA (ACRES)=  50
TIME OF CONCENTRATION (MINUTES)=  60
PERCENT IMPERVIOUS =  40 %
PERCENTAGE OF IMPERV. AREA THAT IS DIRECTLY DRAINED  50
INITIAL ABSTRACTION FOR IMPERV. AREA (INCHES OVER IMPERVIOUS) 0
INITIAL ABSTRACTION FOR PERVIOUS AREA  (INCHES OVER PERVIOUS) 0
SCS CURVE NUMBER FOR THE PERVIOUS PORTION    61
```

continued

TABLE I.6 *(Continued)*

```
TABLE: WATERSHED HYDROGRAPH

***********************************************
TIME        TIME      RAINFALL   WATERSHED
INCREMENT             DEPTH      HYDROGRAPH
           (MINUTES)  (INCHES)   (CFS)
===============================================

PEAK DISCHARGE IN CFS IS   46.38      TIME TO PEAK IN HOURS IS     1.0

   1        10        0.20        7.73
   2        20        0.40       15.46
   3        30        0.70       23.19
   4        40        0.60       30.92
   5        50        0.30       38.65
   6        60        0.10       46.38
   7        70        0.00       38.78
   8        80        0.00       31.18
   9        90        0.00       23.58
  10       100        0.00       15.98
  11       110        0.00        8.38
  12       120        0.00        0.78
  13       130        0.00        0.00
  14       140        0.00        0.00
  15       150        0.00        0.00
  16       160        0.00        0.00
  17       170        0.00        0.00
  18       180        0.00        0.00
                                          Note:  C = 0.40

TOTAL RAIN=  2.30 TOTAL INFILTRATION & ABSTRACTION=  1.24  TOTAL RUNOFF=  1.06

*******************************************************************************

**********  P O L L U T A N T   A N A L Y S I S  *********
TABLE : ANNUAL POLLUTANT DISCHARGE

POLLUTANT           KILOGRAMS/YEAR
======================================

BOD               708.2
SS               8498.6
TN                133.5
TP                 36.4

***********************************

DIVERSION DEPTH =  .5   INCHES

SIDE SLOPE OF OFF LINE RETENTION BASIN =  .25  (VERT/HORIZ)
TABLE: RETENTION FACILITY ANALYSIS FOR SCS TYPE A & D SOILS
```

continued

TABLE I.6   *(Continued)*

```
 FOR VARYING DEPTHS.
 ******************************************************************
                S C S   TYPE   A              S C S   TYPE   D
 STORAGE    -----------------------    -----------------------

 DEPTH    VOLUME        SURFACE AREA   VOLUME       SURFACE AREA
 (FEET)   (ACRE-FT)     (ACRES)        (ACRE-FT)    (ACRES)
 ================================================================
    1      2.08          2.20           2.66         2.78
    2      2.58          1.42           3.80         2.06
    3      3.07          1.19           4.95         1.85
    4      3.57          1.08
    5      4.06          1.03
 ******************************************************************

         TABLE: FINAL DISCHARGE HYDROGRAPH
 **************************************************
 TIME        TIME          HYDROGRAPH
 STEP        (MINUTES)     (CFS)
 ==================================================

    1          10             0.00
    2          20             0.00
    3          30             0.00
    4          40             0.00
    5          50             0.00
    6          60            12.34
    7          70            38.78
    8          80            31.18
    9          90            23.58
   10         100            15.98
   11         110             8.38
   12         120             0.78
   13         130             0.00
   14         140             0.00
   15         150             0.00
   16         160             0.00
   17         170             0.00
   18         180             0.00


 ************************************************
```

TABLE I.7   SCS – Unit – Graph Hydrograph

```
*****************************************************************
*                                                               *
*       SMADA   -   STORMWATER  MANAGEMENT  AND  DESIGN  AID     *
*                                                               *
*                                                               *
*****************************************************************

=============
PROJECT TITLE :  SCS UNIT-GRAPH
=============

===========
DATE & TIME :  06-10-1986    09:24:42
===========

*****************************************************************
***************  R A I N F A L L   D A T A ******************
*****************************************************************

RA1HR :

TIME            RAINFALL
(MIN)           (INCHES)
----            --------
 10                .2
 20                .4
 30                .7
 40                .6
 50                .3
 60                .1

*****************************************************************
*********** W A T E R S H E D   A N A L Y S I S ***********
*****************************************************************

WATERSHED DATA FILE NAME = A:FWSPRE.DAT
SCS CURVE METHOD USED
DRAINAGE AREA (ACRES)=  50
TIME OF CONCENTRATION (MINUTES)=  60
PERCENT IMPERVIOUS =  40 %
PERCENTAGE OF IMPERV. AREA THAT IS DIRECTLY DRAINED  50
INITIAL ABSTRACTION FOR IMPERV. AREA (INCHES OVER IMPERVIOUS) 0
INITIAL ABSTRACTION FOR PERVIOUS AREA  (INCHES OVER PERVIOUS) 0
SCS CURVE NUMBER FOR THE PERVIOUS PORTION   61
```

continued

TABLE I.7   *(Continued)*

TABLE: WATERSHED HYDROGRAPH

****

TIME INCREMENT	TIME (MINUTES)	RAINFALL DEPTH (INCHES)	WATERSHED HYDROGRAPH (CFS)
1	10	0.20	0.00
2	20	0.40	0.00
3	30	0.70	0.44
4	40	0.60	2.97
5	50	0.30	7.04
6	60	0.10	11.68
7	70	0.00	15.61
8	80	0.00	16.21
9	90	0.00	14.34
10	100	0.00	11.56
11	110	0.00	8.78
12	120	0.00	5.99
13	130	0.00	3.30
14	140	0.00	1.19
15	150	0.00	0.23
16	160	0.00	0.00
17	170	0.00	0.00
18	180	0.00	0.00

Note: $I_A = 0.20$
$K = 484$

TOTAL RAIN= 2.30 TOTAL INFILTRATION & ABSTRACTION= 1.24   TOTAL RUNOFF= 1.06

****

TABLE: FINAL DISCHARGE HYDROGRAPH

****

TIME STEP	TIME (MINUTES)	HYDROGRAPH (CFS)
1	10	0.00
2	20	0.00
3	30	0.44
4	40	2.97
5	50	7.04
6	60	11.68
7	70	15.61
8	80	16.21
9	90	14.34
10	100	11.56
11	110	8.78
12	120	5.99
13	130	3.30
14	140	1.19
15	150	0.23
16	160	0.00
17	170	0.00
18	180	0.00

****

TABLE I.8   Santa Barbara Routing

```
***************************************************************
*                                                             *
*     SMADA  -   STORMWATER MANAGEMENT AND DESIGN AID         *
*                                                             *
*                                                             *
***************************************************************

=============
PROJECT TITLE :   SANTA BARBARA ROUTING
=============

===========
DATE & TIME :   06-10-1986    09:50:20
===========


***************************************************************
**************** R A I N F A L L   D A T A ****************
***************************************************************

RA1HR :

TIME          RAINFALL
(MIN)         (INCHES)
----          --------
  10             .2
  20             .4
  30             .7
  40             .6
  50             .3
  60             .1


***************************************************************
*********** W A T E R S H E D   A N A L Y S I S ***********
***************************************************************

WATERSHED DATA FILE NAME = A:FWSPRE.DAT
SCS CURVE METHOD USED
DRAINAGE AREA (ACRES)=  50
TIME OF CONCENTRATION (MINUTES)=  60
PERCENT IMPERVIOUS =  40 %
PERCENTAGE OF IMPERV. AREA THAT IS DIRECTLY DRAINED  50
INITIAL ABSTRACTION FOR IMPERV. AREA (INCHES OVER IMPERVIOUS) 0
INITIAL ABSTRACTION FOR PERVIOUS AREA  (INCHES OVER PERVIOUS) 0
SCS CURVE NUMBER FOR THE PERVIOUS PORTION   61
```

continued

TABLE I.8   *(Continued)*

TABLE: WATERSHED HYDROGRAPH USING SANTA BARBARA ROUTING

```
****************************************************************************
TIME        TIME       RAINFALL   INFILTRATION   RUNOFF    INSTANT      WATERSHED
INCREMENT              DEPTH      & INIT ABST    DEPTH     HYDROGRAPH   HYDROGRAPH
            (MINUTES)  (INCHES)   (INCHES)       (INCHES)  (CFS)        (CFS)
==========================================================================
```

TIME INCREMENT	TIME (MINUTES)	RAINFALL DEPTH (INCHES)	INFILTRATION & INIT ABST (INCHES)	RUNOFF DEPTH (INCHES)	INSTANT HYDROGRAPH (CFS)	WATERSHED HYDROGRAPH (CFS)
1	10	0.20	0.154	0.046	13.92	1.07
2	20	0.40	0.273	0.127	38.09	4.91
3	30	0.70	0.392	0.308	92.53	14.20
4	40	0.60	0.270	0.330	98.86	26.74
5	50	0.30	0.118	0.182	54.65	34.43
6	60	0.10	0.037	0.063	18.88	34.79
7	70	0.00	0.000	0.000	0.00	30.89
8	80	0.00	0.000	0.000	0.00	26.14
9	90	0.00	0.000	0.000	0.00	22.12
10	100	0.00	0.000	0.000	0.00	18.72
11	110	0.00	0.000	0.000	0.00	15.84
12	120	0.00	0.000	0.000	0.00	13.40
13	130	0.00	0.000	0.000	0.00	11.34
14	140	0.00	0.000	0.000	0.00	9.59
15	150	0.00	0.000	0.000	0.00	8.12
16	160	0.00	0.000	0.000	0.00	6.87
17	170	0.00	0.000	0.000	0.00	5.81
18	180	0.00	0.000	0.000	0.00	4.92

TOTAL RAIN= 2.30 TOTAL INFILTRATION & ABSTRACTION= 1.24   TOTAL RUNOFF= 1.06

```
****************************************************************************
```

TABLE: FINAL DISCHARGE HYDROGRAPH
```
***************************************************
TIME       TIME         HYDROGRAPH
STEP       (MINUTES)    (CFS)
===================================================
```

TIME STEP	TIME (MINUTES)	HYDROGRAPH (CFS)
1	10	1.07
2	20	4.91
3	30	14.20
4	40	26.74
5	50	34.43
6	60	34.79
7	70	30.89
8	80	26.14
9	90	22.12
10	100	18.72
11	110	15.84
12	120	13.40
13	130	11.34
14	140	9.59
15	150	8.12
16	160	6.87
17	170	5.81
18	180	4.92

```
***************************************************
```

TABLE I.9   Two-Watershed Example

```
***************************************************************
*                                                             *
*       SMADA  -  STORMWATER MANAGEMENT AND DESIGN AID        *
*                                                             *
*                                                             *
***************************************************************


=============
PROJECT TITLE :   TWO WATERSHED EXAMPLE
=============


===========
DATE & TIME :   06-10-1986    13:43:21
===========


***************************************************************
*************** R A I N F A L L   D A T A ****************
***************************************************************


RA1HR :

TIME            RAINFALL
(MIN)           (INCHES)
----            --------
 10                 .2
 20                 .4
 30                 .7
 40                 .6
 50                 .3
 60                 .1


***************************************************************
************* S U B W A T E R S H E D   1 *************
***************************************************************

WATERSHED DATA FILE NAME = A:FWSPRE.DAT
SCS CURVE METHOD USED
DRAINAGE AREA (ACRES)=   50
TIME OF CONCENTRATION (MINUTES)=   60
PERCENT IMPERVIOUS =   40 %
PERCENTAGE OF IMPERV. AREA THAT IS DIRECTLY DRAINED   50
INITIAL ABSTRACTION FOR IMPERV. AREA (INCHES OVER IMPERVIOUS) 0
INITIAL ABSTRACTION FOR PERVIOUS AREA  (INCHES OVER PERVIOUS) 0
SCS CURVE NUMBER FOR THE PERVIOUS PORTION   61
***************************************************************
************* S U B W A T E R S H E D   2 *************
***************************************************************

WATERSHED DATA FILE NAME = A:SWSPRE.DAT
SCS CURVE METHOD USED
DRAINAGE AREA (ACRES)=   100
TIME OF CONCENTRATION (MINUTES)=   200
PERCENT IMPERVIOUS =   25 %
PERCENTAGE OF IMPERV. AREA THAT IS DIRECTLY DRAINED   100
INITIAL ABSTRACTION FOR IMPERV. AREA (INCHES OVER IMPERVIOUS) 0
INITIAL ABSTRACTION FOR PERVIOUS AREA  (INCHES OVER PERVIOUS) 0
SCS CURVE NUMBER FOR THE PERVIOUS PORTION   54
```

continued

TABLE I.9 *(Continued)*

WATERSHED #1
TABLE: WATERSHED HYDROGRAPH USING SANTA BARBARA ROUTING

```
*********************************************************************************
```

TIME INCREMENT	TIME (MINUTES)	RAINFALL DEPTH (INCHES)	INFILTRATION & INIT ABST (INCHES)	RUNOFF DEPTH (INCHES)	INSTANT HYDROGRAPH (CFS)	WATERSHED HYDROGRAPH (CFS)
1	10	0.20	0.154	0.046	13.92	1.07
2	20	0.40	0.273	0.127	38.09	4.91
3	30	0.70	0.392	0.308	92.53	14.20
4	40	0.60	0.270	0.330	98.86	26.74
5	50	0.30	0.118	0.182	54.65	34.43
6	60	0.10	0.037	0.063	18.88	34.79
7	70	0.00	0.000	0.000	0.00	30.89
8	80	0.00	0.000	0.000	0.00	26.14
9	90	0.00	0.000	0.000	0.00	22.12
10	100	0.00	0.000	0.000	0.00	18.72
11	110	0.00	0.000	0.000	0.00	15.84
12	120	0.00	0.000	0.000	0.00	13.40
13	130	0.00	0.000	0.000	0.00	11.34
14	140	0.00	0.000	0.000	0.00	9.59
15	150	0.00	0.000	0.000	0.00	8.12
16	160	0.00	0.000	0.000	0.00	6.87
17	170	0.00	0.000	0.000	0.00	5.81
18	180	0.00	0.000	0.000	0.00	4.92
19	190	0.00	0.000	0.000	0.00	4.16
20	200	0.00	0.000	0.000	0.00	3.52
21	210	0.00	0.000	0.000	0.00	2.98
22	220	0.00	0.000	0.000	0.00	2.52
23	230	0.00	0.000	0.000	0.00	2.13
24	240	0.00	0.000	0.000	0.00	1.81
25	250	0.00	0.000	0.000	0.00	1.53
26	260	0.00	0.000	0.000	0.00	1.29
27	270	0.00	0.000	0.000	0.00	1.09
28	280	0.00	0.000	0.000	0.00	0.93
29	290	0.00	0.000	0.000	0.00	0.78
30	300	0.00	0.000	0.000	0.00	0.66
31	310	0.00	0.000	0.000	0.00	0.56
32	320	0.00	0.000	0.000	0.00	0.47
33	330	0.00	0.000	0.000	0.00	0.40
34	340	0.00	0.000	0.000	0.00	0.34
35	350	0.00	0.000	0.000	0.00	0.29
36	360	0.00	0.000	0.000	0.00	0.24
37	370	0.00	0.000	0.000	0.00	0.21
38	380	0.00	0.000	0.000	0.00	0.17
39	390	0.00	0.000	0.000	0.00	0.15
40	400	0.00	0.000	0.000	0.00	0.12

TOTAL RAIN= 2.30 TOTAL INFILTRATION & ABSTRACTION= 1.24 TOTAL RUNOFF= 1.06

```
*********************************************************************************
```

continued

TABLE I.9   *(Continued)*

WATERSHED #2
TABLE: WATERSHED HYDROGRAPH USING SANTA BARBARA ROUTING

****

TIME INCREMENT	TIME (MINUTES)	RAINFALL DEPTH (INCHES)	INFILTRATION & INIT ABST (INCHES)	RUNOFF DEPTH (INCHES)	INSTANT HYDROGRAPH (CFS)	WATERSHED HYDROGRAPH (CFS)
1	10	0.20	0.147	0.053	32.06	0.78
2	20	0.40	0.274	0.126	75.70	3.37
3	30	0.70	0.426	0.274	164.69	9.07
4	40	0.60	0.319	0.281	168.47	16.75
5	50	0.30	0.146	0.154	92.28	22.30
6	60	0.10	0.047	0.053	31.84	24.24
7	70	0.00	0.000	0.000	0.00	23.83
8	80	0.00	0.000	0.000	0.00	22.67
9	90	0.00	0.000	0.000	0.00	21.56
10	100	0.00	0.000	0.000	0.00	20.51
11	110	0.00	0.000	0.000	0.00	19.51
12	120	0.00	0.000	0.000	0.00	18.56
13	130	0.00	0.000	0.000	0.00	17.65
14	140	0.00	0.000	0.000	0.00	16.79
15	150	0.00	0.000	0.000	0.00	15.97
16	160	0.00	0.000	0.000	0.00	15.19
17	170	0.00	0.000	0.000	0.00	14.45
18	180	0.00	0.000	0.000	0.00	13.75
19	190	0.00	0.000	0.000	0.00	13.08
20	200	0.00	0.000	0.000	0.00	12.44
21	210	0.00	0.000	0.000	0.00	11.83
22	220	0.00	0.000	0.000	0.00	11.26
23	230	0.00	0.000	0.000	0.00	10.71
24	240	0.00	0.000	0.000	0.00	10.18
25	250	0.00	0.000	0.000	0.00	9.69
26	260	0.00	0.000	0.000	0.00	9.21
27	270	0.00	0.000	0.000	0.00	8.76
28	280	0.00	0.000	0.000	0.00	8.34
29	290	0.00	0.000	0.000	0.00	7.93
30	300	0.00	0.000	0.000	0.00	7.54
31	310	0.00	0.000	0.000	0.00	7.18
32	320	0.00	0.000	0.000	0.00	6.83
33	330	0.00	0.000	0.000	0.00	6.49
34	340	0.00	0.000	0.000	0.00	6.18
35	350	0.00	0.000	0.000	0.00	5.87
36	360	0.00	0.000	0.000	0.00	5.59
37	370	0.00	0.000	0.000	0.00	5.32
38	380	0.00	0.000	0.000	0.00	5.06
39	390	0.00	0.000	0.000	0.00	4.81
40	400	0.00	0.000	0.000	0.00	4.58

TOTAL RAIN= 2.30 TOTAL INFILTRATION & ABSTRACTION= 1.36 TOTAL RUNOFF= 0.94

****

continued

TABLE I.9   *(Continued)*

```
        TABLE:       DISCHARGE HYDROGRAPH  WATERSHED #2
*************************************************
TIME            TIME            HYDROGRAPH
STEP            (MINUTES)       (CFS)
=================================================

    1              10               0.78
    2              20               3.37
    3              30               9.07
    4              40              16.75
    5              50              22.30
    6              60              24.24
    7              70              23.83
    8              80              22.67
    9              90              21.56
   10             100              20.51
   11             110              19.51
   12             120              18.56
   13             130              17.65
   14             140              16.79
   15             150              15.97
   16             160              15.19
   17             170              14.45
   18             180              13.75
   19             190              13.08
   20             200              12.44
   21             210              11.83
   22             220              11.26
   23             230              10.71
   24             240              10.18
   25             250               9.69
   26             260               9.21
   27             270               8.76
   28             280               8.34
   29             290               7.93
   30             300               7.54
   31             310               7.18
   32             320               6.83
   33             330               6.49
   34             340               6.18
   35             350               5.87
   36             360               5.59
   37             370               5.32
   38             380               5.06
   39             390               4.81
   40             400               4.58


*************************************************

*****************************************************************
*************** N O D A L   A N A L Y S I S  ***************
*****************************************************************
TRANSMISSION FROM NODE   1 IS RECEIVED BY NODE   2
        DISTANCE BETWEEN THESE NODES (FEET) = 4000
        DESIRED SIDE SLOPE OF THE CANAL (VERT/HORIZ) EXPRESSED AS A FRACTION
        (eg. 0.25)   .5
        SLOPE  OF PROPOSED DRAINAGE EXPRESSED AS A FRACTION (eg. .01) = .02
        MANNING FRICTION COEFFICIENT N = .013
*************************************************
CALCULATED PIPE DIAMETER (INCHES) =   24.8

COMMERICAL SIZE (INCHES) =   24
*************************************************
```

continued

TABLE I.9 *(Continued)*

```
TRANSMISSION FROM NODE   2 IS RECEIVED BY NODE   3
         DISTANCE BETWEEN THESE NODES (FEET) = 3500
         DESIRED SIDE SLOPE OF THE CANAL (VERT/HORIZ) EXPRESSED AS A FRACTION
         (eg. 0.25)   .5
         SLOPE  OF PROPOSED DRAINAGE EXPRESSED AS A FRACTION (eg. .01) = .02
         MANNING FRICTION COEFFICIENT N = .013
*******************************************************
CALCULATED PIPE DIAMETER (INCHES) =   27.3
COMMERICAL SIZE (INCHES) =   27
*******************************************************


TABLE : SUMMARY OF FLOWS AT EACH NODE
*************************************************
```

TIME (MINUTES)	NODE 1 (CFS)	NODE 2 (CFS)	NODE 3 (CFS)
10	1.1	0.9	0.1
20	4.9	4.1	0.7
30	14.2	11.8	2.6
40	26.7	23.5	6.4
50	34.4	34.4	12.1
60	34.8	41.4	18.6
70	30.9	44.5	24.7
80	26.1	45.1	29.8
90	22.1	44.4	33.6
100	18.7	42.8	36.1
110	15.8	40.7	37.5
120	13.4	38.2	38.0
130	11.3	35.7	37.7
140	9.6	33.1	36.9
150	8.1	30.6	35.6
160	6.9	28.2	34.1
170	5.8	26.0	32.3
180	4.9	23.9	30.5
190	4.2	22.0	28.6
200	3.5	20.2	26.7
210	3.0	18.6	24.8
220	2.5	17.1	23.1
230	2.1	15.8	21.4
240	1.8	14.5	19.8
250	1.5	13.4	18.3
260	1.3	12.4	17.0
270	1.1	11.5	15.7
280	0.9	10.7	14.6
290	0.8	10.0	13.5
300	0.7	9.3	12.5
310	0.6	8.7	11.6
320	0.5	8.1	10.8
330	0.4	7.6	10.1
340	0.3	7.1	9.4
350	0.3	6.7	8.7
360	0.2	6.3	8.2
370	0.2	5.9	7.6
380	0.2	5.5	7.1
390	0.1	5.2	6.7
400	0.1	4.9	6.3

```
*************************************************
```

I.9

KINEMAT (TIME OF CONCENTRATION)
(HYDROLOGY PROGRAMS MENU 2)

The program is accessed from the main menu using the kinematic option. The program estimates the time of concentration for overland flow using the following equation.

$$t_c = \frac{(0.93L^{0.6}N^{.6})}{(i^{0.4}S^{0.3})}$$

where

t_c = time of concentration (min)
L = overland flow length (ft)
N = Manning's roughness coefficient for overland flow
i = rainfall intensity (in./hr)
S = average overland slope (ft/ft)

The solution for the equation usually involves a trial-and-error solution because rainfall intensity is related to time of concentration by Frequency–Intensity–Duration (FID) curves. Thus, when using the computer program these curves (intensity-duration) as a function of frequency (return period) must be entered. The computer has resident on a file (KINEMAT.DAT) the FID curves for the eleven zones in Florida (see appendix C for the zone locations). However, the program creates files for a given frequency assuming a polynomial fit to the intensity duration curve. When solving for t_c, the program will ask for the frequency curve as shown in Table I.10. The result of creating a new file as shown in Table I.11.

TABLE I.10   KINEMAT Menu

KINEMATIC WAVE
PRESS `ESC` KEY TO END ELSE ANY KEY TO CONTINUE
AND ENTER
2 YR***
3 YR
5 YR
10 YR
25 YR
50 YR

TABLE I.11   KINENAME Program and KINEMAT Result

You will be asked to enter the zone number, the return period (frequency), and
the coefficients for a polynomial that can be obtained from the statistical analysis
programs. The polynomial is of the third order and has the form:

$$I = A + BT + CT^2 + DT^3$$

where
$$I = \text{intensity (in./hr)}$$
$$T = \text{duration}$$
$$A, B, C, D = \text{coefficients}$$

Note: You will erase all previous data. This program will not edit but will create a file
in drive B. Key enter to continue. An example file creation is:

```
Zone:? 6
Frequency:? 25
Coefficient(1) = ? 35
Coefficient(2) = ? -1.2
Coefficient(3) = ? -.05
Coefficient(4) = ? -.007
```

An example of the use of the existing data base is:

The zone number under consideration = 7
The length of overland flow (ft)   = 200
The slope (ft/vert/ft hort, eg. .01)   = 0.01
Manning's overland flow   = 0.033
Then intensity (in./hr)   = 9.168335
The time of concentration is   = 8 min
Would you like another run Y/N?

INDEX

COMMONLY USED ENGLISH CONVERSIONS

Area

$43{,}560 \ \text{ft}^2 = 1 \ \text{ac}$

$4{,}840 \ \text{yd}^2 = 1 \ \text{ac}$

$144 \ \text{in}^2 = 1 \ \text{ft}^2$

$640 \ \text{ac} = 1 \ \text{mi}^2$

Volume

$7.48 \ \text{gal} = 1 \ \text{ft}^3$

$1728 \ \text{in}^3 = 1 \ \text{ft}^3$

$.326 \ \text{MG} = 1 \ \text{ac} \cdot \text{ft}$

$8.34 \ \text{lb} = 1 \ \text{gal (of water)}$

$62.43 \ \text{lb} = 1 \ \text{ft}^3 \text{ (of water)}$

Mass

$2000 \ \text{lb} = 1 \ \text{ton}$

$454 \ \text{g} = 1 \ \text{lb}$

$7000 \ \text{gr} = 1 \ \text{lb}$

$2240 \ \text{lb} = 1 \ \text{long ton}$